Architectural Drafting and Design

Sixth Edition

Solutions Manual

Alan Jefferis

Principal, Residential Designs
Autodesk Developer Network Member
Architectural Specialist
Drafting Technology Department
Autodesk Premier Training Center
Clackamas Community College, Oregon City, Oregon

David A. Madsen

President, Madsen Designs Inc.
www.madsendesigns.com
Faculty Emeritus
Former Department Chairperson
Drafting Technology

Autodesk Premier Training Center **Autodesk**®
Authorised Author
Clackamas Community College, Oregon City, Oregon
Autodesk Developer Network Member
Director Emeritus
American Design Drafting Association

DELMAR
CENGAGE Learning™

Australia • Brazil • Japan • Korea • Mexico • Singapore • Spain • United Kingdom • United States

© 2011 Cengage Learning. All Rights Reserved. May not be scanned, copied or duplicated, or posted to a publicly accessible website, in whole or in part.

DELMAR
CENGAGE Learning™

**Architectural Drafting and Design,
Sixth Edition, Solutions Manual**
Alan Jefferis and David A. Madsen

Vice President, Career and Professional
Editorial: Dave Garza

Director of Learning Solutions: Sandy Clark

Senior Acquisitions Editor: Jim DeVoe

Managing Editor: Larry Main

Senior Product Manager: Sharon Chambliss

Editorial Assistant: Cris Savino

Vice President, Career and Professional
Marketing: Jennifer Baker

Marketing Director: Deborah Yarnell

Marketing Coordinator: Mark Pierro

Production Director: Wendy Troeger

Production Manager: Mark Bernard

Content Project Manager: David Plagenza

Art Director: Casey Kirchmayer

Technology Project Manager: Joe Pliss

© 2011, 2005, 2001, 1996, 1991 Delmar, Cengage Learning

ALL RIGHTS RESERVED. No part of this work covered by the copyright
herein may be reproduced, transmitted, stored, or used in any form or by
any means graphic, electronic, or mechanical, including but not limited to
photocopying, recording, scanning, digitizing, taping, Web distribution,
information networks, or information storage and retrieval systems, except
as permitted under Section 107 or 108 of the 1976 United States Copyright
Act, without the prior written permission of the publisher.

For product information and technology assistance, contact us at
Cengage Learning Customer & Sales Support, 1-800-354-9706

For permission to use material from this text or product,
submit all requests online at **www.cengage.com/permissions**
Further permissions questions can be e-mailed to
permissionrequest@cengage.com

Library of Congress Control Number: 2009921885

ISBN-13: 978-1-4354-8165-7

ISBN-10: 1-4354-8165-8

Delmar
5 Maxwell Drive
Clifton Park, NY 12065-2919
USA

Cengage Learning is a leading provider of customized learning solutions with
office locations around the globe, including Singapore, the United Kingdom,
Australia, Mexico, Brazil, and Japan. Locate your local office at:
international.cengage.com/region

Cengage Learning products are represented in Canada by Nelson Education, Ltd.

To learn more about Delmar, visit **www.cengage.com/delmar**

Purchase any of our products at your local college store or at our preferred
online store **www.ichapters.com**

Notice to the Reader
Publisher does not warrant or guarantee any of the products described herein
or perform any independent analysis in connection with any of the product
information contained herein. Publisher does not assume, and expressly dis-
claims, any obligation to obtain and include information other than that provided to it by the manufacturer. The reader is expressly warned to consider
and adopt all safety precautions that might be indicated by the activities
described herein and to avoid all potential hazards. By following the instructions contained herein, the reader willingly assumes all risks in connection
with such instructions. The publisher makes no representations or warranties
of any kind, including but not limited to, the warranties of fitness for particular
purpose or merchantability, nor are any such representations implied with
respect to the material set forth herein, and the publisher takes no responsibility with respect to such material. The publisher shall not be liable for any special, consequential, or exemplary damages resulting, in whole or part, from the
readers' use of, or reliance upon, this material.

Printed in the United States of America
1 2 3 4 5 6 7 12 11 10

© 2011 Cengage Learning. All Rights Reserved. May not be scanned, copied or duplicated, or posted to a publicly accessible website, in whole or in part.

CONTENTS

PART I ANSWERS TO END-OF-CHAPTER TEST QUESTIONS AND PROBLEM SOLUTIONS

© 2011 Cengage Learning. All Rights Reserved. May not be scanned, copied or duplicated, or posted to a publicly accessible website, in whole or in part.

PART 2 SOLUTIONS TO WORKBOOK PROBLEMS

© 2011 Cengage Learning. All Rights Reserved. May not be scanned, copied or duplicated, or posted to a publicly accessible website, in whole or in part.

PREFACE

For over 22 years, students have relied on *Architectural Drafting and Design* for easy-to-read, comprehensive coverage of architectural drafting and design instruction that complies with and reinforces architectural, engineering, and construction industry standards and practices.

Architectural Drafting and Design, 6e, is a practical, comprehensive textbook that is easy to use and understand. The content can be used as presented by following a logical sequence of learning activities for residential and light commercial architectural drafting and design, or the chapters can be rearranged to accommodate alternate formats for traditional or individualized instruction.

APPROACH

Architectural Drafting and Design, 6e, provides a practical and realistic approach to solving problems that are encountered in the architectural design world.

Practical

Architectural Drafting and Design provides a practical approach to architectural drafting as it relates to current standard practices. The emphasis on standardization is an excellent and necessary foundation of drafting training as well as for implementing a common approach to drafting nationwide. After students become professional drafters, this text will serve as a valuable desk reference.

Realistic

Chapters contain professional examples, illustrations, step-by-step layout techniques, drafting problems, and related tests. The examples demonstrate recommended drafting presentation with actual architectural drawings used for reinforcement. The correlated text explains drafting practices and provides useful information for knowledge building and skill development. Step-by-step layout methods provide a logical approach to beginning and finishing complete sets of working drawings.

Practical Approach to Problem Solving

The professional architectural drafter's responsibility is to convert architects', engineers', and designers' sketches and ideas into formal drawings. This textbook explains how to prepare formal drawings from design sketches by providing the learner with basic guidelines for drafting layout and minimum design and code requirements in a knowledge-building format. One concept is learned before the next is introduced. The concepts and skills learned from one chapter to the next allow students to prepare complete sets of working drawings for residential and light commercial construction projects. Problem assignments are presented in order of difficulty and in a manner that provides students with a wide variety of architectural drafting experiences.

Real-World Architectural Problems

The problems are presented as preliminary designs or design sketches in a manner that is consistent with actual architectural office practices. It is not enough for students to duplicate drawings from given assignments; they must be able

© 2011 Cengage Learning. All Rights Reserved. May not be scanned, copied or duplicated, or posted to a publicly accessible website, in whole or in part.

to think through the process of drawing development with a foundation based on how drawing and construction components are put into practice. The goals and objectives of each problem assignment are consistent with recommended evaluation criteria based on the progression of learning activities. The drafting problems and tests recommend that work be done using drafting skills on actual drafting materials with either professional manual or computer-aided drafting equipment. A problem solution or test answer should be accurate and demonstrate proper drafting practice.

FEATURES OF THE TEXT

Major features of this text that guide you through the world of architectural design and drafting include realistic application of the information presented throughout each chapter, professional illustrations of each concept to be explored, CADD applications of each type of the working drawings, and exploration of the newest building codes and standards produced by the International Code Council, the NAHB, and LEED.

Applications

Special emphasis has been placed on providing realistic drafting problems. Problems are presented as design sketches or preliminary drawings in a manner that is consistent with architectural practices. The problems have been supplied by architects and architectural designers. Each problem solution is based on the step-by-step layout procedures provided in the chapter discussions.

Problems are given in order of complexity to expose students to a variety of drafting experiences. Problems require students to go through the same thought and decision-making processes that a professional drafter faces daily, including scale and paper size selection, view layout, dimension placement, section placement, and many other activities. Problems can be solved using manual or computer-aided drafting, as determined by individual course guidelines. Chapter tests provide complete coverage of each chapter and can be used for student evaluation or as review.

Illustrations

Drawings and photos are used liberally throughout this textbook to strengthen the concepts presented. Full-color treatment enhances the clarity. Abundant step-by-step illustrations take students through the detailed stages of the drafting process for each application. The step-by-step illustrations are created using computer-aided drafting for the highest accuracy and quality.

Computer-Aided Design Drafting (CADD)

CADD is presented as a valuable tool that has revolutionized the architectural design and drafting industry. The complete discussion of CADD introduces the workstation environment, terminology, drafting techniques, and sample drawings. Although individual course guidelines may elect to solve architectural drafting problems using either computer-aided or manual drafting equipment, the concepts remain the same, with the only difference being the method of presentation.

Construction Techniques and Building Codes

Construction techniques differ throughout the country. This text clearly acknowledges the difference in construction methods and introduces the student to the format used to make a complete set of working drawings for each method of construction. Students may learn to prepare drawings from each construction method or, more commonly, for the specific construction techniques that are used in their locality. The problem assignments are designed to provide drawings that involve a variety of construction alternatives.

To provide oversight of the wide range of construction methods and materials used throughout the country, the 2009 model codes written by the International Code Council are referenced throughout this textbook. The major ICC codes addressed in this textbook include the International Residential Code in Chapters 1 through 41 and the International Building Code in Chapters 42 through 45. Although many municipalities have adopted their own versions of these codes, the use of these model codes provides a firm background before exploring local variations.

Additional Resources

An Additional Resources section is provided at the end of each chapter to provide students with information on additional resources related to chapter topics. This section lists Web sites for companies or organizations that offer

© 2011 Cengage Learning. All Rights Reserved. May not be scanned, copied or duplicated, or posted to a publicly accessible website, in whole or in part.

materials, services, and standards related to the chapter content. The following is an example of how the Additional Resources are presented in the textbook.

Chapter Tests

Chapter tests are found at the end of each chapter. Pick the chapter tests link on the Student CD to access chapter tests using Microsoft Word. The chapter tests allow you to review or test your knowledge of the related chapter content, depending on your course objectives. Open the related link and answer the questions electronically, unless otherwise directed by your instructor.

NEW TO THE SIXTH EDITION

Architectural Drafting and Design, Sixth Edition, provides the following improvements over the fifth edition.

Codes And Standards Compliance

Each chapter is based on information provided by the following major industry leaders:

- 2009 editions of the International Residential Code and the International Building Code published by the International Code Council
- National CAD Standards Version 4
- MasterFormat™ and UniFormat™ published by The Construction Specifications Institute (CSI) and Construction Specifications Canada (CSC)
- LEED rating system published by the U.S. Green Building Council (USGBC)
- Model Green Home Building Guidelines (MGHBG) developed by the National Association of Home Builders (NAHB) and the International Code Council (ICC) that publishes the International Residential Code (IRC)

Going Green

Protecting the environment is one of the most important worldwide issues today. A new flagship feature called *Going Green* is found throughout this textbook, providing current, practical, and experimental energy-efficient architectural design and construction techniques that result in a significant reduction in energy consumption. As the building industry grows to meet the demands of our increasing population, we must take care of the environment and allow for current and future development. As a student, it is very important for you to learn what is available today and to find ways to improve energy efficiency in architectural design and construction for the future in an effort to protect the earth. National and local programs have been established to meet this need.

A leading program is often referred to as *green building.* The U.S. Green Building Council (USGBC) is a key organization developed to promote building design and construction that is environmentally responsible and healthy, while allowing construction to remain profitable. Modern advances in building construction are available to designers, builders, and owners who want to "build green" and make the most of environmental protection in the architectural and construction industries.

Supplemental Chapter Readings

Students are directed to supplemental chapter readings that are found on the Student CD and are identified by a CD icon in appropriate locations throughout this textbook. The supplemental reference material provides optional learning opportunities that can be commonly known topics available for students desiring a review, or this content can be advanced and beyond the scope of this textbook for students desiring further exploration.

CADD Applications

CADD Applications is a special boxed feature that provides a variety of real-world examples, professional presentations, software applications, tips, standards, and procedures used with computer-aided design and drafting. CADD Applications were first introduced in the fourth edition but have been revised, improved, and expanded due to the rapidly changing CADD industry. CADD Applications in the sixth edition range from one sentence

© 2011 Cengage Learning. All Rights Reserved. May not be scanned, copied or duplicated, or posted to a publicly accessible website, in whole or in part.

statements to multi-page content. The following is an example of part of one of the CADD Applications found in the sixth edition.

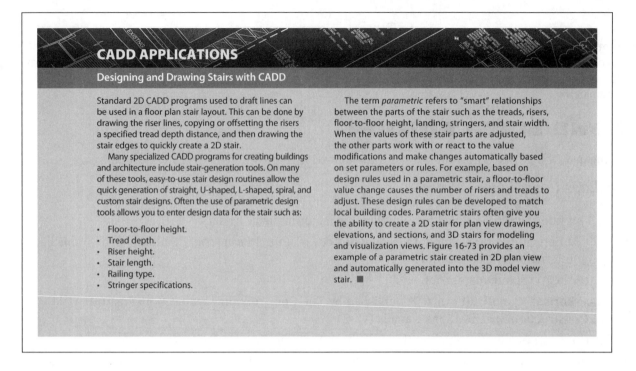

Note

The Note feature is provided throughout this textbook to provide brief information related to the specific content where the note is found.

The Student CD

Although not new to the sixth edition, the student CD has new and improved content that is outlined in the following sections.

Supplemental Chapter Readings

There is a Student CD icon found throughout this textbook guiding you to chapter-related content provided for additional reading and research.

Step-by-Step Layout Drawings

The step-by-step residential house plan drawings link contains the figure drawings found in various chapters with steps for completing the set of working drawings. You can use these to view the drawings and the steps on your computer screen.

Chapter Tests

Chapter Tests are found at the end of each chapter. Pick the Chapter Tests link on the Student CD to access chapter tests. The chapter tests allow you to review or test your knowledge of the related chapter content, depending on your course objectives. Open the related link and answer the questions electronically, unless otherwise directed by your instructor.

Drawing Checklists

Drawing checklists are provided at the end of each layout chapter. The drawing checklists allow you to confirm that you included the features found on the drawing problems related to the specific chapter. The drawing checklists are also found on the Student CD where you can view them on your computer screen and print them, as desired, to check off each item as you complete the drawing problems.

© 2011 Cengage Learning. All Rights Reserved. May not be scanned, copied or duplicated, or posted to a publicly accessible website, in whole or in part.

Drawing Problems

Some of the chapter-ending Drawing Problems are found on the Student CD. These problems are identified in the textbook with a Student CD icon.

Drawing Templates

Pick the Drawing Templates link on the Student CD to access a page containing a link to ARCHITECTURAL-METRIC, ARCHITECTURAL-US, CIVIL-METRIC, and CIVIL-US AutoCAD drawing template (DWT) files. Use these files to begin a new drawing session with predefined drawing settings. Links to AutoCAD drawing (DWG) files are also available. The ARCH-C-TITLE, CIVIL-A1-TITLE, CIVIL-A2-TITLE, CIVIL-C-TITLE, and CIVIL-D-TITLE files contain individual border and title block combinations, associated with a specific sheet size and drawing style. The ARCHITECTURAL CONTENT file includes a variety of AutoCAD content that can be added to existing drawings and templates. Use the Drawing Templates link and the available drawing template and drawing files to create new drawings, as a resource for drawing content, or for inspiration when developing your own templates. Confirm which template drawing and drawing content to use with your instructor.

Architectural Blocks and Symbols

This link contains a variety of useful architectural symbols that you can use in your drawings as you desire or as directed by your instructor. The architectural symbols are AutoCAD drawing (DWG) files for use in creating your own blocks as needed.

Related Web Links

Internet research is an excellent way for you to gain additional knowledge related to architectural drafting and the professional organizations related to architectural drafting and design. This link contains a variety of related Web site links for you to explore as preferred or as directed by your instructor. Pick a link to automatically go to the designated Web site.

Workbook

The Workbook was previously available as a separate bound product. *Architectural Drafting and Design*, Sixth Edition, provides the Workbook on the Student CD with added new and bonus features. Additional problems have been provided to reinforce the knowledge and skills introduced throughout the textbook. These problems are divided into the categories titled WORKBOOK and PROBLEM Files.

Workbook

This Student CD folder contains drawing problems to help you master basic residential drawing skills. Projects are divided into 18 different subfolders that must be mastered to successfully develop architectural working drawings. These problems correspond to the site, floor, electrical, plumbing and HVAC, roof and foundation plans, elevations, details, and sections. These projects can be completed either manually or using a CADD program.

Problems

This Student CD folder is divided into two sections including:

Section 1—Advanced Residential Projects. This Student CD folder contains AutoCAD .dwg files that are arranged by chapter numbers which correspond to the chapter numbers found in the WORKBOOK folder of the Student CD. Drawings are related to the floor, roof and foundation plans, elevations, and sections.

Section 2—Additional Advanced Residential Projects. This section of the Student CD provides AutoCAD .dwg files of the floor plan and elevations for five one-level and multi-level homes.

ORGANIZING YOUR COURSE

Architectural drafting is the primary emphasis of many technical drafting curricula, whereas other programs offer only an exploratory course in this field. This text is appropriate for either application, as its content reflects the common elements in any architectural drafting curriculum.

© 2011 Cengage Learning. All Rights Reserved. May not be scanned, copied or duplicated, or posted to a publicly accessible website, in whole or in part.

Prerequisites

An interest in architectural drafting, plus basic arithmetic, written communication, and reading skills are the only pre-requisites required. Basic drafting skills and layout techniques are presented as appropriate. Students with an interest in architectural drafting who begin using this text will finish with the knowledge and skills required to prepare complete sets of working drawings for residential and light commercial architectural construction projects.

Fundamental through Advanced Coverage

This textbook can be used in an architectural drafting curriculum that covers the basics of residential architecture in a one-, two-, or three-semester sequence. In this application, students use the chapters directly associated with the preparation of a complete set of working drawings for a residence, where the emphasis is on the use of fundamental skills and techniques. The rest of the text can remain as a reference for future study or as a valuable desk reference.

This textbook can also be used in the comprehensive architectural drafting program where a four- to six-semester sequence of residential and light commercial architectural drafting and design is required. In this application, students can expand on the primary objective of preparing a complete set of working drawings for the design of residential and light commercial projects with the coverage of any one or all of the following areas: energy-efficient construction techniques, solar and site orientation design applications, heating and cooling thermal performance calculations, structural load calculations, and presentation drawings.

Section Length

Chapters are presented in individual learning segments that begin with elementary concepts and build until each chapter provides complete coverage of every topic. Instructors can choose to present lectures in short, 15-minute discussions or divide each chapter into 40- to 50-minute lectures.

Drafting Equipment and Materials

Identification and use of manual and computer-aided drafting equipment is given. Students need an inventory of equipment available for use as listed in the chapters. Professional drafting materials are explained, and it is recommended that students prepare problem solutions using actual drafting materials.

SUPPLEMENTS

Instructor's Resource

Spend Less Time Planning and More Time Teaching with Delmar, Cengage Learning's *Instructor Resources to Accompany Architectural Drafting and Design* 6e, preparing for class and evaluating students has never been easier! This invaluable instructor CD-ROM (ISBN: 1435481631) allows you anywhere, anytime access to all of your resources.

Features contained in the e.resource include:

- *Syllabus:* Lesson plans created by chapter. You have the option of using these lesson plans with your own course information. (www.worldclasslearning.com)
- *Chapter Hints:* Objectives and teaching hints that provide the basis for a lecture outline that helps you to present concepts and material. Key points and concepts can be graphically highlighted for student retention.
- *PowerPoint® Presentation:* Slides for each chapter of the text provide the basis for a lecture outline that helps you to present concepts and material. Key points and concepts can be graphically highlighted for student retention.
- *Exam View Computerized Test Bank:* Over 800 questions of varying levels of difficulty are provided in true/false and multiple choice formats so you can assess student comprehension.
- *CADD Drawing Files:* Drawing files for many of the plans in the text are listed in chapter folders. You can modify these plans to create new illustrations or chapter problems, or you can make them available to students who desire to work within AutoCAD.

© 2011 Cengage Learning. All Rights Reserved. May not be scanned, copied or duplicated, or posted to a publicly accessible website, in whole or in part.

Video and Animation Resources

These AVI files graphically depict the execution of key concepts and commands in drafting, design, and AutoCAD and let you bring multimedia presentations into the classroom.

Workbook

A drafting and design workbook, found on the Student CD, correlates with *Architectural Drafting and Design*. The plentiful problem assignments take the beginning architectural drafting student from the basics of line and lettering techniques to drawing a complete set of residential plans. Problems can be done manually or using CADD.

The workbook also provides a series of complete residential plans presented as architectural design problems. The plans range from simple to complex and give the student an opportunity to vary the design elements of the home.

Advanced coverage includes a variety of complete light commercial drafting and design projects. The types of projects include multifamily residential, tilt-up concrete, steel, and heavy timber construction. This information leads the student into the comprehensive drafting and design projects.

When using CADD to create the working drawings of the designs found in the workbook, use the templates found on the Student CD as a basis for project development. (ISBN: 143548164X)

Solutions Manual

A solutions manual is available with answers to end-of-chapter review questions and solutions to end-of-chapter problems. Solutions are also provided for the Workbook problems. (ISBN: 1435481658)

Videos

Two video sets, containing four 20-minute tapes each, are available. The videos correspond to the topics addressed in the text.

- Set #1, ISBN 0–7668–3094–2

- Set #2, ISBN 0–7668–3095–0

Video sets are also available on interactive video CD-ROM.

- Set #1, ISBN 0–7668–3116–7

- Set #2, ISBN 0–7668–3117–5

© 2011 Cengage Learning. All Rights Reserved. May not be scanned, copied or duplicated, or posted to a publicly accessible website, in whole or in part.

© 2011 Cengage Learning. All Rights Reserved. May not be scanned, copied or duplicated, or posted to a publicly accessible website, in whole or in part.

Answers to End-of-Chapter Test Questions and Problem Solutions

© 2011 Cengage Learning. All Rights Reserved. May not be scanned, copied or duplicated, or posted to a publicly accessible website, in whole or in part.

© 2011 Cengage Learning. All Rights Reserved. May not be scanned, copied or duplicated, or posted to a publicly accessible website, in whole or in part.

CHAPTER 1
PROFESSIONAL ARCHITECTURAL CAREERS, OFFICE PRACTICE, AND OPPORTUNITIES

OBJECTIVES

When students have completed this chapter, they will:

- Know the educational requirements for a drafter, designer, architect, and engineer.
- Know the typical office function of a drafter, designer, architect, and engineer.
- Be aware of related fields that drafting may prepare you for.
- Be familiar with the drawing required for a single-family residence.
- Understand their role in creating sustainable homes.

TEST ANSWERS

1. Making corrections, making deliveries, running prints, obtaining permits, and drawing simple drawings from detailed sketches.
2. An understanding of construction methods, mastery of office standards and drawing conventions, and confidence in ability and an effective manager of your time.
3. Simple drawings designed by someone else such as cabinets, site plans, and roof plans.
4. Detailed sketches or examples of similar jobs.
5. Building codes, National Association of Home Builders or other local standards, Sweets, Architectural Graphics, and Time-Saver Standards.
6. Engineering—drafting would be helpful for producing high-quality sketches to give to drafters, and would provide the engineer the ability to draw structures that he or she had designed without requiring the aid of a drafter.

   Model Maker—drafting would aid in properly interpreting plans to produce the models.

   Specification Writer—drafting would help to provide an understanding of the structure so that specifications could be accurate, and would aid in communication with the architect or designer.

   Construction Worker—aid in interpreting plans quickly.

© 2011 Cengage Learning. All Rights Reserved. May not be scanned, copied or duplicated, or posted to a publicly accessible website, in whole or in part.

7. Freehand sketches used to determine room locations and relationships to site and energy efficiency of the home.

8. So that the design will be functional.

9. Floor, foundation, site plans, elevations, and sections.

10. Roof, electrical, framing and grading plans, cabinets, and construction details.

11. Initial contact, preliminary design studies, room planning, initial working drawings, final design considerations, completion of working drawings, permit procedure, job supervision.

12. Preparing preliminary designs for floor and elevations. Make changes and revisions to drawings.

13. Sketches will vary depending on students' imaginations.

CHAPTER 1 PROBLEM SOLUTIONS

Chapter 1 of the text has no problems.

CHAPTER 2
INTRODUCTION TO CONSTRUCTION PROCEDURES

OBJECTIVES

When students have completed this chapter, they will:

- Define and list the elements of given construction documents.
- Outline the required building construction inspection requirements.
- Complete a building permit application.
- Complete a building contract.
- Complete a change order form.
- Fill out a completion notice.

TEST ANSWERS

1. Elements of construction-related documents are defined as follows:

   a. Loan applications—in applying to borrow money for a construction project, the following may be required:

      1. Plot plan
      2. Prints (should include floor plans, foundation plans, wall sections, roof plans, elevations, cross sections, cabinet details, fireplace details, truss details, and heating layout)
      3. Specifications (everything not covered on plans or schedules)
      4. Public Utility District (PUD) heat loss calculations
      5. Proposed sale price
      6. Copy of earnest money agreements

   b. Contracts are an agreement between the client, general contractor and architect. The main concern in preparation of the contract is that all parties specifically understand what will be done, in what period of time, and for what reimbursement. The contract will specify:

      1. The date the project is to be completed
      2. The amount of payment and when the contractor will receive it
      3. The owner's responsibilities during construction
      4. Insurance

© 2011 Cengage Learning. All Rights Reserved. May not be scanned, copied or duplicated, or posted to a publicly accessible website, in whole or in part.

c. Building permits are necessary before construction begins. They are generally given by local government agencies when local requirements are met. A building permit application is a basic form that identifies the major characteristics of the structure to be built, the legal description, location of the property, and information about the applicant. The application is accompanied by plans and plot plans.

d. A completion notice is a document that should be posted in a conspicuous place on or adjacent to the structure. This legal document notifies all parties involved in the project that work has been substantially completed. The completion notice must be recorded in the local jurisdiction.

e. Bids are often obtained by the architect for the client. The purpose is to obtain the best price for the best work. The bid is part of the legal documents for completion of the project. The bid can include the:

    1. Plans

    2. Permits

    3. Roads

    4. Excavation

    5. Water connections

    6. Sewer connections

    7. Foundation

    8. Framing

    9. Fireplace

    10. Plumbing

    11. Wiring

    12. Windows

    13. Roofing

    14. Insulation

    15. Drywall

    16. Siding

    17. Concrete

    18. Painting, and every other element of the construction

f. Change orders are any physical change in plans or specs. It should be noted whether the described change will be an increase or decrease in value and by what dollar amount. It must be signed by the lender, the builder and, if sold, the purchaser must also sign.

2. When the architect or designer is responsible for the supervision of the construction project, it is necessary to work closely with the building contractor to get the proper inspections at the necessary times. Two types of inspections occur most frequently. The regularly scheduled code inspections that are required during specific phases of construction help ensure that the construction methods and materials meet local and national code requirements. The general intent of these inspections is to protect the safety of the occupants and the public. Another type of inspection is often conducted by the lender during certain phases of construction. The purpose of these inspections is to ensure that the materials and methods described in the plans and specifications are being used. The lender has a valuable interest here. If the materials and methods are inferior or not of the standard expected, then the value of the structure may not be what the lender had considered when a preliminary appraisal was made. Another reason for these inspections, and probably the reason that the builder likes best, has to do with disbursement. Disbursement inspections may be requested at various times, such as monthly, or they may be related to a specific disbursement schedule: four times during construction, for example. The intended result of these inspections is the release of funds for payment of work completed.

© 2011 Cengage Learning. All Rights Reserved. May not be scanned, copied or duplicated, or posted to a publicly accessible website, in whole or in part.

When architects or designers supervise the total construction, then they must work closely with the contractor to ensure that the project is completed in a timely manner. When a building project remains idle, the overhead costs, such as construction interest, begin to add up quickly. A contractor who bids a job high but builds quickly may be able to save money in the final analysis. Some overhead costs go on daily even when work has stopped or slowed. The supervisor should also have a good knowledge of scheduling so that inspections can be obtained at the proper time. If an inspection is requested when the project is not ready, the building official may charge a fee for excess time spent. Always try to develop a good rapport with building officials so each encounter goes as smoothly as possible.

© 2011 Cengage Learning. All Rights Reserved. May not be scanned, copied or duplicated, or posted to a publicly accessible website, in whole or in part.

CHAPTER 2 PROBLEM SOLUTIONS

2-1

BUILDING PERMIT APPLICATION | Amount Due _____

Project Location (Address) __**3456 Barrington Drive, Your City, State Zip Code**__

Nearest Cross Street __**Washington Street**__

Subdivision Name __**Barrington Heights**__

Township __**25**__ Range __**1E**__ Section __**36**__ Lot __**8**__ Block __**1**__

Lot Size __**15000**__ (Sq. Ft.) Building Area __**2000**__ (Sq. Ft.) Basement Area __**—**__ (Sq. Ft.) Tax Lot __**2400**__ Garage Area __**576**__ (Sq. Ft.)

Stories __**1**__ Bedrooms __**3**__ Water Source __**Public**__ Sewage Disposal __**Public**__

Estimated Cost of Labor and Material __**$88,500**__

Plans and Specifications made by __**[Student name]**__ accompany this application.

Owner's Name __**[Instructor name]**__ Builder's Name __**[Student name]**__

Address __**[fictitious]**__ Address __**[Student address]**__

City _____ State _____ City _____ State _____

Phone _____ Zip _____ Phone _____ Zip _____

I certify that I am registered under the provisions of ORS Chapter 701 and my registration is in full force and effect. I also agree to build according to the above description, accompanying plans and specifications, the State of Oregon Building Code, and to the conditions set forth below.

__**[Student signature]**__ __**[SS# or fictitious]**__

APPLICANT HOMEBUILDER'S REGISTRATION NO. DATE

I agree to build according to the above description, accompanying plans and specifications, the State of Oregon Building Code, and to the conditions set forth below.

__**[Today's date]**__

APPLICANT DATE

TO BE FILLED IN BY APPLICANT

© 2011 Cengage Learning. All Rights Reserved. May not be scanned, copied or duplicated, or posted to a publicly accessible website, in whole or in part.

2-2

FORM No. 144—BUILDING CONTRACT (Fixed Price—No Service Charge).

TN

THIS AGREEMENT, Made the .... today .... *day of* .... this month ...., 19.. yr., *by and*
between .... [Student name] ...., *hereinafter called*
the Contractor, and .... [Instructor name] ...., *hereinafter called*
the Owner, WITNESSETH:

The parties hereto, each in consideration of the promises of the other, agree as follows:
ARTICLE I: The contractor shall and will perform all the work for the

**Construction of approximate 2000–square foot house to be located at 3456 Barrington Drive, your
City, State, Zip Code. Also known as Lot 8, Block 1, Barrington Heights, your County and State.**

as shown on the drawings and described in the specifications therefor prepared by .... [Student name] ....
....;
said drawings, specifications and this contract hereinafter, for brevity, are called "contract documents"; they are identified by the sig-
natures of the parties hereto and hereby are made a part hereof. All said work is to be done under the direction of ....
.... [Student name] .... *who, for*
brevity hereinafter is designated as "supervisor." (Publisher's note: If the owner himself is to supervise said work, simply insert the
word "owner" in the blank space immediately preceding.) The supervisor's decision as to the true construction and meaning of the
drawings and specifications shall be final and binding upon both parties. All of said drawings and specifications including those herein-
after mentioned have been and will be prepared by the owner at his expense and are to remain his property; said drawings and speci-
fications are loaned to the contractor for the purposes of this contract and at the completion of the work are to be returned to the
owner; none of said contract documents shall be used by, submitted or shown to third parties without owner's written consent.

ARTICLE II: The contractor shall commence work within .... 10 .... *days from the date hereof and substantially com-*
plete the same on or before 4 mos. from date above, 19 .... *. At all times the supervisor shall have access to said work for the*
purpose of inspecting the same and the progress thereof. Should completion be delayed by reason of the fault of the owner or of any
other contractor employed by him or by fire, casualty, strikes, delays in obtaining materials or other reasons beyond the contractor's con-
trol, then the completion date shall be extended for a period equivalent to the time lost for such reasons. Should the parties be unable
to agree as to the period of such extension, the question shall be referred to arbitration as hereunder provided. However, the contractor
shall take special precautions to protect his work during freezing weather and shall be fully responsible for the effect of such weather
upon said work.

ARTICLE III: Subject to the provisions for adjustment set forth in ARTICLE V hereof, the owner shall pay to the contractor
for the performance of this contract, in current funds, the sum of $ .... 88,500 ...., *payable at the following times:*

1. **One–third upon completion of foundation.**

2. **One–third upon completion of drywall.**

3. **One–third 30 days after posting completion notice.**

NOTE—This form not suitable for use as a retail installment contract where a finance charge is being made.

© 2011 Cengage Learning. All Rights Reserved. May not be scanned, copied or duplicated, or posted to a publicly accessible website, in whole or in part.

2-2 (Continued)

Sales tax, if any, shall be paid by the owner in addition to the fixed price mentioned above. Should any progress payments be provided for above, the same shall not include or be based upon any salary, allowance or compensation to the contractor, if an individual, or any officer of the contractor, if a corporation, nor shall it include any of the contractor's overhead or general expenses of any kind; before any such progress payment is made, the contractor shall deliver to the supervisor receipts, vouchers or other evidence satisfactory to the supervisor showing contractor's payment for materials, labor and other items for which the contractor seeks payment, including payments to subcontractors, if any. After three days' written notice to the contractor, bills for labor or materials not paid by the contractor when due, may be paid by the owner and deducted from any payment due or to become due to the contractor. After similar notice, liens, if any are filed, including attorney's fees and costs claimed therein, may be paid, settled or compromised by the owner and amounts paid therefor shall likewise be deducted. However, the contractor shall have the right to contest any such bills, claims or liens. Final payment shall be made within .... days after the completion of said work as certified in writing by the supervisor; however, before the latter shall so certify, the contractor shall submit evidence satisfactory to the supervisor that all payrolls, material bills and other indebtedness connected with the work have been fully paid, including those incurred by each and all of contractor's subcontractors. Provided always, that no payment made to the contractor pursuant to the terms hereof shall be construed as an acceptance of any work or materials not in accordance with the contract documents.

ARTICLE IV: In his performance of said work, contractor shall obtain at his own expense all necessary permits and comply with all applicable laws, ordinances, building codes and regulations of any public authority and be responsible for any infraction or violation thereof and any expense or damages resulting from any such infraction or violation. If the parties are unable to agree upon the dollar amount of contractor's responsibility under this paragraph, the matter shall be referred to arbitration as hereinafter provided. Any work claimed by the supervisor to be defective shall be uncovered by the contractor so that a complete inspection may be made; the contractor further agrees promptly (1) to remove from the job site all materials, whether or not incorporated in the work, condemned by any public authority, (2) to take down and remove all portions of the work likewise condemned or deemed by the supervisor as failing in any way to conform to any of said contract documents and (3) to replace all faulty work and materials.

ARTICLE V: No eliminations or alterations shall be made in the work except upon written order of the supervisor. Should any such eliminations or alterations require new plans or specifications, the owner shall supply the same at his expense. Should any of said eliminations or alterations require an adjustment of the agreed price (upward or downward) such adjustment shall be evidenced by the written agreement of the parties. Should they not be able so to agree, the work shall go on nevertheless under the order mentioned above and the determination of the proper adjustment shall be referred to arbitration as hereinafter provided.

ARTICLE VI: The owner reserves the right to let other contracts in connection with the improvement of which the work herein undertaken by the contractor is a part. In such event, due written notice of such other contracts shall be given promptly to the contractor and the latter shall afford said other contractors a reasonable opportunity for the storage of their materials and the execution of their contracts and shall properly coordinate his work within theirs. In this connection, should the contractor suffer loss by reason of any delay brought about by said other contractors, the owner agrees to reimburse the contractor for such loss; on the other hand, the contractor agrees that if he shall delay the work of said other contractors so as to cause loss for which the owner shall become liable, then he shall reimburse the owner for any such loss. If the parties are unable to agree as to the amounts so to be reimbursed, all questions relative thereto shall be submitted to arbitration as hereinafter provided.

ARTICLE VII: The contractor may subcontract any part of said work but not the whole thereof. Within seven days after entering into any such subcontract, the contractor shall notify the supervisor in writing of the names of said subcontractors and the work to be undertaken by each of them. In this connection, the contractor shall be fully responsible to the owner for the acts and omissions of any of said subcontractors or of persons either directly or indirectly employed by them. Nothing contained herein shall create any contractual relation between any such subcontractor and the owner.

ARTICLE VIII: At no time shall the contractor or any of his subcontractors employ on the work any unfit person or anyone not skilled in the work assigned to him. Any employee adjudged by the supervisor to be incompetent or unfit immediately shall be discharged and shall not again be employed upon the work. Should the contractor at any time be adjudged a bankrupt or should a receiver be appointed for his affairs or should he neglect to supply sufficient properly skilled workmen or supply materials of the proper quality or fail in any respect to prosecute the work with promptness and diligence (except because of matters for which an extension of the completion date is above provided for) or comply with said contract documents or any thereof, then in any of such events, after seven days' written notice to the contractor, the owner may, if the contractor is still in default, terminate the contractor's right to continue said work and may take exclusive possession of the premises and of all materials, tools and appliances thereon and finish the work by whatever method he may deem expedient. In such case the contractor shall not be entitled to receive any further payment until the work is finished. If the unpaid balance of the contract price shall exceed the expense of finishing the work, including compensation to the owner for additional managerial and administrative expenses, such excess shall be paid to the contractor; however, if such expense shall exceed such unpaid balance, the contractor shall pay the difference to the owner. If the parties are unable to agree upon the amounts so to be paid, the question shall be submitted to arbitration as hereinafter provided.

ARTICLE IX: All materials incorporated in any structure in connection with said work by the contractor shall, as soon as incorporated, become the property of the owner. At all times the owner, at his expense, shall effect and maintain fire insurance, with extended coverage, upon the entire structure on which the work under this contract is to be done, in an amount equal to the full insurable value thereof; said insurance shall cover materials on the work site intended by the contractor to be incorporated into said structure but not yet incorporated as well as contractor's temporary buildings incident to the said work. The insured in such policy or policies shall include the owner, the contractor and such other persons as either of them may designate. Loss, if any, shall be made payable to said insured as their respective interests may appear. Certificates showing the existence of such insurance shall be delivered to the contractor if he so requests. The owner shall have power, in his sole discretion to adjust and settle any loss with the insurer which he may deem reasonable. If loss should occur and the parties hereto are unable to agree as to the division of the proceeds thereof, the question as to the amount as to which each insured shall be entitled shall be referred to arbitration as hereinafter provided.

ARTICLE X: At all times the contractor shall take all necessary precautions for the safety of persons on the work by whomsoever employed; he shall comply with all workers' compensation and similar legislation and further shall maintain at his expense public liability insurance against claims for damages because of bodily injury, including death and property damage, which may arise during his operations and those of all subcontractors under him. The insured in all such liability policies shall be the parties hereto and any others which they, or either of them, shall designate. The said insurance shall be written for not less than $ 250,000 for injuries, including death, to any one person in any one accident; not less than $ 500,000 for bodily injury, including death, to more than one person in any one accident, and $ 50,000 property damage. The contractor shall deliver to the owner within ten days after the date hereof, one or more certificates from a responsible insurance company or companies satisfactory to the owner, showing the existence of such insurance. No such insurance shall be cancelled without ten days' prior written notice to the owner.

ARTICLE XI: All disputes, claims or questions subject to arbitration under this contract shall be submitted to three arbitrators, one to be designated by the owner, one by the contractor and the two thus selected to choose the third arbitrator; each party hereto shall have the right to appear before said arbitrators either in person, by attorney or other representative and to present witnesses or evidence, if desired; the decision of the majority of said arbitrators shall be final, binding and conclusive upon all parties hereto; the parties further agree that the decision of the arbitrators shall be a condition precedent to any right of legal action which either party hereto may have against the other. The work herein contracted for shall not be delayed during any arbitration proceedings except by mutual written agreement of the parties. The expense of such arbitration shall be shared equally by the parties hereto.

© 2011 Cengage Learning. All Rights Reserved. May not be scanned, copied or duplicated, or posted to a publicly accessible website, in whole or in part.

2-2 (Continued)

ARTICLE XII: The contractor shall keep the premises (especially that part thereof under the floors thereof) free from accumulation of waste materials or rubbish and at the completion of the work shall remove all of his tools, scaffoldings and supplies and leave the premises broom-clean, or its equivalent.

ARTICLE XIII: If the owner should require a completion bond from the contractor, the premium therefor shall be added to the contract price and paid by the owner on delivery of said bond to him.

ARTICLE XIV: If the contractor employs a foreman or superintendent on said work, all directions and instructions given to the latter shall be as binding as if given to the contractor.

ARTICLE XV: The contractor agrees at all times to keep said work and the real estate on which the same is to be constructed free and clear of all construction and materialmen's liens, including liens on behalf of any subcontractor or person claiming under any such subcontractor and to defend and save the owner harmless therefrom.

ARTICLE XVI: In all respects the contractor shall be deemed to be an independent contractor.

ARTICLE XVII: In the event of any suit or action arising out of this contract, the losing party therein agrees to pay to the prevailing party therein the latter's costs and reasonable attorney's fees to be fixed by the trial court and in the event of an appeal, the prevailing party's costs and reasonable attorney's fees in the appellate court to be fixed by the appellate court.

ARTICLE XVIII: Any notice given by one party hereto to the other shall be sufficient if in writing, contained in a sealed envelope with postage thereon fully prepaid and deposited in the U. S. Registered Mails; any such notice conclusively shall be deemed received by the addressee thereof on the day of such deposit. If such notice is intended for the owner, the envelope containing the same shall be addressed to the owner at the following address: [Instructor's name, fictitious address and phone number may be used]

and if intended for the contractor, if addressed to [Student name, address, and phone number]

ARTICLE XIX: In construing this contract and where the context so requires, the singular shall be deemed to include the plural, the masculine shall include the feminine and the neuter and all grammatical changes shall be made and implied so that this contract shall apply equally to individuals and to corporations; further, the word "work" shall mean and include the entire job undertaken to be performed by the contractor as described in the contract documents, and each thereof, together with all services, labor and materials necessary to be used and furnished to complete the same, except for the preparation of the said plans and specifications and further except the compensation of the said supervisor.

ARTICLE XX: The parties hereto further agree

that this contract is valid for a period of 60 days. If, for reasons out of the contractor's control, construction has not begun by the end of this 60–day period, contractor has the right to rebid and revise the contract.

IN WITNESS WHEREOF, the parties have hereunto set their hands in duplicate.

[Student signature]

CONTRACTOR

[Fictitious signature]

OWNER

© 2011 Cengage Learning. All Rights Reserved. May not be scanned, copied or duplicated, or posted to a publicly accessible website, in whole or in part.

2-3

CHANGE ORDER

Date: ___**today**_____

Project Name: ___**[Instructor name]**_____

Location: ___**3456 Barrington Drive, [Student city, state zip]**_____
___**AKA Lot 8 Block 2, Barrington Heights, [Student county, state]**_____

Description of Change:

Additional Cost: _____

Reduction in Cost: _____

Adjusted Total Project Cost: _____

_____
OWNER

_____
BUILDER

_____
LENDER

© 2011 Cengage Learning. All Rights Reserved. May not be scanned, copied or duplicated, or posted to a publicly accessible website, in whole or in part.

2-4

FORM No. 748
STEVENS-NESS LAW PUBLISHING CO., PORTLAND. OR. 97204
1976

RECORD WHITE COPY
RETAIN PINK COPY

COMPLETION NOTICE

Notice hereby is given that the building or structure on the following described premises, to-wit (insert legal description including street address, if known):

[Student address and legal description]

has been completed.

All persons claiming a lien upon the same under Oregon's Construction Lien Law hereby are notified to file a claim of lien as required by ORS 87.035.

Dated ....[Today's date]............., 19 yr..

Owner or Mortgagee

By ...[Student name]...

P. O. Address ...[Student address]...

....

STATE OF _____)
)ss.
County of ....)

I, ..., being first duly sworn, depose and say:

That on my behalf or as agent for..

....

I did on the_____day of................................. , 19........, duly post a notice of which the above is a true copy, in a conspicuous place upon the land or upon the improvement situated thereon described in said notice, to-wit: by posting, nailing, tacking, pasting, fastening or .... (indicate which) such notice at the front entrance on the building or improvement constructed, altered or repaired on the above described land. (If no building, state in what manner posted.)

....

....

....

Subscribed and sworn to before me this

day of .... , 19.........

....
Notary Public for _____

My commission expires:

(SEAL)

Record with recording officer within 5 days after posting
—ORS 87.045 (3).

STATE OF _____)
) ss.
County of   )

I certify that the within instrument was filed in my office on the.............day of .... , 19........., at ....o'clock .....M., and recorded in book.......................on page.................. or as file/reel number............................ of the Construction Lien Book of said County.

Witness my hand and seal of County affixed.

....
Recording Officer.

By ....
Deputy.

© 2011 Cengage Learning. All Rights Reserved. May not be scanned, copied or duplicated, or posted to a publicly accessible website, in whole or in part.

CHAPTER 3
ARCHITECTURAL DRAFTING EQUIPMENT

OBJECTIVES

When students have completed this chapter, they will:

- Identify and use the following manual drafting equipment, tools, and supplies: pencils, leads, sharpeners, technical pens and accessories, erasers and erasing agents, dusting brush, compass, dividers, drafting machine, parallel bars, templates, triangles, irregular curves, and scales.
- Read the architect's, civil engineer's, and metric scales.

TEST ANSWERS

1. A mechanical pencil is that which has to have a piece of lead manually put into the pencil, and by some mechanical means, twist, push, or pull, the lead is mechanically or semi-automatically advanced into the tip.

2. An automatic pencil is one with a lead chamber that, at the push of a button or tab, will advance the lead from the chamber to the writing tip. When a new piece of lead is needed, it will advance to the tip by action of the push button or tab.

3. Lead sizes available for automatic pencils are 0.3mm, 0.5mm, 0.7mm, and 0.9mm.

4. Common drafting leads range in hardness from F to 6H. The 2H through F leads are used for thick lines while leads for thin lines range from 4H to H.

5. The mechanical pencil is properly used with a slightly rounded point. The lead extends out of the holder about 1/4". The pencil is held at an angle of about 45 degrees in the direction of the line. Rotate the pencil while drawing. This helps maintain a uniform line and keeps the lead uniformly sharp. Sharpen the pencil frequently or as needed.

6. The lead projects out slightly from the pencil tip. The pencil is held nearly perpendicular to the paper. Rotating the pencil while drawing is optional, but preferred by some drafters.

7. Drafting ink should be opaque, matte, or semiflat black finish that will not reflect light. The ink should reproduce without hot spots or line variation. Drafting ink should have excellent adhesion properties for use on paper or film.

8. An electric eraser will remove lines quickly, but without care can also remove paper quickly.

9. The Bow Compass (center-wheel) is the type of compass most commonly used by professionals.

10. Templates should be used when possible because the use of a compass is more time consuming.

11. A compass point should have a shoulder to keep the point from penetrating the paper any more than necessary.

12. Two common lead points that may be used in a compass are the elliptical point and the conical point.

13. Placing drafting tape or plastic stick-ons at the center of a circle before using the compass will keep the compass point from making a hole in the paper.

14. A good divider should not be too loose or too tight so that it can be adjusted easily with one hand.

15. Two uses for dividers are to lay out equal increments and to transfer dimensions from one feature to another.

16. Most drafting machine heads will automatically lock at 15-degree increments.

17. There are 60 minutes in one degree and 60 seconds in one minute.

© 2011 Cengage Learning. All Rights Reserved. May not be scanned, copied or duplicated, or posted to a publicly accessible website, in whole or in part.

18. The soft green and pink erasers contain no pumice and are designed for use on even the most delicate types of paper without doing damage to the surface. The color difference is established only to satisfy long-established personal preferences.

19. Vinyl eraser

20. Remove the unwanted image without removing the surface. Erase only hard enough to remove the desired image. However, you must apply enough pressure to remove the desired line completely.

21. Circles, door swings, sinks, bathroom fixtures, kitchen appliances, electrical symbols

22. Irregular curve, also known as a French curve

23. The parallel bar slides up and down the drafting table on cables that are connected to pulleys mounted at the top and bottom corners of the table surface. The parallel bar allows you to draw horizontal lines, and supports triangles for drawing vertical lines and angles.

24. Parallel bars are common for architectural drafting because architectural drawings are commonly very large. This requires that straight lines be drawn the length of the table. The parallel bar can also be used with the table inclined.

25. Angles from 15% to 75%

26. 1/8" = 1'-0", 1/4" = 1'-0", 1/2" = 1'-0", 3/4" = 1'-0", 1 1/2" = 1'-0", 3" = 1'-0"

27. 1" = 50'

28. 1/4" = 1'-0"

29. Drawing dimensions, amount of information required, paper size standard practices

30. The architect's scale is commonly used, because it has scale calibrations that are typically used on architectural drawings.

31. 25.4

32. All measurements are in units of 10.

    Questions 33–40 allow some tolerance.

33. 32'-0", 40'-0", 102 mm

34. 16'-0", 80'-0", 204 mm

35. 10'-9", 120'-0", 510 mm

36. 8'-0", 160'-0", 1020 mm

37. 5'-4 1/2", 200'-0", 2040 mm

38. 4'-0 1/4", 240'-0", 5.1 m

39. 2'-8 1/4", 400'-0"

40. 1'-4 1/8", 800'-0"

CHAPTER 3 PROBLEM SOLUTIONS

Chapter 3 of the textbook contains no problems.

© 2011 Cengage Learning. All Rights Reserved. May not be scanned, copied or duplicated, or posted to a publicly accessible website, in whole or in part.

CHAPTER 4
DRAFTING MEDIA AND REPRODUCTION METHODS

OBJECTIVES

When students have completed this chapter, they will:

- Identify the factors that influence the selection of drafting media.
- Explain the difference between drafting papers and films.
- Identify sheet sizes and title block information.
- Identify and use diazo reproduction equipment and materials.
- Explain the uses of photocopy reproduction.
- Discuss the advantages and uses of microfilm.
- Explain computerized reproduction and information retrieval.

TEST ANSWERS

1. Factors that influence the purchase and use of drafting materials are durability, smoothness, erasability, dimensional stability, transparency, and cost.

2. Material transparency is important because the diazo reproduction methods require that light pass through the material. The goal of a drawing is good reproduction, so the more transparent the material the better the reproduction.

3. Vellum is drafting paper specifically designed to accept pencil or ink drawings.

4. Polyester film, also known as mylar, is a plastic material that offers excellent dimensional stability, erasability, transparency, and durability.

5. Polyester film is also known by its trade name, Mylar.

6. Mat is surface texture. The double mat has texture on both sides so that drawing can be done on either side if necessary. The single mat is the most common with one side a slick non-drawing surface.

7. The combination that would yield the best reproduction is ink on polyester film.

8. The primary elements that will give the best reproduction is the blackest, most opaque lines or images on the most transparent base or material.

9. Standard cut sheets are 18" × 24", 24" × 36", 28" × 42", 30" × 42", 30" × 48", 36" × 48". Standard roll sizes are 18" to 48" wide.

10. Some companies use a system of numbers along the top and bottom margin and letters along the left and right margins called zoning. The reader can refer to the location of a specific item as D-4, which means that the item can be found at or near the intersection of D across and 4 up or down.

11. Drawing number, company name, project or client name, drawing name or title, scale, sheet identification, date, drawn by, checked by, architect, or designer, revisions

12. Either in the title block or in conjunction with the drawing title on the field of the drawing or both

13. The title block and sheet identification number ends up on the front.

14. There is usually a written request for a change that comes from the contractor, owner, or architect. The change is then implemented on the drawings. Where changes are made on the drawing, a circle revision number accompanies the change. The revision number is keyed to a place in the title block where the revision number, date, initials of the person making the change, and an optional brief description of the change appear. For further record, the person making the change may also fill out a form called a change notice that has complete information about the change.

© 2011 Cengage Learning. All Rights Reserved. May not be scanned, copied or duplicated, or posted to a publicly accessible website, in whole or in part.

15. Another name for the diazo print is blue-line print.

16. A diazo print is not the same as a blueprint. Diazo prints are blue lines on a white background while true blueprints are white lines on a blue background.

17. The diazo process is a printing process that uses an ultraviolet light source to pass through a translucent "original" material and expose a chemical coated print material underneath. The chemically coated print material is then exposed to ammonia vapor which will activate the chemical coating that remains unexposed forming blue images on a white background.

18. A good quality print should have lines and letters that are dark blue and the background almost all white.

19. Sepias are diazo materials that are used to make secondary originals. A secondary or second generation original is actually a print of the original drawing that can be used as an original. The diazo process is performed with a material called sepia.

20. Extreme care should be taken to avoid direct contact of ammonia with your eyes. Always wear safety goggles or other equivalent eye protection. Avoid contact of ammonia and filter with your skin or clothing. Ammonia can cause uncomfortable irritation and burns when in direct contact with your skin.

21. If ammonia is spilled on the skin, promptly wash with plenty of water. Remove clothing if necessary to flush the affected parts adequately. If the eyes are exposed to ammonia, irrigate as quickly as possible with water for at least 15 minutes.

    Anyone overcome by ammonia vapor should be removed to fresh air at once. Apply artificial respiration, preferably with the aid of oxygen if breathing is labored or has stopped.

22. The advantage of photocopy over diazo is that prints can be made on all types of paper, bond, vellum, polyester film, colored paper, or other translucent materials. The reproduction capabilities also include instant print sizes ranging from 45% to 141% of the original size. Larger or smaller sizes are possible by making a print from a print by enlarging or reducing in two or more steps. Reproduction clarity is also excellent.

23. For mailing or filing

24. The big advantage of microfilm is that large quantities of information can be stored in a very small area.

25. Computer-aided drafting is rapidly replacing the need for drawings to be stored on microfilm. CAD drawings are stored in computer files that can be easily copied for use in numerous places or for safe storage.

CHAPTER 4 PROBLEM SOLUTION

1. a. sheet number, b. company logo and name, c. plot/completion date, d. revision date, e. file number, f. drawing title, g. job number, h. title block identification

© 2011 Cengage Learning. All Rights Reserved. May not be scanned, copied or duplicated, or posted to a publicly accessible website, in whole or in part.

CHAPTER 5
SKETCHING APPLICATIONS

OBJECTIVES

When students have completed this chapter, they will:

- Define and discuss the advantages and uses of freehand sketching.
- Prepare orthographic and pictorial sketches.
- Perform basic geometric constructions.

TEST ANSWERS

1. Sketching is freehand drawing without the aid of formal drafting equipment. All that is needed is paper and pencil.

2. The computer graphics technician will prepare a sketch on graph paper to help establish the coordinates for drawing components.

3. For sketching all you need is a pencil and paper. The pencil should have soft lead, a common number 2 pencil will work fine. A mechanical pencil with F or HB or an automatic 0.7 or 0.9 mm pencil with F or HB lead is a good alternative. The pencil lead should not be sharp, a dull slightly rounded point is best. A good sketching paper is newsprint, although most anything will work.

4. When sketching, the sketching paper should not be taped down to the table. The best sketches are made when you are able to move the paper to the most comfortable position.

5. If a long straight line is drawn without moving the hand, your arm tends to make the line curve rather than remain straight.

6. A good sketching paper is newsprint, although most anything will work. A surface that is not too smooth is best.

7. Two methods that can be used to sketch irregular shapes are the box-in method and frame of reference.

8. A pictorial sketch where the receding axes of the object are approximately 30%

9. Isometric lines are on or parallel to the isometric axis and nonisometric lines are not.

10. Proportions are used rather than actual measurements to save time and have the resulting sketch look like the real object.

11. Any projection of the features of an object onto an imaginary plane

12. Perpendicular

13. When the surface is at an angle to the plane of projection

14. 6

15. a. Easier to draw and read when you can project from one view to the next
    b. Standard view relationship allows uniform communications for any reader

16. Elevation

17. Round, true size and shape

18. Elliptical

19. Take a strip of paper and mark two ends of the approximate radius of the desired circle. Place one point at the desired center. Rotate the paper keeping the point at the center while you make marks at the other point creating the circumference of the circle. After doing this all the way around, connect the marks by sketching the desired circle.

© 2011 Cengage Learning. All Rights Reserved. May not be scanned, copied or duplicated, or posted to a publicly accessible website, in whole or in part.

20. The paper needs to be free to rotate, because you want to turn the paper in one continuous motion without interruption.

21. Radius

22. Diameter

23. For the 14" circle, tie a string between a pencil and a pin, with a distance of 7" between the pencil and the pin. Stick the pin at the desired center and rotate the pencil around to draw a circle. On a construction site, the pin is replaced with a nail that is driven at the desired center. The string is 3'-3" from the nail to the pencil and a circle is drawn in the same manner.

24. All of the lines in a sketch are related by size and direction. For the sketch to communicate accurately it should be drawn to the proper proportions of the object.

25. The sketch of the object can be surrounded by a block to help determine the desired shape and proportions.

26. Exterior elevations and cabinet elevations

27. Plan

28. Front, rear, right, and left sides

29. For better control and so the point does not break easily

30. Hold the pencil at arm's length and establish the proportions of the sketch to match the length of the pencil to the features on the house.

CHAPTER 5 PROBLEM SOLUTIONS

5-1   Students should sketch the front view of their homes. Student solutions will vary.

5-2   Students should sketch one 4-inch diameter circle using the box or trammel method and another using the hand compass method.

5-3   Students should sketch an object. Student solutions will vary.

5-4   Students should make an isometric sketch of a structure. Student solutions will vary.

5-5   Students should sketch a front and side view of the structure in Problem 5-4. Student solutions will vary.

5-6

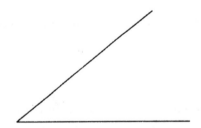

© 2011 Cengage Learning. All Rights Reserved. May not be scanned, copied or duplicated, or posted to a publicly accessible website, in whole or in part.

5-7

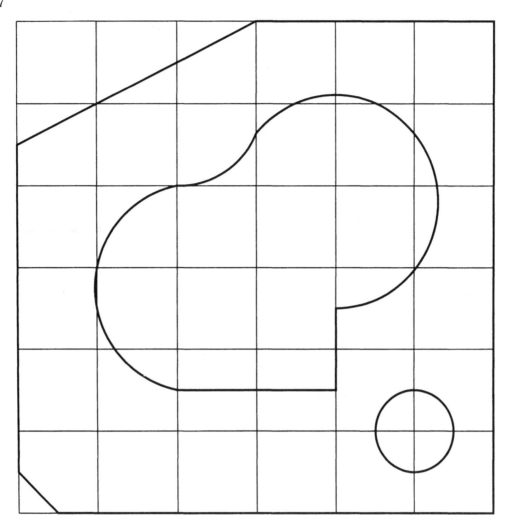

© 2011 Cengage Learning. All Rights Reserved. May not be scanned, copied or duplicated, or posted to a publicly accessible website, in whole or in part.

5-8

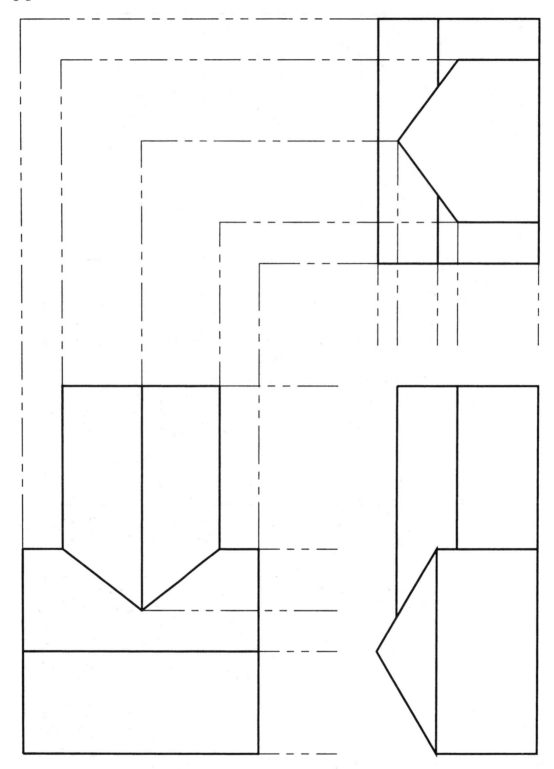

© 2011 Cengage Learning. All Rights Reserved. May not be scanned, copied or duplicated, or posted to a publicly accessible website, in whole or in part.

5-9

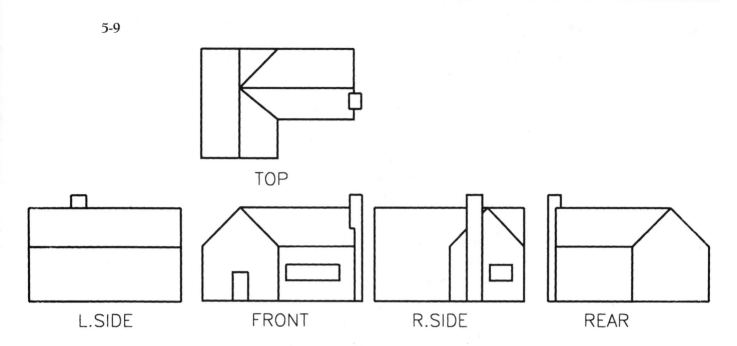

TOP

L.SIDE   FRONT   R.SIDE   REAR

5-10

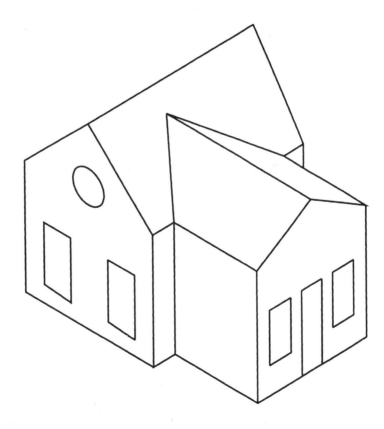

© 2011 Cengage Learning. All Rights Reserved. May not be scanned, copied or duplicated, or posted to a publicly accessible website, in whole or in part.

CHAPTER 6
ARCHITECTURAL LINES AND LETTERING

OBJECTIVES

When students have completed this chapter, they will:

- Discuss and implement proper line uniformity, contrast, and darkness.
- Describe and draw the following lines: guidelines, outlines, extension lines, dimension lines, and leaders.
- Discuss the use of graphite lead with mechanical and automatic pencils.
- Describe proper technical pen usage.
- Discuss and use proper architectural lettering technique.
- Describe the following display lettering methods: lettering template, lettering guides, lettering machines, and transfer materials.
- Draw a given floor plan using two different presentation techniques.

TEST ANSWERS

1. All properly drawn lines are the same darkness.
2. Construction lines are used for laying out a drawing. Construction lines are drawn very lightly so that they will not reproduce and will not be mistaken for any other lines on the drawing.
3. All lines should be drawn dark, crisp, sharp, and uniform in thickness. There is no variation in darkness, only a variation in line thickness known as line contrast. Certain lines may be drawn thick so that they stand out clearly from other information on the drawing.
4. Guidelines are the same as construction lines and do not reproduce when properly drawn. They are drawn to guidelines of lettering.
5. The recommended thickness for outlines is 0.7 mm or a thick line.
6. Dashed lines are used to denote drawing features that are not visible in relationship to the view or plan. Dashed lines can represent beams, headers, upper kitchen cabinets, or electrical circuit runs.
7. Extension lines show the extent of a dimension. Extension lines are used to denote the center of a window or sliding door, and also the center of interior walls.
8. Extension lines show the extent of a dimension.
9. Extension lines begin at the feature, with a small space from the feature and extend about 1/8" beyond the last dimension line.
10. Leader lines are thin, sharp, crisp lines. These lines are used to connect notes to related features on a drawing. Leaders may be drawn freehand or with an irregular curve. The leader should begin centered at the beginning or end of the note and be terminated with an arrowhead at the feature.

© 2011 Cengage Learning. All Rights Reserved. May not be scanned, copied or duplicated, or posted to a publicly accessible website, in whole or in part.

11. When dimension lines terminate at extension lines they have a slash, dot, or arrowhead to indicate termination. Examples of each are shown below:

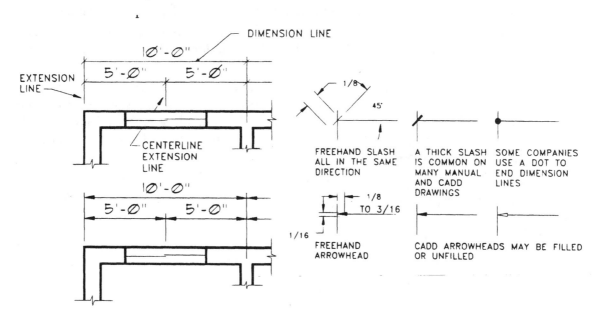

12. Architectural line work does not differ from mechanical drafting line work except that architectural line work is not as rigidly standardized.

13. The advantage of drawing certain outlines thicker than others enhances certain features so that they clearly stand out from other items on the drawing.

14. Dark shading can be used to accentuate features such as walls and partitions when all lines are drawn the same thickness.

15. When drawing with a technical fountain pen, hold the pen perpendicular to the vellum or Mylar. Move the pen at a constant speed. Do not apply any pressure to the pen. Care should be taken to provide space between instrument and drawing surface so that ink does not flow and cause ink smears.

16. Architectural lettering style is derived from the single-stroke Gothic style but is more individualized. Architectural styles can range from standard Gothic form to avant garde characters.

17. Minimum recommended lettering heights should be 1/8 inch.

18. Letters within a word should be uniformly spaced with approximately equal background areas. The minimum space between letters is 1/16 inch.

19. The spaces between words should be the same as the letter height.

20. The recommended horizontal space between sentences or lines should be a minimum of one-half the height of the letters.

21. Guidelines should always be used for lettering.

22. Guidelines are necessary for freehand lettering so that each letter will be of uniform height.

23. When doing freehand lettering with an automatic pencil, try a 0.5 mm with an H, F, or HB lead. The same leads can be used with a mechanical pencil, but a slightly rounded point is recommended.

24. To avoid smudging the drawing while lettering, protect the drawing by resting your hand on a clean protective sheet of paper placed over the drawing.

25. Fraction numerals shall be full size; the fraction division line may be either horizontal or diagonal with clear space between the line and numerals; provide adequate space from whole numbers.

26. The Ames lettering guide and the lettering aid are two quick ways to make guidelines.

© 2011 Cengage Learning. All Rights Reserved. May not be scanned, copied or duplicated, or posted to a publicly accessible website, in whole or in part.

27. Mechanical lettering templates should be placed along a straight edge so that lines are straight and the template can easily be moved from letter to letter.

28. An advantage for using lettering guides is that uniformity of lettering is maintained.

29. Lettering machines are used to prepare drawing titles, labels, or special headings in a variety of fonts, styles, and letter sizes. This is especially useful for making display, cover, or rendering drawing titles.

30. Transfer letters may be used in any combination to prepare drawing titles, labels, or special headings. Special drawing transfers are also made that can be used on presentation drawings. For example, a wide assortment of home furnishings or plant and office products may be purchased to prepare layout drawings. Other special items available are scales, call outs, trees, landscaping items, people representations and transportation figures.

31. Rectangular coordinate

32. Based on selecting points that are a given distance from the horizontal and vertical axes

33. X = 0, and Y = 0

34. Always measured from the origin

35. 4,3

36. From the previous point

37. @ 0,2

38. From the previous point using a distance and angle

39. @ 2 < 90

40. The CADD system might have a command such as SNAP that allows you to move the cursor in exact increments to pick points where desired.

41. Gives you the coordinates of the cursor location

42. A complete assortment of any one size and style of lettering or text

43. Refers to text, notes, dimensions, and text symbols

44. Any value that is maintained by the computer for a command or function that has variable parameters

45. The basis for starting a drawing. It contains all the standard elements that you need.

46. Template

47. Establishes the text height when plotted at the desired scale

48. 1/4" = 1'-0" (1/4" = .25), .25" = 12", 12/.25 = 48

49. Consistent shape and size and a variety of styles

50. There are CADD text styles that look like quality freehand architectural lettering.

CHAPTER 6 PROBLEM SOLUTIONS

Problems 6–1 through 6–2: See instructions for problem solutions.
Problem 6–3

a. extension line

b. dimension line

c. center line/extension line

d. hidden line

e. leader

f. thin object line for symbol

g. long break line

h. dimension line

i. center line/extension line

j. extension line

k. hidden line

© 2011 Cengage Learning. All Rights Reserved. May not be scanned, copied or duplicated, or posted to a publicly accessible website, in whole or in part.

CHAPTER 7
COMPUTER-AIDED DESIGN AND DRAFTING IN ARCHITECTURE

OBJECTIVES

When students have completed this chapter, they will:

- Define CADD-related terminology.
- Identify at least three factors that influence an increase in productivity with CADD.
- Describe potential advantages and disadvantages with CADD.
- Describe elements of the U.S. National CAD Standard.
- Discuss layers and layer names.

TEST ANSWERS

1. Computer-aided design and drafting

2. There is agreement among users that CADD increases drafting productivity over traditional manual drafting methods. Estimates range from two times to tens times productivity increase over manual drafting. In reality, any increase in productivity depends on the task, the system, and how quickly employees learn to use CADD. Productivity is also directly related to the amount of time a company has had CADD in use and to employee acceptance experience with the technology. Most companies can expect more productivity after the users become comfortable with the capabilities of the equipment and software.

   For many duties, CADD does multiply productivity several times. This is especially true of multiple and time-consuming tasks, which CADD performs much faster and more accurately than manual techniques. A great advantage of CADD is that it increases the time available to designers and drafters for creativity by reducing the time they spend on the actual preparation of drawings. A big increase in productivity over manual drafting is evident when drawings are revised. CADD makes the drawing revision process quick and easy. Some of the business tasks related to architectural design and drafting, such as analyzing construction costs, writing specifications, computing, taking materials inventories, scheduling time, and storing information, are also done better and faster on a computer.

   With some CADD systems, a designer can look at several design alternatives at one time. The drafter draws in layers; one layer can be the plan perimeter, the next layer fixtures, the next electrical, and the next dimensions and notes. Each layer appears in a different color for easy comparison.

3. Analyzing construction costs, writing specifications, computing, taking materials inventories, scheduling time, and storing information

4. Drawings are made in layers, each perfectly aligned with the others. Each layer contains its own independent information. Layers can be reproduced individually, in combination, or together as one composite drawing.

   Using layers increases productivity in several ways:

   - Each layer can be assigned a different color, line type, and line weight to correspond to line standards and to help improve clarity.
   - Changes can be made to a layer easily, affecting all objects drawn on the layer.
   - Selected layers can be turned off or frozen to decrease the amount of information displayed on the screen or to speed screen regeneration.
   - Each layer can be plotted in a different color, line type, or line weight, or set not to plot at all.

© 2011 Cengage Learning. All Rights Reserved. May not be scanned, copied or duplicated, or posted to a publicly accessible website, in whole or in part.

- Specific information can be grouped on separate layers. For example, a floor plan can be drawn using specific floor plan layers, the electrical plan on electrical layers, and the plumbing plan on plumbing layers.

- Several plot sheets can be created from the same drawing file by controlling layer visibility to separate or combine drawing information. For example, a floor plan and electrical plan can be reproduced together and sent to an electrical contractor for a bid. The floor plan and plumbing plan can be reproduced together and sent to a plumbing contractor.

5. The CADD system can perform a number of design functions in a manner that often exceeds expectations. Plan components, such as room arrangements, can be stored in a design file; this allows the designer to call on a series of these components and rearrange them in a new design. Another aid to design is that a given plan can be quickly reduced or enlarged in size, with all components remaining in proportion. One particular room can be changed while the rest of the design stays the same. The design capability of drawing layers allows the architect to prepare a preliminary layout on one layer while changing and rearranging components on another layer.

6. There is concern about the effect of the CADD working environment on the individual worker. Some studies have found that people should not work at a computer workstation for longer than about four hours without a break. Physical problems can develop when someone is working at a poorly designed CADD workstation. These problems can range from injury to eyestrain. In general, a workstation should be designed so you sit with your feet flat on the floor, your calves perpendicular to the floor, and your thighs parallel to the floor. Your back should be straight, your forearms should be parallel to the floor, and your wrists should be straight. For some people, the keyboard should either be adjustable or separate from the computer, to provide more flexibility. The keyboard should be properly positioned, and arm or wrist supports used to reduce elbow and wrist tension. Also, when the keys are depressed, a slight sound should be heard to assure the user that the key has made contact.

The monitor should be 18" to 28" (450–700 mm), or approximately one arm's length, away from your head. The screen should be adjusted to 15 to 30° below your horizontal line of sight. Eyestrain and headache can be a problem with extended use. If the position of the monitor is adjustable, you can tilt or turn the screen to reduce glare from overhead or adjacent lighting. Some users have found that a small amount of background light is helpful. Monitor manufacturers offer large, flat, nonglare screens that help reduce eyestrain. Some CADD users have suggested changing screen background and text colors weekly to give variety and reduce eyestrain.

The chair should be designed for easy adjustments to give you optimum comfort. It should be comfortably padded. Your back should be straight or up to 10° back, your feet should be flat on the floor, and your elbow-to-hand movement should be horizontal when you are using the keyboard, mouse, or digitizer. The mouse or digitizer puck should be close to the monitor so movement is not strained and equipment use is flexible. You should not have to move a great deal to look directly over the cursor to activate commands.

In addition to an ergonomically designed workstation, your own personal work habits can contribute to a healthy environment. Try to concentrate on good posture until it becomes second nature. Keeping your feet flat on the floor helps improve posture. Try to keep your stress level low because increased stress can contribute to tension, which may aggravate physical problems. Take breaks periodically to help reduce muscle fatigue and tension. You should consult with your doctor for further advice and recommendations.

The plotter makes some noise and is best located in a separate room next to the workstation. Some companies put the plotter in a central room, with small office workstations around it. Others prefer to have plotters near the individual workstations, which may be surrounded by acoustical partition walls or partial walls.

© 2011 Cengage Learning. All Rights Reserved. May not be scanned, copied or duplicated, or posted to a publicly accessible website, in whole or in part.

7. World Wide Web

8. Outsourcing means sending parts of a project out to subcontractors for completion. Outsourcing to multiple resources requires consistency in procedure and similarity in tools. This interactive teamwork of the future requires clear measurement of progress. The collaboration tools now being developed give architects a higher level of communication and control over the production process.

9. Virtual reality refers to a world that appears to be a real or actual world, having many of the properties of a real world. The VR world often appears and feels so real that it almost is real. This is where the computer is used to simulate environments, including the inside and outside of buildings, sound, and touch.

10. An intranet links computers within a company or organization; the Internet is a worldwide network of communication between computers.

11. Walk-through can be described as a camera in a computer program that is set up like a person walking through a building, around a building, or through a landscape. Fly-through is similar, but the camera is like a helicopter flying over the area. Fly-through is generally not used to describe a tour through a building.

12. A scale factor is a numerical value that is used in the proper scaling of text and dimension objects, such as dimension text, arrowheads or slashes, and the size of the model limits. When drawing in CADD, the objects are always full scale.

13. An example of a complete model file name is PR2004A-FPF1XX.dwg, where:
    - PR2004 is the project code.
    - A- is the discipline designator.
    - FP is the model file type.
    - F1XX is the user definable code.
    - .dwg is the AutoCAD file extension. .dgn is used for a MicroStation file; .dwf is a design web format file; .dxf is a drawing exchange file.

14. A sample sheet name is PR2004AD102XXX.dwg, where:
    - PR2004 is the project code.
    - AD is the discipline designator with level 2, Architectural Demolition.
    - 1 is the sheet type.
    - 02XXX is the sheet sequence number and user definable characters.
    - .dwg is the AutoCAD file extension (.dgn for a MicroStation file).

15. A template (CADD) is a pattern of a standard or commonly used feature or features that is created once and then used on following drawings.

16. An architectural drawing to be plotted at 1/4" = 1'-0" has a scale factor calculated like this:

    1/4" = 1'-0"

    25" = 12"

    12/25" = 48"

    The scale factor is 48.

17. AutoCAD, for example, refers to the place where drawing objects are created as *model space,* and sheet space is called layout space. *Layout space* is an area used to lay out the sheet of paper to be plotted. Everything you draw in CADD is drawn full scale in model space. When you enter layout (sheet) space, a real-size sheet of paper is placed over the top of the model space drawing. Border line, title blocks, and notes are also found on the real-size paper layout space.

© 2011 Cengage Learning. All Rights Reserved. May not be scanned, copied or duplicated, or posted to a publicly accessible website, in whole or in part.

18.

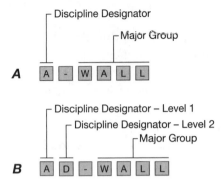

19. Drawing content is the variety of information in the drawing, such as layers, layouts, line types, text styles, and symbols.

20. Sheet grid coordinates is a system of numbers along the top and bottom margins and letters along the left and right margins, allowing a drawing to read like a road map.

OPTIONAL QUESTIONS

Refer to the student CD: Supplemental Reference: THE CADD WORKSTATION to answer the following:

CD7–1 Personal computer: a small digital computer based on a microprocessor and designed to be used by one person at a time

CD7–2 Ergonomics is the study of a worker's relationship to physical and psychological environments.

CD7–3 Describe the following components of a computer-aided drafting workstation:

   a. Computer—A machine that manipulates data according to a list of instructions

   b. Monitor—Similar to a TV screen, and resting below it or attached to it is the keyboard. The monitor displays alphanumeric information (characters and numbers) from input given at the keyboard. *Input* is any data or information that the operator puts into the computer. The monitor also displays graphics (lines, symbols, or pictures) as input from the keyboard, mouse, or digitizer.

   c. Digitizer—An electronically sensitized drafting board. The digitizer can be adjacent to the monitor or built into the unit

   d. Plotter—An output device used in computer-aided drafting to create a hardcopy of a drawing

CD7–4 Define the following CADD terms:

   a. Hardware—Workstation components

   b. Software—Instructions that tell a computer what to do and how to do it

   c. Program—A sequence of instructions that a computer can interpret and execute

   d. Commands—Computer instructions

   e. Soft copy files stored in a computer

   f. Default value—A preassigned value or a value that is used when no ther value is assigned

   g. Disk drive—A typical CADD system has one or two disk drives for floppy diskettes, which are referred to as disks. These removable disks are convenient for storing and transferring data to and from your computer

   h. Storage—Computer data storage, often called storage or memory; refers to computer components, devices, and recording media that retain digital data used for computing

   i. Floppy disk—Removable disks are convenient for storing and transferring data to and from your computer

   j. Menu—A list of symbols, lines, or words

   k. Hard copy—Printed or paper copy of computer file

© 2011 Cengage Learning. All Rights Reserved. May not be scanned, copied or duplicated, or posted to a publicly accessible website, in whole or in part.

l. File—A file maintained in computer-readable form

m. Network—A communication or connection system that allows each computer to be linked to other computers, to printers and plotters, to data storage devices, and to other equipment

n. PC—Personal computer

o. Puck—Electronic computer input device

p. Mouse—Has a small ball on the underside that rolls as you move it across a flat surface. Optical mice have a tracking system that works with light, which illuminates the surface on which the mouse is moving. A mouse typically has two or three buttons. When the cursor is in the desired position, the pick button can be pressed to cause the desired input to the computer.

q. Stylus—Electronic computer input device

r. Windows—Microsoft Corporation operating system

s. Attribute—Computer text

t. Font—A specific size and style of type within a type family

u. Optical mouse—An optical sensor observes the surface through a lens and takes very rapid pictures to compute tracking movement. Sensors inside the mouse send messages to the software that operates the screen cursor or crosshairs.

v. Facsimile—Duplicator that transmits the copy by wire or radio

w. Resolution—Print quality is measured in *dots per inch* (dpi). This is also referred to as resolution.

x. Text—Letters and numbers

y. Layers—Allow for details of a design or different drafting information to be separated. Layers are generally of different colors and have their own names. Layers can be kept together, or individual layers can be turned on or off as needed.

z. Backup—A copy of a file or directory on a separate storage device

CD7–5 The most common type of injury is referred to as repetitive strain injury (RSI), but it also has other names, which include repetitive movement injury (RMI), cumulative trauma disorder (CTD), and occupational overuse syndrome (OOS). One of the most common effects is carpal tunnel syndrome (CTS), which develops when inflamed muscles trap the nerves that run through your wrists.

CD7–6 In addition to an ergonomically designed workstation, your own personal work habits can contribute to a healthy environment. Try to concentrate on good posture until it becomes second nature. Keeping your feet flat on the floor helps improve posture. Try to keep your stress level low because increased stress can contribute to tension, which may aggravate physical problems. Take breaks periodically to help reduce muscle fatigue and tension. You should consult with your doctor for further advice and recommendations.

CD7–7 The cursor is an on-screen symbol, which is usually an arrow or a box, and crosshairs are made up of a horizontal and a vertical line.

CD7–8 Briefly discuss each of the following data storage devices:

a. Disk—A typical CADD system has one or two disk drives for *floppy diskettes,* which are referred to as *disks*. These removable disks are convenient for storing and transferring data to and from your computer. The most commonly used disk is the 3 1/2" *diskette*, which stores up to 1.44 megabytes (MB). 1 MB = 1 million bytes of data files. The 3 1/2" disk is in a hard case that makes it easy to transport. Most new computers are purchased without floppy disk drives because this technology is outdated and is being replaced by optical disk drives.

b. Hard drive—Computers normally have non-removable or internal hard drives. The hard drives are used to store program files and to store your work. Hard drives are available in many sizes, but large hard drives are recommended for CADD applications. Three to four *gigabyte* or larger hard drives are common because the operating system and the CADD program can occupy 100 MB or more of disk space.

© 2011 Cengage Learning. All Rights Reserved. May not be scanned, copied or duplicated, or posted to a publicly accessible website, in whole or in part.

   c. Optical disk—Commonly called *compact disk* (CD) drives. One CD can store up to 4 gigabytes (GB).

   d. High-capacity disk drive—Gives you high-capacity and high-performance storage. These drives are available in 1- to 10-GB drives. Also available are 3-, 5-, 7-, and 10-GB tape drives. These products provide you with large movable storage capabilities. High-capacity disks are commonly used to store one or more projects or individual customer accounts. They are also used to back up the hard drive and to archive files or to share large files or many files with coworkers or other company sites. The high-capacity drive, CD, or DVD drive can also be used to store items that you want to save but do not want to fill up the hard drive.

CHAPTER 7 PROBLEM SOLUTIONS

Problems 7–1 through 7–25 are written reports of 250 words or less. Student solutions vary.

© 2011 Cengage Learning. All Rights Reserved. May not be scanned, copied or duplicated, or posted to a publicly accessible website, in whole or in part.

SECTION 2
Residential Design

CHAPTER 8
CONSTRUCTION SPECIFICATIONS

OBJECTIVES

When students have completed this chapter, they will:

- Give a general definition of construction specifications.
- Explain the basic difference between residential and commercial specifications.
- List at least four factors that influence the specific requirements of minimum construction specifications.
- Define in general typical minimum construction requirements.
- Describe the format used by the Construction Specifications Institute.
- Complete a given Description of Materials form based on a previously drawn set of architectural plans.

TEST ANSWERS

1. Information that cannot be clearly or completely provided on the drawings or in schedules, is provided in construction specifications. (See Figure 8–1 in the text.)

2. The basic difference between residential and commercial specifications is that commercial constructions are often more complex and comprehensive. The commercial specifications may provide very detailed instructions for each phase of construction.

3. Factors that influence the specific requirements of minimum construction are local ordinances, climates, codes used, and the extent of coverage.

4. Typical minimum construction requirements for the following categories are as follows:

   a. room dimensions: (1) minimum room size; (2) ceiling height

   b. light and ventilation: (1) window area; (2) tempered glass; (3) glass doors; (4) venting to outside

   c. foundation: (1) concrete mix; (2) foundation mud sills; (3) crawl space; (4) basement foundation walls; (5) footings

   d. framing: (1) lumber grades; (2) beams bearing; (3) wall bracing; (4) joist; (5) solid blocking of floor joist; (6) clearance between combustible material and walls; (7) rafter perlin braces; (8) to plate; (9) tie downs; (10) fire blocking; (11) water splash areas; (12) post-beam connections

   e. stairways: (1) rise and run; (2) space under stairway; (3) handrails; (4) guardrails

   f. roof: (1) composition shingles; (2) shake roofs; (3) attic

© 2011 Cengage Learning. All Rights Reserved. May not be scanned, copied or duplicated, or posted to a publicly accessible website, in whole or in part.

     g. chimney and fireplace: (1) reinforcing; (2) anchorage

     h. thermal insulation and heating: (1) R factors, (2) thermal glazing; (3) duct insulation; (4) heating

     i. fire warning system: (1) fire detectors

5. The Construction Specifications Institute (CSI) format for construction specifications is made up of seventeen major divisions. Within each major division are several subsections. The major categories are numbered in a standard order beginning at Division 0, Bidding and Contract Requirements through Division 16, Electrical. The subdivisions of each general category are numbered with five-digit numbers. When specific divisions or subdivisions are not required, they are excluded.

6. *Work results* are traditional construction practices that typically result from an application of skills to construction products or resource.

7. *Functional elements*, often referred to as systems or assemblies, are major components, common to building, that perform a known function regardless of the design specification, construction method, or materials used.

8. *Systems or assemblies,* see number 7, functional elements

9. *Building life cycle* refers to the observation and examination of a building over the course of its entire life.

10. *Construction documents* are drawings and written specifications prepared and assembled by architects and engineers for communicating the design of the project and administering the construction contract.

11. *Bidding requirements* are the construction documents issued to bidders for the purpose of providing construction bids.

12. *Contract documents* are the legal requirements that become part of the construction contract.

CHAPTER 8 PROBLEM SOLUTIONS

Solutions for Problem 8–1 through 8–4 will vary based on individual student applications.

CHAPTER 9
GUIDELINES AND REQUIRED CODES THAT AFFECT BUILDING DESIGN

OBJECTIVES

When students have completed this chapter, they will:

- Be familiar with the basic concepts of the IRC that impact residential design.
- Know how the IRC affects exit facilities.
- Know how the IRC affects light, ventilation, and sanitation requirements.
- Know how the IRC affects room dimensions.
- Know how the IRC and ANSI A117.1-2003 affect the access of multi-family sleeping units.
- Know how LEED's and NAHB quidelines affect residential design and construction.

TEST ANSWERS

1. 3'-0" × 6'-8"
2. IRC, UBC, BOCA, SBCCI, CABO
3. 8 percent

© 2011 Cengage Learning. All Rights Reserved. May not be scanned, copied or duplicated, or posted to a publicly accessible website, in whole or in part.

4. 36"

5. 36"

6. 7'-0"

7. 44"

8. 30"

9. No, only multi-family projects

10. Water closet, lavatory, and either a shower or tub.

11. 26" C/R width, 7 1/2" run within 12" of narrow edge and 6'-6" head room.

12. IRC. = 4.8 sq. ft.

13. 1 room must equal 120 sq. ft., other 70 sq. ft.

14. 5'-0"

15. 5.7 sq. ft. 20" wide, 24" high, within 44" of floor

16. One door that is 36 inches (914 mm) wide.

17. Loads will vary greatly depending on your area of the country.

18. The climate zone will vary but should be based on IECC zones.

19. The size and placement of shear panels or braced wall panels required to resist wind and seismic factors will influence window placement.

20. The IECC defines *fenestration* as the openings in the building envelope including glazed blocks, glazed doors, opaque doors, roof windows, skylights, vertical windows including fixed and moveable, or any products with glass or other types of glazing.

21. The building envelope is comprised of the elements of a structure that enclose heated and cooled air through which thermal energy transfers to or from the exterior.

22. Answers will vary but should be based on minimum local standards.

23. Students should be able to find articles discussing the adoption of state codes, and articles about periodic reviews of code requirements.

24. Material found will vary to reflect class assignments.

25. Students should be able to find articles discussing the application of state codes, articles about periodic review of code requirements, and state adoption guidelines.

CHAPTER 9 PROBLEM SOLUTIONS

Chapter 9 of the text has no drawing problems.

CHAPTER 10
ROOM RELATIONSHIPS AND SIZES

OBJECTIVES

When students have completed this chapter, they will:

- Have an understanding of basic interior design considerations.
- Be able to identify the relationship of the living, sleeping, and service areas of a residence.

TEST ANSWERS

1. Living, sleeping, and service areas
2. 4' × 2'. FHA recommends a length of 48" for males and 72" for females. Min. closet depth is 24".

© 2011 Cengage Learning. All Rights Reserved. May not be scanned, copied or duplicated, or posted to a publicly accessible website, in whole or in part.

3. Dining—for serving ease

   Family/Living—near family activities

   Utility—near other main service areas

   Garage—for ease of storage and unloading

   Play Areas—for ease of supervision

4. Laundry, sewing, storage

5. 21' × 21' or 22' × 24'

6. Informal family activities, entertainment, eating, game room, and sorting laundry

7. Heated by natural convection and provides a quiet sleeping area

8. Cooler

9. Near formal living areas

   Overall size of house

   Room relationships

   Near kitchen for serving

   Atmosphere of residence

   Room usage

10. Kitchen, utility, baths, and garage

11. The main entry should provide a focal point from the outside of the house, and may serve as a transition area to other living areas of the home. It is preferred to have the main entry open to the foyer rather than directly into a living area of the home. The service entry is the family's main access into the house. The service entry links the garage, kitchen, utility room, bathrooms, and patios or decks.

12. Information will vary but should reflect on seating, speaker, and television placement.

13. The foyer serves as a place either for welcoming guests or saying final good-byes. A foyer should have a closet where guests may hang their coats and jackets. The foyer also provides access to other areas of the home. It provides access to the living room or dining areas, a hall leading to the sleeping area, or stairs leading to another level.

14. A formal living room is not a multi-purpose room, unlike a casual living room that allows for a wide variety of activities.

15. When placing a living room within a home, consider the number of people that will use it and the type of activities it will be used for. Also determine the type of furniture intended for that space. Placement of furniture in square rooms is harder than in rectangular spaces.

16. A single bedroom will decrease the value of the home. A room that can be use as a den or library can also double as a guest room and will greatly increase the resale value.

17. Student answers will vary depending on the homes visited.

18. Student answers will vary depending on the sites visited, but should include built-in storage, furniture, and storage systems.

19. Student answers will vary.

20. Student answers will vary depending on sites visited.

CHAPTER 10 PROBLEM SOLUTIONS

Chapter 10 of the text contains no drawing problems.

© 2011 Cengage Learning. All Rights Reserved. May not be scanned, copied or duplicated, or posted to a publicly accessible website, in whole or in part.

CHAPTER 11
EXTERIOR DESIGN FACTORS

OBJECTIVES

When students have completed this chapter, they will:

- Identify methods of gaining access to a lot.
- List benefits of different floor plan styles.
- Describe how the shape of a house can affect the design.
- Identify exterior features of common architectural residential styles.
- Describe how the home style will affect sustainable construction.

TEST ANSWERS

1. The value and style of surrounding structures should be considered.

2. Lines can be curved, horizontal, vertical, or diagonal and can accent or disguise a feature. Horizontal lines can be used to minimize the height of a structure. Vertical lines accent the height. Curves are used in decorative arches, curved walls, and round windows and doorways. Diagonal lines are used to create a sense of transition.

3. Student sketches will vary greatly.

4. To keep the value of the neighborhood uniform, to establish square footage minimums, to set height limitations, to establish the type and color of siding and roofing materials

5. Any four of the following:

    Single—simple construction, easy to maintain, no stairs, can be used with many styles

    Split-level—good for sloping lots, reduced stair runs between floors

    Daylite basement—can appear as a one-level structure, benefits of a one- and two-level structure

    Two-story—provides good separation between living areas, minimum land areas required for structures of equal square footage, lower cost per square foot, less building materials required

    Dormer—well suited for traditional styling, second level built into attic area

    Multi-level—unlimited levels, free shape to fit job site

6. Less material used in the construction of foundation, wall, and roof

7. Dome

8. Photos and sketches will vary.

9. Rectangles, squares, circles, ovals, and ellipses

10. Hue, value, and intensity. Hue represents color. Value is the darkening or lightening of the color. Intensity is the brightness of the color.

11. Primary—red, yellow, blue

    Secondary—orange, green, violet

12. a. one level, rambling layout

    b. unsymmetrical layout, walls of stone, brick, or heavy timber, diamond grill window shapes

    c. one level, with a steep roof

    d. adobe or plaster construction, usually one level

13. Tint is created by adding white to a color.

14. Sketches will vary.

© 2011 Cengage Learning. All Rights Reserved. May not be scanned, copied or duplicated, or posted to a publicly accessible website, in whole or in part.

15. Designed to follow ancient Roman styling

16. Student sketches should reflect elements of a Dutch colonial structure as shown in the reading material.

17. Sketches will vary.

18. Usually have very small rooms with poor traffic flow

19. Common proportions of classical Greek design include 2:3, 3:5, and 5:8.

20. The French plantation style

21. a. Portico—A covered entry porch supported on Greek-style columns centered over the front door

    b. Quatrefoil window—A round window composed of four equal lobes that resemble a four-leafed clover

    c. Balusters—A row of repetitive, small decorative posts (balusters) that support the hand railing

    d. Corbel—Decorative brackets used to support bays

    e. Palladian window—A large window that is divided into three parts, with the center section that is usually arched and larger than the two side sections

22. Georgian homes followed the classical principles of design used by ancient Romans. The homes were rectangular in shape, usually two or three stories in height, and had symmetrical floor plans. The roofs had a medium roof pitch with small overhangs. Dentil molding is often placed along the eaves.

    Federal homes combined Georgian architecture with classical Roman and Greek styles to form a very dignified style. Federal-style buildings have curved lines and decorative flourishes such as swags, garlands, and elliptical windows. Federal homes were built of wood or brick with low-sloped roofs with dentil moldings below the eaves. A common alternative to the dentil molding was a flat roof surrounded with a balustrade.

23. Foursquare-style homes feature a simple box shape that is two stories tall with an attic and a full basement. Large overhangs supported with cornice-line brackets or other details drawn from Craftsman and Italian Renaissance styles are a common feature. Others features sometimes associated with a foursquare home are a large central dormer, and a front porch that covers the majority of the front facade of the home.

24. Prairie-style homes feature low horizontal lines, one-story projections, low-pitched hipped roofs and large overhanging eaves that are designed to help the home blend into the landscape. Roofs are typically tile or shingles depending on the area of the country where the home is built.

25. Styles will vary greatly depending on your area.

CHAPTER 11 PROBLEM SOLUTIONS

Chapter 11 of the text contains no drawing problems.

CHAPTER 12
CONSERVATION AND ENVIRONMENTAL
DESIGN AND CONSTRUCTION

OBJECTIVES

When students have completed this chapter, they will:

- Define and discuss environmental design and construction concepts such as sustainable buildings, green building, brownfields, green power, and Energy Star.
- Discuss and list methods that contribute to a healthier home.

© 2011 Cengage Learning. All Rights Reserved. May not be scanned, copied or duplicated, or posted to a publicly accessible website, in whole or in part.

- Discuss why energy-efficient construction techniques are becoming important.
- Explain the primary goal of energy-efficient design and construction.
- Identify site factors that contribute to energy-efficient design.
- Give room layout factors that contribute to energy-efficient design.
- List window placement factors that contribute to energy-efficient design.
- Describe passive and active solar heating.
- List and describe three factors that influence a good solar design.
- Describe each of the following solar systems and make a sketch to show how each functions:
    a. South-facing glass
    b. Clerestory windows
    c. Thermal storage wall
    d. Roof ponds
    e. Solarium
- Describe applications of geothermal heating and cooling systems.
- Describe the function of photovoltaic cells.
- Describe insulated windows.
- Define direct solar gain.
- Discuss wind power generation.
- Describe the green building concept.
- Define green power.
- List at least three reasons why energy-efficient construction techniques are becoming important.
- Discuss how energy-efficient construction design will affect future building codes.
- Identify the goals of conservation design.
- Discuss individual architectural and construction factors that contribute to energy-efficient design.
- Identify the two basic residential and commercial uses for solar heat.
- Describe passive and active solar heating.
- Define and sketch examples of given solar system techniques.
- Describe solar collectors.
- Discuss at least three applications for geothermal heating and cooling applications.
- Describe the function of photovoltaic cells.

TEST ANSWERS

1. List any three of the following.
    a. Better living environment
    b. Demand for economical living
    c. Establish future building codes
    d. Consume natural resources
    e. Preserve ozone layer
    f. Save the environment
2. a. Evaluate expensive and complex construction techniques
    b. Airtight construction may create an unhealthy environment; the use of air-to-air heat exchangers may be required.
3. Reduce energy costs
4. Improve construction methods and provide alternative energy sources
5. The energy-efficient design concepts may not be apparent in the external appearance of the structure. This is done by the use of framing techniques, caulking, vapor retarders, radiant barriers and insulation.

© 2011 Cengage Learning. All Rights Reserved. May not be scanned, copied or duplicated, or posted to a publicly accessible website, in whole or in part.

6. The basic energy-efficient design concepts are simple and easy to implement. For example, additional insulation, double- or triple-pane windows, and air infiltration barriers.

7. a. Avoid windy locations

    b. Solar orientation

    c. Effective use of terrain

8. a. Placement of living spaces on south side

    b. Placement of inactive rooms on north side

    c. Provide airlock entry

9. Reduce north-facing windows, increase south-facing windows

10. The two basic residential and commercial uses for solar heat are heating spaces and hot water.

11. Passive heat uses no mechanical devices to retain, store, and radiate solar heat. Active or mechanical systems use mechanics to absorb, store, and utilize solar heat.

12. Three factors that influence a good solar design are:

    a. The structure should be carefully insulated to reduce heat loss and air infiltration.

    b. Southern exposure provides the best site orientation for solar construction.

    c. Room design is important. Living areas should be on the south side of the house, while inactive rooms should be located on the north side of the structure.

13. The concept of *right to light* is the idea that a person has the right to receive solar light (energy) at his or her home or business. Individuals' rights to solar access are not always guaranteed. A solar home may be built in an area that has excellent solar orientation, and then a few years later a tall structure may be built across the street that blocks the sun. Some local zoning ordinances do protect the individual's "right to light."

14. a. South-facing windows create a direct solar gain in heat created by the sun.

© 2011 Cengage Learning. All Rights Reserved. May not be scanned, copied or duplicated, or posted to a publicly accessible website, in whole or in part.

b. Clerestory windows are generally at a second floor or adjacent to the room ridge. They may be used for solar gain and for ventilation.

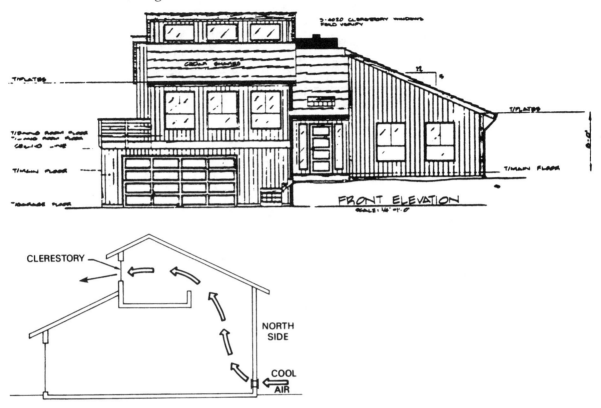

c. Thermal storage walls can be constructed of any good heat-absorbing material such as concrete, masonry, or water-filled cylinders. The wall receives and stores the energy during the day and releases the heat slowly at night.

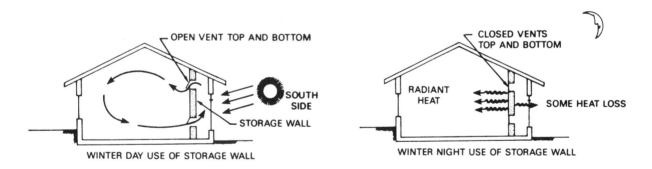

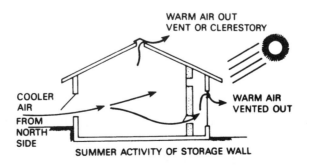

© 2011 Cengage Learning. All Rights Reserved. May not be scanned, copied or duplicated, or posted to a publicly accessible website, in whole or in part.

d. Roof ponds are antifreeze water-filled containers placed on a flat roof. The water is heated during the winter days and then at night the structure is covered with insulation, which allows the absorbed heat to radiate to the living space.

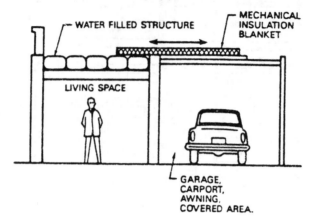

e. A solarium is designed to be built on the south side adjacent to the living areas of the structure. The idea is to absorb a great deal of direct solar gain and in turn to transmit this solar energy to the balance of the structure.

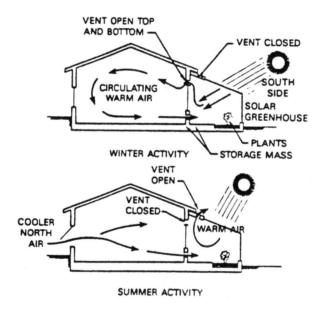

15. *Solar collectors* are devices that catch sunlight and convert this light to heat.

16. Solar architectural cement products are architectural products that are part of the home that can double as solar collectors. Solar architectural cement products absorb and collect heat from the sun and outside air, transferring this heat into the water, glycol, or heat-transferring fluid passing through the tubes. The nature of the special formulation allows it to store heat, which is transferred to water after the sun goes down.

17. Applications for geothermal heating and cooling systems are:

    a. The utilization of ground water pumped from a supply well and circulated through the system, where either heat or cold is transferred by the freon before the water is recycled through a discharge well back to the strata.

    b. When not enough water is available, the ground itself, which maintains a constant temperature at all times, can be utilized to extract either cooling or heating through the use of a closed-loop system consisting of polybutylene tubing filled with a glycol solution and circulated through the geothermal system.

© 2011 Cengage Learning. All Rights Reserved. May not be scanned, copied or duplicated, or posted to a publicly accessible website, in whole or in part.

c. A vertical dry-hole well sealed to enable it to function as a closed system by circulating a glycol solution through the system after it has extracted either heating or cooling.

d. A solar-assisted system created by transferring heat from solar collectors that have been stored in a tank and circulated through a water coil until the temperature of the water is below 100°F. Then the storage tank water will be used as a water source for the operation of the geothermal system.

18. Photovoltaic cells turn light into electricity. Photo means light and voltaic means to produce electricity by chemical action. Photons of light strike the surfaces of a silicon wafer. This stimulates the release of mobile electric charges that can be guided into a circuit to become a useful electric current.

19. 1'-10"

20. 3'-3"

21. A *direct solar gain* in heat created by the sun

22. A free renewable resource and one that is clean

23. Quality insulation, caulking, and vapor retarders. Airtight well-insulated windows. Unbleached fiberboard. Heat recovery ventilation system. High-performance particle air filtration system. Use low-toxicity ceramic tiles and hardwood floors or natural fiber carpets. Wood decking. Low toxicity foam insulation or other nonchemical insulation. Water base solvent free. Low toxicity paints and finishes. Tightly sealed foundation. Use a heat pump. Gas appliances and fireplaces with outdoor air and exhaust to the outside. An electrical system that is designed to reduce stray voltage. Sealed and well-balanced metal ducts. Central vacuum system. Garage ventilation system. Ceramic roofing.

24. Sustainable buildings are buildings capable of maintaining their desired function in the future.

25. As the building industry grows to meet the demands of our increasing population, there is a strong need to take care of the environment and allow for current and future development. National and local programs have been established to meet this need. A leading program is often referred to as green building.

26. *Brownfields,* as taken from the National Brownfield Association Web site, include properties that are contaminated or perceived to be contaminated. They may also include properties that are underutilized for various socioeconomic reasons, such as abandonment, obsolescence, tax delinquency, and/or blight.

27. *Green power,* as taken from the Environmental Protection Agency Web site, is electricity that is generated from resources such as solar, wind, geothermal, biomass, and low-impact hydro facilities.

28. As taken in part from the Energy Star Web site, Energy Star is a government-backed program helping businesses and individuals protect the environment through superior energy efficiency.

STUDENT CD ANSWERS

CD12–1. Close and seal all cracks and openings, use a vapor barrier

CD12–2. The goal of energy-efficient construction is to decrease dependency on the heating and cooling system.

CD12–3. 1. Caulking

2. Vapor retarders

3. Insulation

CD12–4. Caulking is the general name of a variety of products that are used to stop or reduce air infiltration. Caulking is used:

1. At exterior joints around window and door frames

2. At joints between wall cavities and window and door frames

3. At joints between the wall framing and the foundation

© 2011 Cengage Learning. All Rights Reserved. May not be scanned, copied or duplicated, or posted to a publicly accessible website, in whole or in part.

4. At joints between the wall and roof

5. At joints between wall panels

6. At penetrations or utility services through exterior walls, floors, and roofs

7. At all openings that may cause air leakage.

CD12–5. Most building codes require 6-mil thick plastic to be placed over the earth in the crawl space.

CD12–6. R values for the following uses:

a. Flat ceilings = R-38

b. Floors = R-25

c. Walls = R-15 to R-24

CD12–7. Envelope design is based on the idea that an envelope or continuous cavity be constructed around the perimeter of the structure. A solar greenhouse is built on the south side with insulating double-pane glass to act as a solar collector.

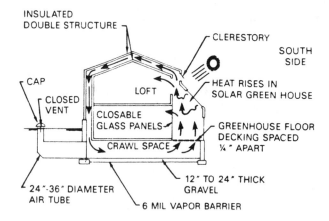

CD12–8. Radiant barriers are made of aluminum foil with a backing. Radiant barriers stop heat from radiating through the attic. They help to reduce attic and roof temperatures in hot climates.

CD12–9. Help reduce air infiltration, heat costs and reduces noise

CD12–10. Local and national codes, local climates, energy costs, personal budget, and personal preference

CD12–11. Thermal resistance

CD12–12. Thermal resistance

CD12–13. Resistance to heat flow

CD12–14. Granules made of cellulose, fiberglass, rock wool, cotton, or other materials

CD12–15. Conforms to and completely fills the space

CD12–16. Roll insulation made of fiberglass or cotton fibers

CD12–17. To avoid gaps that reduce their effectiveness

CD12–18. High R-values, sound insulation, some structural strength, air sealing

CD12–19. In foundations, under siding, and in tight places

CD12–20. High R-value per inch and air sealing

CD12–21. Loose fill

CD12–22. 2.9 to 3.8

CD12–23. Two or more panes of glass with a sealed space between

CD12–24. Raises the window's insulative value

CD12–25. Has a transparent coating that acts like a thermal mirror, which increases insulating value, blocks heat from the sun, and reduces the fading of objects inside the house

© 2011 Cengage Learning. All Rights Reserved. May not be scanned, copied or duplicated, or posted to a publicly accessible website, in whole or in part.

CD12–26. CL40

CD12–27. Spray-in foam

CD12–28. a. Walls—R-15–R-24

     b. Flat ceilings—R-38

     c. Vaulted ceilings—R-30 not to exceed 50% of the floor space unless insulated to R-38

     d. Under floor—R-25

     e. Basement walls—R-21

     f. Slab floor edge—R-15

     g. Forced-air ducts—R-8

     h. Windows—U = 0.40, CL40

     i. Front entry door—U = 0.54, maximum 24 sq. ft.

     j. Other exterior doors—U = 0.20.

     K. Skylights—U = 0.50, CL50, not to exceed 2% of the heated space

CHAPTER 12 PROBLEM SOLUTIONS

Problems 12-1 through 12-28 require a report of 250 words related to given topics. Student results vary.

© 2011 Cengage Learning. All Rights Reserved. May not be scanned, copied or duplicated, or posted to a publicly accessible website, in whole or in part.

© 2011 Cengage Learning. All Rights Reserved. May not be scanned, copied or duplicated, or posted to a publicly accessible website, in whole or in part.

SECTION 3
Site Planning

CHAPTER 13
SITE ORIENTATION

OBJECTIVES

When students have completed this chapter, they will:

- Define site orientation.
- Describe at least five factors that influence site orientation.
- Define magnetic declination.
- Discuss the characteristics of solar, terrain, and wind orientation.
- List at least five advantages of considering site orientation in architectural planning.

TEST ANSWERS

1. *Site orientation* is the placement of the structure on the property with certain environmental and physical factors taken into consideration.

2. Five factors that influence site orientation are as follows:

   a. Terrain—Terrain is the characteristic of land upon which the proposed structure will be placed.

   b. View—Many sites are bought for the view: a view of the mountains, the city lights, a lake, the ocean or even a golf course.

   c. Solar—The sun is an important factor in home orientation.

   d. Wind—The direction of the prevailing winds is the direction that the winds blow most frequently.

   e. Sound—Undesirable sounds need to be taken into consideration in site orientation. Freeway and road sounds can plague an otherwise charming site.

3. The *magnetic declination* is the difference between true north and magnetic north.

4. The magnetic declination of the area where I live is about 21%.

5. Tall trees or tall buildings can block the sun in an otherwise good solar site. Select a site where zone restrictions have maximum height requirements. This will not allow future neighborhood development to block the sun from a good solar layout. Avoid a site where coniferous trees hinder the full potential of the sun.

6. Deciduous trees can be an asset in solar orientation by providing shade relief from the very hot summer sun. In the winter trees lose their leaves so that winter sun exposure is not substantially reduced.

© 2011 Cengage Learning. All Rights Reserved. May not be scanned, copied or duplicated, or posted to a publicly accessible website, in whole or in part.

7. Prevailing winds refer to the direction that winds blow most frequently in a given area of the country.

8. Features that protect a structure from wind are a hill, mountain, or forest.

9. A sketch of how landscaping can be used for winter problems and summer cooling

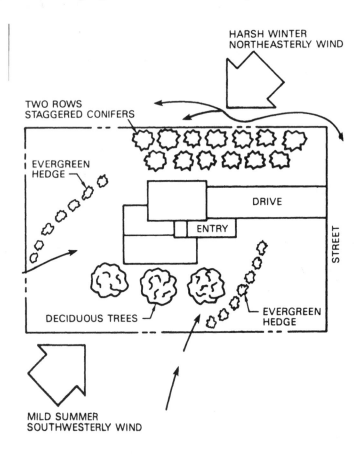

10. A sketch of how landscaping can be used for effective sound control

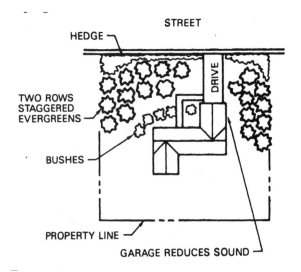

© 2011 Cengage Learning. All Rights Reserved. May not be scanned, copied or duplicated, or posted to a publicly accessible website, in whole or in part.

Problem 15–9

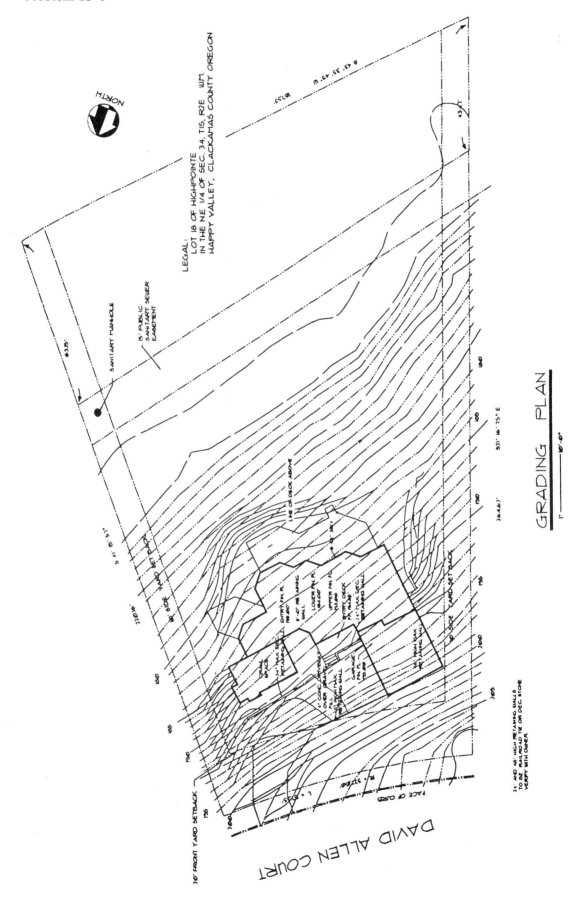

© 2011 Cengage Learning. All Rights Reserved. May not be scanned, copied or duplicated, or posted to a publicly accessible website, in whole or in part.

© 2011 Cengage Learning. All Rights Reserved. May not be scanned, copied or duplicated, or posted to a publicly accessible website, in whole or in part.

CHAPTER 16
FLOOR PLAN SYMBOLS

OBJECTIVES

When students have completed this chapter, they will:

- Identify the proper representation for exterior walls and interior partitions.
- Describe and draw given floor plan symbols.
- Determine minimum dimensions for floor plan features.
- Describe the use of schedules.
- Ba able to complete Litter-specific notes for floor plan features.
- Identify at least four factors to consider when planning stairs.

TEST ANSWERS

1. Exterior walls for a wood-frame residence are usually drawn 6" thick at a 1/4" = 1'-0" scale when using manual drafting, or 5" with CADD using 2 × 4 framing and 7" with CADD using 2 × 6 studs.

2. Interior walls are frequently drawn 4" thick when 2 × 4 studs are used with drywall on each side when using manual drafting, or the exact 4 1/2" when using CADD.

3. Interior doors are drawn without a sill while exterior doors have a sill drawn with them.

4. Recommended spaces required for the following are:

   a. Wardrobe closet depth is a minimum of 24".

   b. Water closet is 30" wide, 18" from center of stool to wall, and a minimum of 18" in front.

   c. Stair width is 36" minimum while 48" to 60" is ideal.

   d. Fireplace hearth depth is minimum of 22".

5. The advantage of using a window or door schedule is that it keeps the drawing clear of unnecessary notes.

© 2011 Cengage Learning. All Rights Reserved. May not be scanned, copied or duplicated, or posted to a publicly accessible website, in whole or in part.

6.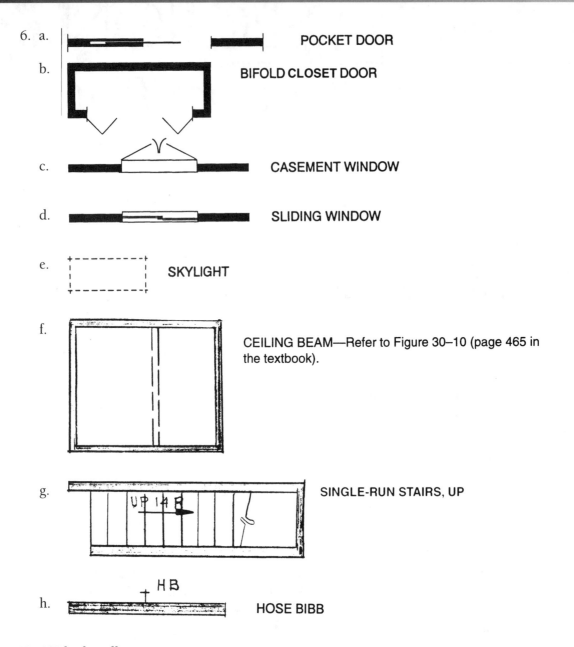

a.   POCKET DOOR

b.   BIFOLD CLOSET DOOR

c.   CASEMENT WINDOW

d.   SLIDING WINDOW

e.   SKYLIGHT

f.   CEILING BEAM—Refer to Figure 30–10 (page 465 in the textbook).

g.   SINGLE-RUN STAIRS, UP

h.   HOSE BIBB

7. 48" high wall

8. Residential—36"

9. The appropriate note to identify a guardrail at a balcony is 36" GUARDRAIL W/OAK CAP.

10. When there is no room for door swing, a pocket door might work.

11. For a 100% openable window a casement window is recommended.

12. The note 6040 next to a window on a floor plan indicates the size of the window. A 6040 window means 6'-0" wide × 4'-0" high.

13. The minimum crawl space or attic access required must be 22" × 30".

14. The abbreviation for garbage disposal is GD.

15. The clothes washer and dryer should be shown with dash lines on the floor plan when these are not part of the construction contract.

16. When planning stairs consider the following:

a. Stair width should be a minimum of 36".

© 2011 Cengage Learning. All Rights Reserved. May not be scanned, copied or duplicated, or posted to a publicly accessible website, in whole or in part.

Problem 18–1

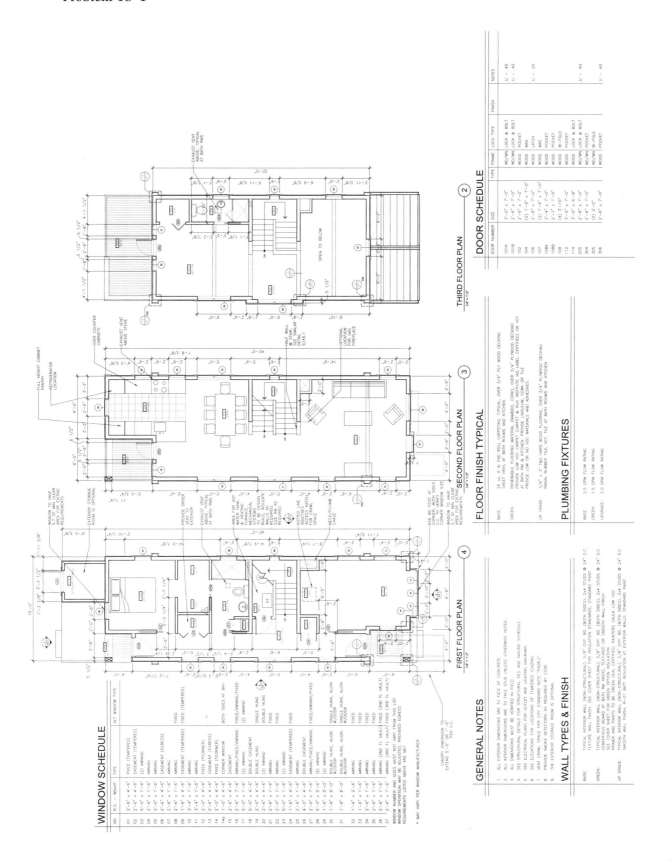

© 2011 Cengage Learning. All Rights Reserved. May not be scanned, copied or duplicated, or posted to a publicly accessible website, in whole or in part.

Problem 18–2

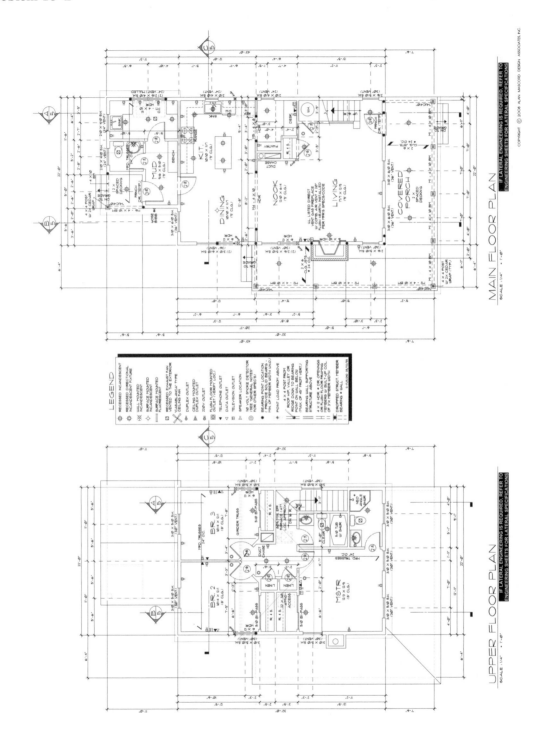

© 2011 Cengage Learning. All Rights Reserved. May not be scanned, copied or duplicated, or posted to a publicly accessible website, in whole or in part.

Problem 18–3

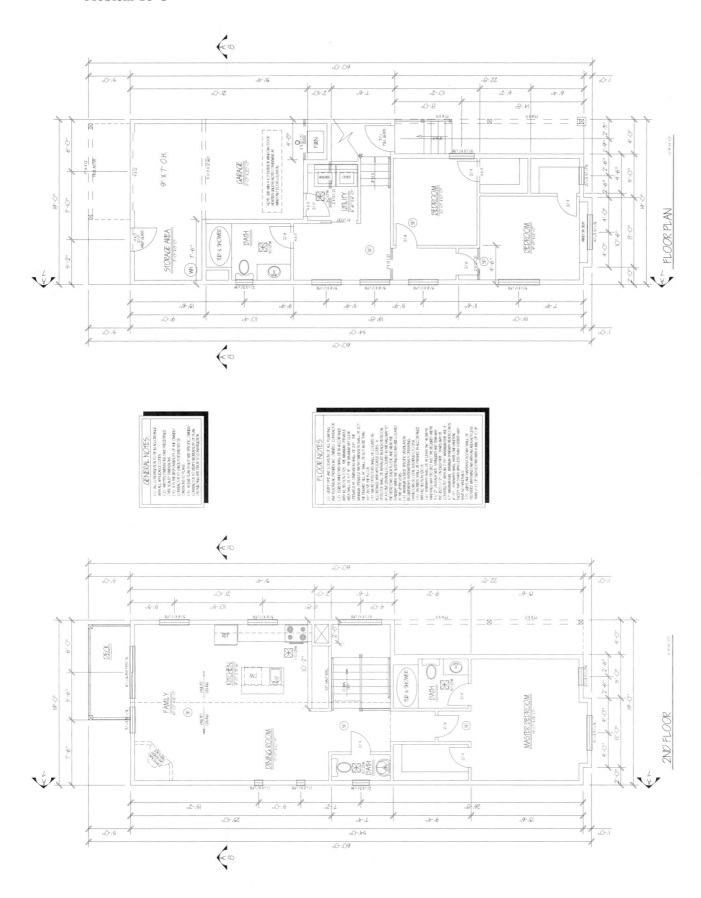

© 2011 Cengage Learning. All Rights Reserved. May not be scanned, copied or duplicated, or posted to a publicly accessible website, in whole or in part.

Problem 18–4

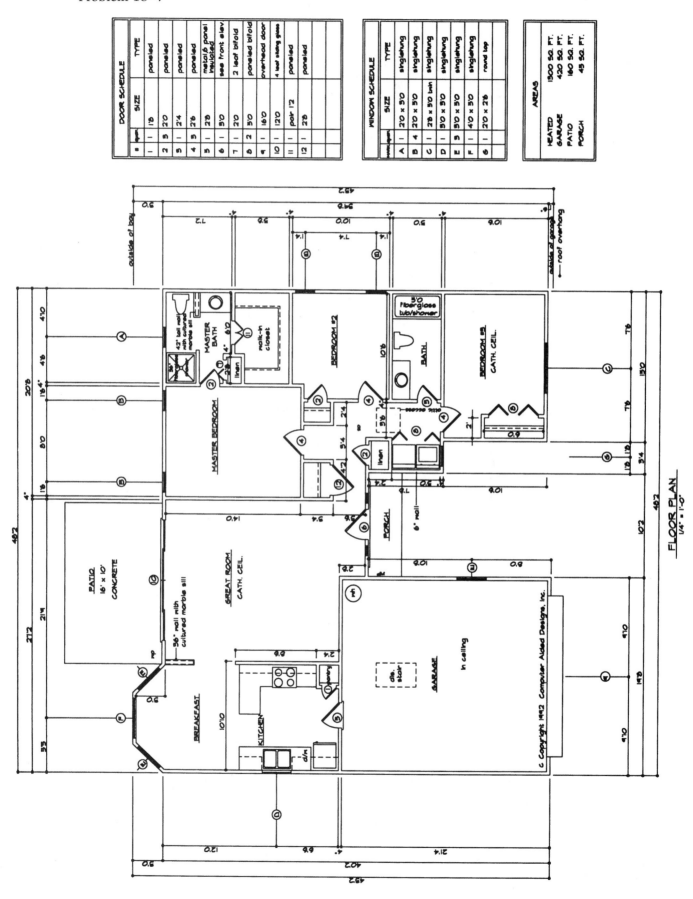

FLOOR PLAN
1/4" = 1'-0"

© 2011 Cengage Learning. All Rights Reserved. May not be scanned, copied or duplicated, or posted to a publicly accessible website, in whole or in part.

Problem 18–9

FLOOR PLAN
SCALE 1/4" = 1'-0"

© 2011 Cengage Learning. All Rights Reserved. May not be scanned, copied or duplicated, or posted to a publicly accessible website, in whole or in part.

Problem 18–10

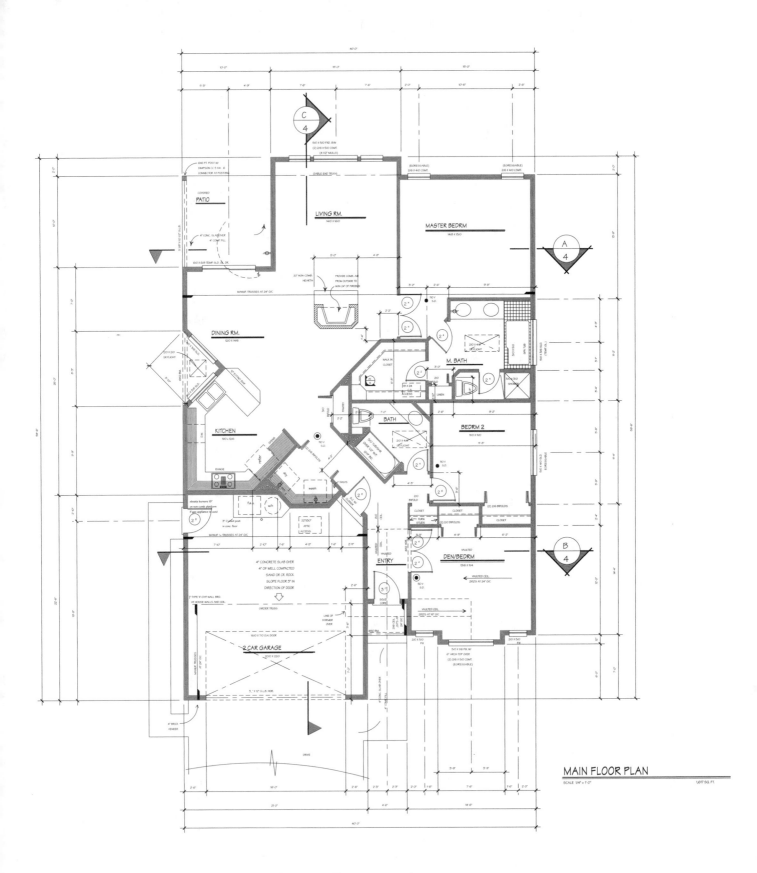

MAIN FLOOR PLAN

© 2011 Cengage Learning. All Rights Reserved. May not be scanned, copied or duplicated, or posted to a publicly accessible website, in whole or in part.

Problem 18–11

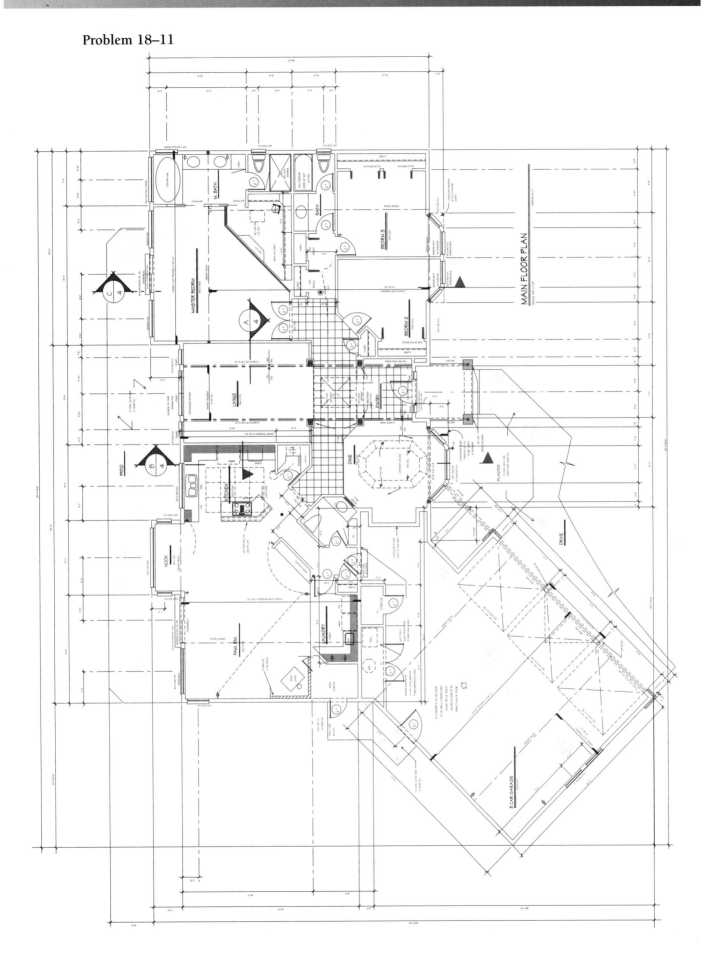

© 2011 Cengage Learning. All Rights Reserved. May not be scanned, copied or duplicated, or posted to a publicly accessible website, in whole or in part.

Problem 18–12

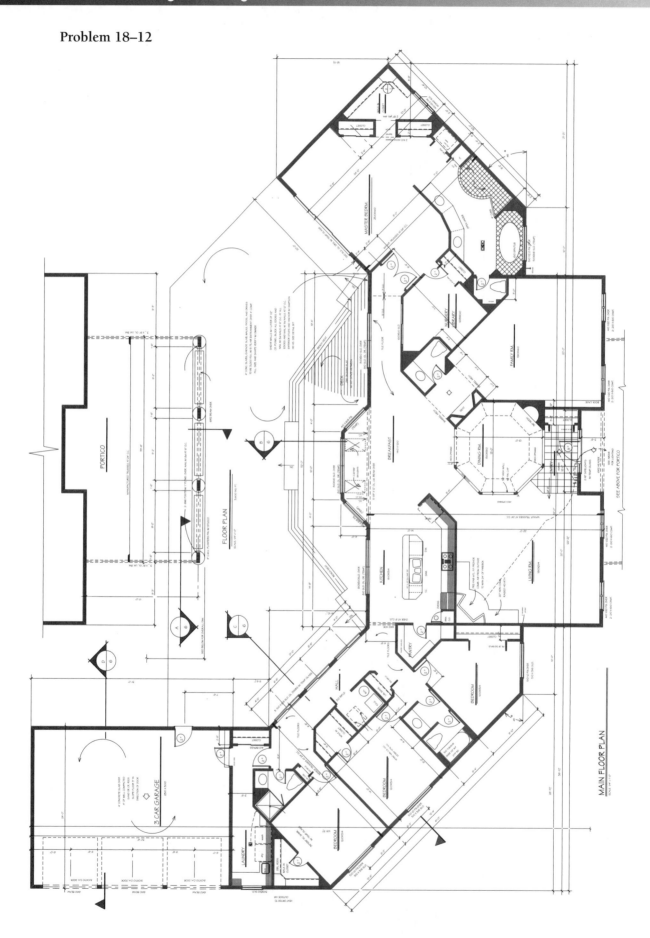

© 2011 Cengage Learning. All Rights Reserved. May not be scanned, copied or duplicated, or posted to a publicly accessible website, in whole or in part.

Problem 18–15, p. 2

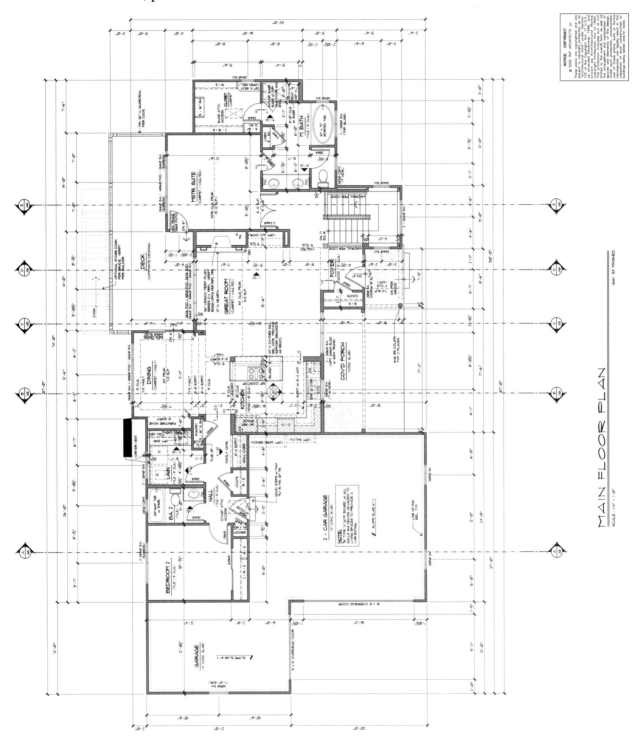

MAIN FLOOR PLAN
SCALE 1/4" = 1'-0"

© 2011 Cengage Learning. All Rights Reserved. May not be scanned, copied or duplicated, or posted to a publicly accessible website, in whole or in part.

Problem 18–16, p. 1

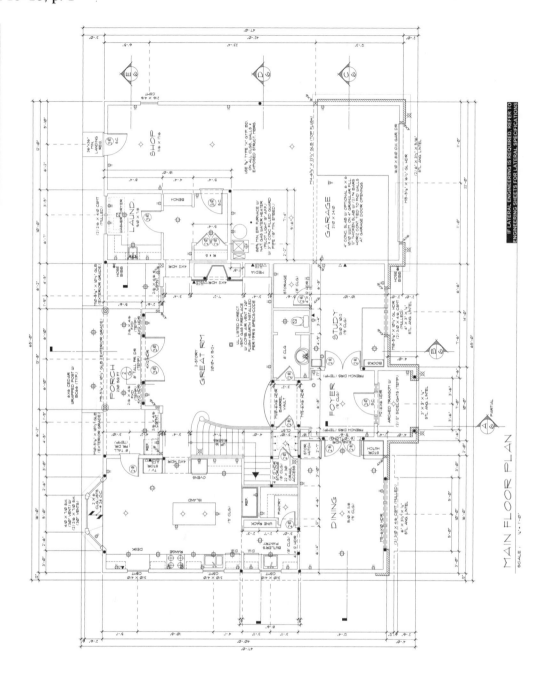

MAIN FLOOR PLAN

SCALE: 1/4" = 1'-0"

© 2011 Cengage Learning. All Rights Reserved. May not be scanned, copied or duplicated, or posted to a publicly accessible website, in whole or in part.

Problem 18–16, p. 2

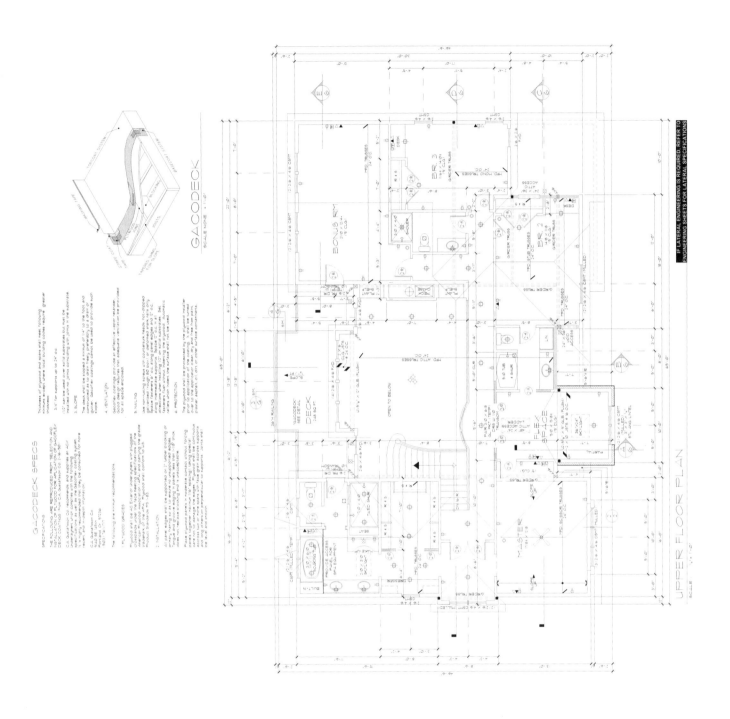

© 2011 Cengage Learning. All Rights Reserved. May not be scanned, copied or duplicated, or posted to a publicly accessible website, in whole or in part.

Problem 18–17, p. 1

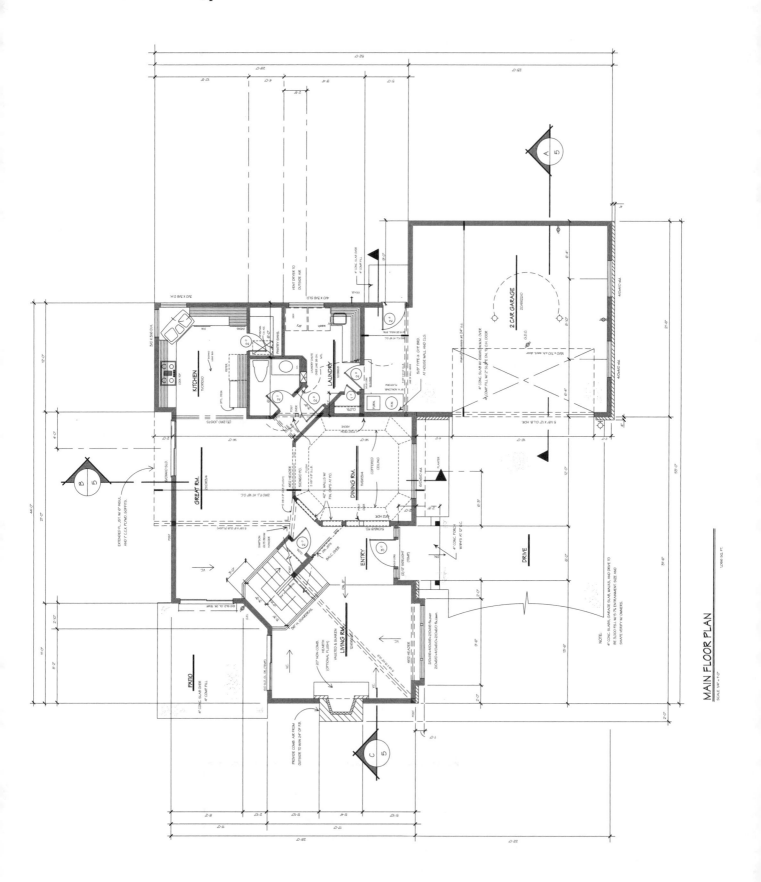

MAIN FLOOR PLAN
SCALE 1/4" = 1'-0"

© 2011 Cengage Learning. All Rights Reserved. May not be scanned, copied or duplicated, or posted to a publicly accessible website, in whole or in part.

Problem 18–17, p. 2

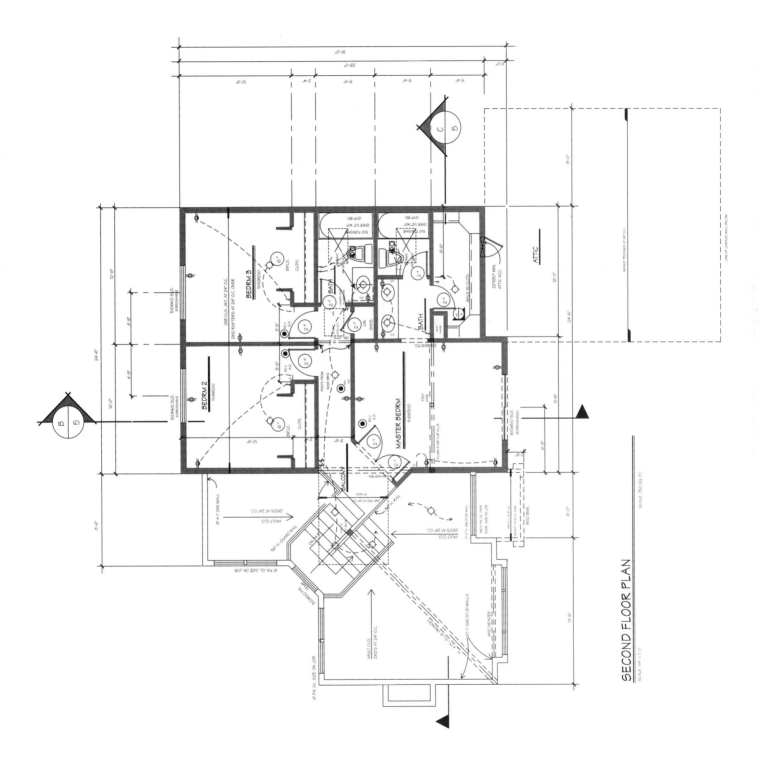

SECOND FLOOR PLAN

SCALE 1/4" = 1'-0"

© 2011 Cengage Learning. All Rights Reserved. May not be scanned, copied or duplicated, or posted to a publicly accessible website, in whole or in part.

Problem 18–18, p. 1

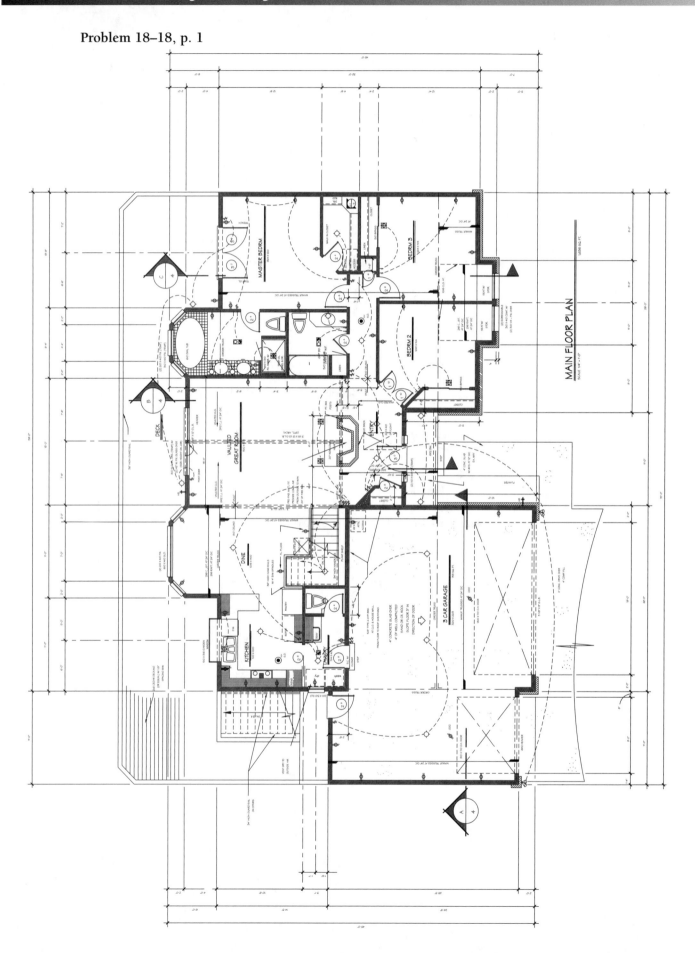

© 2011 Cengage Learning. All Rights Reserved. May not be scanned, copied or duplicated, or posted to a publicly accessible website, in whole or in part.

Problem 18–18, p. 2

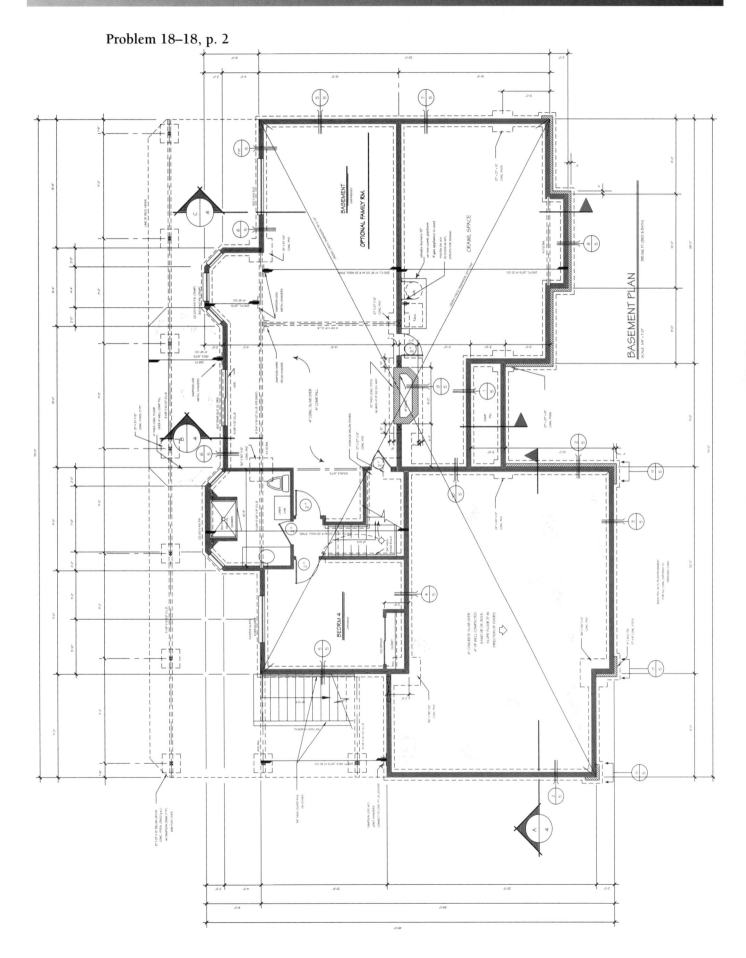

© 2011 Cengage Learning. All Rights Reserved. May not be scanned, copied or duplicated, or posted to a publicly accessible website, in whole or in part.

Problem 18–19, p. 1

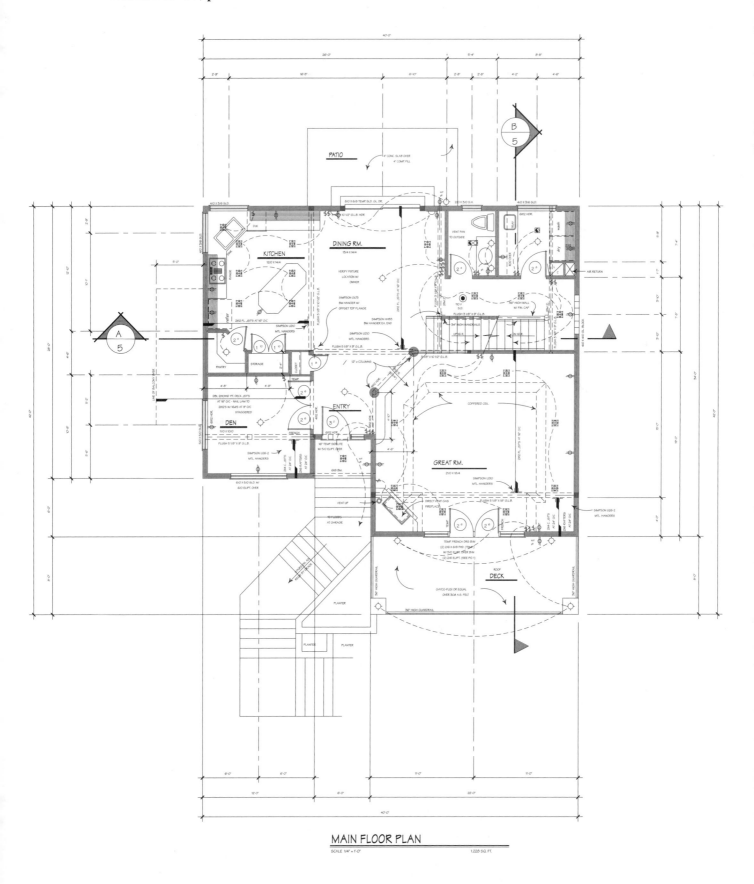

MAIN FLOOR PLAN

SCALE 1/4" = 1'-0"   1,228 SQ. FT.

© 2011 Cengage Learning. All Rights Reserved. May not be scanned, copied or duplicated, or posted to a publicly accessible website, in whole or in part.

Problem 18–19, p. 2

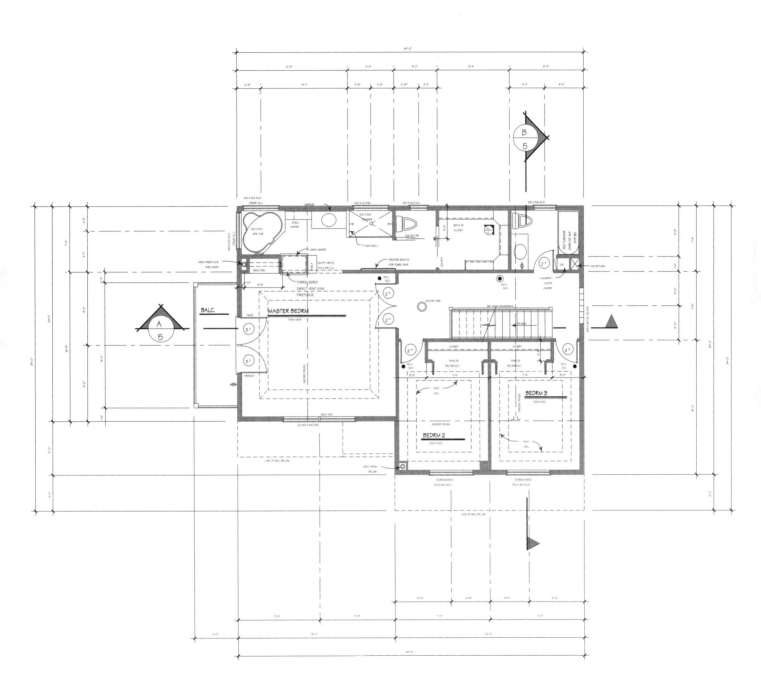

SECOND FLOOR PLAN

SCALE 1/4" = 1'-0"   1,058 SQ. FT.

© 2011 Cengage Learning. All Rights Reserved. May not be scanned, copied or duplicated, or posted to a publicly accessible website, in whole or in part.

Problem 18–19, p. 3

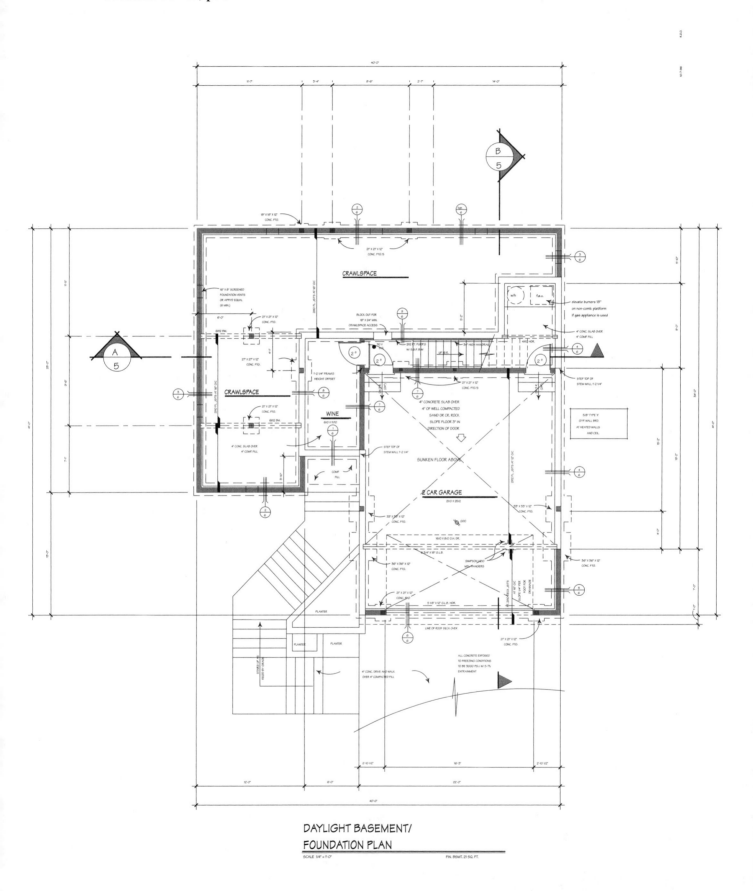

DAYLIGHT BASEMENT/
FOUNDATION PLAN

SCALE 1/4" = 1'-0"   FIN. BSMT. 21 SQ. FT.

© 2011 Cengage Learning. All Rights Reserved. May not be scanned, copied or duplicated, or posted to a publicly accessible website, in whole or in part.

Problem 18–20, p. 1

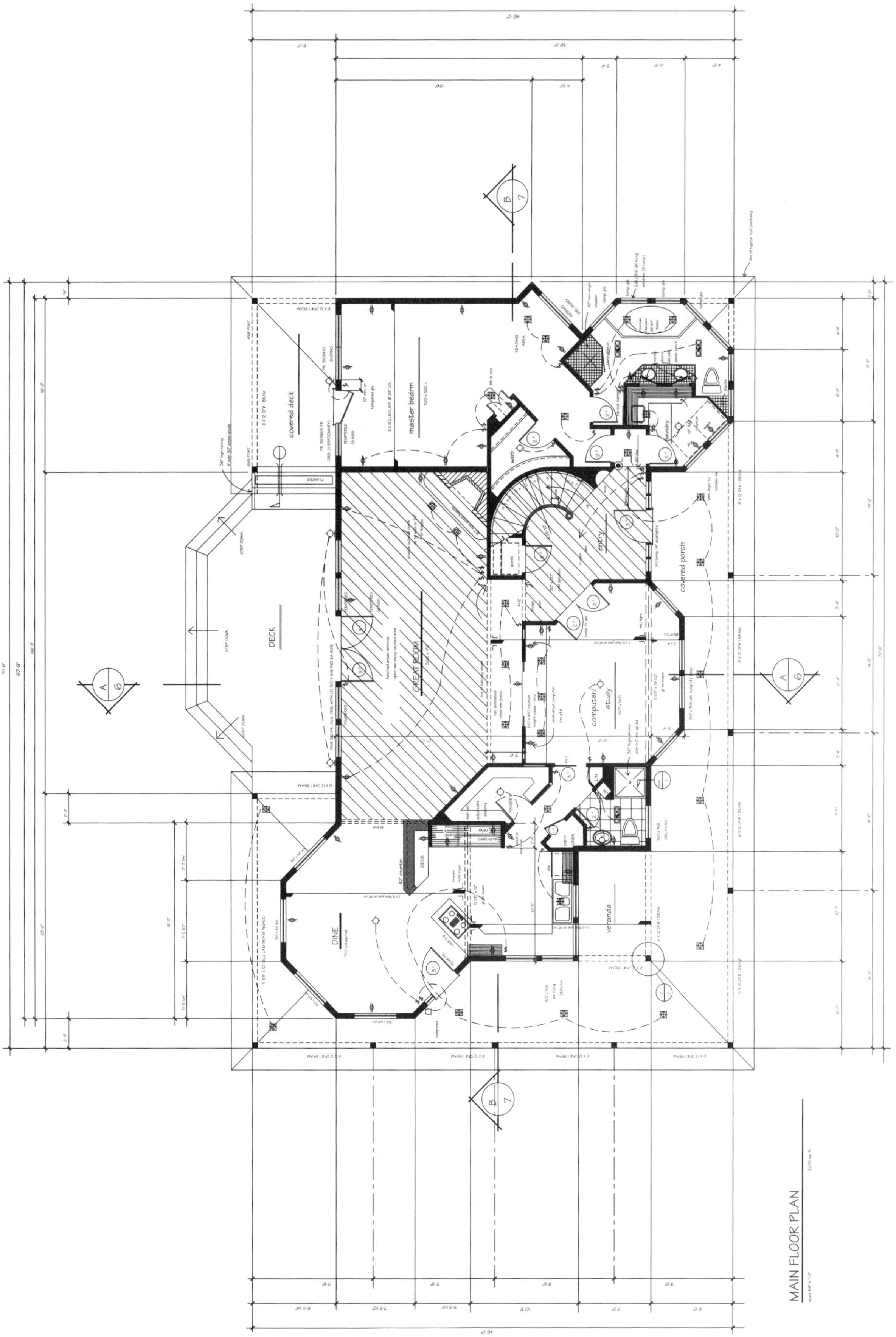

MAIN FLOOR PLAN

© 2011 Cengage Learning. All Rights Reserved. May not be scanned, copied or duplicated, or posted to a publicly accessible website, in whole or in part.

Problem 18–20, p. 2

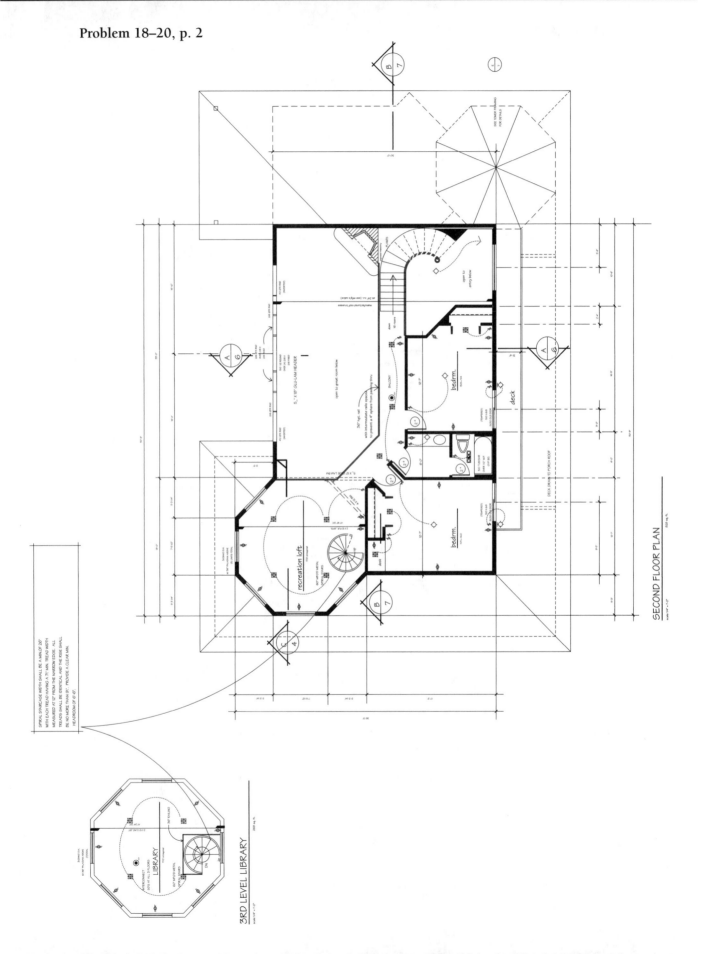

© 2011 Cengage Learning. All Rights Reserved. May not be scanned, copied or duplicated, or posted to a publicly accessible website, in whole or in part.

Problem 18–21, p. 1

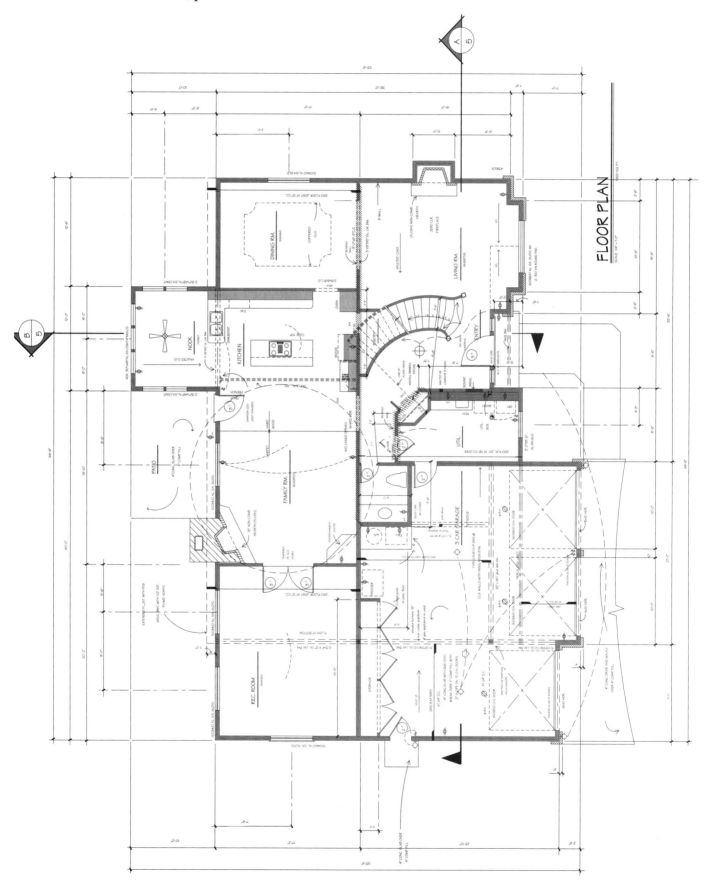

© 2011 Cengage Learning. All Rights Reserved. May not be scanned, copied or duplicated, or posted to a publicly accessible website, in whole or in part.

Problem 18–21, p. 2

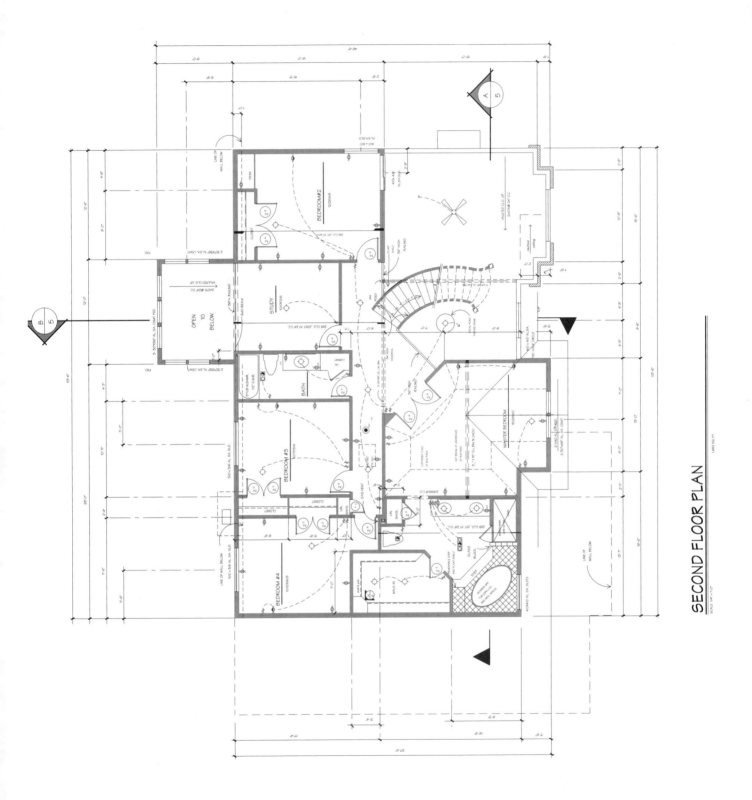

SECOND FLOOR PLAN

Problem 18–22
Residential duplex design problem. Solutions vary.

© 2011 Cengage Learning. All Rights Reserved. May not be scanned, copied or duplicated, or posted to a publicly accessible website, in whole or in part.

SECTION 5

Supplemental Floor Plan Drawings

CHAPTER 19
ELECTRICAL PLANS

OBJECTIVES

When students have completed this chapter, they will:

- Identify specific code and design requirements for electrical installations.
- Describe at least four electrical energy-efficient construction techniques.
- Properly draw given electrical floor plan symbols.
- Draw given typical floor plan representations.

TEST ANSWERS

1. Duplex convenience outlets should be a maximum of 12' apart.
2. Duplex convenience outlets should be no more than 6' from an opening.
3. Energy-efficient considerations related to electrical design are:
   a. Keep electrical outlets and recessed appliances or panels to a minimum at exterior walls.
   b. Timed switches should be installed with exhaust fans to prevent unnecessary operation.
   c. Electrical wire should run along the bottom of the studs to keep insulation from being compacted.
   d. Use energy saving fluorescent lights.
   e. Carefully caulk and seal around all light and convenience outlets.
4. a. Duplex convenience outlet (Wall outlet) 120 Volts

   b. Range outlet 220 Volts

   c. Recessed circuit breaker panel

   d. Phone

   e. ○ Light

© 2011 Cengage Learning. All Rights Reserved. May not be scanned, copied or duplicated, or posted to a publicly accessible website, in whole or in part.

f. Wall-mounted light

g. Single-pole switch

h. Simplified fluorescent light fixture
Solid surface mount
Dashed recessed

i. Ⓕ Ⓒ Fan
Note: if required, vent out

5. It is poor practice to place a switch behind a door because it is difficult to get to or find when entering or leaving a room.

6. Ground fault circuit interrupter (GFCI or GFI) A 110-convenience outlet with a built-in circuit breaker.

7. An average single-family residence should be equipped with 200-amp electrical service.

8. A box equipped with a clamp, used to terminate a conduit

9. After the framing is completed and the structure is dried-in

10. An electrical connector used to plug in devices

11. An electrical outlet that is intended for the direct connection of a lighting fixture

12. Every 4' (1,200 mm) of counter space, with no more than 2' (600 mm) from a corner end of counter or appliance.

13. GFI or GFCI

14. High-speed voice and data lines and video cables wired to a central service location

15. At each sleeping area and on each additional story and basement of a living unit

CHAPTER 19 PROBLEM SOLUTIONS

Problem 19–1

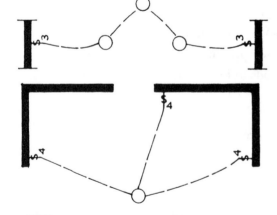

a. Three-way switch: Two switches control one or more lights.

b. Four-way switch: Three switches control one or more lights.

c. Single-pole switch to wall-mounted light. Typical installation at an entry or porch.

© 2011 Cengage Learning. All Rights Reserved. May not be scanned, copied or duplicated, or posted to a publicly accessible website, in whole or in part.

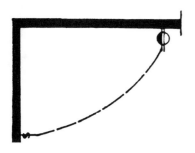

d. Single-pole switch to split-wired outlet. Common application in a room without a ceiling light. Allows switching a table lamp.

Problem 19–2

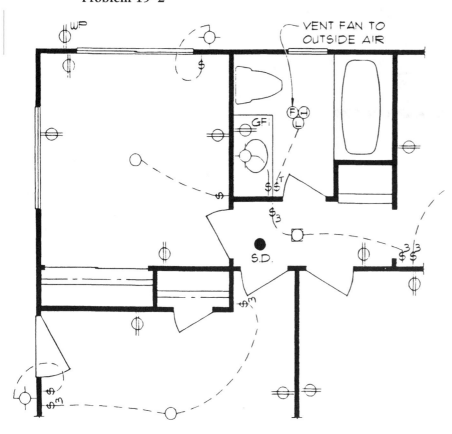

© 2011 Cengage Learning. All Rights Reserved. May not be scanned, copied or duplicated, or posted to a publicly accessible website, in whole or in part.

Problem 19–3

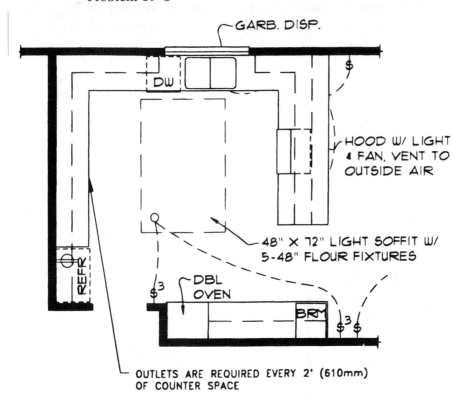

GARB. DISP.

DW

HOOD W/ LIGHT
& FAN, VENT TO
OUTSIDE AIR

48" X 72" LIGHT SOFFIT W/
5-48" FLOUR FIXTURES

REFR

DBL
OVEN

BRM

OUTLETS ARE REQUIRED EVERY 2' (610mm)
OF COUNTER SPACE

Problem 19–4 Solutions vary. Instructions: Use the drawing of the house floor plan that you started in Chapter 18 and do one of the following as directed by your instructor:

a. Continue by drawing the electrical plan on the same floor plan or plans that you completed in Chapter 18. Use the steps provided in this chapter.

b. Use the floor plan or plans that you created in Chapter 18 as the base drawing and create a separate electrical plan as outlined in the steps provided in this chapter.

c. Prepare your CADD drawing using the appropriate electrical plan layers.

© 2011 Cengage Learning. All Rights Reserved. May not be scanned, copied or duplicated, or posted to a publicly accessible website, in whole or in part.

CHAPTER 20
PLUMBING PLANS

OBJECTIVES

When students have completed this chapter, they will:

- Draw given plumbing floor plan symbols.
- Identify at least four methods related to energy-efficient plumbing.
- Draw given plumbing piping symbols.
- Define given plumbing abbreviations.
- Draw typical plumbing isometric layouts.
- Describe plumbing schedules.
- Discuss the advantages and disadvantages of solar hot water.
- Describe public and private sewage disposal systems.

TEST ANSWERS

1. Floor plan plumbing symbols are generally drawn at 1/4" = 1'-0".
2. Four methods that can contribute to energy-efficient plumbing are:
   a. Insulate all exposed hot water pipes.
   b. Keep water pipes out of exterior walls where practical.
   c. Locate the hot water heater in a heated space and insulate it well.
   d. Put flow restrictors on the faucets.
   e. Completely caulk plumbing pipes where they pass through plates.
   f. Run water pipes in insulated spaces.
   g. Place thermosiphon traps in hot water pipes to reduce heat loss.
   h. Seal and cover drain penetrations.
   i. Seal wall penetrations.
3. a. CO—Clean out
   b. FD—Floor drain
   c. VTR—Vent through roof
   d. WC—Water closet
   e. WH—Water heater
   f. SH—Shower
4. The information required on a plumbing schedule is the fixture, number required, location, make, manufacturer's fixture identification number, size, and color.
5. No, plumbing drawings are not required by all contractors. Residential plans, in many cases, do not require a complete plumbing plan. In most cases, the required plumbing can be clearly and easily provided on the floor plan in the form of symbols for fixtures and notes for specific applications or conditions.
6. One not covered advantage of a solar hot-water system is cost saving and energy saving. Disadvantages not covered of solar hot-water systems are the cost of installation, the danger of freezing if you have a water system, and the danger of transfer to the water system if antifreeze is used.

© 2011 Cengage Learning. All Rights Reserved. May not be scanned, copied or duplicated, or posted to a publicly accessible website, in whole or in part.

7. The public sewer system is comprised of lines that carry the waste water to a central waste water treatment plant. A private sewage disposal system, a septic system, is a combination of storage tank and ground absorption field. The solid and liquid waste enters the septic storage tank where it is stored and begins to decompose into sludge. Liquid material or effluent flows from the tank outlet and disperses into a soil absorption field or drain field. When solid waste has effectively decomposed, it also moves into the soil absorption field. The cesspool is similar to the septic tank in that solid and liquid waste collect for decomposition and eventual absorption into the soil. The cesspool does not have a drain field, but is perforated so that effluent will filter directly into the gravel casing and then directly into the soil.

8. Galvanize pipe

9. Black pipe

10. Corrugated stainless steel tubing is a flexible piping system that is easier and less expensive to install than black pipe.

11. Corrosion resistance

12. A pipe that carries the discharge of water closets or other similar fixtures

13. Trap

14. The pipe installed to ventilate the building drainage system and to prevent drawing liquid out of traps and stopping back pressure

15. Amount of water needed, supply pressure, pipe length, number of stories, flow pressure needed at the farthest point from the source

CHAPTER 20 PROBLEM SOLUTIONS

Problem 20–1

Problem 20–2

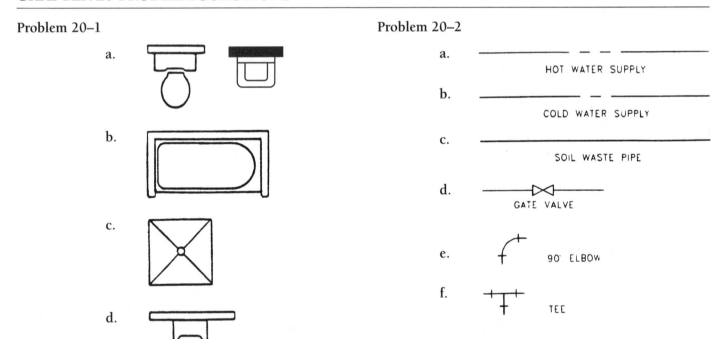

© 2011 Cengage Learning. All Rights Reserved. May not be scanned, copied or duplicated, or posted to a publicly accessible website, in whole or in part.

Problem 20–3

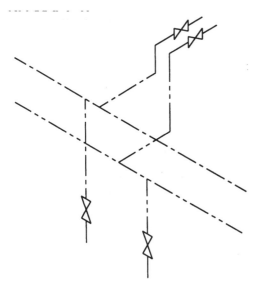

Problem 20–4

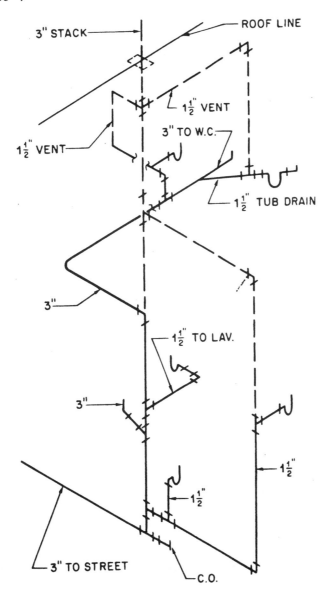

© 2011 Cengage Learning. All Rights Reserved. May not be scanned, copied or duplicated, or posted to a publicly accessible website, in whole or in part.

Problem 20–5

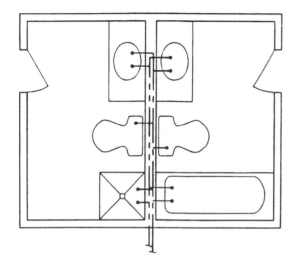

Problem 20–6

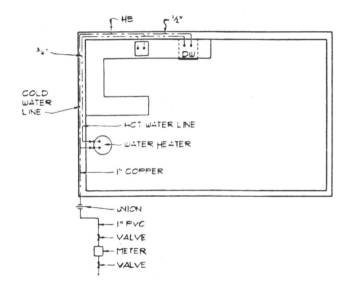

Problem 20–7

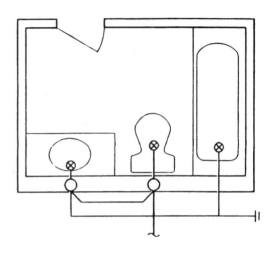

Problem 20–8

Solutions vary. Instructions: Continue the floor plan or floor plans that you started in Chapter 18 by adding any additional symbols and notes related to the plumbing, such as hose bibbs, clothes washer, laundry trays, sinks, and water heater.

CHAPTER 21
HEATING, VENTILATING, AND AIR-CONDITIONING

OBJECTIVES

When students have completed this chapter, they will:

- Describe at least four standard heating and cooling systems.
- Discuss at least four factors that influence the placement of a thermostat.
- Describe at least five sources that contribute to an unhealthy living environment.
- Discuss the function of an air-to-air heat exchanger.
- Define given thermal performance terminology.
- Prepare heat loss and heat gain calculations from given floor plan and specifications.

© 2011 Cengage Learning. All Rights Reserved. May not be scanned, copied or duplicated, or posted to a publicly accessible website, in whole or in part.

TEST ANSWERS

1. a. Central forced-air—The air from the living spaces is circulated through or around heating or cooling devices. A fan forces the air into sheet metal or plastic pipes called ducts. These ducts connect to openings called diffusers in the room. The air enters the room and either heats it or cools it as needed.

   b. Hot water—In the hot water system, the water is heated in an oil- or gas-filled boiler, then circulated through pipes to radiators or convectors in the rooms.

   c. Heat pump—The heat pump is a forced-air central heating and cooling system. It operates using a compressor and a circulating system of liquid gas refrigerant. Heat is extracted from the outside air and pumped inside the structure. In the summer the cycle is reversed and the unit operates as an air conditioner. In this mode, the heat is extracted from the inside air and pumped outside.

   d. Zoned heating—A zoned system allows for one heater and one thermostat per room. No ductwork is required and only the heaters in occupied rooms need to be turned on.

2. Radiant heating and cooling systems function on the basis of providing a comfortable environment by means of controlling surface temperatures and minimizing excessive air motion within the space. Radiant systems vary from oil or gas hot water piping in the floor or ceiling, to electric coils, wiring, or elements in the ceiling and two heavy metal panels mounted about an inch below the ceiling surface.

3. The advantages of zonal heat are that no ductwork is required and only the heaters in occupied rooms need to be turned on. Homeowners can save up to 60% on energy costs through controlled heating.

   The disadvantages of zonal heat are that the units often project a few inches into the room, which can be unsightly, and the furniture arrangement is more complicated with the wall units.

4. A heat pump supplies up to three times as much heat per year for the same amount of electrical consumption as a standard electric forced-air system.

5. Factors that influence the placement of a thermostat are:

   1. a good common location near the center of the structure

   2. close to a return air duct

   3. a stable location where an average temperature reading can be achieved

   4. there should be no drafts that would adversely affect temperature settings

   5. the thermostat should not be placed in a location where sunlight, or a heat register would cause an unreliable reading

6. Sources that can contribute to an unhealthy living environment are:

   1. moisture in the form of relative humidity

   2. indoor combustion from such items as gas fired or wood burning appliances or fireplaces

   3. humans and pets can transmit diseases through the air by the exhale of a variety of bacterial and viral contaminants

   4. tobacco smoke may contribute chemical compounds to the air environment

   5. formaldehyde in glues used in such construction materials as plywood, particle board, or even carpet and furniture causes pollution

7. An air-to-air heat exchanger is a heat recovery ventilation device that pulls stale polluted water air from the living space and transfers the heat in that air to the fresh cold air being pulled into the house. Heat exchangers do not produce heat; they only exchange heat from one air stream to the other.

8. The advantages of a central vacuum system are:

   a. it costs no more than a major appliance

   b. increased resale value of the home

© 2011 Cengage Learning. All Rights Reserved. May not be scanned, copied or duplicated, or posted to a publicly accessible website, in whole or in part.

    c. removes dirt too heavy for most portable units

    d. exhausts dirt and dust out of the house

    e. no noise

    f. saves cleaning time

9. Located with clearances to allow access for servicing and replacement of the largest piece of equipment

10. Air that is provided at a burner for proper combustion

11. Kitchens, bathrooms, garages, or other dwelling units

12. Underwriters' laboratories

13. R-4.2

14. An enclosed duct or area that is connected to a number of branch ducts

15. Aid the drawing by keeping it clear of unneccessary notes

CHAPTER 21 PROBLEM SOLUTIONS

21–1   Answers will depend on the floor plan chosen in Chapter 18. Student solutions will vary.

21–2   Students should prepare their drawings as instructed. Student solutions will vary, but final drawings should be similar to the engineering sketch.

21–3   Students should prepare their drawings as instructed. Student solutions will vary, but final drawings should be similar to the engineering sketch.

21–4, 21–5, 21–6   Student solutions vary depending on the problem selected from Chapter 18.

© 2011 Cengage Learning. All Rights Reserved. May not be scanned, copied or duplicated, or posted to a publicly accessible website, in whole or in part.

Problem 21–7 The following pages are the heat loss and heat gain forms, which are explained in the text-book. These forms can be copied for student use in solving Problem 21–7.

LENNOX RESIDENTIAL HEATING DATA SHEET

JOB NAME:	DATE
ADDRESS:	

OUTDOOR TEMP:	INDOOR TEMP:	TEMP. DIFFERENCE:

MOVABLE GLASS WINDOWS	SQUARE FEET	DESIGN TEMPERATURE DIFFERENCE													BTUH HEAT LOSS
		30	35	40	45	50	55	60	65	70	75	80	85	90	95	
		HEAT TRANSFER MULTIPLIER														
SINGLE GLASS		39	45	52	58	65	71	78	84	90	97	103	110	116	123	
SINGLE GLASS W/STORM		21	25	28	31	35	38	42	45	49	52	56	59	63	66	
DOUBLE GLASS		28	32	37	41	46	50	55	60	64	69	73	78	82	87	
DOUBLE GLASS W/STORM		16	19	21	24	27	29	32	35	37	40	42	45	48	50	

SLIDING GLASS DOORS	SQUARE FEET	DESIGN TEMPERATURE DIFFERENCE													BTUH HEAT LOSS
		30	35	40	45	50	55	60	65	70	75	80	85	90	95	
		HEAT TRANSFER MULTIPLIER														
SINGLE GLASS		42	48	55	62	69	76	83	90	97	104	110	117	124	131	
SINGLE GLASS W/STORM		22	26	29	33	37	40	44	48	51	55	59	62	66	70	
DOUBLE GLASS		29	34	39	43	48	53	58	63	67	72	77	82	87	91	

DOORS	SQUARE FEET	DESIGN TEMPERATURE DIFFERENCE													BTUH HEAT LOSS
		30	35	40	45	50	55	60	65	70	75	80	85	90	95	
		HEAT TRANSFER MULTIPLIER														
SOLID WOOD		31	36	41	46	51	56	62	67	72	77	82	87	92	97	
SOLID WOOD**		18	21	24	27	30	33	36	39	42	45	47	50	53	56	
METAL URETHANE		23	27	30	34	38	42	45	49	53	57	60	64	68	72	
METAL URETHANE**		13	16	18	20	22	25	27	29	31	33	36	38	40	42	

**Weatherstripped or Storm

WALLS	RUNNING FEET _____
	CEILING HEIGHT X _____
	GROSS WALL = _____
	WINDOWS & DOOR AREAS − _____
	NET WALL AREA [_____]

FRAME WALL	SQUARE FEET	DESIGN TEMPERATURE DIFFERENCE													BTUH HEAT LOSS
		30	35	40	45	50	55	60	65	70	75	80	85	90	95	
		HEAT TRANSFER MULTIPLIER														
NO INSULATION		8	10	11	12	14	15	17	18	19	21	22	23	25	26	
R-11, 3" INSULATION		2.7	3.1	3.6	4.0	4.5	4.9	5.4	5.8	6.3	6.7	7.2	7.6	8.1	8.5	
R-13, 3-1/2" INSULATION		2.1	2.4	2.8	3.2	3.5	3.8	4.2	4.6	4.9	5.3	5.6	5.9	6.3	6.6	
R-13 + 1" POLYSTYRENE		1.8	2.1	2.4	2.7	3.0	3.3	3.6	3.9	4.2	4.5	4.8	5.1	5.4	5.7	
R-19 + 1/2" POLYSTYRENE		1.6	1.9	2.2	2.5	2.8	3.0	3.3	3.6	3.8	4.1	4.4	4.7	4.9	5.2	

MASONRY WALL ABOVE GRADE	SQUARE FEET	DESIGN TEMPERATURE DIFFERENCE													BTUH HEAT LOSS
		30	35	40	45	50	55	60	65	70	75	80	85	90	95	
		HEAT TRANSFER MULTIPLIER														
NO INSULATION		16	18	21	23	26	28	31	33	36	38	41	44	46	49	
R-5, 1" INSULATION		4.3	5.0	5.8	6.5	7.2	7.9	8.6	9.4	10.1	10.8	11.5	12.2	13.0	13.7	
R-11, 3" INSULATION		2.3	2.7	3.1	3.5	3.8	4.2	4.6	5.0	5.4	5.8	6.2	6.5	6.9	7.3	
R-19, 6" INSULATION		1.4	1.7	1.9	2.2	2.4	2.6	2.9	3.1	3.4	3.6	3.8	4.1	4.3	4.6	

MASONRY WALL BELOW GRADE	SQUARE FEET	DESIGN TEMPERATURE DIFFERENCE													BTUH HEAT LOSS
		30	35	40	45	50	55	60	65	70	75	80	85	90	95	
		HEAT TRANSFER MULTIPLIER														
NO INSULATION		4.4	5.1	5.9	6.6	7.3	8.1	8.8	9.6	10.3	11.0	11.8	12.5	13.2	14.0	
R-5, 1" INSULATION		2.6	3.0	3.5	3.9	4.3	4.8	5.2	5.7	6.1	6.5	7.0	7.4	7.8	8.3	
R-11, 3" INSULATION		1.8	2.1	2.4	2.7	3.0	3.3	3.6	3.9	4.2	4.5	4.8	5.1	5.4	5.7	
R-19, 6" INSULATION		1.2	1.4	1.6	1.8	2.0	2.2	2.4	2.6	2.8	3.0	3.2	3.4	3.6	3.8	

HEAT LOSS SUBTOTAL	[ ]

© 2011 Cengage Learning. All Rights Reserved. May not be scanned, copied or duplicated, or posted to a publicly accessible website, in whole or in part.

Problem 21–7 (Continued)

Heat Loss Subtotal from Page 1

CEILING	SQUARE FEET	DESIGN TEMPERATURE DIFFERENCE														BTUH HEAT LOSS
		30	35	40	45	50	55	60	65	70	75	80	85	90	95	
		HEAT TRANSFER MULTIPLIER														
NO INSULATION		18	21	24	27	30	33	36	39	42	45	48	51	54	57	
R-11, 3" INSULATION		2.6	3.1	3.5	4.0	4.4	4.8	5.3	5.7	6.2	6.6	7.0	7.5	7.9	8.4	
R-19, 6" INSULATION		1.6	1.9	2.1	2.4	2.6	2.9	3.2	3.4	3.7	4.0	4.2	4.5	4.8	5.0	
R-30, 10" INSULATION		1.0	1.2	1.3	1.5	1.6	1.8	2.0	2.1	2.3	2.5	2.6	2.8	3.0	3.1	
R-38, 12" INSULATION		0.8	0.9	1.0	1.2	1.3	1.4	1.6	1.7	1.8	2.0	2.1	2.2	2.3	2.5	

FLOOR OVER AN UNCONDITIONED SPACE	SQUARE FEET	DESIGN TEMPERATURE DIFFERENCE														BTUH HEAT LOSS
		30	35	40	45	50	55	60	65	70	75	80	85	90	95	
		HEAT TRANSFER MULTIPLIER														
NO INSULATION		10	11	13	14	16	17	19	21	22	24	25	27	28	30	
R-11, 3" INSULATION		2.4	2.8	3.2	3.6	4.0	4.4	4.8	5.2	5.6	6.0	6.4	6.8	7.2	7.6	
R-19, 6" INSULATION		1.6	1.8	2.1	2.3	2.6	2.9	3.1	3.4	3.6	3.9	4.2	4.4	4.7	4.9	
R-30, 10" INSULATION		1.1	1.3	1.5	1.7	1.8	2.0	2.2	2.4	2.6	2.8	3.0	3.1	3.3	3.5	

BASEMENT FLOOR	SQUARE FEET	DESIGN TEMPERATURE DIFFERENCE														BTUH HEAT LOSS
		30	35	40	45	50	55	60	65	70	75	80	85	90	95	
		HEAT TRANSFER MULTIPLIER														
BASEMENT FLOOR		0.8	1.0	1.1	1.3	1.4	1.5	1.7	1.8	2.0	2.1	2.2	2.4	2.5	2.7	

CONCRETE SLAB WITHOUT PERIMETER SYSTEM	LINEAR FOOT	DESIGN TEMPERATURE DIFFERENCE														BTUH HEAT LOSS
		30	35	40	45	50	55	60	65	70	75	80	85	90	95	
		HEAT TRANSFER MULTIPLIER														
NO EDGE INSULATION		25	29	33	37	41	45	49	53	57	61	65	69	73	77	
1" EDGE INSULATION		13	15	17	19	21	23	25	27	29	31	33	35	37	39	
2" INSULATION		6.3	7.4	8.4	9.4	10.5	11.5	12.6	13.6	14.7	15.8	16.8	17.8	18.9	20.0	

CONCRETE SLAB WITH PERIMETER SYSTEM	LINEAR FOOT	DESIGN TEMPERATURE DIFFERENCE														BTUH HEAT LOSS
		30	35	40	45	50	55	60	65	70	75	80	85	90	95	
		HEAT TRANSFER MULTIPLIER														
NO EDGE INSULATION		57	67	76	86	95	105	114	124	133	143	152	162	171	181	
1" EDGE INSULATION		34	40	46	52	57	63	69	74	80	86	91	97	103	109	
2" EDGE INSULATION		28	33	37	42	47	51	56	61	65	70	75	79	84	89	

An additional infiltration load is calculated only if the home is loosely constructed or when window infiltration is greater than .5 CFM per linear foot of crack.

INFILTRATION/ VENTILATION	_____ FLOOR SQ. FT. x _____ CEILING HEIGHT = _____ CUBIC FT
	0.40 x _____ CUBIC FT + 60 = _____ CFM
	MECHANICAL VENTILATION CFM = FRESH AIR INTAKE

	CFM	DESIGN TEMPERATURE DIFFERENCE														BTUH HEAT LOSS
		30	35	40	45	50	55	60	65	70	75	80	85	90	95	
		HEAT TRANSFER MULTIPLIER														
INFILTRATION		33	39	44	50	55	61	66	72	77	83	88	94	99	105	
MECHANICAL VENTILATION		33	39	44	50	55	61	66	72	77	83	88	94	99	105	

HEAT LOSS SUBTOTAL

DUCT LOSS	BTUH HEAT LOSS
R-4, 1" Flexible Blanket Insulation: ADD 15% (.15)	
R-7, 2" Flexible Blanket Insulation: ADD 10% (.10)	

TOTAL HEAT LOSS

NOTE: All Heat Transfer Multipliers from ACCA Manual "J" Sixth Edition.

HL-841-L7   OU2344

Litho U.S.A.

© 2011 Cengage Learning. All Rights Reserved. May not be scanned, copied or duplicated, or posted to a publicly accessible website, in whole or in part.

Problem 21–7 (Continued)

LENNOX RESIDENTIAL COOLING DATA SHEET

JOB NAME:	DATE
ADDRESS:	

OUTDOOR TEMP:	INDOOR TEMP:	TEMP DIFFERENCE:

SENSIBLE LOAD CALCULATIONS

GLASS NO SHADE		SINGLE						DOUBLE						TRIPLE						BTUH HEAT GAIN
COMPASS POINT	GLASS AREA SQ. FEET	DESIGN TEMPERATURE DIFFERENCE																		
		10	15	20	25	30	35	10	15	20	25	30	35	10	15	20	25	30	35	
		HEAT TRANSFER MULTIPLIER																		
N		25	29	33	37	41	45	20	22	24	26	28	30	15	16	18	19	20	21	
NE & NW		55	60	65	70	75	80	50	52	54	56	58	60	37	38	40	41	42	44	
E & W		80	85	90	95	100	105	70	72	74	76	78	80	55	56	58	59	60	62	
SE & SW		70	74	78	82	86	90	60	62	64	66	68	70	47	49	51	52	53	54	
S		40	44	48	52	56	60	35	37	39	41	43	45	26	27	29	31	32	33	

GLASS INSIDE SHADE		SINGLE						DOUBLE						TRIPLE						BTUH HEAT GAIN
COMPASS POINT	GLASS AREA SQ. FEET	DESIGN TEMPERATURE DIFFERENCE·																		
		10	15	20	25	30	35	10	15	20	25	30	35	10	15	20	25	30	35	
		HEAT TRANSFER MULTIPLIER																		
N		15	19	23	27	31	35	15	17	19	21	23	25	10	12	14	16	17	19	
NE & NW		35	39	43	47	51	55	30	32	34	36	38	40	22	24	26	28	30	31	
E & W		50	54	58	62	66	70	45	47	49	51	53	55	35	36	38	40	42	44	
SE & SW		40	44	48	52	56	60	35	37	39	41	43	45	29	30	32	34	36	38	
S		25	29	33	37	41	45	20	22	24	26	28	30	16	18	20	22	24	26	

DOORS	SQUARE FEET	DESIGN TEMPERATURE DIFFERENCE						BTUH HEAT GAIN
		10	15	20	25	30	35	
		HEAT TRANSFER MULTIPLIER						
SOLID WOOD		6.3	8.6	10.9	13.2	14.4	15.5	
SOLID WOOD **		4.2	5.7	7.3	8.8	9.6	10.4	
METAL URETHANE		2.6	3.5	4.5	5.4	5.9	6.4	
METAL URETHANE **		2.2	3.0	3.8	4.6	5.0	5.4	

** Weatherstripped or Storm

WALLS	RUNNING FEET	_____
	CEILING HEIGHT	X _____
	GROSS WALL	= _____
	WINDOWS & DOOR AREAS	− _____
	NET WALL AREA	[_____]

FRAME WALL	SQUARE FEET	DESIGN TEMPERATURE DIFFERENCE						BTUH HEAT GAIN
		10	15	20	25	30	35	
		HEAT TRANSFER MULTIPLIER						
NO INSULATION		3.7	5.0	6.4	7.8	8.5	9.1	
R-11, 3" INSULATION		1.2	1.7	2.1	2.6	2.8	3.0	
R-13, 3-1/2" INSULATION		1.1	1.5	1.9	2.3	2.5	2.7	
R-13 + 1" POLYSTYRENE		0.8	1.1	1.4	1.7	1.8	2.0	
R-19 + 1/2" POLYSTYRENE		0.7	1.0	1.3	1.6	1.7	1.8	

MASONRY WALL ABOVE GRADE	SQUARE FEET	DESIGN TEMPERATURE DIFFERENCE						BTUH HEAT GAIN
		10	15	20	25	30	35	
		HEAT TRANSFER MULTIPLIER						
NO INSULATION		3.2	5.8	8.3	10.9	12.2	13.4	
R-5, 1" INSULATION		0.9	1.6	2.3	3.1	3.5	3.8	
R-11, 3" INSULATION		0.5	0.9	1.3	1.6	1.8	2.0	
R-19, 6" INSULATION		0.3	0.5	0.8	1.0	1.2	1.3	

SENSIBLE HEAT GAIN SUBTOTAL	

© 2011 Cengage Learning. All Rights Reserved. May not be scanned, copied or duplicated, or posted to a publicly accessible website, in whole or in part.

Problem 21–7 (Continued)

		Sensible Heat Gain Subtotal from Page 1							

CEILING	SQUARE FEET	DESIGN TEMPERATURE DIFFERENCE						BTUH HEAT GAIN
		10	15	20	25	30	35	
		HEAT TRANSFER MULTIPLIER						
No Insulation		14.9	17.0	19.2	21.4	22.5	23.6	
R-11, 3″ Insulation		2.8	3.2	3.7	4.1	4.3	4.5	
R-19, 6″ Insulation		1.8	2.1	2.3	2.6	2.8	2.9	
R-30, 10″ Insulation		1.1	1.3	1.5	1.6	1.7	1.8	
R-38, 12″ Insulation		0.9	1.0	1.1	1.3	1.3	1.4	

FLOOR OVER UNCONDITIONED SPACE	SQUARE FEET	DESIGN TEMPERATURE DIFFERENCE						BTUH HEAT GAIN
		10	15	20	25	30	35	
		HEAT TRANSFER MULTIPLIER						
No Insulation		1.9	3.9	5.8	7.7	8.7	9.6	
CARPET FLOOR-NO INSULATION		1.3	2.5	3.8	5.1	5.7	6.3	
R-11, 3″ INSULATION		0.4	0.8	1.3	1.7	1.9	2.1	
R-19, 6″ INSULATION		0.3	0.5	0.8	1.1	1.2	1.3	
R-30, 10″ INSULATION		0.2	0.4	0.6	0.7	0.8	0.9	

INFILTRATION/ VENTILATION	_____ FLOOR SQ. FT. x _____ CEILING HEIGHT = _____ CUBIC FT

0.40 x _____ CUBIC FT ÷ 60 = _____ CFM

MECHANICAL VENTILATION CFM = FRESH AIR INTAKE

	CFM	DESIGN TEMPERATURE DIFFERENCE						BTUH HEAT GAIN
		10	15	20	25	30	35	
		HEAT TRANSFER MULTIPLIER						
INFILTRATION		11.0	16.5	22.0	27.0	32.0	38.0	
MECHANICAL VENTILATION		11.0	16.5	22.0	27.0	32.0	38.0	

INTERNAL HEAT GAIN	BTUH HEAT GAIN
Number of People _____ × 300	
Kitchen Allowance	1,200

SENSIBLE HEAT GAIN SUBTOTAL	

DUCT GAIN	BTUH HEAT GAIN
R-4, 1″ Flexible Blanket Insulation: ADD 15% (.15)	
R-7, 2″ Flexible Blanket Insulation: ADD 10% (.10)	

TOTAL SENSIBLE HEAT GAIN	

LATENT LOAD CALCULATIONS

Conditions	Outdoor Wet Bulb	Indoor Wet Bulb	Grains
Wet	80	62.5	50
Medium	75	62.5	35
Medium Dry	70	62.5	20
Dry	65	62.5	0

Based on 75ºF Indoor Dry Bulb at 50% RH.

LATENT LOAD-INFILTRATION	
0.68 × _____ Grains × _____ Infiltration CFM	
LATENT LOAD-VENTILATION	
0.68 × _____ Grains × _____ Ventilation CFM	

LATENT LOAD-PEOPLE	
Number of People _____ x 230	

TOTAL LATENT HEAT GAIN	

TOTAL SENSIBLE AND LATENT HEAT GAIN	

NOTE: All Heat Transfer Multipliers from ACCA Manual "J" Sixth Edition and for a medium outdoor daily temperature range.

CL-841-L7   002345

Litho U.S.A.

© 2011 Cengage Learning. All Rights Reserved. May not be scanned, copied or duplicated, or posted to a publicly accessible website, in whole or in part.

Problem 21–8

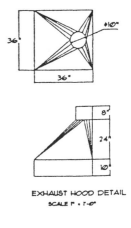

EXHAUST HOOD DETAIL
SCALE 1" = 1'-0"

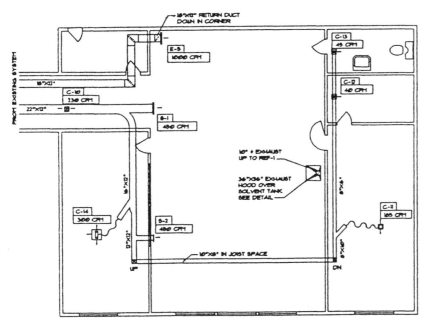

PROPOSED HVAC ADDITION TO EXISTING FLOOR PLAN
SCALE 1/8" = 1'-0"

CEILING OUTLET SCHEDULE

Symbol	Size	CFM	Damper Type	Panel Size
C-10	9X9	230	KEY OPERATED	12X12
C-11	8X8	188	KEY OPERATED	12X12
C-12	6X6	40	KEY OPERATED	12X12
C-13	6X6	45	KEY OPERATED	12X12
C-14	6X18	300	FIRE DAMPER	24X24

SUPPLY GRILL SCHEDULE

Symbol	Size	CFM	Location	Damper Type
S-1	20X8	480	HIGH WALL	KEY OPERATED
S-2	20X8	480	HIGH WALL	EXTERNAL OPERATION

EXHAUST GRILL SCHEDULE

Symbol	Size	CFM	Location	Damper Type
E-5	18X14	1000	LOW WALL	NO DAMPER

ROOF EXHAUST FAN SCHEDULE

Symbol	Area Served	CFM	Fan Specifications
REF-1	SOLVENT TANK	300	1/4 HP, 12" NON-SPARK WHEEL, 1050 MAX OUTLET VELOCITY

© 2011 Cengage Learning. All Rights Reserved. May not be scanned, copied or duplicated, or posted to a publicly accessible website, in whole or in part.

© 2011 Cengage Learning. All Rights Reserved. May not be scanned, copied or duplicated, or posted to a publicly accessible website, in whole or in part.

SECTION 6
Roof Plans

CHAPTER 22
ROOF PLAN COMPONENTS

OBJECTIVES

When students have completed this chapter, they will:
- Identify three types of roof plans.
- Determine roof pitches and how to represent them in plan view.
- Identify and describe common roof shapes.
- Describe major types of roof materials.
- Determine proper amounts of attic ventilation and access.

TEST ANSWERS

1. Roof plan showing shape only; roof drainage, showing downspouts; roof framing, showing framing members
2. The 4 represents the vertical rise and the 12 represents the horizontal run.
3. 26 1/2 degrees
4. A wall
5. It is an economical roof to construct, and it can provide an area for mechanical equipment.
6. Water and snow build-up
7. Steep gable, hip, gambrel

© 2011 Cengage Learning. All Rights Reserved. May not be scanned, copied or duplicated, or posted to a publicly accessible website, in whole or in part.

8. A hip roof has four or more angled surfaces that meet at the ridge. A dutch hip roof is a combination of a hip and a gable roof with the center section framed as a gable roof, and each end framed with a partial hip.

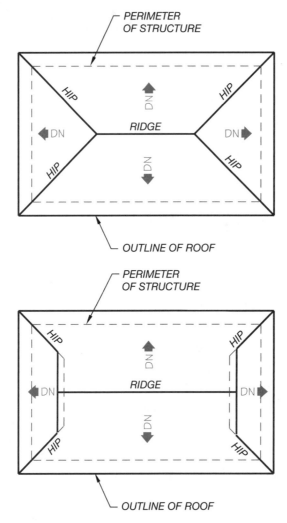

9. As a parapet roof to hide mechanical equipment on the roof, or to help hide the height of the structure

10. 235# and 300#

11. Flat and curved

12. Ease of installation, durable, fire resistant

13. 30" minimum headroom

14. 22" × 30"

15. The "A" frame roof

16. Answers will vary but should reflect suitable waterproof materials.

17. A cool roof is a roof that features highly reflective materials that are used to reflect heat.

18. To be considered sustainable, a roofing system must meet key criteria in the areas of energy, environment, endurance, and economics.

19. LEED credits typically are achieved based on the Material and Resource division, from Thermal Protection area, or from Transportation.

20. Listing of companies that provide green roofing products vary greatly.

© 2011 Cengage Learning. All Rights Reserved. May not be scanned, copied or duplicated, or posted to a publicly accessible website, in whole or in part.

CHAPTER 22 PROBLEM SOLUTIONS

Chapter 22 of the text contains no problems.

CHAPTER 23
ROOF PLAN LAYOUT

OBJECTIVES

When students have completed this chapter, they will:

- Be familiar with the line types, line weights, and symbols used to represent materials on roof plans.
- Draw, label, and dimension a roof plan.

TEST ANSWERS

Chapter 23 contains no written test questions.

© 2011 Cengage Learning. All Rights Reserved. May not be scanned, copied or duplicated, or posted to a publicly accessible website, in whole or in part.

CHAPTER 23 PROBLEM SOLUTIONS

Problem 23–1

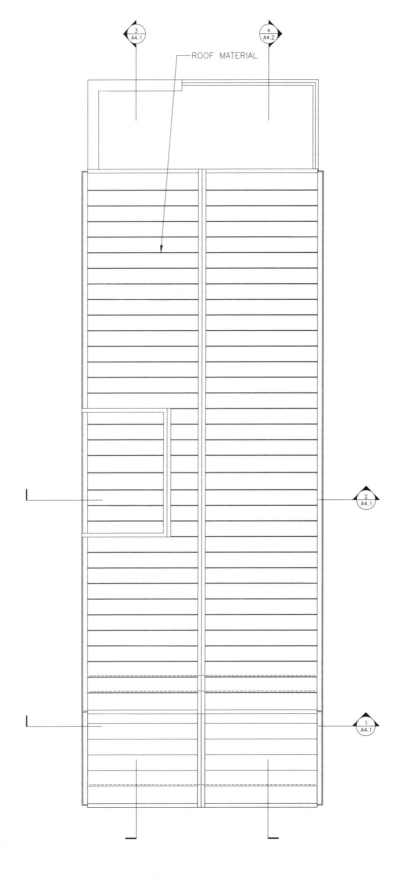

© 2011 Cengage Learning. All Rights Reserved. May not be scanned, copied or duplicated, or posted to a publicly accessible website, in whole or in part.

Problem 23–2

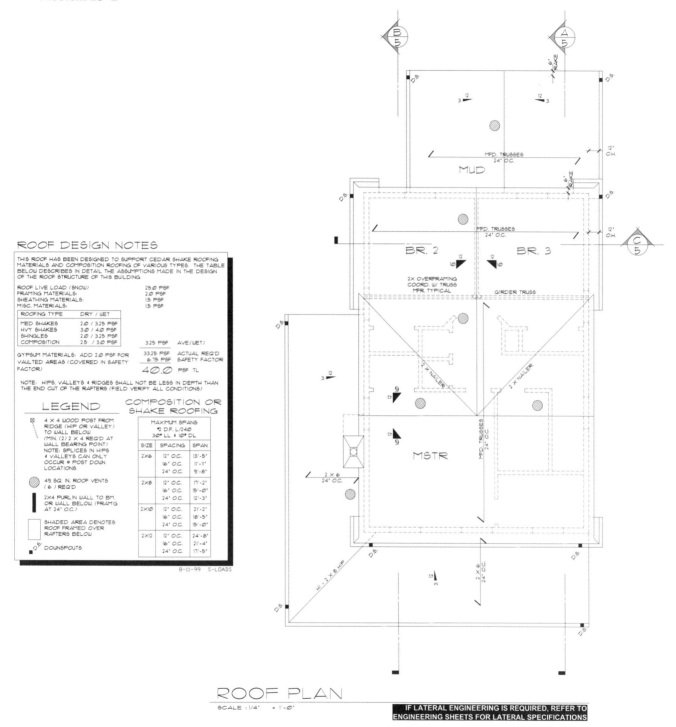

ROOF DESIGN NOTES

THIS ROOF HAS BEEN DESIGNED TO SUPPORT CEDAR SHAKE ROOFING MATERIALS AND COMPOSITION ROOFING OF VARIOUS TYPES. THE TABLE BELOW DESCRIBES IN DETAIL THE ASSUMPTIONS MADE IN THE DESIGN OF THE ROOF STRUCTURE OF THIS BUILDING.

ROOF LIVE LOAD (SNOW)	25.0 PSF
FRAMING MATERIALS:	2.0 PSF
SHEATHING MATERIALS:	1.5 PSF
MISC. MATERIALS:	1.5 PSF

ROOFING TYPE	DRY / WET
MED SHAKES	2.0 / 3.25 PSF
HVY SHAKES	3.0 / 4.0 PSF
SHINGLES	2.0 / 3.25 PSF
COMPOSITION	2.5 / 3.0 PSF

GYPSUM MATERIALS: ADD 2.0 PSF FOR VAULTED AREAS (COVERED IN SAFETY FACTOR)

3.25 PSF   AVE.(WET)

33.25 PSF   ACTUAL REQ'D
6.75 PSF   SAFETY FACTOR

40.0 PSF TL

NOTE: HIPS, VALLEYS & RIDGES SHALL NOT BE LESS IN DEPTH THAN THE END CUT OF THE RAFTERS (FIELD VERIFY ALL CONDITIONS)

LEGEND

⊠ 4 X 4 WOOD POST FROM RIDGE (HIP OR VALLEY) TO WALL BELOW (MIN. (2) 2 X 4 REQ'D AT WALL BEARING POINT) NOTE: SPLICES IN HIPS & VALLEYS CAN ONLY OCCUR @ POST DOWN LOCATIONS

◯ 48 SQ. IN. ROOF VENTS (6) REQ'D

▪ 2X4 PURLIN WALL TO BM. OR WALL BELOW. (FRAM'G AT 24" O.C.)

▢ SHADED AREA DENOTES ROOF FRAMED OVER RAFTERS BELOW

▪ D.S   DOWNSPOUTS

COMPOSITION OR SHAKE ROOFING

MAXIMUM SPANS #2 D.F. L/240 30# LL & 10# DL		
SIZE	SPACING	SPAN
2×6	12' O.C.	13'-5"
	16' O.C.	11'-11"
	24' O.C.	9'-8"
2×8	12' O.C.	17'-2"
	16' O.C.	15'-0"
	24' O.C.	12'-3"
2×10	12' O.C.	21'-5"
	16' O.C.	18'-5"
	24' O.C.	15'-0"
2×12	12' O.C.	24'-8"
	16' O.C.	21'-4"
	24' O.C.	17'-5"

8-11-99   S-LOADS

ROOF PLAN

SCALE : 1/4" = 1'-0"

IF LATERAL ENGINEERING IS REQUIRED, REFER TO ENGINEERING SHEETS FOR LATERAL SPECIFICATIONS

© 2011 Cengage Learning. All Rights Reserved. May not be scanned, copied or duplicated, or posted to a publicly accessible website, in whole or in part.

Problem 23–3

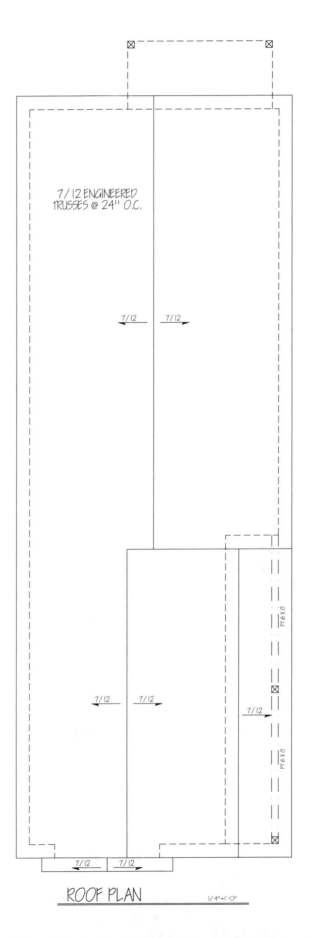

7/12 ENGINEERED
TRUSSES @ 24" O.C.

7/12   7/12

PT 6×8

7/12   7/12

PT 6×8

7/12

7/12   7/12

ROOF PLAN   1/4"=1'-0"

© 2011 Cengage Learning. All Rights Reserved. May not be scanned, copied or duplicated, or posted to a publicly accessible website, in whole or in part.

Problem 23–4

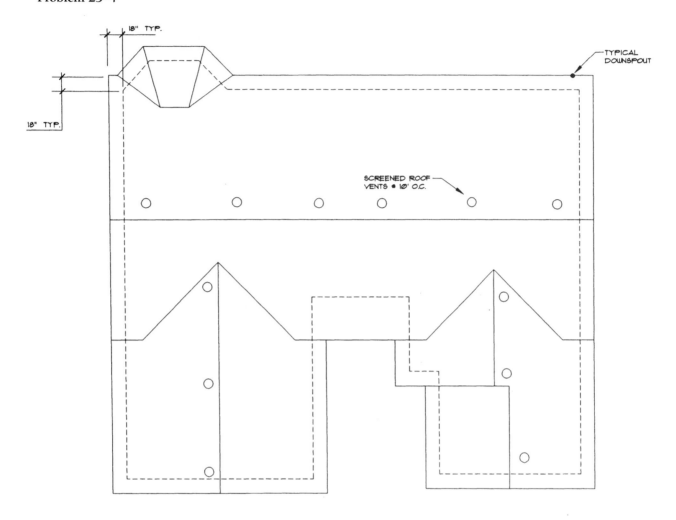

18" TYP.

18" TYP.

TYPICAL
DOWNSPOUT

SCREENED ROOF
VENTS @ 10' O.C.

ROOF PLAN

SCALE 1/4" = 1'-0"

ROOF NOTES:
1. ALL FRAMING LUMBER TO BE DFL #2 OR
   BETTER UNLESS NOTED.
2. ALL VAULTED CEILINGS TO BE FRAMED WITH
   TRUSSES UNLESS NOTED.
3. PROVIDE SCREENED VENTS 2 EA. 3rd
   TRUSS SPACE.
4. USE 1/2" 'CCX EXTERIOR PLY @ ALL
   EXPOSED EAVES.
5. USE 300# COMPO. ROOF SHINGLE OVER 15# FELT
   W/ 5/8" PLY. APA RATED 32/16 W/
   8d @ 6" O.C. EDGES AND 12" O.C. FIELD.
6. BUILDING CONTRACTOR TO SUBMIT TRUSS MANUF.
   DRAWINGS TO BUILDING DEPT. PRIOR TO ERECTION.

© 2011 Cengage Learning. All Rights Reserved. May not be scanned, copied or duplicated, or posted to a publicly accessible website, in whole or in part.

Problem 23–5

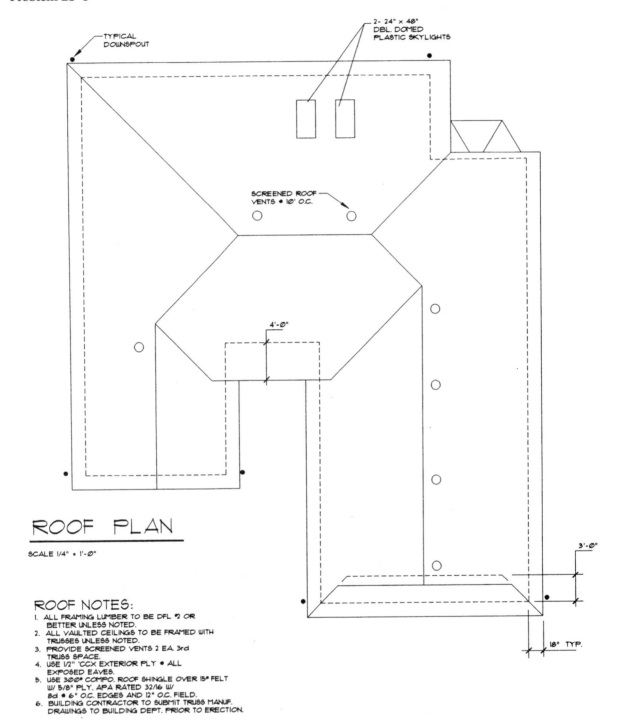

TYPICAL DOWNSPOUT

2- 24" x 48"
DBL. DOMED
PLASTIC SKYLIGHTS

SCREENED ROOF VENTS ● 10' O.C.

4'-0"

3'-0"

18" TYP.

ROOF PLAN

SCALE 1/4" ■ 1'-0"

ROOF NOTES:

1. ALL FRAMING LUMBER TO BE DFL #2 OR BETTER UNLESS NOTED.
2. ALL VAULTED CEILINGS TO BE FRAMED WITH TRUSSES UNLESS NOTED.
3. PROVIDE SCREENED VENTS 2 EA. 3rd TRUSS SPACE.
4. USE 1/2" 'CCX EXTERIOR PLY ● ALL EXPOSED EAVES.
5. USE 300# COMPO. ROOF SHINGLE OVER 15# FELT W/ 5/8" PLY. APA RATED 32/16 W/ 8d ● 6" O.C. EDGES AND 12" O.C. FIELD.
6. BUILDING CONTRACTOR TO SUBMIT TRUSS MANUF. DRAWINGS TO BUILDING DEPT. PRIOR TO ERECTION.

© 2011 Cengage Learning. All Rights Reserved. May not be scanned, copied or duplicated, or posted to a publicly accessible website, in whole or in part.

Problem 23–6

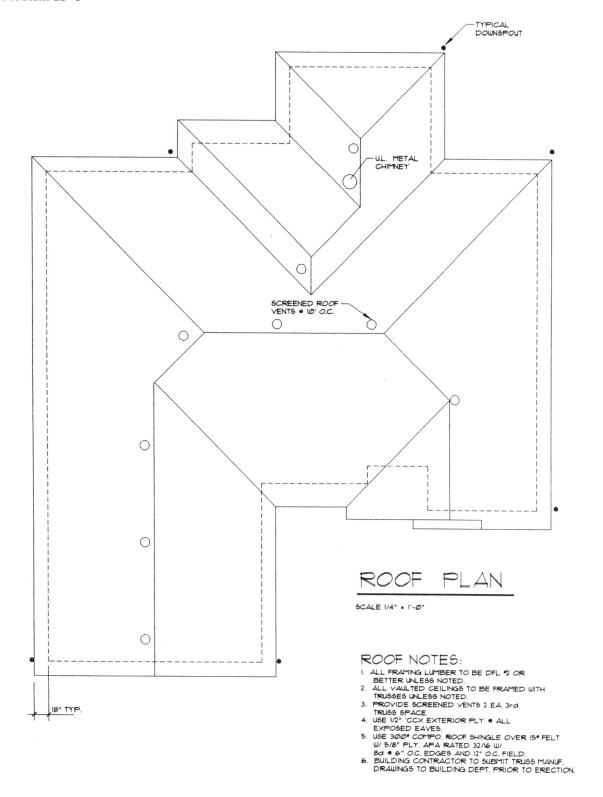

TYPICAL
DOWNSPOUT

U.L. METAL
CHIMNEY

SCREENED ROOF
VENTS ● 10' O.C.

18" TYP.

ROOF PLAN

SCALE 1/4" ● 1'-Ø"

ROOF NOTES:

1. ALL FRAMING LUMBER TO BE DFL #2 OR BETTER UNLESS NOTED.
2. ALL VAULTED CEILINGS TO BE FRAMED WITH TRUSSES UNLESS NOTED.
3. PROVIDE SCREENED VENTS 2 EA. 3rd TRUSS SPACE.
4. USE 1/2" 'CCX EXTERIOR PLY ● ALL EXPOSED EAVES.
5. USE 300# COMPO. ROOF SHINGLE OVER 15# FELT W/ 5/8" PLY. APA RATED 32/16 W/ 8d ● 6" O.C. EDGES AND 12" O.C. FIELD.
6. BUILDING CONTRACTOR TO SUBMIT TRUSS MANUF. DRAWINGS TO BUILDING DEPT. PRIOR TO ERECTION.

© 2011 Cengage Learning. All Rights Reserved. May not be scanned, copied or duplicated, or posted to a publicly accessible website, in whole or in part.

Problem 23–7

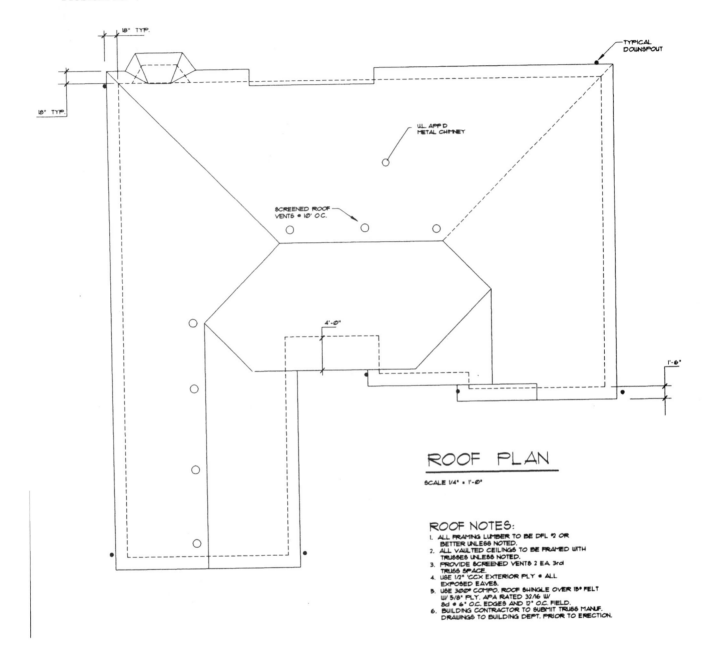

18" TYP.

18" TYP.

TYPICAL
DOWNSPOUT

U.L. APP'D
METAL CHIMNEY

SCREENED ROOF
VENTS @ 10' O.C.

4'-0"

1'-6"

ROOF PLAN

SCALE 1/4" = 1'-0"

ROOF NOTES:

1. ALL FRAMING LUMBER TO BE DFL #2 OR
   BETTER UNLESS NOTED.
2. ALL VAULTED CEILINGS TO BE FRAMED WITH
   TRUSSES UNLESS NOTED.
3. PROVIDE SCREENED VENTS 2 EA 3rd
   TRUSS SPACE.
4. USE 1/2" 'CCX EXTERIOR PLY @ ALL
   EXPOSED EAVES.
5. USE 300# COMPO. ROOF SHINGLE OVER 15# FELT
   W/ 5/8" PLY. APA RATED 32/16 W/
   8d @ 6" O.C. EDGES AND 12" O.C. FIELD.
6. BUILDING CONTRACTOR TO SUBMIT TRUSS MANUF.
   DRAWINGS TO BUILDING DEPT. PRIOR TO ERECTION.

© 2011 Cengage Learning. All Rights Reserved. May not be scanned, copied or duplicated, or posted to a publicly accessible website, in whole or in part.

Problem 23–8

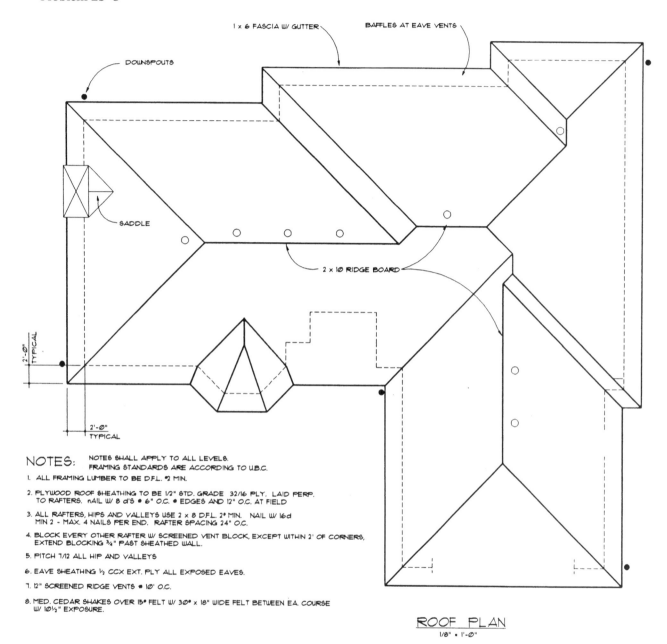

1 x 6 FASCIA W/ GUTTER

BAFFLES AT EAVE VENTS

DOWNSPOUTS

SADDLE

2'-0" TYPICAL

2'-0" TYPICAL

2 x 10 RIDGE BOARD

NOTES: NOTES SHALL APPLY TO ALL LEVELS.
FRAMING STANDARDS ARE ACCORDING TO U.B.C.

1. ALL FRAMING LUMBER TO BE D.F.L. #2 MIN.

2. PLYWOOD ROOF SHEATHING TO BE 1/2" STD. GRADE 32/16 PLY. LAID PERP.
   TO RAFTERS. NAIL W/ 8 d'S @ 6" O.C. @ EDGES AND 12" O.C. AT FIELD

3. ALL RAFTERS, HIPS AND VALLEYS USE 2 x 8 D.F.L. 2° MIN. NAIL W/ 16d
   MIN 2 - MAX. 4 NAILS PER END. RAFTER SPACING 24" O.C.

4. BLOCK EVERY OTHER RAFTER W/ SCREENED VENT BLOCK, EXCEPT WITHIN 2' OF CORNERS,
   EXTEND BLOCKING 3/4" PAST SHEATHED WALL.

5. PITCH 7/12 ALL HIP AND VALLEYS

6. EAVE SHEATHING 1/2 CCX EXT. PLY ALL EXPOSED EAVES.

7. 12" SCREENED RIDGE VENTS @ 10' O.C.

8. MED. CEDAR SHAKES OVER 15° FELT W/ 30° x 18" WIDE FELT BETWEEN EA. COURSE
   W/ 10½" EXPOSURE.

ROOF PLAN
1/8" = 1'-0"

© 2011 Cengage Learning. All Rights Reserved. May not be scanned, copied or duplicated, or posted to a publicly accessible website, in whole or in part.

Problem 23–9

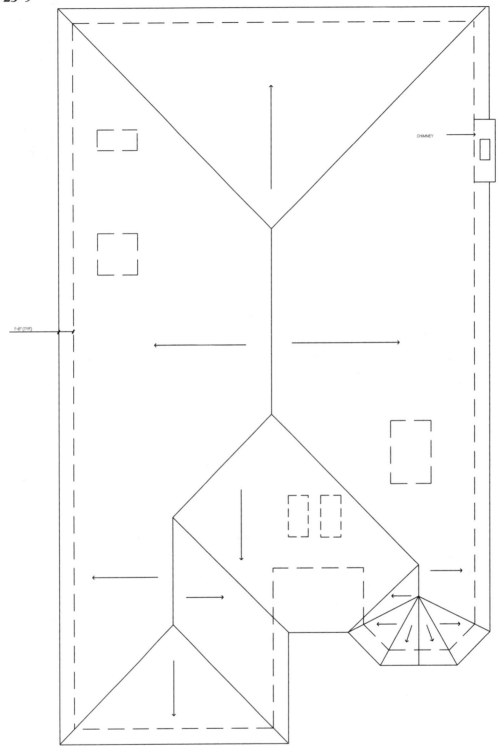

CHIMNEY

1'-6" (TYP.)

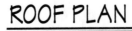

ROOF PLAN

SCALE 1/8" = 1'-0"

© 2011 Cengage Learning. All Rights Reserved. May not be scanned, copied or duplicated, or posted to a publicly accessible website, in whole or in part.

Problem 23–10

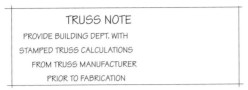

TRUSS NOTE
PROVIDE BUILDING DEPT. WITH
STAMPED TRUSS CALCULATIONS
FROM TRUSS MANUFACTURER
PRIOR TO FABRICATION

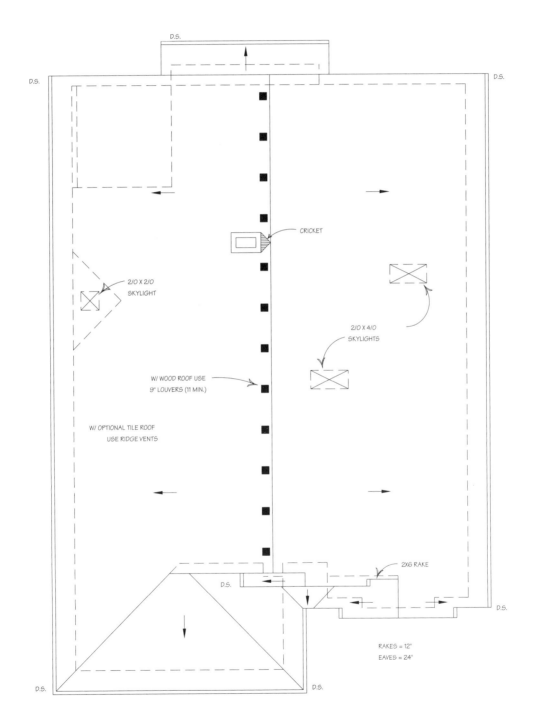

D.S.

D.S.   D.S.

CRICKET

2/0 X 2/0
SKYLIGHT

2/0 X 4/0
SKYLIGHTS

W/ WOOD ROOF USE
9" LOUVERS (11 MIN.)

W/ OPTIONAL TILE ROOF
USE RIDGE VENTS

2X6 RAKE

D.S.   D.S.

RAKES = 12"
EAVES = 24"

D.S.   D.S.

ROOF PLAN

SCALE 1/8" = 1'-0"

© 2011 Cengage Learning. All Rights Reserved. May not be scanned, copied or duplicated, or posted to a publicly accessible website, in whole or in part.

Problem 23–11

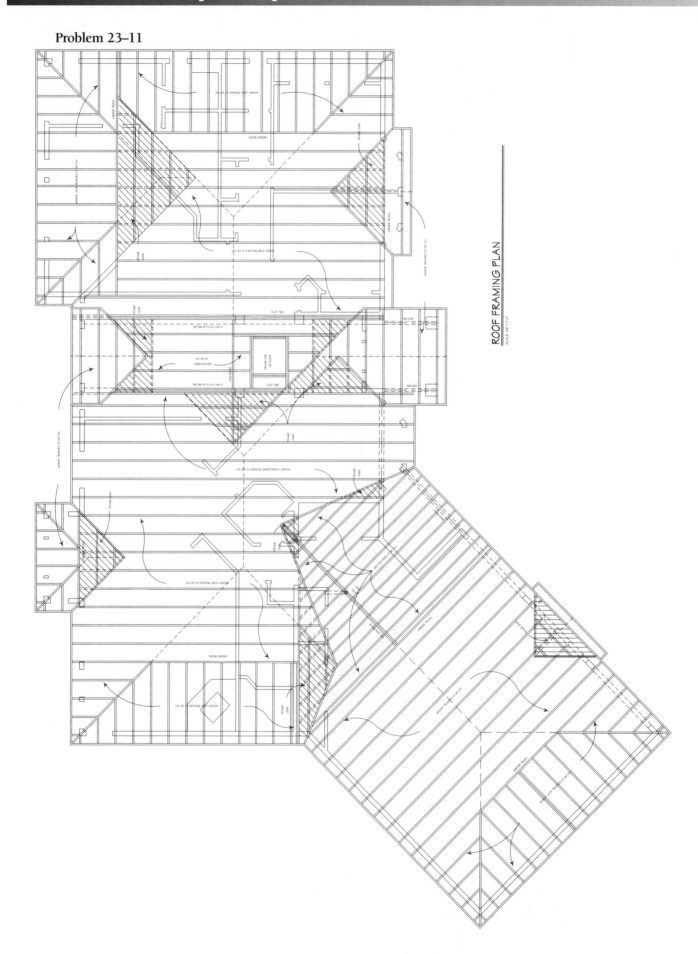

ROOF FRAMING PLAN
SCALE 1/4" = 1'-0"

© 2011 Cengage Learning. All Rights Reserved. May not be scanned, copied or duplicated, or posted to a publicly accessible website, in whole or in part.

Problem 23–12

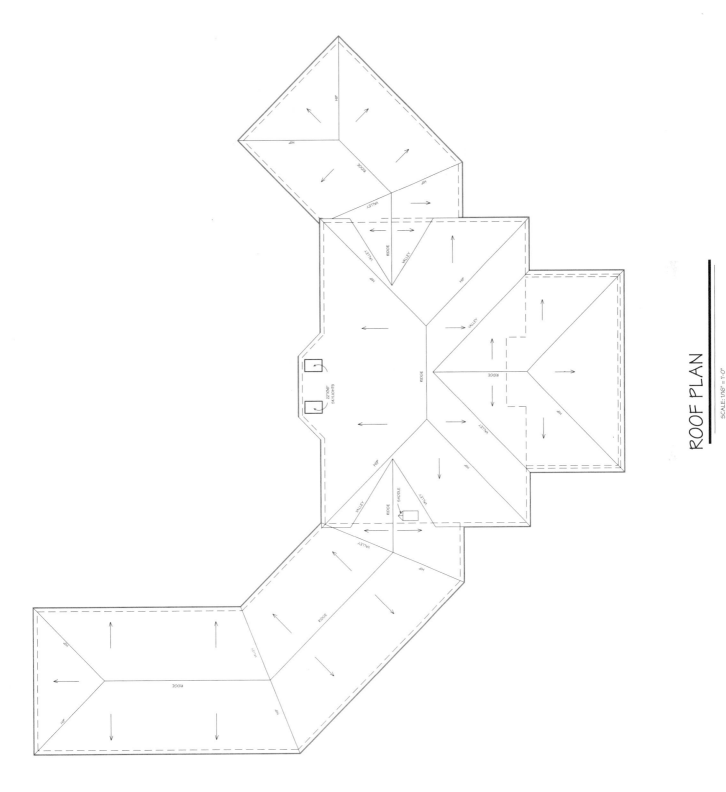

ROOF PLAN

SCALE: 1/16" = 1'-0"

© 2011 Cengage Learning. All Rights Reserved. May not be scanned, copied or duplicated, or posted to a publicly accessible website, in whole or in part.

Problem 23–13

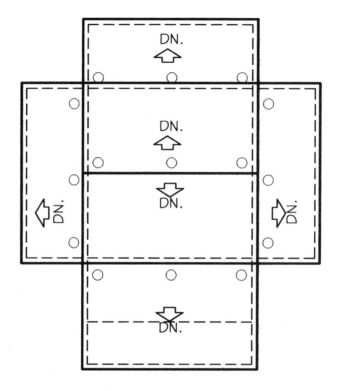

ROOF PLAN

1/8"═══ 1'-0"

ALL FRAMING LUMBER TO BE DFL #2 OR
BETTER UNLESS NOTED.

PROVIDE SCREENED VENTS @ EA. 3rd.
JOIST SPACE @ ALL EAVES.

USE 1/2" 'CCX' EXTERIOR PLY @ ALL
EXPOSED EAVES

USE MED. CEDAR SHAKES OVER 15#
FELT W/ 30# x 18" WIDE FELT BTWN
EA. COURSE W/ 10 1/2" EXPOSURE.

© 2011 Cengage Learning. All Rights Reserved. May not be scanned, copied or duplicated, or posted to a publicly accessible website, in whole or in part.

Problem 23–14

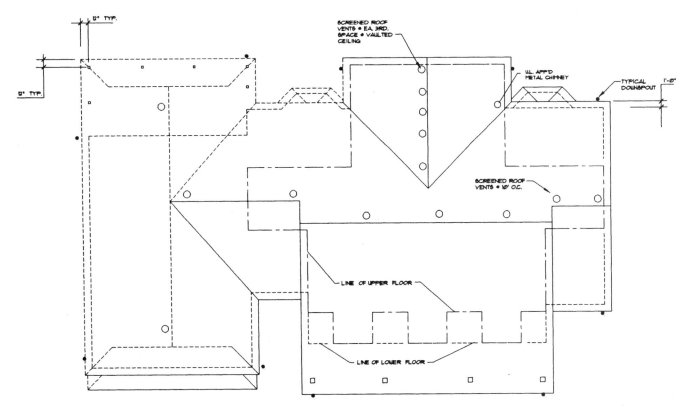

12" TYP.

12" TYP.

SCREENED ROOF
VENTS @ EA. 3RD.
SPACE @ VAULTED
CEILING

U.L. APP'D
METAL CHIMNEY

TYPICAL
DOWNSPOUT

1'-0"

SCREENED ROOF
VENTS @ 10' O.C.

LINE OF UPPER FLOOR

LINE OF LOWER FLOOR

ROOF PLAN

SCALE 1/4" = 1'-0"

ROOF NOTES:

1. ALL FRAMING LUMBER TO BE DFL #2 OR
   BETTER UNLESS NOTED.
2. ALL VAULTED CEILINGS TO BE FRAMED WITH
   TRUSSES UNLESS NOTED.
3. PROVIDE SCREENED VENTS 2 EA. 3rd
   TRUSS SPACE.
4. USE 1/2" 'CCX EXTERIOR PLY @ ALL
   EXPOSED EAVES.
5. USE 300# COMPO. ROOF SHINGLE OVER 15# FELT
   W/ 5/8" PLY. APA RATED 32/16 W/
   8d @ 6" O.C. EDGES AND 12" O.C. FIELD.
6. BUILDING CONTRACTOR TO SUBMIT TRUSS MANUF.
   DRAWINGS TO BUILDING DEPT. PRIOR TO ERECTION.

© 2011 Cengage Learning. All Rights Reserved. May not be scanned, copied or duplicated, or posted to a publicly accessible website, in whole or in part.

Problem 23–15   No drawing provided for this home. See the solution for 32–15.

Problem 23–16   No drawing provided for this home. See the solution for 32–16.

Problem 23–17

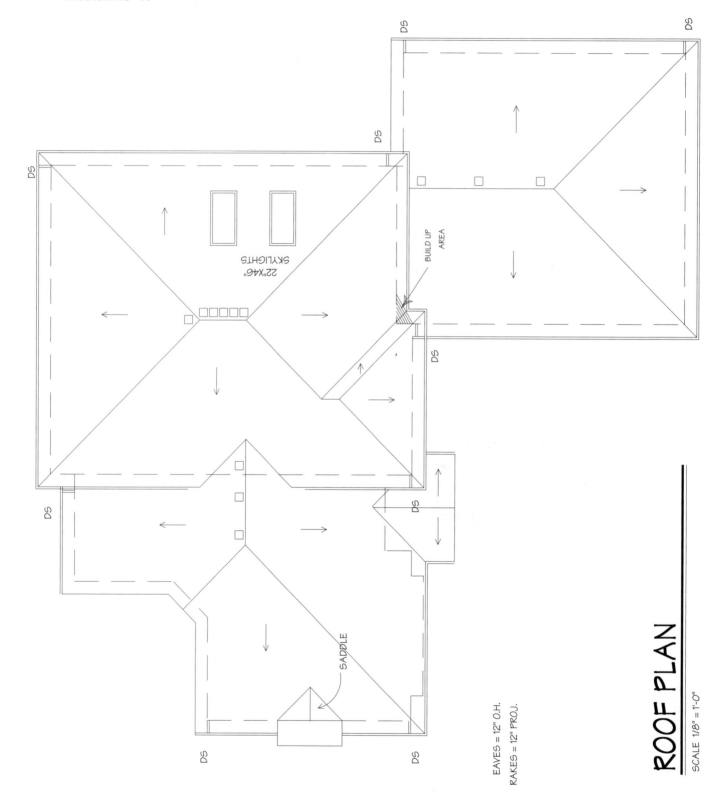

ROOF PLAN

SCALE 1/8" = 1'-0"

EAVES = 12" O.H.
RAKES = 12" PROJ.

© 2011 Cengage Learning. All Rights Reserved. May not be scanned, copied or duplicated, or posted to a publicly accessible website, in whole or in part.

Problem 23–18

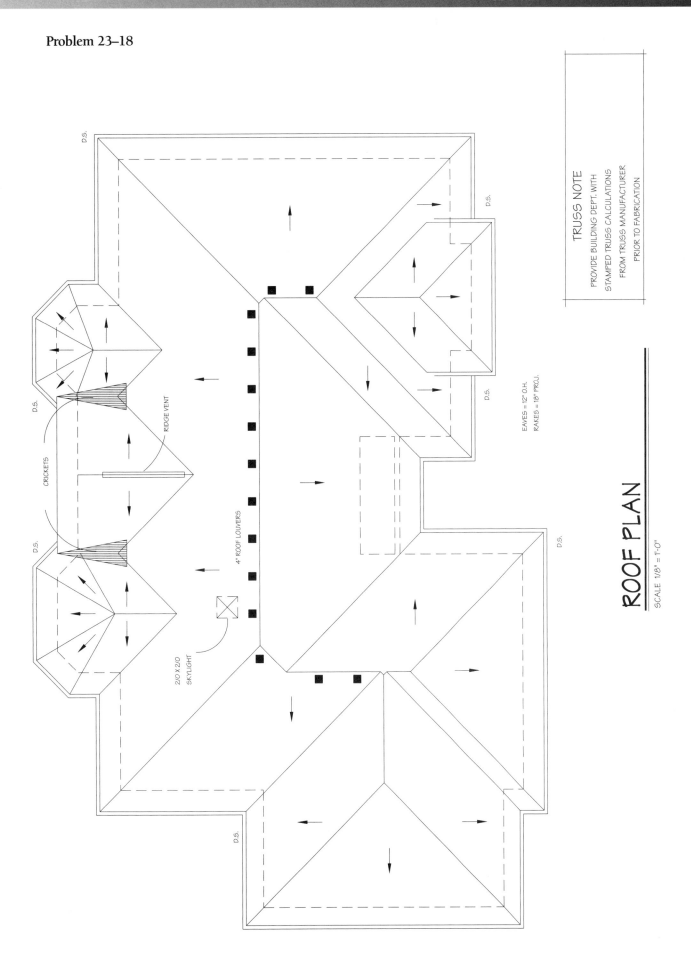

TRUSS NOTE

PROVIDE BUILDING DEPT. WITH
STAMPED TRUSS CALCULATIONS
FROM TRUSS MANUFACTURER
PRIOR TO FABRICATION

D.S.

D.S.

D.S.

D.S.

D.S.

D.S.

D.S.

RIDGE VENT

CRICKETS

4" ROOF LOUVERS

2/0 X 2/0
SKYLIGHT

EAVES = 12" O.H.
RAKES = 18" PROJ.

ROOF PLAN

SCALE 1/8" = 1'-0"

© 2011 Cengage Learning. All Rights Reserved. May not be scanned, copied or duplicated, or posted to a publicly accessible website, in whole or in part.

Problem 23–19

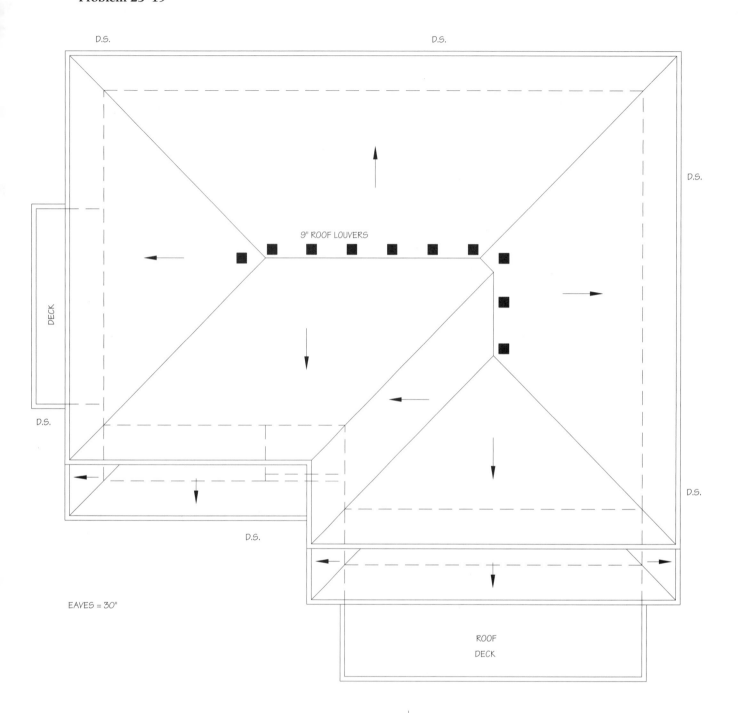

D.S.   D.S.

D.S.

9" ROOF LOUVERS

DECK

D.S.

EAVES = 30"

D.S.

D.S.

ROOF

DECK

ROOF PLAN

SCALE 1/8" = 1'-0"

TRUSS NOTE

PROVIDE BUILDING DEPT. WITH

STAMPED TRUSS CALCULATIONS

FROM TRUSS MANUFACTURER

PRIOR TO FABRICATION

© 2011 Cengage Learning. All Rights Reserved. May not be scanned, copied or duplicated, or posted to a publicly accessible website, in whole or in part.

Problem 23–20

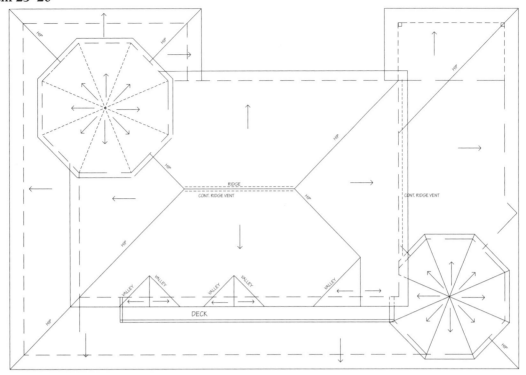

ROOF PLAN

SCALE 1/8" = 1'-0"

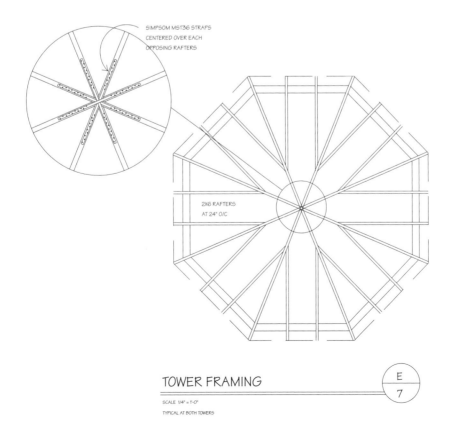

SIMPSON MST36 STRAPS
CENTERED OVER EACH
OPPOSING RAFTERS

2X6 RAFTERS
AT 24" O/C

TOWER FRAMING

SCALE 1/4" = 1'-0"

TYPICAL AT BOTH TOWERS

E
7

© 2011 Cengage Learning. All Rights Reserved. May not be scanned, copied or duplicated, or posted to a publicly accessible website, in whole or in part.

Problem 23–21

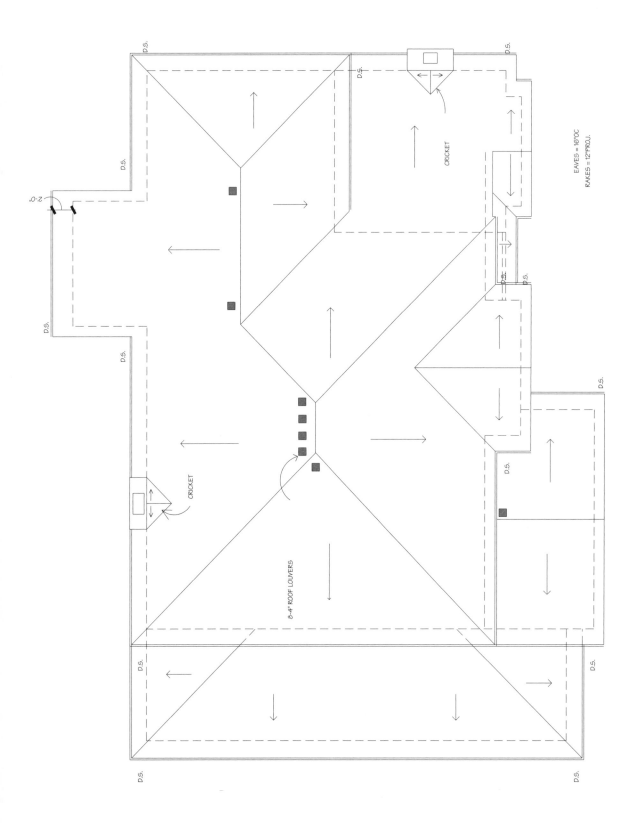
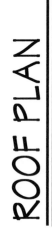

ROOF PLAN

SCALE 1/8" = 1'-0"

EAVES = 16"OC
RAKES = 12"PROJ.

CRICKET

CRICKET

8-4" ROOF LOUVERS

D.S.

2'-0"

© 2011 Cengage Learning. All Rights Reserved. May not be scanned, copied or duplicated, or posted to a publicly accessible website, in whole or in part.

Problem 23–22

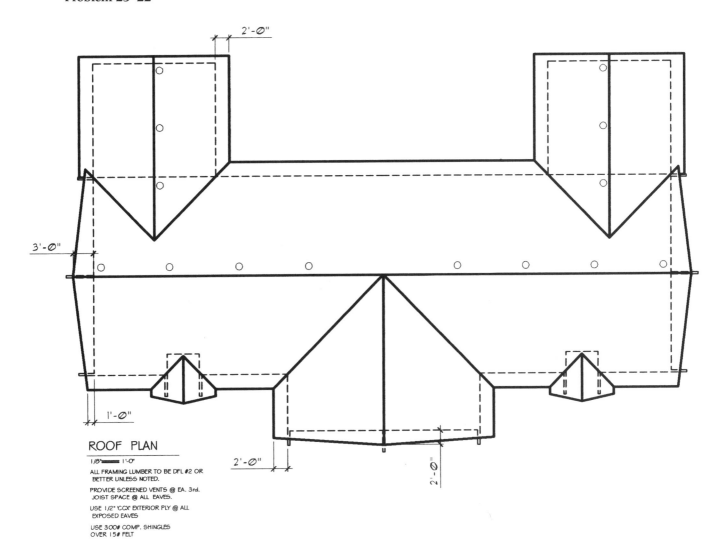

2'-∅"

3'-∅"

1'-∅"

ROOF PLAN

1/8" = 1'-0"

ALL FRAMING LUMBER TO BE DFL #2 OR
BETTER UNLESS NOTED.

PROVIDE SCREENED VENTS @ EA. 3rd.
JOIST SPACE @ ALL EAVES.

USE 1/2" 'CCX' EXTERIOR PLY @ ALL
EXPOSED EAVES

USE 300# COMP. SHINGLES
OVER 15# FELT

2'-∅"

2'-∅"

© 2011 Cengage Learning. All Rights Reserved. May not be scanned, copied or duplicated, or posted to a publicly accessible website, in whole or in part.

© 2011 Cengage Learning. All Rights Reserved. May not be scanned, copied or duplicated, or posted to a publicly accessible website, in whole or in part.

SECTION 7
Elevations

CHAPTER 24
INTRODUCTION TO ELEVATIONS

OBJECTIVES

When students have completed this chapter, they will:

- List and describe required elevations for a structure.
- Describe two types of elevations.
- Be familiar with common scales used for drawing elevations.
- Describe and draw common materials used for roofing, walls, doors, and windows.

TEST ANSWERS

1. When two sides of the structure are similar, or a simple building may only require three elevations.
2. When the structure has an irregular shape causing some surfaces to be distorted, or when some surfaces are hidden by other surfaces
3. To show exterior shape, exterior building materials, and vertical relationships
4. The elevations should be drawn at the same scale used to draw the elevations. When drawn using CADD, this should be full scale. When plotted, the elevations should be plotted at the same scale used to plot the floor plan.
5. The same symbols would be used, but not as much of the material is usually drawn.
6. Direct orthographic projection, projection from a print, drawing a partial section, or projecting heights
7. Flat Barr tiles, or curved Spanish tiles
8. Large plywood sheets or individual members
9. It is not drawn, but specified in a note.

© 2011 Cengage Learning. All Rights Reserved. May not be scanned, copied or duplicated, or posted to a publicly accessible website, in whole or in part.

10.

11. Representing the irregular shape without letting it look mechanical

12.

13. Doors should be drawn so that they resemble a type of door, but not so detailed as to waste a lot of time.

14. Wood or wrought iron

15. With dots placed together in groups, not with small straight lines

CHAPTER 24 PROBLEM SOLUTIONS

Chapter 24 of the text contains no problems.

CHAPTER 25
ELEVATION LAYOUT AND DRAWING TECHNIQUES

OBJECTIVES

When students have completed this chapter, they will:

- Lay out exterior elevations.
- Use finished line quality to complete an elevation.
- Label elevations to describe exterior materials.
- Draw elevations of irregular shaped structures.
- Project grades onto an elevation.

TEST ANSWERS

1. The architect, designer, or senior drafter will usually draw the Front elevation of a structure because these drawings usually provide such a creative outlet. The drafter will usually get to draw the rear or side elevations after the initial design work has been done.

2. Direct orthographic projection, indirect orthographic projection from a print that has been taped by the drawing area, or lightly drawing a section in the area where the elevation will be drawn

© 2011 Cengage Learning. All Rights Reserved. May not be scanned, copied or duplicated, or posted to a publicly accessible website, in whole or in part.

3. Elevations are typically drawn at the same scale as the floor plan. Common scales include 1/4" = 1'-0"; 1/8" = 1'-0"; and 1/16" = 1'-0".

4. Lightly draw a section and project heights.

5. Start at the top of the page and work to the bottom of the page. Within each elevation start at the roof and work to ground level. When drawn using CADD, draw general shapes first and then lines to represent openings, trim, siding and roof patterns using appropriate layers to separate materials.

6. A grading plan and a floor plan. Information from the grading plan is projected onto a print of the floor plan and then into the elevation.

7. The floor and roof plans

8.
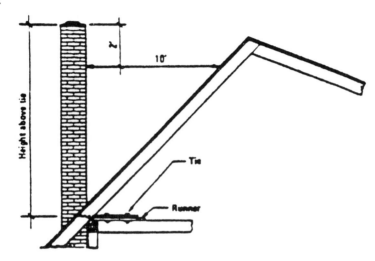

9. Finish floor to ceiling, roof pitch, and chimney to roof height

10. 18 1/2°

© 2011 Cengage Learning. All Rights Reserved. May not be scanned, copied or duplicated, or posted to a publicly accessible website, in whole or in part.

CHAPTER 25 PROBLEM SOLUTIONS

Problem 25–1

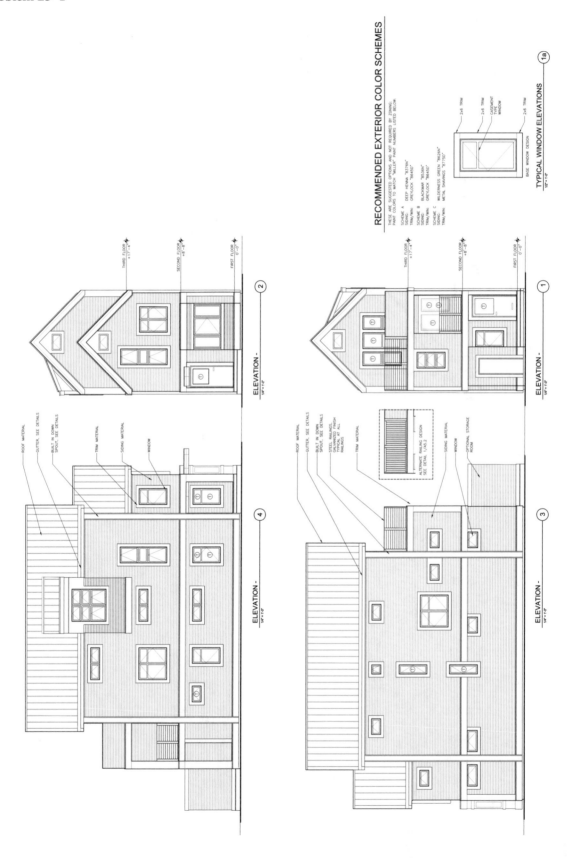

© 2011 Cengage Learning. All Rights Reserved. May not be scanned, copied or duplicated, or posted to a publicly accessible website, in whole or in part.

Problem 25–2

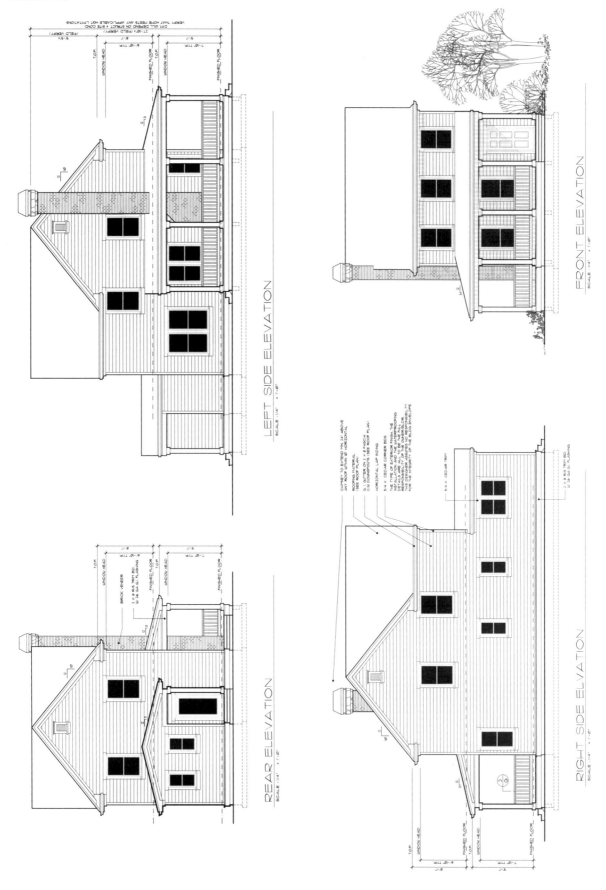

© 2011 Cengage Learning. All Rights Reserved. May not be scanned, copied or duplicated, or posted to a publicly accessible website, in whole or in part.

Problem 25–3

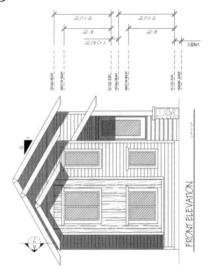

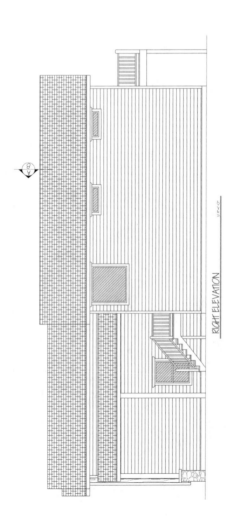

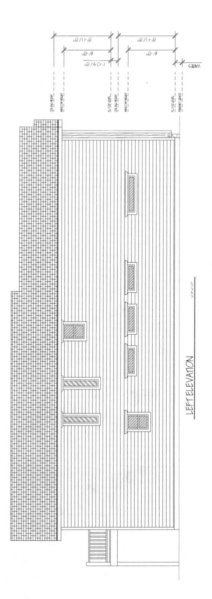

© 2011 Cengage Learning. All Rights Reserved. May not be scanned, copied or duplicated, or posted to a publicly accessible website, in whole or in part.

Problem 25–4

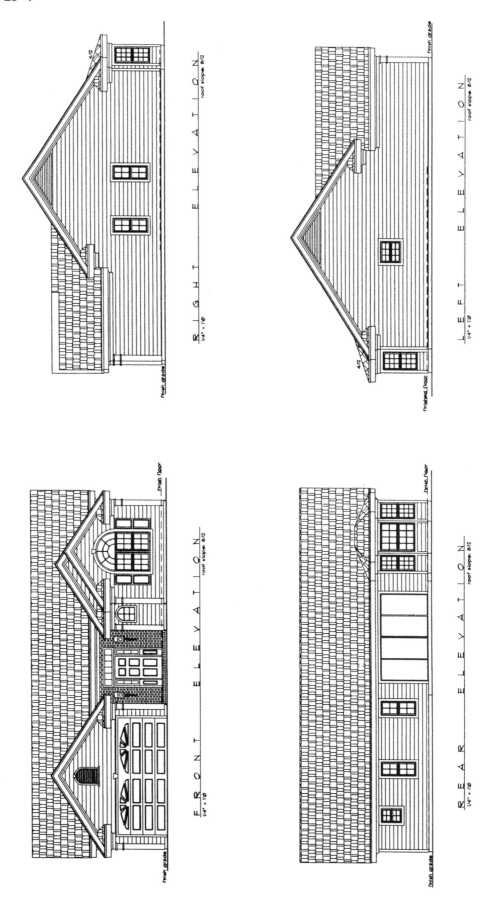

© 2011 Cengage Learning. All Rights Reserved. May not be scanned, copied or duplicated, or posted to a publicly accessible website, in whole or in part.

Problem 25–5

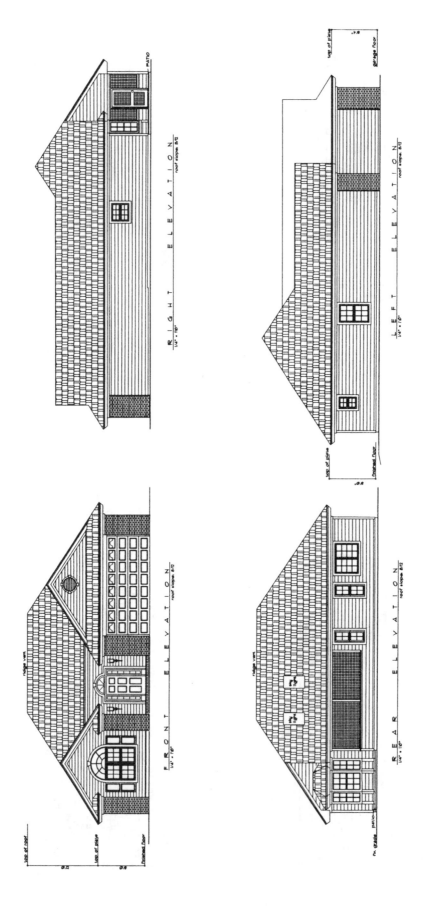

© 2011 Cengage Learning. All Rights Reserved. May not be scanned, copied or duplicated, or posted to a publicly accessible website, in whole or in part.

Problem 25–6

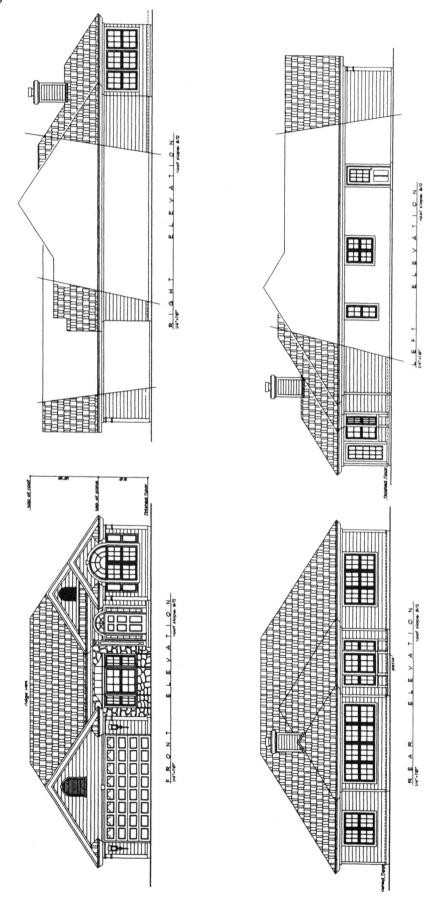

© 2011 Cengage Learning. All Rights Reserved. May not be scanned, copied or duplicated, or posted to a publicly accessible website, in whole or in part.

Problem 25–7

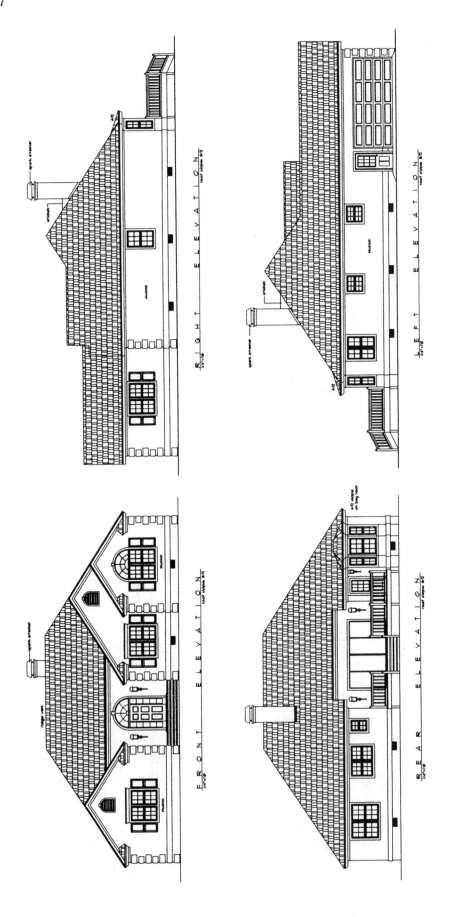

© 2011 Cengage Learning. All Rights Reserved. May not be scanned, copied or duplicated, or posted to a publicly accessible website, in whole or in part.

Problem 25–8

RIGHT SIDE

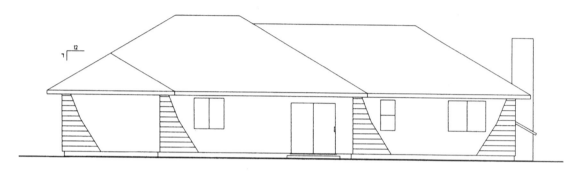

REAR VIEW

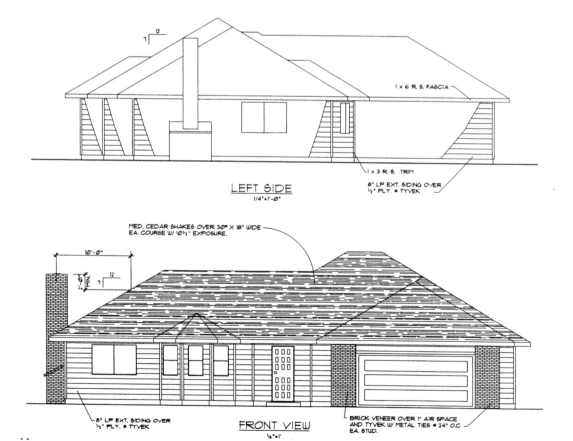

1 x 6 R.S. FASCIA

LEFT SIDE
1/4"=1'-0"

1 x 3 R.S. TRIM

8" LP EXT. SIDING OVER
½" PLY. • TYVEK

MED. CEDAR SHAKES OVER 30# X 18" WIDE
EA. COURSE W/ 10½" EXPOSURE.

10'-0"

2'-0"
MIN.

8" LP EXT. SIDING OVER
½" PLY. • TYVEK

FRONT VIEW
¼"=1'

BRICK VENEER OVER 1" AIR SPACE
AND TYVEK W/ METAL TIES • 24" O.C.
EA. STUD.

© 2011 Cengage Learning. All Rights Reserved. May not be scanned, copied or duplicated, or posted to a publicly accessible website, in whole or in part.

Problem 25–9

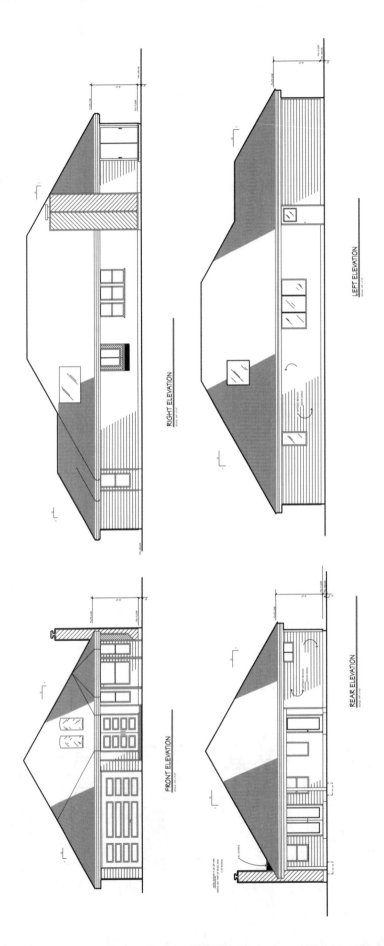

© 2011 Cengage Learning. All Rights Reserved. May not be scanned, copied or duplicated, or posted to a publicly accessible website, in whole or in part.

Problem 25–10

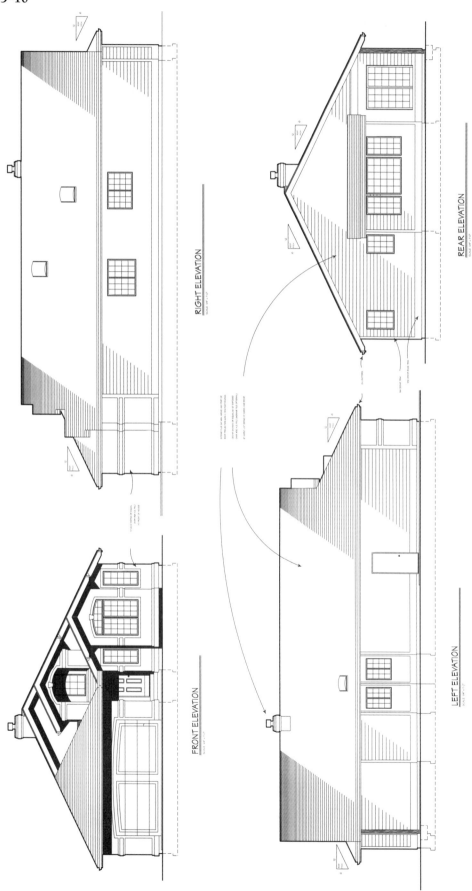

RIGHT ELEVATION
SCALE: 1/4" = 1'-0"

REAR ELEVATION
SCALE: 1/4" = 1'-0"

FRONT ELEVATION
SCALE: 1/4" = 1'-0"

LEFT ELEVATION
SCALE: 1/4" = 1'-0"

© 2011 Cengage Learning. All Rights Reserved. May not be scanned, copied or duplicated, or posted to a publicly accessible website, in whole or in part.

Problem 25–11

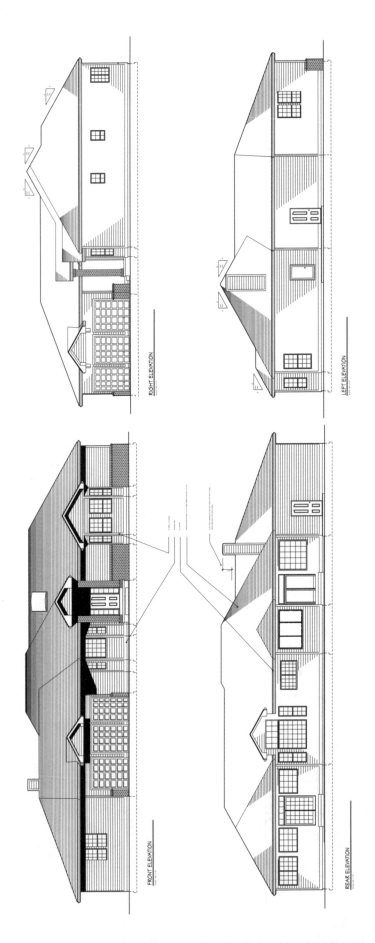

Problem 25–12

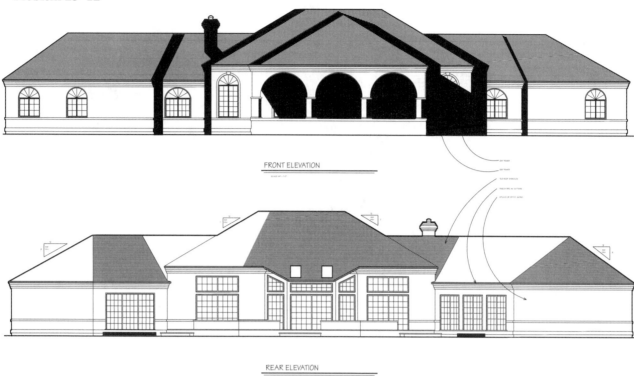

FRONT ELEVATION

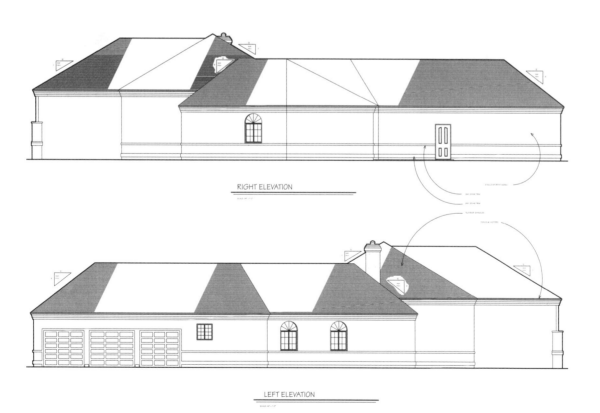

REAR ELEVATION

RIGHT ELEVATION

LEFT ELEVATION

© 2011 Cengage Learning. All Rights Reserved. May not be scanned, copied or duplicated, or posted to a publicly accessible website, in whole or in part.

Problem 25–13

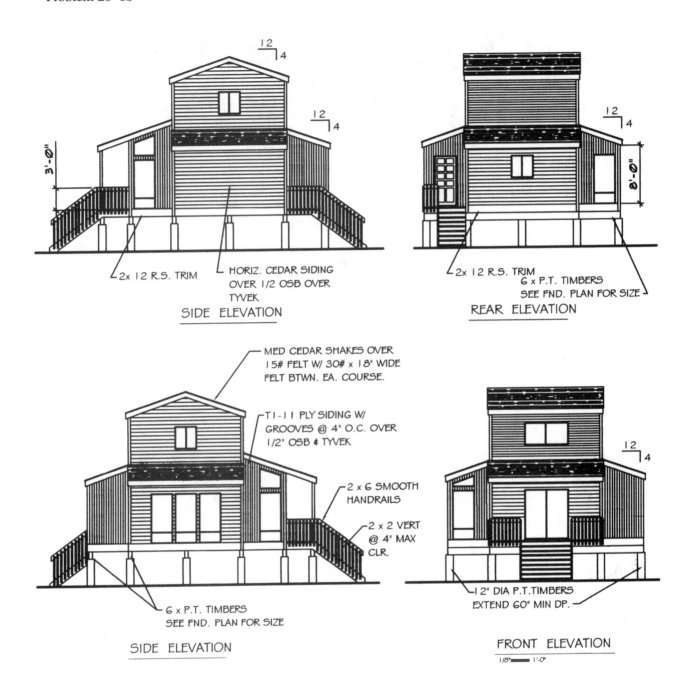

SIDE ELEVATION

2x 12 R.S. TRIM

HORIZ. CEDAR SIDING
OVER 1/2 OSB OVER
TYVEK

REAR ELEVATION

2x 12 R.S. TRIM

6 x P.T. TIMBERS
SEE FND. PLAN FOR SIZE

MED CEDAR SHAKES OVER
15# FELT W/ 30# x 18" WIDE
FELT BTWN. EA. COURSE.

T1-11 PLY SIDING W/
GROOVES @ 4" O.C. OVER
1/2" OSB & TYVEK

2 x 6 SMOOTH
HANDRAILS

2 x 2 VERT
@ 4" MAX
CLR.

SIDE ELEVATION

6 x P.T. TIMBERS
SEE FND. PLAN FOR SIZE

FRONT ELEVATION

12" DIA P.T. TIMBERS
EXTEND 60" MIN DP.

1/8" = 1'-0"

© 2011 Cengage Learning. All Rights Reserved. May not be scanned, copied or duplicated, or posted to a publicly accessible website, in whole or in part.

Problem 25–14

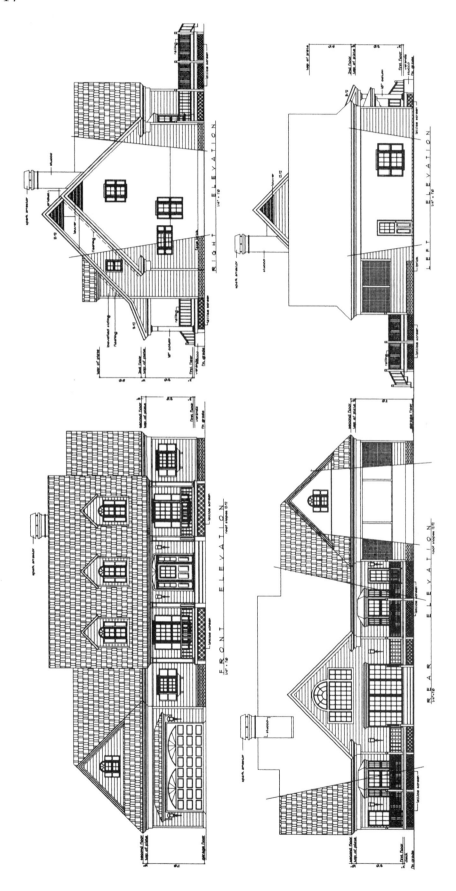

© 2011 Cengage Learning. All Rights Reserved. May not be scanned, copied or duplicated, or posted to a publicly accessible website, in whole or in part.

Problem 25–15A

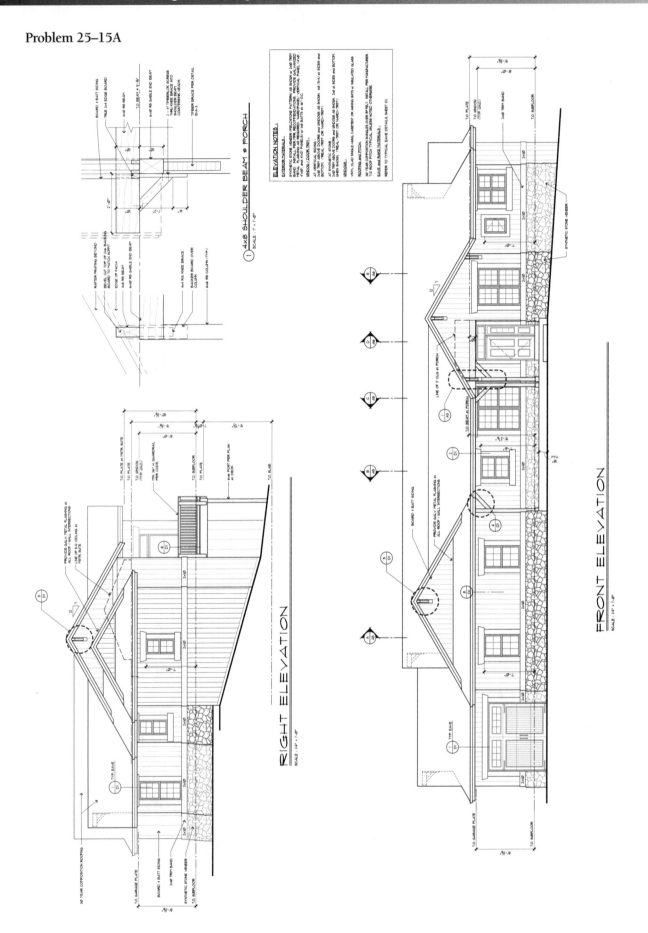

© 2011 Cengage Learning. All Rights Reserved. May not be scanned, copied or duplicated, or posted to a publicly accessible website, in whole or in part.

Problem 25–15B

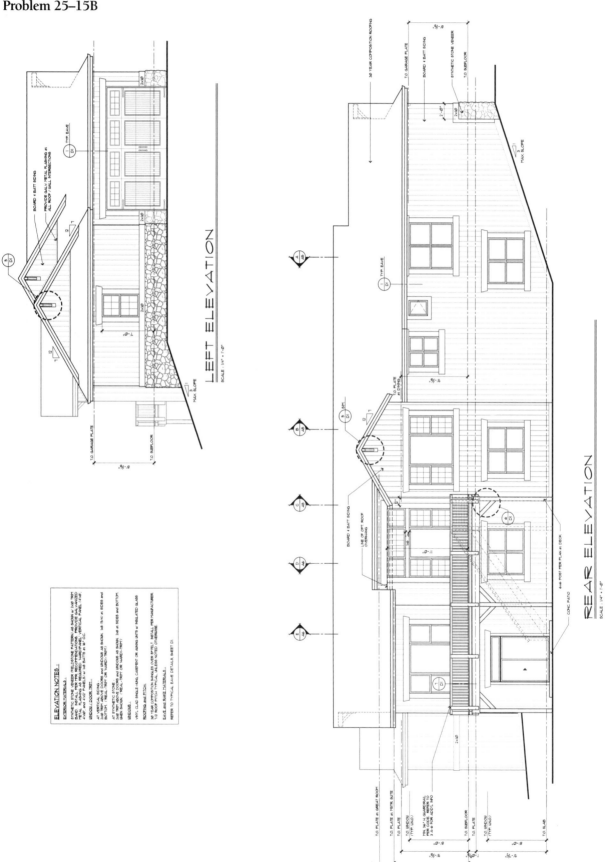

© 2011 Cengage Learning. All Rights Reserved. May not be scanned, copied or duplicated, or posted to a publicly accessible website, in whole or in part.

Problem 25–16A

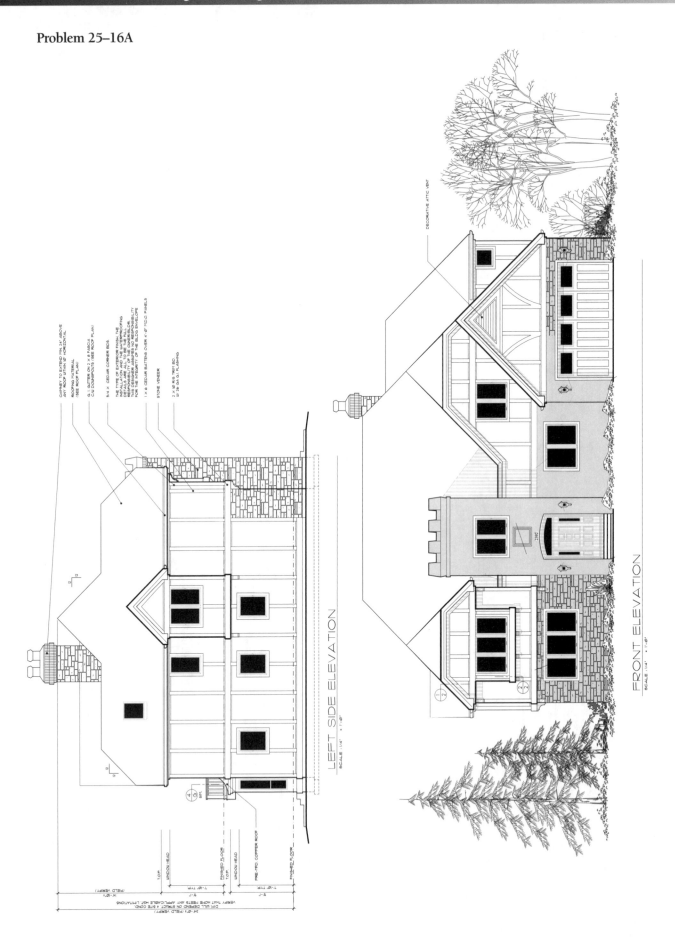

© 2011 Cengage Learning. All Rights Reserved. May not be scanned, copied or duplicated, or posted to a publicly accessible website, in whole or in part.

Problem 25–16B

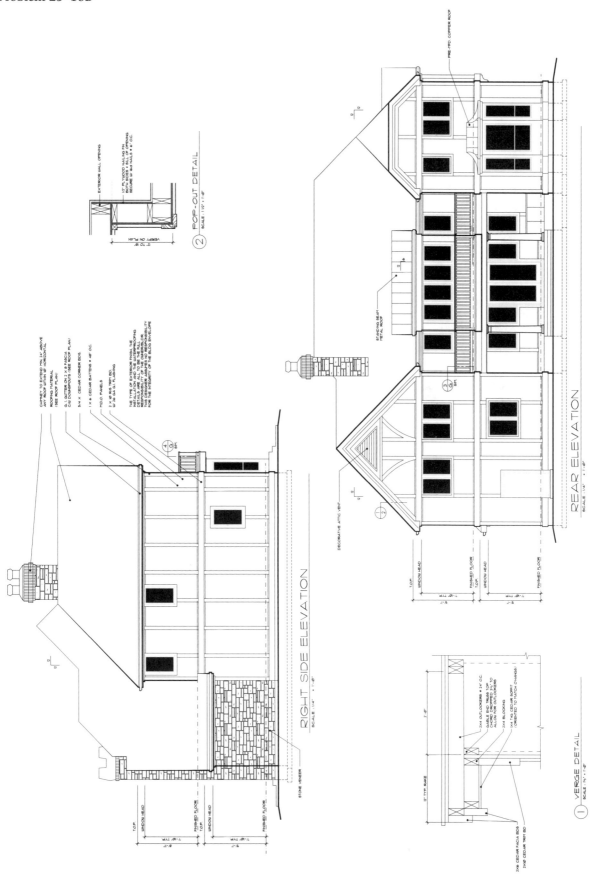

© 2011 Cengage Learning. All Rights Reserved. May not be scanned, copied or duplicated, or posted to a publicly accessible website, in whole or in part.

Problem 25–17

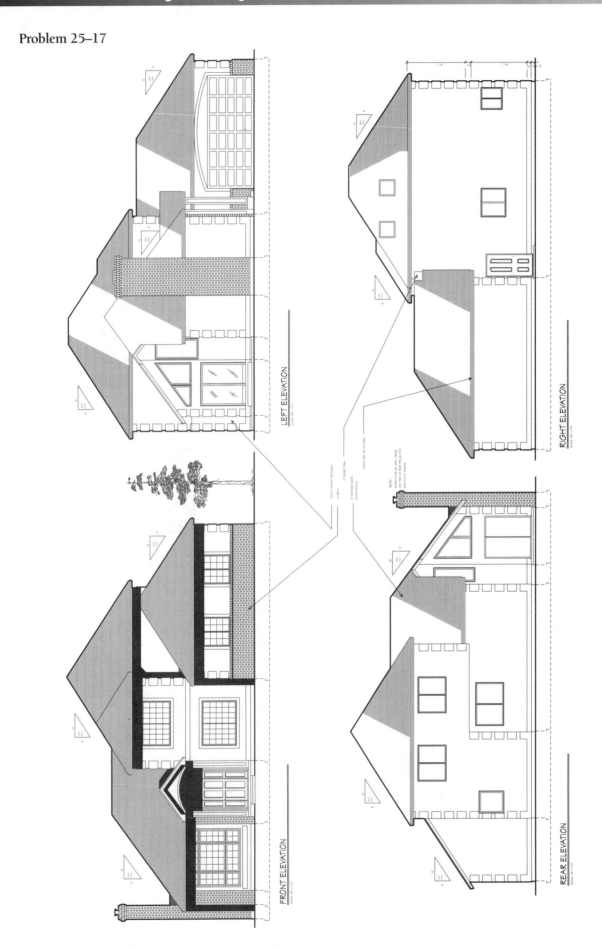

© 2011 Cengage Learning. All Rights Reserved. May not be scanned, copied or duplicated, or posted to a publicly accessible website, in whole or in part.

Problem 25–18

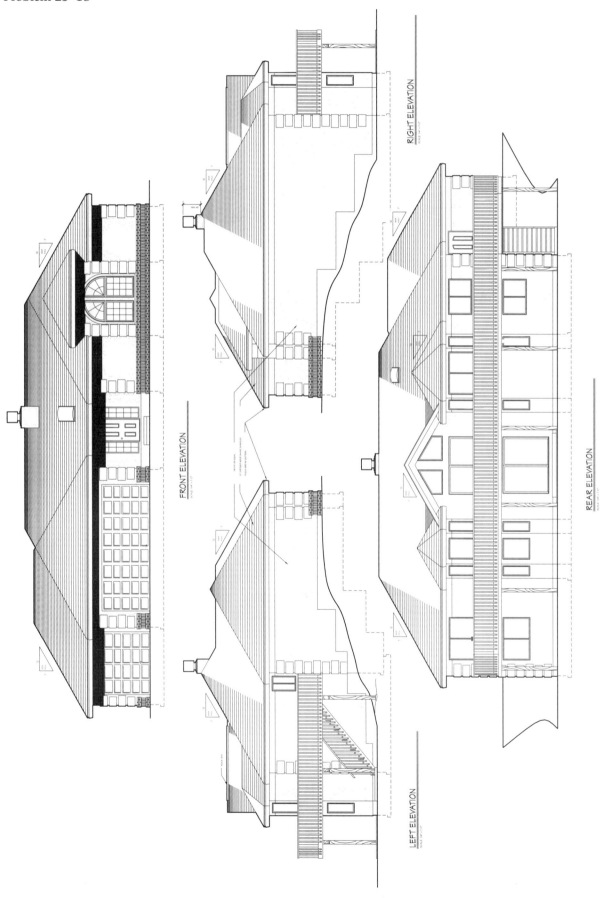

RIGHT ELEVATION

FRONT ELEVATION

LEFT ELEVATION

REAR ELEVATION

© 2011 Cengage Learning. All Rights Reserved. May not be scanned, copied or duplicated, or posted to a publicly accessible website, in whole or in part.

Problem 25–19

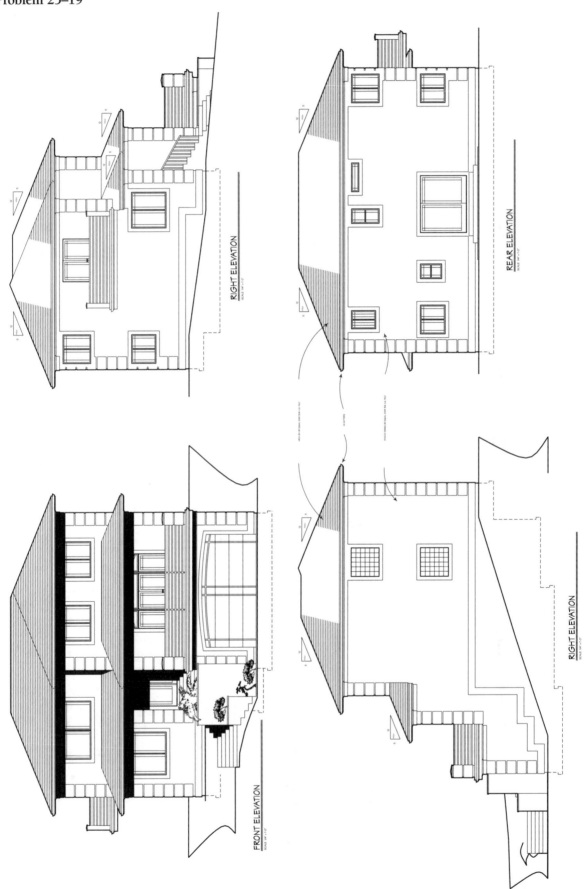

RIGHT ELEVATION

REAR ELEVATION

FRONT ELEVATION

RIGHT ELEVATION

© 2011 Cengage Learning. All Rights Reserved. May not be scanned, copied or duplicated, or posted to a publicly accessible website, in whole or in part.

Problem 25–20

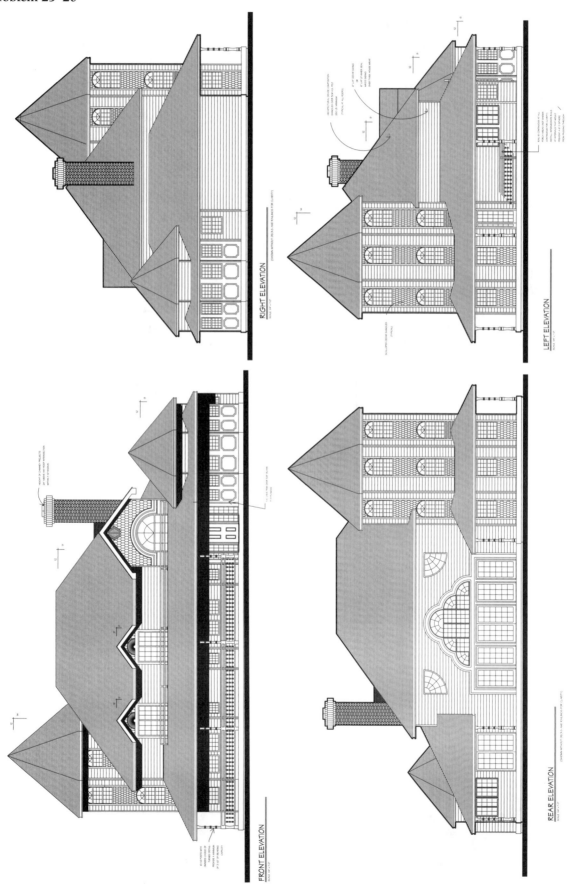

© 2011 Cengage Learning. All Rights Reserved. May not be scanned, copied or duplicated, or posted to a publicly accessible website, in whole or in part.

Problem 25–21

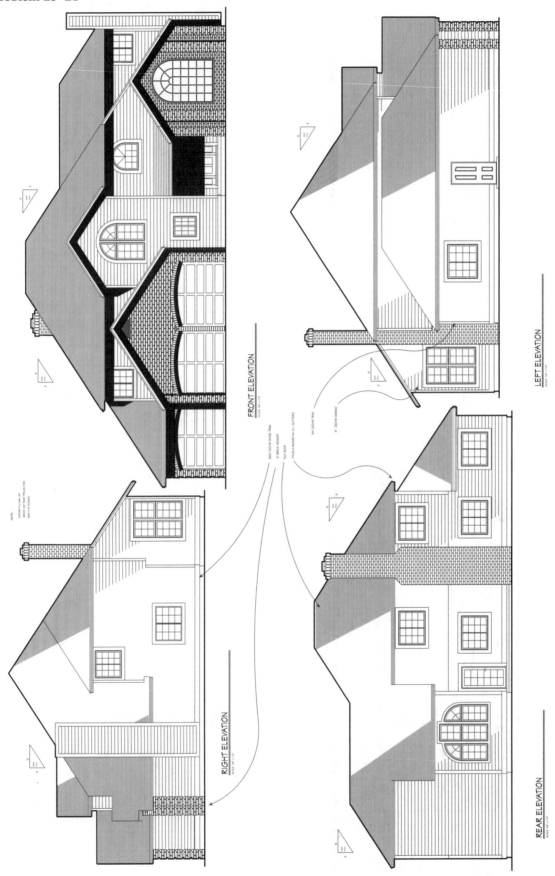

FRONT ELEVATION

LEFT ELEVATION

RIGHT ELEVATION

REAR ELEVATION

© 2011 Cengage Learning. All Rights Reserved. May not be scanned, copied or duplicated, or posted to a publicly accessible website, in whole or in part.

Problem 25–22

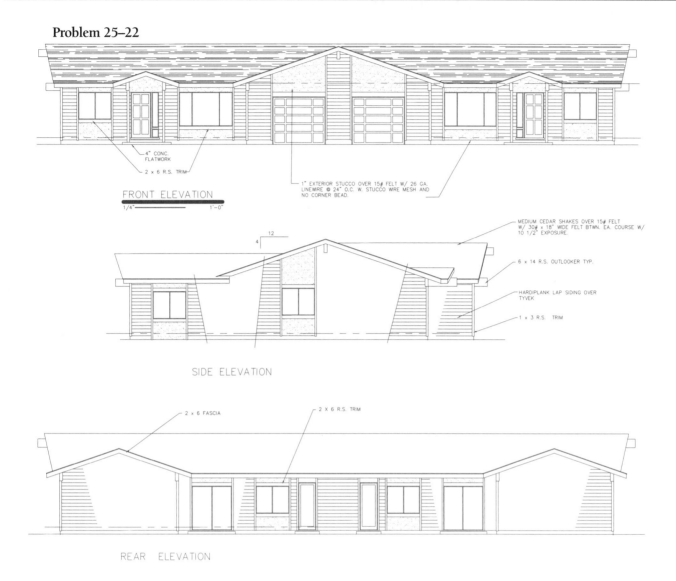

4" CONC.
FLATWORK

2 x 6 R.S. TRIM

FRONT ELEVATION
1/4" ———— 1'–0"

1" EXTERIOR STUCCO OVER 15# FELT W/ 26 GA.
LINEWIRE @ 24" O.C. W. STUCCO WIRE MESH AND
NO CORNER BEAD.

MEDIUM CEDAR SHAKES OVER 15# FELT
W/ 30# x 18" WIDE FELT BTWN. EA. COURSE W/
10 1/2" EXPOSURE.

6 x 14 R.S. OUTLOOKER TYP.

HARDIPLANK LAP SIDING OVER
TYVEK

1 x 3 R.S. TRIM

12
4

SIDE ELEVATION

2 x 6 FASCIA

2 x 6 R.S. TRIM

REAR ELEVATION

CHAPTER 26
MILLWORK AND CABINET TECHNOLOGY, CABINET
ELEVATIONS, AND LAYOUT

OBJECTIVES

When students have completed this chapter, they will:

- Define millwork.
- Describe the following millwork items: baseboards, wainscots, cornices, casings, mantels, bookshelves, and railings.
- Describe modular and custom cabinetry.
- Explain the purpose of cabinet elevations and when they are used.
- Show by sketching and/or explanation how cabinet elevations may be keyed to the floor plans.
- Sketch a typical kitchen and bath vanity cabinet elevation.
- Given the floor plan problem previously drawn, draw appropriate cabinet elevations and key the elevations to the floor plan.

© 2011 Cengage Learning. All Rights Reserved. May not be scanned, copied or duplicated, or posted to a publicly accessible website, in whole or in part.

TEST ANSWERS

1. *Millwork* is any item that is considered finish trim or finish woodwork.

2. Plastic or ceramic products may be used rather than wood millwork in a public restroom or in a home laundry where plastic strip or ceramic tile may be used around the wall at the floor to protect the wall.

3. Baseboards are placed at the intersection of walls and floors and are generally used to protect the wall from damage.

4. Wainscot is any wall finish material application where the bottom portion of the wall is different from the upper portion. The lower portion is called wainscot.

5. The *cornice* is decorative trim placed in the corner where the wall meets the ceiling.

6. Cornice boards are appropriate in specific types of architectural styles such as English Tudor, Victorian, and Colonial.

7. Casings are the members that are used to trim around windows and doors. Casings are attached to the window or door jamb and the adjacent wall.

8. Mantel is an ornamental shelf or structure that is built above the fireplace opening.

9. Bookshelves may be used effectively as millwork in the interior design of a structure in a den or study or on each side of a fireplace or in nearly any room of a house.

10. Railings are used for safety at stairs, landings, decks, and open balconies where people could fall off.

11. The term *modular cabinets* refers to prefabricated cabinets, because they are constructed in specific sizes called modules.

12. Custom cabinets are made to order. Custom cabinets are generally locally fabricated in a shop to the specifications of an architect or designer, and after they are completely constructed they are delivered to the job site and installed in large sections.

13. Another name for modular cabinets is prefabricated cabinets.

14. The big difference between custom cabinets and modular cabinets is that custom cabinets are generally locally fabricated in a shop to the specifications of an architect or designer, and after they are completely constructed they are delivered to the job site and installed in large sections. The modular cabinets are often nationally manufactured, and delivered in modules.

15. There is a fine line between good quality, well-designed cabinetry, and fine furniture.

16. The purpose of cabinet elevations is to show how the exterior of the cabinets will look when completed, giving general dimensions, notes, and specifications.

17. Elevations may not be a part of a complete set of architectural drawings because this is left up to the cabinet supplier or is not required by the local building authority or lending institution.

18. Three methods used to key the cabinet elevations to the floor plan are:

   1. The designer keys the cabinet elevations to the floor plan with room titles such as KITCHEN CABINET ELEVATIONS.

   2. The designer uses an arrow with a letter inside to correlate the elevation to the floor plan.

   3. The designer may use circle arrows with identification numbers pointing to various areas that correlate with the same arrow-number symbols labeled below the related elevations.

© 2011 Cengage Learning. All Rights Reserved. May not be scanned, copied or duplicated, or posted to a publicly accessible website, in whole or in part.

19. A sketch of a kitchen cabinet elevation:

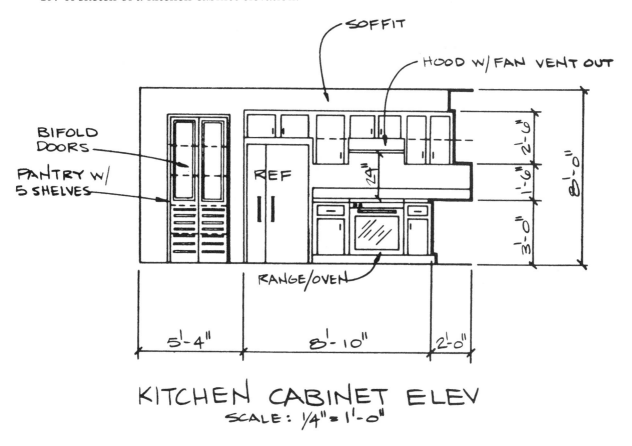

SOFFIT

HOOD W/ FAN VENT OUT

BIFOLD DOORS

PANTRY W/ 5 SHELVES

REF

2'-0"

1'-6"

8'-0"

24"

3'-0"

RANGE/OVEN

5'-4"   8'-10"   2'-0"

KITCHEN CABINET ELEV
SCALE: 1/4" = 1'-0"

20. A sketch of a bath vanity elevation:

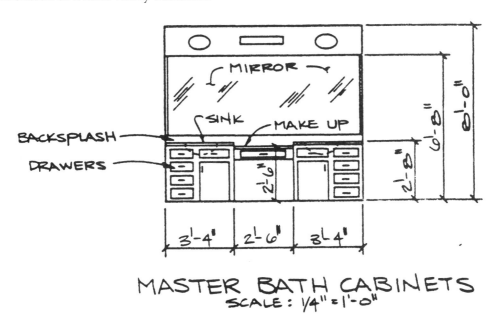

MIRROR

BACKSPLASH

SINK   MAKE UP

DRAWERS

2'-6"

6'-8"

8'-0"

2'-8"

3'-4"   2'-6"   3'-4"

MASTER BATH CABINETS
SCALE: 1/4"=1'-0"

© 2011 Cengage Learning. All Rights Reserved. May not be scanned, copied or duplicated, or posted to a publicly accessible website, in whole or in part.

CHAPTER 26 PROBLEM SOLUTIONS

For the Problem in Chapter 26, students should prepare the required cabinet elevations as instructed, using the floor plans chosen or assigned in Chapter 18. Make sure that students follow the general directions given in the textbook when preparing drawings. Student solutions vary depending on the floor plan chosen but should resemble examples given in the textbook.

Cabinets for Problem 18–2

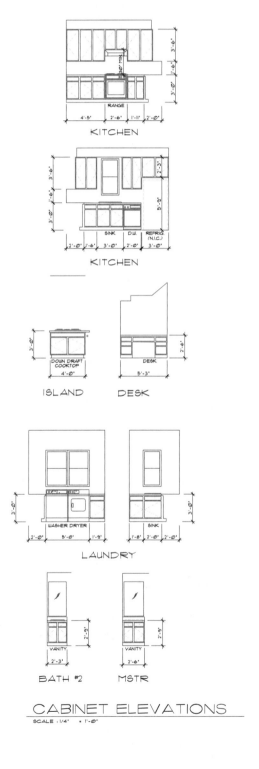

© 2011 Cengage Learning. All Rights Reserved. May not be scanned, copied or duplicated, or posted to a publicly accessible website, in whole or in part.

Cabinets for Problem 18–9

SINK   D.W.   OVEN W/ M.W.   JENN-AIR W/ OVEN

W/ BREAD BD. BETWEEN

5'-0"

3'-0"

TRAY   WASH/DRY   TRAY   WASH/DRY   MARBLE CUTTING BLOCK   WET BAR

5'-3"

2'-9"

SINK   SHELF   SPA TUB   SINK   SINK

CABINET ELEVATIONS

SCALE 1/4" = 1'-0"

© 2011 Cengage Learning. All Rights Reserved. May not be scanned, copied or duplicated, or posted to a publicly accessible website, in whole or in part.

Cabinets for Problem 18–10

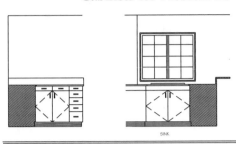

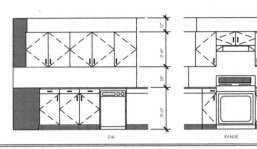

SINK

D.W.

RANGE

OVENS REFER

KITCHEN CABINETS

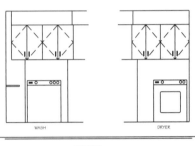

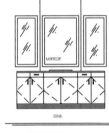

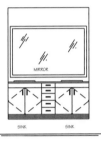

WASH

DRYER

SINK

MIRROR

SINK SINK

MIRROR

LAUNDRY

UPPER BATH

MASTER BATH

CABINET ELEVATIONS

SCALE 1/4" = 1'-0"

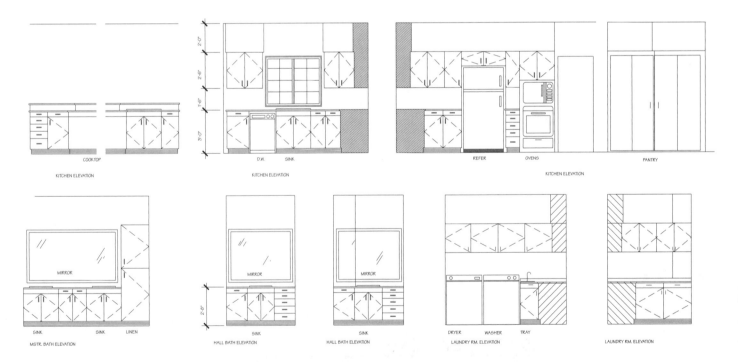

COOKTOP

KITCHEN ELEVATION

D.W. SINK

KITCHEN ELEVATION

REFER OVENS

KITCHEN ELEVATION

PANTRY

SINK SINK LINEN

MSTR. BATH ELEVATION

MIRROR

SINK

HALL BATH ELEVATION

MIRROR

SINK

HALL BATH ELEVATION

DRYER WASHER TRAY

LAUNDRY RM. ELEVATION

LAUNDRY RM. ELEVATION

CABINET ELEVATIONS

SCALE 1/4" = 1'-0"

© 2011 Cengage Learnings. All Rights Reserved. May not be scanned, copied or duplicated, or posted to a publicly accessible website, in whole or in part.

Cabinets for Problem 18–12

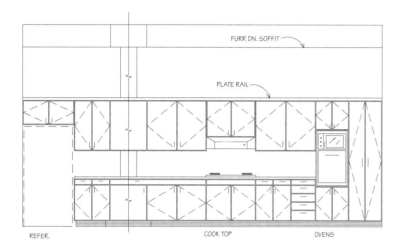

FURR DN. SOFFIT

PLATE RAIL

REFER.   COOK TOP   OVENS

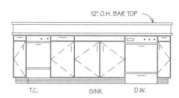

12" O.H. BAR TOP

T.C.   SINK   D.W.

SINK

SINK

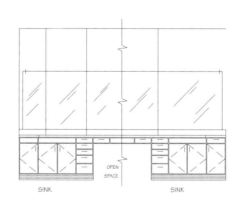

SINK   OPEN SPACE   SINK

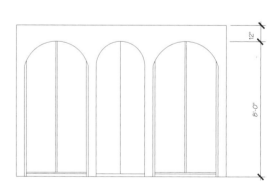

12"

8'-0"

CABINET ELEVATIONS

SCALE: 1/4" = 1'-0"

F
6

ELEVATION

© 2011 Cengage Learning. All Rights Reserved. May not be scanned, copied or duplicated, or posted to a publicly accessible website, in whole or in part.

Cabinets for Problem 18–15

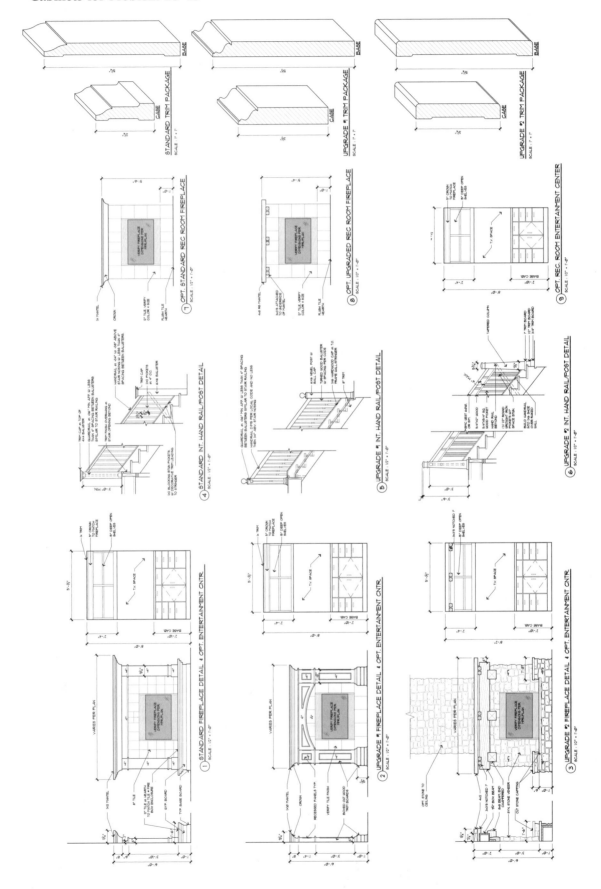

© 2011 Cengage Learnies. All Rights Reserved. May not be scanned, copied or duplicated, or posted to a publicly accessible website, in whole or in part.

Cabinets for Problem 18–16

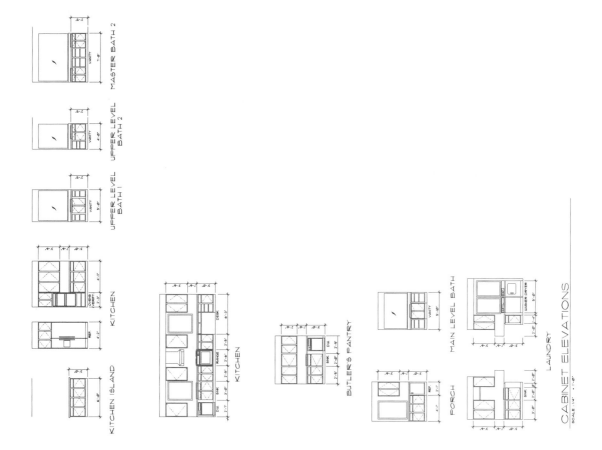

© 2011 Cengage Learning. All Rights Reserved. May not be scanned, copied or duplicated, or posted to a publicly accessible website, in whole or in part.

Cabinets for Problem 18–17

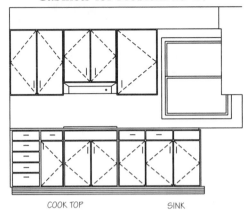

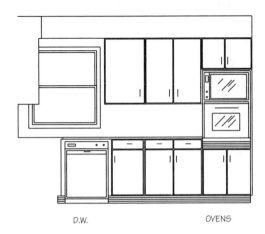

COOK TOP   SINK

D.W.   OVENS

KITCHEN

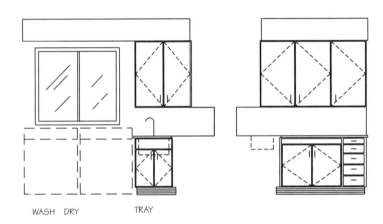

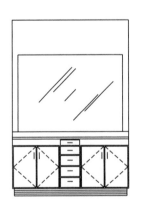

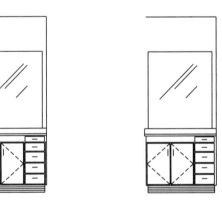

WASH   DRY   TRAY

LAUNDRY

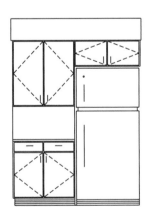

CABINET ELEVATIONS

SCALE 1/4" = 1'-0"

© 2011 Cengage Learnings. All Rights Reserved. May not be scanned, copied or duplicated, or posted to a publicly accessible website, in whole or in part.

Cabinets for Problem 18–18

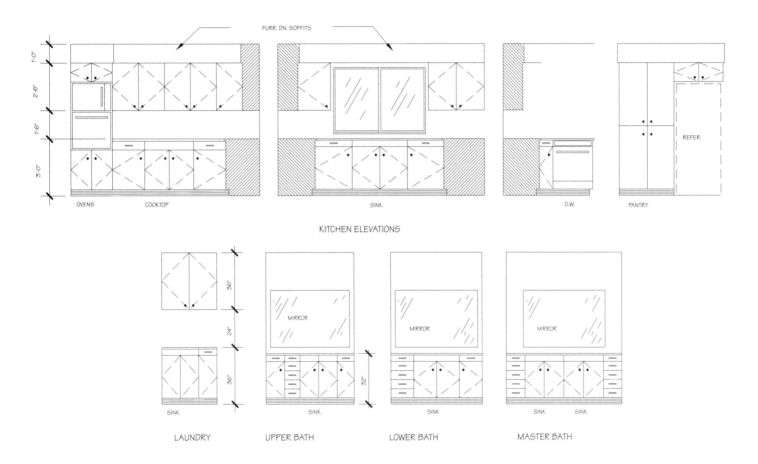

FURR. DN. SOFFITS

1'-0" 2'-6" 1'-6" 3'-0"

OVENS   COOKTOP   SINK   D.W.   PANTRY

REFER

KITCHEN ELEVATIONS

36" 24" 36" 32"

SINK   SINK   MIRROR   SINK   MIRROR   SINK   MIRROR   SINK   SINK

LAUNDRY   UPPER BATH   LOWER BATH   MASTER BATH

CABINET ELEVATIONS

SCALE 1/4" = 1'-0"

© 2011 Cengage Learning. All Rights Reserved. May not be scanned, copied or duplicated, or posted to a publicly accessible website, in whole or in part.

Cabinets for Problem 18–19

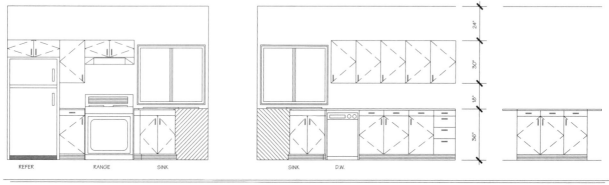

KITCHEN CABINET ELEVATIONS

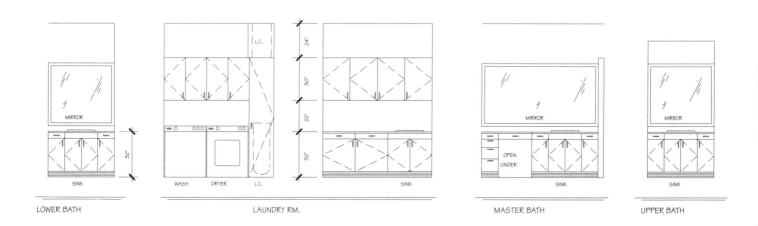

LOWER BATH   LAUNDRY RM.   MASTER BATH   UPPER BATH

CABINET ELEVATIONS

SCALE 1/4" = 1'-0"

© 2011 Cengage Learning. All Rights Reserved. May not be scanned, copied or duplicated, or posted to a publicly accessible website, in whole or in part.

Cabinets for Problem 18–21

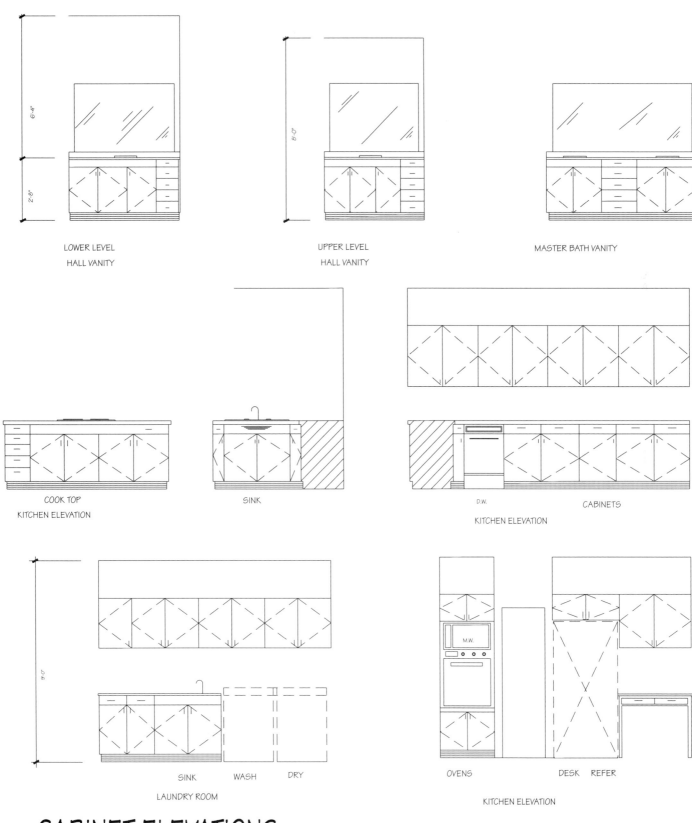

LOWER LEVEL
HALL VANITY

UPPER LEVEL
HALL VANITY

MASTER BATH VANITY

COOK TOP
KITCHEN ELEVATION

SINK

D.W.   CABINETS
KITCHEN ELEVATION

SINK   WASH   DRY
LAUNDRY ROOM

OVENS   DESK   REFER
KITCHEN ELEVATION

CABINET ELEVATIONS

SCALE 1/4" = 1'-0"

© 2011 Cengage Learning. All Rights Reserved. May not be scanned, copied or duplicated, or posted to a publicly accessible website, in whole or in part.

© 2011 Cengage Learning. All Rights Reserved. May not be scanned, copied or duplicated, or posted to a publicly accessible website, in whole or in part.

SECTION 8

Framing Methods and Plans

CHAPTER 27
ENVIROMENTALLY FRIENDLY FRAMING METHODS

OBJECTIVES

When students have completed this chapter, they will:

- Describe the balloon framing method.
- List and describe the components of platform construction.
- List and describe the components of post-and-beam and timber construction.
- Identify common uses for brick and stone.
- List common elements of energy-efficient construction and describe the use of each.
- Describe major green construction qualities of materials such as:
  - Engineered lumber
  - Structurally engineered panels
  - Steel framing
  - Concrete masonry units
  - Solid masonry units

TEST ANSWERS

1. Platform construction provides a level surface to form walls for upper levels, requires shorter lumber, and helps reduce the spread of fire.
2. Sketches should resemble the lower portion of Figure 27–6.
3. Because of the fire danger and the length of lumber required
4. a. Western platform
    b. Post-and-beam
    c. Energy-efficient framing
    d. Timber
    e. Steel
    f. Concrete and block
5. Sketches will vary, but should resemble Figure 27–9.
6. As a veneer

© 2011 Cengage Learning. All Rights Reserved. May not be scanned, copied or duplicated, or posted to a publicly accessible website, in whole or in part.

7. Seismic zone and the wall height

8. Because of the appearance of an open beam ceiling

9. R-4 for uninsulated wall

   R-14-33 for insulated

10. 48" O.C.

11. Lower energy cost, higher strength, and insurance considerations

12. Hollow, load bearing, solid load bearing, and nonload bearing

13. Sketches should be similar to Figure 27–15.

14. A firecut is an angle cut at the end of a floor joist that is supported by a masonry wall. The angle allows the joist to fall out of the wall during a fire without destroying the wall.

15. Moisture is removed from a masonry cavity wall by providing weep holes in the bottom course of the exterior wythe.

16. Steel rebar, steel mesh

17. Studs cannot exceed 10' high.

18. Advanced framing techniques

19. Most steel used in construction contains approximately 50% recycled materials.

20. A traditional corner has three studs; AFT corners can have two or three studs.

21. Because they are made from wood scraps making efficient use of materials, and because they are made from fast growing trees

22. Engineered products can be made with sawdust, wood scraps, small pieces of lumber, or whole pieces of lumber.

23. Sips are panels made with OSB outer layers and an inner layer of rigid foam used for framing roof, wall, and floor construction.

24. VOCs are volatile organic compounds that can be released into the environment by poor product selection or poor design.

25. Student answers will vary, but will generally relate to ground water and air pollution, radon, and recycled materials.

CHAPTER 27 PROBLEM SOLUTIONS

Chapter 27 of the text contains no drawing problems.

CHAPTER 28
STRUCTURAL COMPONENTS OF FRAMED CONSTRUCTION

OBJECTIVES

When students have completed this chapter, they will:

- Define terms associated with floor systems.
- Distinguish between bearing and nonbearing walls.
- Describe typical wall construction.
- List common features of masonry wall construction.
- Identify framing members of conventional and trussed frame roofs.

© 2011 Cengage Learning. All Rights Reserved. May not be scanned, copied or duplicated, or posted to a publicly accessible website, in whole or in part.

TEST ANSWERS

1. Post-and-beam and conventional (stick) flooring. Stick framing uses 2" wide members, typically spaced at 16" O.C. with either 1/2", 5/8", or 3/4" plywood sheathing. Post-and-beam flooring typically uses 4" wide beams spaced at 48" O.C. with 1 1/8" plywood sheathing or 2 × 6 or 2 × 8 decking.

2. Each is used to support loads. A girder is used at the foundation level; a header and a beam are used in walls and roof construction.

3. A rim joist is a continuous member placed perpendicular to the edge of the floor joists. Solid blocking is placed between floor joists.

4. 4 or 6 inches wide

5. Let-in braces and wall sheathing are used to resist lateral movement of wall members caused by wind or earthquakes.

6. 45%

7. PSL—Parallel strand lumber

   OSB—Oriented strand board

   LVL—Laminated veneer lumber

   MDF—Medium density fiberboard

   EXP—Exposure

   HDF—High density fiberboard

   APA—The Engineered Wood Association (formerly the American Plywood Association)

   EXT—Exterior

   STRUCT—Structural

8. 55# felt or a roofing shingle

9. 10'

10. Sawn lumber, Glu-lam beams, steel girders, PSL beams, LVL

11. The notch increases the contact area of the rafter by placing more rafter surface against the top of the wall.

12. The 4 represents the vertical rise and the 12 represents the horizontal run.

13. The ridge is the highest part of a roof where two roof surfaces intersect. Ridge blocking is placed between trusses to maintain a uniform spacing. The ridge board is used to align the rafters.

14. Open webs with tube steel, I-joist with plywood or OSB webs

15. Common, hip, valley, jack, rafter/ceiling joist (sketches should resemble Figure 28–44)

16. To resist the outward force from the rafters, and to support the finished ceiling

17. Top chord, bottom chord, webs, gusset, or metal connectors

18. Heat and pressure

19. It is a horizontal wood member bolted to a masonry foundation, to which other wood members can be nailed.

20. It is a horizontal rafter support that allows the rafter size to be decreased because of the shorter span.

21. A bearing wall supports the weight of floors, roofing, or loads from other bearing walls. A nonbearing wall only supports its own weight or ceiling loads.

22. 48"

© 2011 Cengage Learning. All Rights Reserved. May not be scanned, copied or duplicated, or posted to a publicly accessible website, in whole or in part.

23.

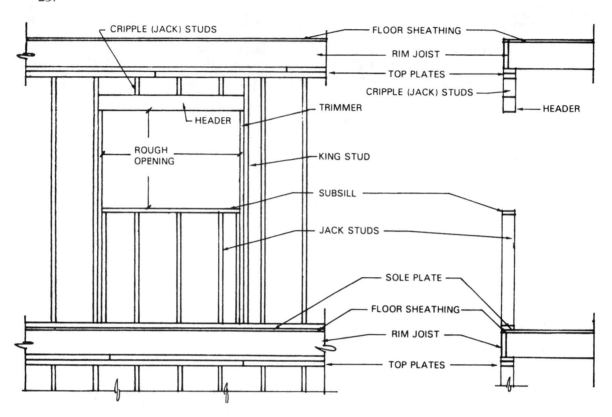

24. 24" O.C. but 12" and 16" spacings are sometimes used.

25. It holds the studs in position and serves as a nailing surface for the interior and exterior finishing materials.

26. Approximately 1/2 to 2 times the design strength is achieved.

27. 2 × 4 or 2 × 6 in 8', 9', and 10' lengths

28. 24/16, 32/16, 40/20, and 48/24

29. EXP1, EXP2, EXT, STRUCT-I EXP1, or STRUCT 1-EXT.

30. In addition to consulting the text, have students consult the APA Web site.

   a. Structural use

   b. Mill number

   c. ANSI number

   d. American wood code number

   e. Laminating specification

   f. Combination number

   g. Species of lumber used

   h. Appearance grade

CHAPTER 28 PROBLEM SOLUTIONS

Chapter 28 of the text contains no drawing problems.

© 2011 Cengage Learning. All Rights Reserved. May not be scanned, copied or duplicated, or posted to a publicly accessible website, in whole or in part.

CHAPTER 29
DESIGN CRITERIA FOR STRUCTURAL LOADING

OBJECTIVES

When students have completed this chapter, they will:

- Calculate loads and determine where they come from.
- Determine how loads are distributed throughout the structure.

TEST ANSWERS

1. Live loads or dead loads
2. 40# nonsleeping; 30# sleeping
3. 50# nonsleeping; 40# sleeping
4. Elevation, wind frequency, and duration
5. The weight is spread equally along the joist. If the joist is supported at each end, half of the total weight will be supported at each end of the joist.
6. 12.5' × 50# = 625# / 7.5 × 50 = 375
7. 12.5' × 50# = 625# per linear foot
8. Wall support = 12' × 55# (tile) = 660# per linear foot

   660# × 30' = total weight on wall = 19,800# on each bearing wall

   Foundation weight = roof weight + wall weight + floor weight

   Wall = (assume 8' high) 8 × 10# = 80

   Floor = 2' × 50# = 100# PLF

   Foundation = 660 + 80 + 100 = 840# per linear foot

   840 × 30 = 25,200# total load supported by each footing
9. Load supported by each girder = 4 × 8 × 50# = 1600#

   Stem wall supports 800# at each girder

CHAPTER 29 PROBLEM SOLUTIONS

1. 250#
2. 350# is supported at the mid support and 175# is supported at each end.
3. 12" spacing = 16' × 40# = 640#

   16" spacing = 16' × 40# × 1.4' = 896#

   24" spacing = 16' × 40# × 2' = 1280#
4. Half the span = 14' × 40# = hanger must support 560# (no overhang is supported)
5. 8' × 1260# = 10,080#
6. 8' × (12' + 2.5') × 40# = 4640# / 0#
7. 6' × (12' + 3') × 40# = 3600#
8. A 5'-6" long header (5' + bearing) will be needed to support the doorway, but it will support no load.
9. A wall can be placed 14' from the left bearing wall, but with trusses it will support no load, and require no footing.
10. 10# × 15' = 150# dead load per foot for roof load
11. 40# × 15' = 600# total load per foot

© 2011 Cengage Learning. All Rights Reserved. May not be scanned, copied or duplicated, or posted to a publicly accessible website, in whole or in part.

CHAPTER 30
SIZING JOISTS AND RAFTERS USING SPAN TABLES

OBJECTIVES

When students have completed this chapter, they will:

- Calculate the size of span for engineered lumber.
- Calculate the size and spans for joists and rafters standard tables.

TEST ANSWERS

Note: Answers are based on DFL #2. Students' answers will vary based on species of lumber that is used.

1. Douglas fir-larch, Hem-fir, Spruce-pine-fir, Southern pine
2. E
3. 2 × 10 @ 16" O.C.
4. No, it will only span 12'-7" @ 16" O.C.; a spacing of 12" will be required.
5. 17'-8"
6. 2 × 12 are required to provide the depth for the required insulation and air space.
7. 2 × 10 @ 16" O.C.
8. 2 × 8 @ 12" O.C.
9. 2 × 10 @ 12" O.C.
10. 2 × 8 @ 16" O.C.
11. 2 × 8 @ 12" O.C.
12. Deflection is the sag in a structural member. Allowable deflection is represented by a symbol such as $L/\Delta = 360$, $L/\Delta = 240$ and $L/\Delta = 180$.
13. Answers will vary greatly. Common answers should reflect major lumber suppliers such as Georgia Pacific, Louisiana Pacific, and Weyerhaeuser.
14. 9 1/2 TJI pro 150 will span 17'-1 @ l/360 and 11 7/8" TJI Pro 150 @ 16" O.C. will work for l/480.
15. A higher quality floor, with less chance of squeaks

CHAPTER 30 PROBLEM SOLUTIONS

1. 2 × 6 @ 12" O.C.
2. Yes, but only for 17'-8" maximum span @ 16" O.C.
3. 2 × 10 at 24" O.C., or 2 × 8 at 12" O.C.
4. 18'—2" @ 24" O.C.
5. 2 × 8 at 24" O.C.
6. 9 1/2" TJI 210 @ 12" O.C. or 11 7/8 TJI 110 @ 16" O.C.
7. The joist will fail using 24" spacing. Reduce spacing to 19.2" and use reinforcing per details on the iLevel Web site.
8. E-I–E-3. Reinforcing is required with 16" spacings per iLevel Web site.
9. 11 7/8 TJI 210 will span 19'–7".
10. 9 1/2" TJI 110 at 16" O.C. is the smallest member that can be used. Also, 11 7/8" TJI 110 can be used at 24" spacings.

© 2011 Cengage Learning. All Rights Reserved. May not be scanned, copied or duplicated, or posted to a publicly accessible website, in whole or in part.

CHAPTER 31
DETERMINING BEAM SIZES

OBJECTIVES

When students have completed this chapter, they will:
- Identify common methods of simple beam design.
- Identify common symbols used in beam formula notations.
- Calculate simple beams using standard formulas.
- Calculate loads for a simple beam with a concentrated load at the center.
- Calculate loads for a simple beam with a concentrated load at any point.
- Calculate loads for a cantilevered beam with a uniformly distributed load (See CD).
- Calculate loads for a cantilevered beam with a concentrated load at the free end (See CD).

TEST ANSWERS

1. A simple beam is a beam that supports a uniform load with supports at each end.
2. A uniform load is equally dispersed over the entire beam. A concentrated load is located on one small portion of the beam.
3. Any three of the following: fiber bending stress, horizontal shear, deflection, vertical shear, and compression.
4. W = total load on beam

   w = load per linear foot of beam

   R = reaction (the amount of the load to be supported at each support)

   L = length of beam expressed in feet

   ℓ = length of beam expressed in inches

   E = modulus of elasticity (the amount of sag expressed as a percentage of the beam length)

   I = moment of inertia expressed in inches

   S = section modulus of a beam

   Fv = horizontal shear

   Fb = fiber bending strength
5. W = area × weight = 10' × 10' × 50# = 5000#

   w = 10' × 50' = 500# or W/L = w

   R = W/2 = 5000#/2 = 2500#

   See Figure 31–9 for sketch.

CHAPTER 31 PROBLEM SOLUTIONS

1. $F_v = \dfrac{3V}{2bd} = \dfrac{\langle 3 \rangle \langle 1400 \rangle}{(2)(3.5)(5.5)} = \dfrac{4200}{38.5} = 109 > 85 = $ beam failure

© 2011 Cengage Learning. All Rights Reserved. May not be scanned, copied or duplicated, or posted to a publicly accessible website, in whole or in part.

2. $\ell = L \times 12'' = 12 \times 12 = 144''$

Safe modulus of elasticity $= \dfrac{\ell}{360} = \dfrac{144}{360} = 0.4$

$D = \dfrac{5 \times W \times \ell^3}{384 \times E \times I} = \dfrac{5 \times 4650 \times 2.985984}{384 \times 1.6 \times 415} = \dfrac{69424}{254976} = .272 < 0.4 =$ safe bm.

3. $\dfrac{\text{load}}{\text{soil psi}} =$ footing size required $= \dfrac{4600\#}{1500} = 3.06$ sq. ft. required

use a 24" diameter or a 21" square footing

4. 6×8 safe according to Wood Beam Safe Load Table in Appendix B

5. $P = 32,000\#; L = 14'; \ell = 168''; \ell^3 = 4,741,632; V = 1,600\#; F_b = 1,300$

$M = \dfrac{P\ell}{4} = \dfrac{3200 \times 168}{1300} = \dfrac{537600}{4} = 134400 = M$

$S = \dfrac{M}{F_b} = \dfrac{134400}{1300} = 103.4 =$ USE: 4×14 or 6×12 beam.

$F_v = \dfrac{3V}{2bd} = \dfrac{3 \times 1600}{2 \times 3.5 \times 13.5} = \dfrac{4800}{94.5} = 50.79 < 85 = 4 \times 14$ beam

Because a 6×12 has a bigger surface than a 4×14, it will also work.

$D_{max.} = \dfrac{\ell}{360} = \dfrac{168}{360} = .47$ max deflection allowed.

$D = \dfrac{P\ell^3}{48EI} = \dfrac{3200 \times 4.741632}{48 \times 1.6 \times 697} = \dfrac{15173}{53530} = .283 = 6 \times 12$ beam will work safety.

Since the I value for a 4×14 is greater than a 6×12, a 4×14 beam will also work safely. Pier size?

Pier Size $= \dfrac{R}{\text{Soil PSF}} = \dfrac{1600\#}{2000} = 0.8$ sq. ft. pier

6. $P = 2500\#; L = 12'; \ell = 144''; \ell^2 = 20,736; a = 36''; b = 108''$

SPF: $F = 900; E = 1.3$

$R_1 = \dfrac{Pb}{\ell} = \dfrac{2500 \times 108}{144} = \dfrac{270000}{144} = 1875 \quad R_2 = P - R_1 = 2500 - 1875 = 625$

$M = \dfrac{Pab}{\ell} = \dfrac{2500 \times 36 \times 108}{144} = \dfrac{9720000}{144} = 67500$

$S = \dfrac{M}{F_b} = \dfrac{67500}{900} = 75 = S \quad$ Try 4×12 or 6×10

$E_{max.} = \dfrac{\ell}{360} = \dfrac{144}{360} = 0.4$ max sag

$E = \dfrac{Pab(a + 2b)\sqrt{3a(a + 2b)}}{27 \times E \times I \times \ell}$

$E = \dfrac{2500 \times 36 \times 108(36 + 2 \times 108)\sqrt{3 \times 36(36 + 2 \times 108)}}{27 \times 1.3 \times 393 \times 144} =$

$E = \dfrac{9720000 \times 252\sqrt{108 \times 252}}{1986379} = \dfrac{2449 \times \sqrt{27216}}{1986379} = \dfrac{2449 \times 165}{1986379}$

© 2011 Cengage Learning. All Rights Reserved. May not be scanned, copied or duplicated, or posted to a publicly accessible website, in whole or in part.

$$E = \frac{404085}{1986379} = 0.2 < 0.4 = 6 \times 10 \text{ SPF \#2 safe}$$

$$R_1 = \frac{1875}{1500 \text{psf}} = 1.25 \text{ sq. ft. piers. use 18" dia. or 15" sq.}$$

7. L = 14' ℓ = 168"

$$R = V = \frac{P}{Z} = 1100$$

$$M_{\text{max.}} = \frac{P\ell}{4} = \frac{(2200)(168)}{4} = \frac{369600}{4} = 92400$$

$$S = \frac{M}{F_b} = S = \frac{92400}{1300} = 71 \quad 4 \times 12 \text{ and } 6 \times 10$$

$$F_v = \frac{3V}{85} = \frac{(3)(1100)}{85} = \frac{3300}{85} = 38.8 \text{ both beams O.K.}$$

$$D_{\text{max.}} = \frac{\ell}{360} = \frac{168}{360} = .46 \text{ max.}$$

$$D = \frac{P\ell^3}{48EI} = \frac{(2200)(4.741632)}{(48)(1.6)(393)} = \frac{10431}{30182} = .34$$

Use 4×12 and 6×10

8. L = 15'6" (15.5) ℓ = 186

   P = 2750 F_b = 1300

$$R = V = \frac{1375\#}{2000} = .687 \text{ pier} \qquad \text{Use a minimum 12" } \phi \text{ pier}$$

Since this beam will react exactly like a beam with a uniform load, the Beam Tables in the Appendix can be used. A 4 × 12 will work.

9. L = 14.5 ℓ = 174 L^2 = 210   l3 = 5,268,024 F_b = 2200

   W = 5500   R = V = 2750   w = 379

$$S = \frac{3(w)(\ell^2)}{(2)F_b} = \frac{(3)(379)(210)}{(2)(2200)} = \frac{238770}{4400} = S = 54.2$$

Use 3 1/8 × 10 1/2 or 5 1/8 × 9

$$F_v = \frac{3V}{165} = \frac{(3)(2750)}{165} = \frac{8250}{165} = 50 \text{ Both O.K.}$$

$$D_{\text{max.}} = \frac{\ell}{360} = \frac{174}{360} = .48 \text{ max.}$$

$$D = \frac{(5)(W)(\ell^3)}{(384)(E)(I)} = \frac{(5)(5500)(5286)}{(384)(1.7)(301)} = \frac{144870}{196493} = .73 \quad 3 \text{ 1/8} \times 10 \text{ 1/2 fail}$$

$$5 \text{ 1/8} \times 9 = \frac{144870}{(653)(311)} = \frac{144870}{203083} = .71 \qquad 5 \text{ 1/8} \times 9 \text{ fail}$$

$$5 \text{ 1/8} \times 10 \text{ 1/2} = \frac{144870}{(653)(494)} = \frac{144870}{322582} = .449 \qquad 5 \text{ 1/8} \times 10 \text{ 1/2 safe}$$

© 2011 Cengage Learning. All Rights Reserved. May not be scanned, copied or duplicated, or posted to a publicly accessible website, in whole or in part.

10. $L = 16'$ $L^2 = 256$ $\ell = 192$ $\ell^3 = 7.077,888$

$w = 800$ $W = 16 \times 800 = 12,800$ $R = V = 6,400$

Assume $F_b = 2200$

$$S = \frac{(3)(W)(L^2)}{(2)(F_b)} = \frac{(3)(800)(256)}{(2)(2200)} = \frac{614400}{4400} = 139.6 = S \quad 5\ 1/8 \times 13\ 1/2?$$

$$F_v = \frac{3V}{165} = \frac{(3)(6400)}{165} = \frac{19200}{165} = 116 < 138 \quad 13\ 1/2" \ O.K.$$

$$D_{max.} = \frac{\ell}{360} = \frac{192}{360} = .53 \ max.$$

I for $5\ 1/8 \times 15 = I = 1441$

$$D = \frac{(5)(W)(\ell^3)}{(384)(E)(I)} = \frac{(5)(12800)(7.077888)}{(384)(1.7)(1051)} = \frac{452985}{686092} = .66 < .53 \quad beam\ fails!$$

$D = 5\ 1/8 \times 15 = I = 1441$

$$D = \frac{452985}{(653)(1441)} = .48 < .53 \quad 5\ 1/8 \times 15\ 1/2" \ glu\text{-}lam\ bean\ safe$$

11. $12" \ PL = 6400 \ 36"$ $\ell = 48$ $a = 12$ $b = 36$ $2b = 72 \ a + 2b = 84$ $3a = 36$

$R_1 \ 4'\text{-}0"R_2$ $DFL\#2 = F_b \ 1300$

$$R_1 = \frac{P_b}{\ell} = \frac{(6400)(36)}{48} = \frac{230400}{48} = 4800$$

$$R_2 = P - R_1 = 6400 - 4800 = 1600$$

$$M = \frac{Pab}{\ell} = \frac{(6400)(12)(36)}{48} = \frac{2764800}{48} = 57600 = M$$

$$S = \frac{M}{F_b} = S = \frac{57600}{1300} = 44 = 4 \times 10$$

$$F_v = \frac{3V}{85} = \frac{(3)(4800)}{85} = \frac{14400}{85} = 169 \quad 4" \ and \ 6" \ members \ fail$$

Glu-lam:

$$\frac{3V}{165} = \frac{14400}{165} = 87 = 3\ 1/8 \times 15$$

$$D_{max.} = \frac{\ell}{360} = \frac{48}{360} = .13 \ max.$$

$$D = \frac{Pab(a + 2b)\sqrt{3a(a + 2b)}}{27EIl} = \frac{(6400)(12)(36)[12 + 72]\sqrt{(3 \bullet 12)(12 + 72)}}{(27)(1.7)(1441)(48)} = \frac{2764800(84)\sqrt{(36)(84)}}{3174811}$$

$$= \frac{232.2432\sqrt{3024}}{3174811} = \frac{12760}{3174811} = .004 < .13 \quad 3\ 1/8 \times 15 \ safe$$

12. $V = P + 4,000;\ F = 1,200;\ L = 3.5';\ \ell = 42";\ \ell^3 = .074088$

$$M = P\ell = 4000 \times 42 = 168000$$

$$S = \frac{M}{F_b} = \frac{168000}{1200} = 140$$

© 2011 Cengage Learning. All Rights Reserved. May not be scanned, copied or duplicated, or posted to a publicly accessible website, in whole or in part.

$$F_v = \frac{3V}{2bd} = \frac{3 \times 4000}{2 \times 5.5 \times 13.5} = \frac{12000}{148.5} = 80.8 < 85 = 6 \times 14 \text{ beam O.K.}$$

$$D_{max} = \frac{\ell}{360} = \frac{42}{360} = 0.117$$

$$D = \frac{P\ell^3}{3EI} = \frac{4000 \times 074088}{3 \times 1.5 \times 1128} = \frac{188}{5076} = 0.037 = 6 \times 14 \text{ beam safe}$$

13. $W = (70\#)(1.5)(1.4) = 147\#$

    $W = (70)(1.4) = 98\#$

    $R = V = (W)(L) = (98)(1.5) = 147\#$

    $$M = \frac{(W)(\ell^2)}{2} = \frac{(98)(324)}{2} = \frac{31752}{2} = 15876$$

    $$S = \frac{M}{F_b} = \frac{15876}{2 \times 6} = 1235 = 12.8 \qquad 2 \times 6 \text{ fails}$$

    $$\frac{15876}{2 \times 8} = 1140 = 13.9 \qquad 2 \times 9 \text{ fails}$$

    $$\frac{15876}{2 \times 10} = 1045 = 15.1 \qquad 2 \times 10 \text{ O.K.}$$

    $$F_v = \frac{3V}{85} = \frac{(3)(147)}{85} = \frac{441}{85} = 5.18 \quad 2 \times 10 \text{ O.K.}$$

    $$D_{max.} = \frac{\ell}{360} = \frac{18}{360} = .05 \text{ max}$$

    $$D = \frac{(W)(\ell^4)}{(8)(E)(I)} = \frac{(98)(104976)}{(8)(1.6)(99)} = \frac{10287648}{1267} = .008 \quad 2 \times 10 \text{ O.K.}$$

14. $R = V = P = 650$

    $M = P\ell = (650)(24) = 15600 = M$

    $$S = \frac{M}{F_b} = \frac{15600}{2 \times 8} = 1140 = S = 13.6 \qquad 2 \times 8 \text{ fails}$$

    $$\frac{15600}{2 \times 10} = 1045 = S = 14.9 \qquad 2 \times 10 \text{ O.K.}$$

    $$F_v = \frac{3V}{85} = \frac{(3)(650)}{85} = \frac{1950}{85} = 22.9 < 27.75 \qquad 2 \times 10 \text{ O.K.}$$

    $$D_{max.} = \frac{\ell}{360} = \frac{24}{360} = .06 \text{ max.}$$

    $$D = \frac{P\ell^3}{3EI} = \frac{(650)(.013842)}{(3)(1.6)(99)} = \frac{8.98}{475} = .018 < .06 \quad 2 \times 10 \text{ O.K.}$$

15. Assuming DFL. Answers will vary as different wood values are used.

    a. RAFTERS. Use Table in Figure 30–7. Span = 14'. Use 2 × 8 raft @ 16" o.c. or 2 × 10 @ 24" o.c.

    b. CEILING JOIST. Refer to Figure 30–4. Max L = 15'. Use 2 × 6 @ 16" o.c.

© 2011 Cengage Learning. All Rights Reserved. May not be scanned, copied or duplicated, or posted to a publicly accessible website, in whole or in part.

c. & d. UPPER FLOOR JOIST.

16' span = 2 × 10 @ 21" required to span 16'

16' span w/point load

Roof load = 14'× 40# = 560# + (8 × 10 wall) = 80

P = 560 + 80 = 640

a = 3' (36")   b = 13'/156"   L = 16' L^2 = 256 ℓ = 192

$$R_1 = \frac{(640 \times 13) + (8)(50)}{16} = \frac{(8320) + (400)}{16} = \frac{8720}{16} = 545\#$$

R_2 = ([(16)(50)] + 640) − 545 = 1440 − 545 = 895#

M = M cannot be accurately checked with the formulas given and should be left for an engineer to design.

e. LOWER FLOOR JOIST.

L = 16' span   Use 2 × 10 @ 12" o.c.

f. 5' HEADER @ UPPER FLOOR.

W = (7.5 + 2') × 40 = 380   W = 1900   L = S   R = V = 950

L^2 = 25 ℓ = 60 ℓ^3 = 216,000

4 × 6

$$S = \frac{(3)(W)(L^2)}{2F_b} = \frac{(3)(380)(25)}{(2)(1300)} = \frac{28500}{2600} = 10.9 \quad 4 \times 6 \text{ O.K.}$$

$$F_v = \frac{3V}{85} = \frac{(3)(950)}{85} - \frac{2850}{85} = 33.5 < 38 \quad 4 \times 6 \text{ O.K.}$$

$$D_{max.} = \frac{\ell}{360} = \frac{60}{360} = .16 \text{ max.}$$

$$D = \frac{(5)(W)(\ell^3)}{(384)(E)(I)} = \frac{(5)(1900)(.216)}{(384)(1.6)(48)} = \frac{2052}{29491} = .07 < .16 \quad 4 \times 6 \text{ safe}$$

UPPER HEADER. Use 4 × 6

g. 8' HEADER @ LOWER FLOOR

Left side max. condition

Roof	= 8.5 × 40#	= 340	W = 8 × 1295 = 10,360	
Upper Wall	= 8 × 10#	= 80	R = V = 5180	
Floor	= 875# (R_2)	= 875	L = 8 L^2 = 64	
		= 1295 = W	ℓ = 96 ℓ^3 = 884,736	

$$S = \frac{(3)(W)(L^2)}{2F_b} = \frac{(3)(1295)(64)}{(2)(1300)} = \frac{248640}{2600} = 96 \quad \text{Use } 4 \times 14 \text{ or } 6 \times 12$$

$$F_v = \frac{3V}{85} = \frac{(3)(5180)}{85} = \frac{15540}{85} = 183 \quad \text{All } 4 \times 4 \text{ and } 6 \times 4 \text{ fail}$$

$$\frac{3V}{165} = \frac{(3)(5180)}{165} = \frac{15540}{165} = 94 \quad \text{Use } 5\,1/8 \times 10$$

© 2011 Cengage Learning. All Rights Reserved. May not be scanned, copied or duplicated, or posted to a publicly accessible website, in whole or in part.

h. GIRDER.

Roof	= 14×40	= 340	5' span	
Wall	= 8×10	= 80	$(5)(2040) = W = 10{,}200$	
Floor	= 13×50	= 650	$V = R = 5{,}100$	
Wall	= 10×10	= 100	$L = 5 \quad L^2 = 25$	
Floor	= 13×50	= 650	$\ell = 60 \quad \ell^3 = 216$	
		= 1295 = W		

$$S = \frac{(3)(W)(L^2)}{2F_b} = \frac{(3)(2040)(25)}{(2)(1300)} = \frac{153000}{2600} = 58.8 \qquad \text{Use } 4 \times 14 \text{ or } 6 \times 12$$

$$F_v = \frac{3V}{85} = \frac{(3)(5180)}{85} = \frac{15540}{85} = 182 \qquad \text{All } 4 \times 4 \text{ and } 6 \times 4 \text{ fail}$$

$$F_v = \frac{15540}{165} = 94$$

$$D_{max.} = \frac{\ell}{360} = \frac{60}{360} = .16 \text{ max.}$$

$$D = \frac{(5)(W)(\ell^3)}{(384)(E)(I)} = \frac{(5)(10200)(.216)}{(384)(1.7)(494)} = \frac{11016}{322483} = .034 < .16$$

Use 5 1/8 × 10 1/2 glu-lam beam.

i. SPOT.

© 2011 Cengage Learning. All Rights Reserved. May not be scanned, copied or duplicated, or posted to a publicly accessible website, in whole or in part.

CHAPTER 32
DRAWING FRAMING PLANS

OBJECTIVES

When students have completed this chapter, they will:

- Identify and draw the needed plans to represent the structural portions of a structure separate from a floor plan. This would include:
  1. a framing plan
  2. a roof framing plan
- Identify, draw, and specify the materials needed to represent the structural considerations of a structure separate from a floor plan. This would include:
  1. bearing and nonbearing walls
  2. structural members such as trusses, joists and rafters
  3. lateral bracing

TEST ANSWERS

1. Lateral loads are determined by using engineering studies or prescriptive methods of the IBC.
2. Rafters are specified on the roof framing plan and on sections.
3. Rafters are shown on the roof framing plan. If a room has a vaulted ceiling, the rafters are shown on a framing plan. Trusses can be shown on the floor plan. If a complex roof shape is used, trusses are shown on the roof framing plan.
4. Ceiling joists are represented on the floor or framing plan.
5. The floor joists that will support the upper floor.
6. 110 mph for prescriptive wall design
7. The strap can be represented on the framing plan with a bold line. The manufacturer, strap model number, and fasteners should be specified on the plan.
8. Maximum wall height is 12'-0" for prescriptive wall design of Braced wall panels and ABWP. 10'-0" high for ABWPAO.
9. ABWPAO: 16" wide, 6' minimum wall opening, 18'-0" maximum wall opening
10. According to Figure 32–19, braced walls are attached with (2) 1/2" Ø anchor bolts.
11. According to Figure 32–19, portal frames require (3) 1/2 Ø anchor bolts, and 2-#4 rebar 3" up from the bottom of a 15' × 7' footing. A #4 vertical bar is required at each steel connector.
12. Student answers should reflect one of the options from the eight listed options.
13. Walls will try to turn into a parallelogram, fail top uplift, or fall from gravity.
14. Maximum distance between braced wall lines is 35'.
15. According to Figure 32–19, nails must be 5d cooler nails at 7" O.C. with blocked edges.
16. According to Figure 32–11, use 16d at 24" O.C. to nail the studs to form a post.
17. According to Figure 32–11, use 6d common or deformed shank.
18. Walls can be offset no more than the depth of the floor joist they support and still be considered aligned.
19. Walls can be offset no more than 4'-0" to be considered one plane.
20. No more than 4'-0", provided the total distance in offsets are not greater than 8'-0".

© 2011 Cengage Learning. All Rights Reserved. May not be scanned, copied or duplicated, or posted to a publicly accessible website, in whole or in part.

CHAPTER 32 PROBLEM SOLUTIONS

Students should use information from the floor plan, the roof plan, and the elevations for the residence started in Chapter 18 to draw the appropriate framing plan. Rafter sizes should be determined using the span tables in Chapter 30 and beam sizes should be determined using the formulas described in Chapter 31. Lateral bracing should be indicated based on area standards. Student solutions will vary, but should resemble the following solutions.

Problem 32–1   Framing plans were unavailable at the time of printing, but should reflect the use of 2 × 10 floor joists @ 16" o.c. or 9 1/2" TJI 110 joists spanning the approximately 15'-0" from the exterior walls. Headers should be referenced as (2) 2 × 12 headers unless noted on Problem 18–1.

Problem 32–2

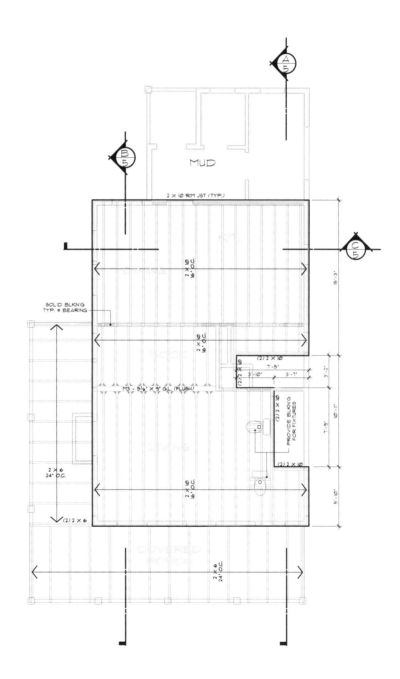

UPPER FLOOR FRAMING

SCALE : 1/4" = 1'-0"

IF LATERAL ENGINEERING IS REQUIRED, REFER TO
ENGINEERING SHEETS FOR LATERAL SPECIFICATIONS

© 2011 Cengage Learning. All Rights Reserved. May not be scanned, copied or duplicated, or posted to a publicly accessible website, in whole or in part.

Problem 32–3

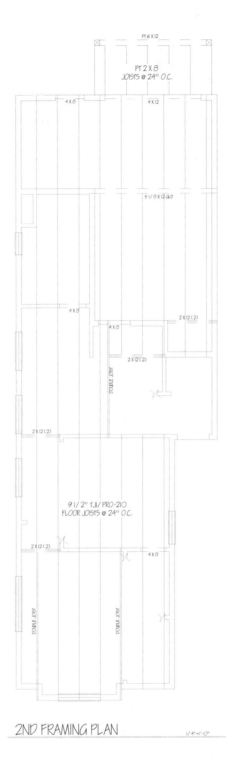

2ND FRAMING PLAN   1/4"=1'-0"

© 2011 Cengage Learning. All Rights Reserved. May not be scanned, copied or duplicated, or posted to a publicly accessible website, in whole or in part.

Problem 32–4

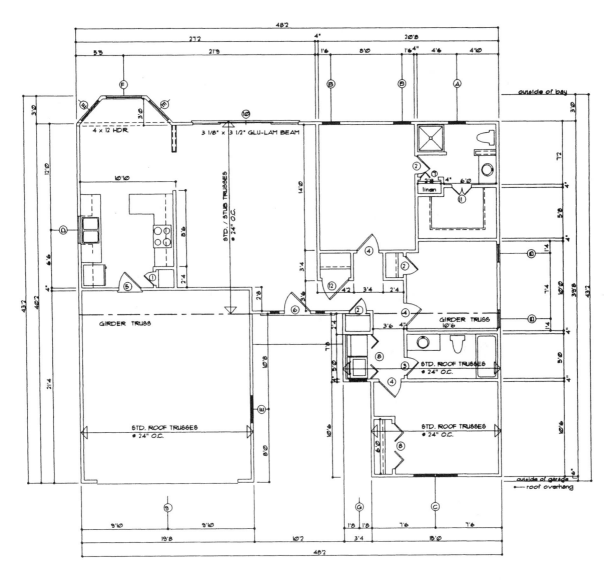

NOTES SHALL APPLY TO ALL LEVELS.

FRAMING PLAN
1/4" = 1'-0"

FRAMING NOTES: FRAMING STANDARDS ARE ACCORDING TO U.B.C. OR C.A.B.O. WITH THE STRICTEST ALTERNATIVE LISTED.

1. ALL FRAMING LUMBER TO BE D.F.L. #2 MIN. ALL GLU-LAM BEAMS TO BE rb2200, V-4, DF/DF

2. FRAME ALL EXTERIOR WALLS W/ 2 x 4 STUDS ● 16" O.C. PROVIDE AN ALTERNATE BID TO FRAME ALL EXTERIOR WALLS W/ 2 x 6 STUDS ● 16" O.C.

3. USE 2-2 x 12 HEADERS ● EXTERIOR WALLS UNLESS NOTED. BACK HEADER W/ 2" RIGID INSULATION.

4. ALL SHEAR PANELS TO BE 1/2" PLY NAILED W/ 8 d'S ● 4" O.C. AT EDGE AND BLOCKING AND 6 d'S ● 8" O.C. ● FIELD.

5. PLYWOOD ROOF SHEATHING TO BE 1/2" STD. GRADE 32/16 PLY. LAID PERP. TO RAFTERS. NAIL W/ 8 d'S ● 6" O.C. ● EDGES AND 12" O.C. AT FIELD

6. BLOCK ALL WALLS OVER 10'-0" HIGH AT MID HEIGHT.

7. LET-IN BRACES TO BE 1 x 4 DIAG. BRACES ● 45° FOR ALL INTERIOR LOAD-BEARING WALLS.

© 2011 Cengage Learning. All Rights Reserved. May not be scanned, copied or duplicated, or posted to a publicly accessible website, in whole or in part.

Problem 32–5

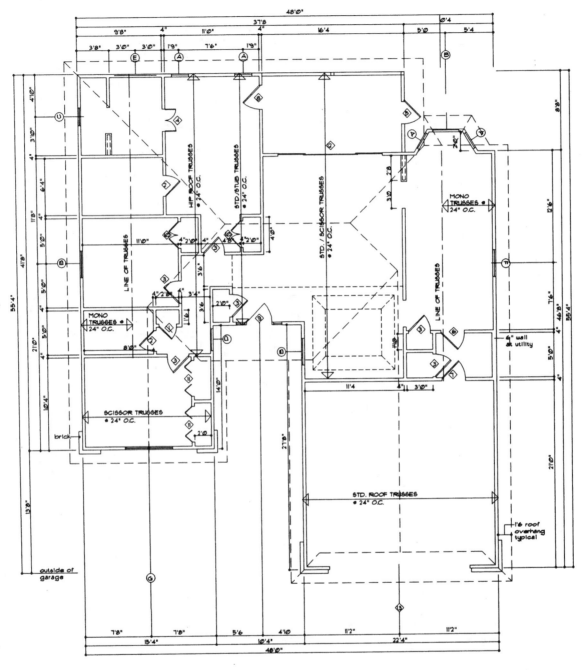

FRAMING PLAN
1/4" = 1'-0"

NOTES SHALL APPLY TO ALL LEVELS.

FRAMING NOTES: FRAMING STANDARDS ARE ACCORDING TO U.B.C. OR C.A.B.O.
WITH THE STRICTEST ALTERNATIVE LISTED.

1. ALL FRAMING LUMBER TO BE D.FL. #2 MIN. ALL GLU-LAM BEAMS TO BE fb2200, V-4, DF/DF

2. FRAME ALL EXTERIOR WALLS W/ 2 x 4 STUDS ● 16" O.C. PROVIDE AN ALTERNATE BID TO
   FRAME ALL EXTERIOR WALLS W/ 2 x 6 STUDS ● 16" O.C.

3. USE 2-2 x 12 HEADERS ● EXTERIOR WALLS UNLESS NOTED.
   BACK HEADER W/ 2" RIGID INSULATION.

4. ALL SHEAR PANELS TO BE 1/2" PLY NAILED W/ 8 d'S ● 4" O.C.
   AT EDGE AND BLOCKING AND 6 d'S ● 8" O.C. ● FIELD.

5. PLYWOOD ROOF SHEATHING TO BE 1/2" STD. GRADE 32/16 PLY. LAID PERP.
   TO RAFTERS. NAIL W/ 8 d'S ● 6" O.C. ● EDGES AND 12" O.C. AT FIELD

6. BLOCK ALL WALLS OVER 10'-0" HIGH AT MID HEIGHT.

7. LET-IN BRACES TO BE 1 x 4 DIAG. BRACES ● 45° FOR ALL INTERIOR
   LOAD-BEARING WALLS.

© 2011 Cengage Learning. All Rights Reserved. May not be scanned, copied or duplicated, or posted to a publicly accessible website, in whole or in part.

Problem 32–6A

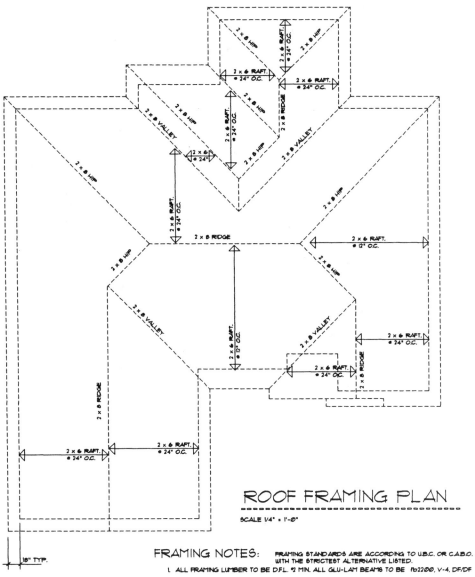

ROOF FRAMING PLAN

SCALE 1/4" = 1'-0"

FRAMING NOTES: FRAMING STANDARDS ARE ACCORDING TO U.B.C. OR C.A.B.O. WITH THE STRICTEST ALTERNATIVE LISTED.

1. ALL FRAMING LUMBER TO BE D.F.L. #2 MIN. ALL GLU-LAM BEAMS TO BE fb2200, V-4, DF/DF

2. PLYWOOD ROOF SHEATHING TO BE 1/2" STD. GRADE 32/16 PLY. LAID PERP. TO RAFTERS. NAIL W/ 8 d'S @ 6" O.C. @ EDGES AND 12" O.C. AT FIELD

3. ALL RIDGES, HIPS AND VALLEYS TO BE 2 x 8.

© 2011 Cengage Learning. All Rights Reserved. May not be scanned, copied or duplicated, or posted to a publicly accessible website, in whole or in part.

Problem 32–6B

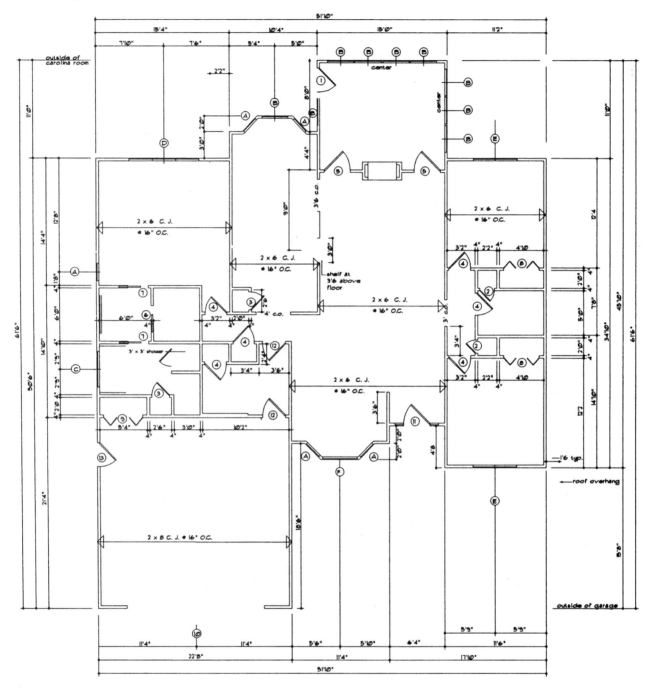

FRAMING PLAN
1/4" = 1'0"

FRAMING NOTES: FRAMING STANDARDS ARE ACCORDING TO U.B.C. OR C.A.B.O.
WITH THE STRICTEST ALTERNATIVE LISTED.

1. ALL FRAMING LUMBER TO BE D.F.L. #2 MIN. ALL GLU-LAM BEAMS TO BE fb2200, V-4, DF/DF

2. FRAME ALL EXTERIOR WALLS W/ 2 x 4 STUDS @ 16" O.C. PROVIDE AN ALTERNATE BID TO
   FRAME ALL EXTERIOR WALLS W/ 2 x 6 STUDS @ 16" O.C.

3. USE 2-2 x 12 HEADERS @ EXTERIOR WALLS UNLESS NOTED.
   BACK HEADER W/ 2" RIGID INSULATION.

4. ALL SHEAR PANELS TO BE 1/2" PLY NAILED W/ 8 d'S @ 4" O.C.
   AT EDGE AND BLOCKING AND 6 d'S @ 8" O.C. @ FIELD.

5. PLYWOOD ROOF SHEATHING TO BE 1/2" STD. GRADE 32/16 PLY. LAID PERP.
   TO RAFTERS. NAIL W/ 8 d'S @ 6" O.C. @ EDGES AND 12" O.C. AT FIELD

6. BLOCK ALL WALLS OVER 10'-0" HIGH AT MID HEIGHT.

7. LET-IN BRACES TO BE 1 X 4 DIAG. BRACES @ 45° FOR ALL INTERIOR
   LOAD-BEARING WALLS.

© 2011 Cengage Learning. All Rights Reserved. May not be scanned, copied or duplicated, or posted to a publicly accessible website, in whole or in part.

Problem 32–7

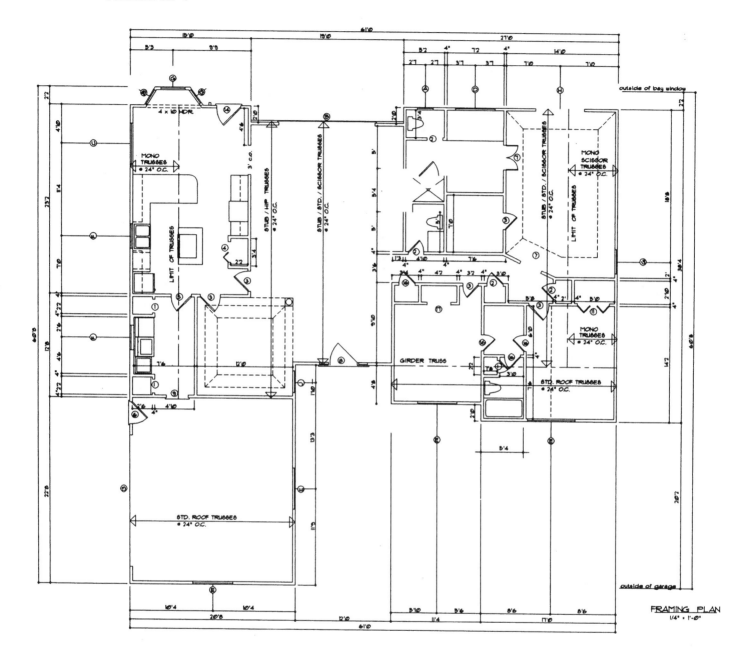

FRAMING PLAN
1/4" = 1'-0"

FRAMING NOTES: FRAMING STANDARDS ARE ACCORDING TO U.B.C. OR C.A.B.O.
WITH THE STRICTEST ALTERNATIVE LISTED.

1. ALL FRAMING LUMBER TO BE D.F.L. #2 MIN. ALL GLU-LAM BEAMS TO BE No2200, V-4, DF/DF

2. FRAME ALL EXTERIOR WALLS W/ 2 x 4 STUDS @ 16" O.C. PROVIDE AN ALTERNATE BID TO
   FRAME ALL EXTERIOR WALLS W/ 2 x 6 STUDS @ 16" O.C.

3. USE 2-2 x 12 HEADERS @ EXTERIOR WALLS UNLESS NOTED.
   BACK HEADER W/ 2" RIGID INSULATION.

4. ALL SHEAR PANELS TO BE 1/2" PLY. NAILED W/ 8 d's @ 4" O.C.
   AT EDGE AND BLOCKING AND 6 d's @ 8" O.C. @ FIELD.

5. PLYWOOD ROOF SHEATHING TO BE 1/2" STD. GRADE 32/16 PLY. LAID PERP.
   TO RAFTERS. NAIL W/ 8 d's @ 6" O.C. @ EDGES AND 12" O.C. AT FIELD

6. BLOCK ALL WALLS OVER 10'-0" HIGH AT MID HEIGHT.

7. LET-IN BRACES TO BE 1 x 4 DIAG. BRACES @ 45° FOR ALL INTERIOR
   LOAD-BEARING WALLS.

© 2011 Cengage Learning. All Rights Reserved. May not be scanned, copied or duplicated, or posted to a publicly accessible website, in whole or in part.

Problem 32–8A

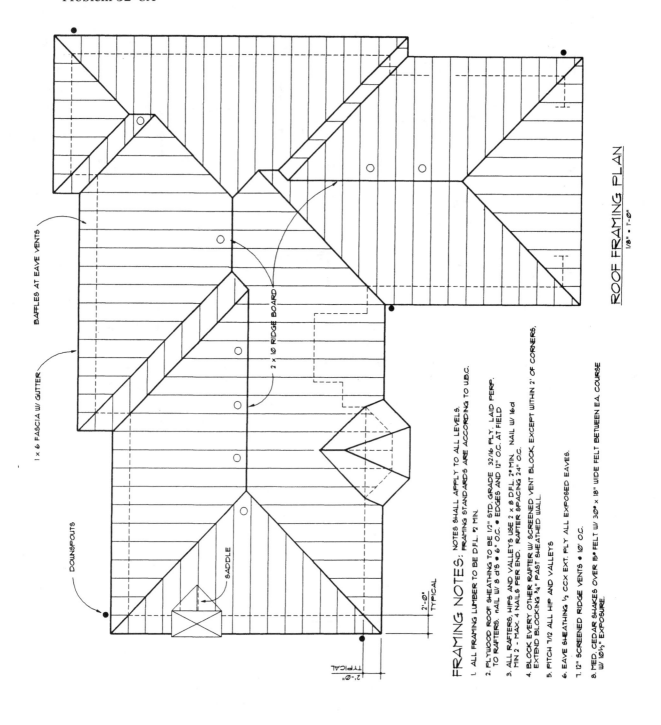

BAFFLES AT EAVE VENTS

1 x 6 FASCIA W/ GUTTER

2 x 10 RIDGE BOARD

DOWNSPOUTS

SADDLE

2'-0" TYPICAL

2'-0" TYPICAL

ROOF FRAMING PLAN
1/8" = 1'-0"

FRAMING NOTES: NOTES SHALL APPLY TO ALL LEVELS.
FRAMING STANDARDS ARE ACCORDING TO U.B.C.

1. ALL FRAMING LUMBER TO BE D.F.L. #2 MIN.

2. PLYWOOD ROOF SHEATHING TO BE 1/2" STD. GRADE 32/16 PLY. LAID PERP.
   TO RAFTERS, NAIL W/ 8 d'S @ 6" O.C. @ EDGES AND 12" O.C. AT FIELD

3. ALL RAFTERS, HIPS AND VALLEYS USE 2 x 8 DF.L. 2" MIN. NAIL W/ 16d
   MIN 2 - MAX. 4 NAILS PER END. RAFTER SPACING 24" O.C.

4. BLOCK EVERY OTHER RAFTER W/ SCREENED VENT BLOCK, EXCEPT WITHIN 2' OF CORNERS,
   EXTEND BLOCKING 3/4" PAST SHEATHED WALL.

5. PITCH 7/12 ALL HIP AND VALLEYS

6. EAVE SHEATHING 1/2 CCX EXT. PLY ALL EXPOSED EAVES.

7. 12" SCREENED RIDGE VENTS @ 10' O.C.

8. MED. CEDAR SHAKES OVER 15# FELT W/ 30# x 18" WIDE FELT BETWEEN EA. COURSE
   W/ 10 1/2" EXPOSURE.

© 2011 Cengage Learning. All Rights Reserved. May not be scanned, copied or duplicated, or posted to a publicly accessible website, in whole or in part.

Problem 32–8B

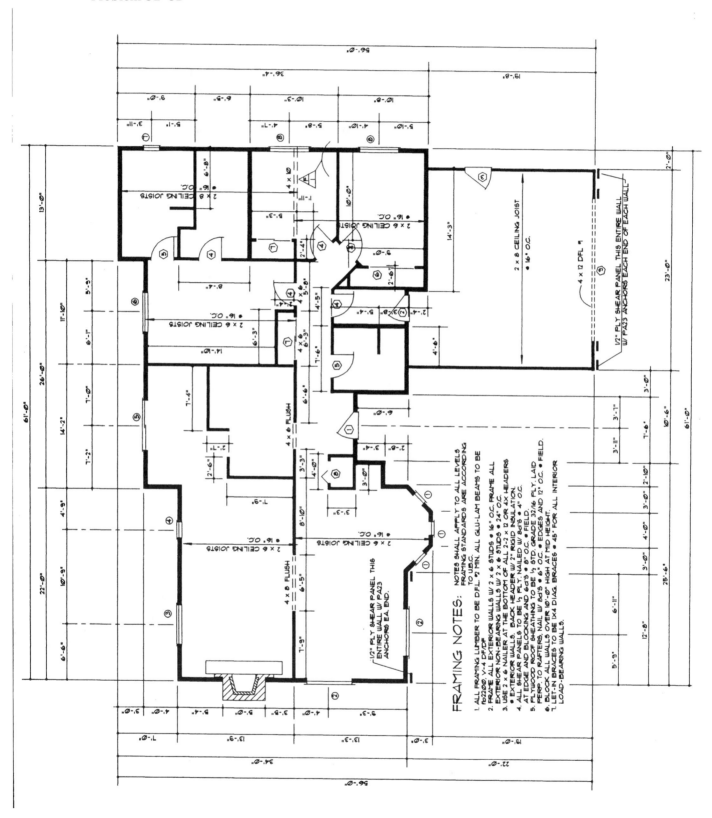

© 2011 Cengage Learning. All Rights Reserved. May not be scanned, copied or duplicated, or posted to a publicly accessible website, in whole or in part.

Problem 32–9

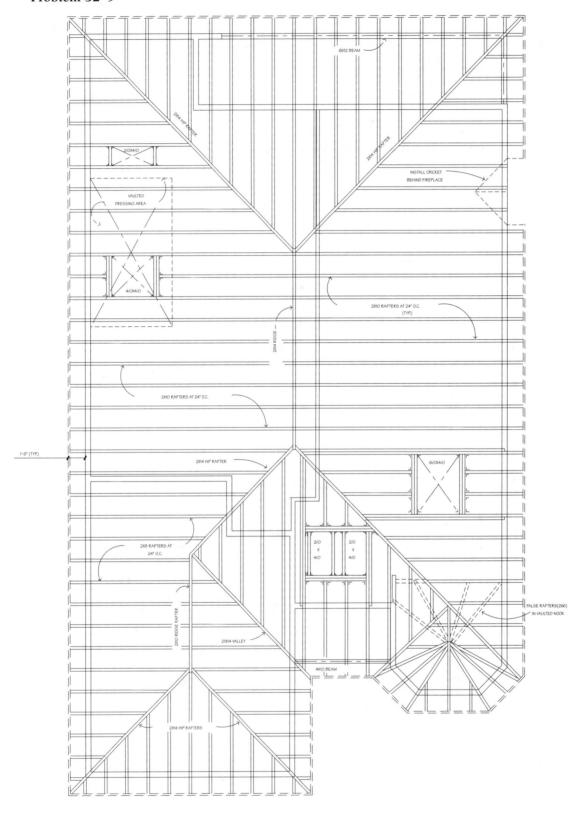

ROOF FRAMING PLAN

SCALE 1/4" = 1'-0"

See solution to Problem 18–9 for balance of framing information.

© 2011 Cengage Learning. All Rights Reserved. May not be scanned, copied or duplicated, or posted to a publicly accessible website, in whole or in part.

32–10   The framing information for this problem has been displayed on the floor plan. See solution for Problem 16–10.

32–11   The framing information for this problem has been displayed on the floor plan. See solution for Problem 16–11.

32–12   The solution for this problem was unavailable at the time of printing.

Problem 32–13A

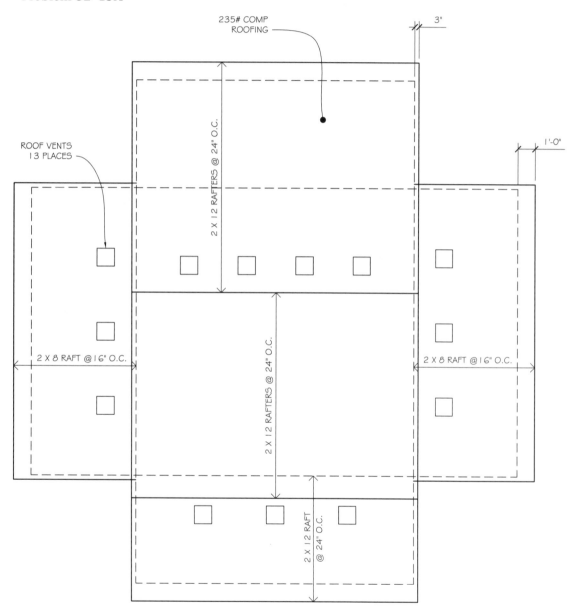

235# COMP ROOFING

ROOF VENTS 13 PLACES

2 X 12 RAFTERS @ 24" O.C.

2 X 8 RAFT @ 16" O.C.

2 X 12 RAFTERS @ 24" O.C.

2 X 8 RAFT @ 16" O.C.

2 X 12 RAFT @ 24" O.C.

3"

1'-0"

ROOF PLAN

© 2011 Cengage Learning. All Rights Reserved. May not be scanned, copied or duplicated, or posted to a publicly accessible website, in whole or in part.

Problem 32–13B

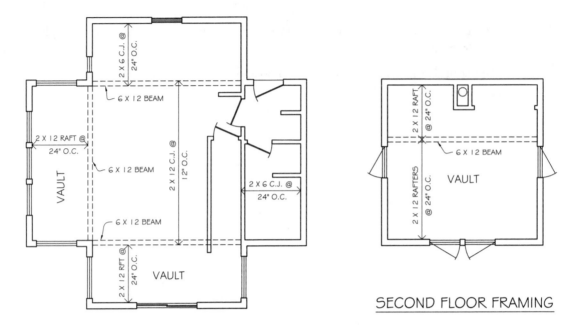

FIRST FLOOR FRAMING

SECOND FLOOR FRAMING

See solution to Problem 18–13 for Additional Framing information.

© 2011 Cengage Learning. All Rights Reserved. May not be scanned, copied or duplicated, or posted to a publicly accessible website, in whole or in part.

Problem 32–14A

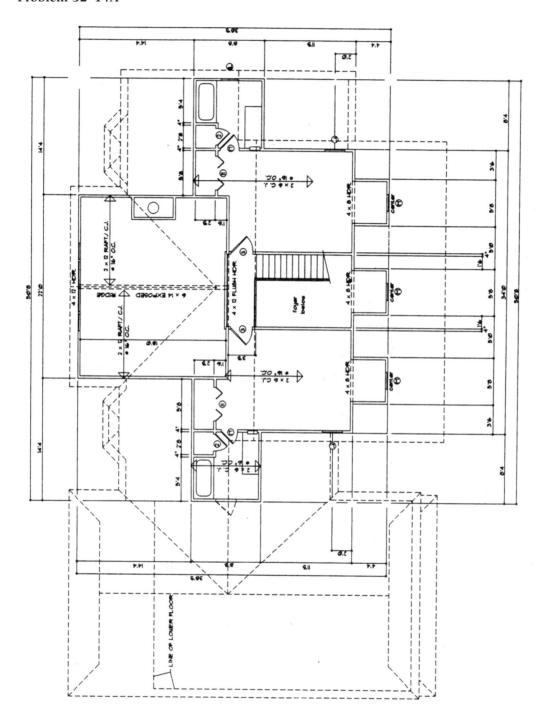

© 2011 Cengage Learning. All Rights Reserved. May not be scanned, copied or duplicated, or posted to a publicly accessible website, in whole or in part.

Problem 32–14B

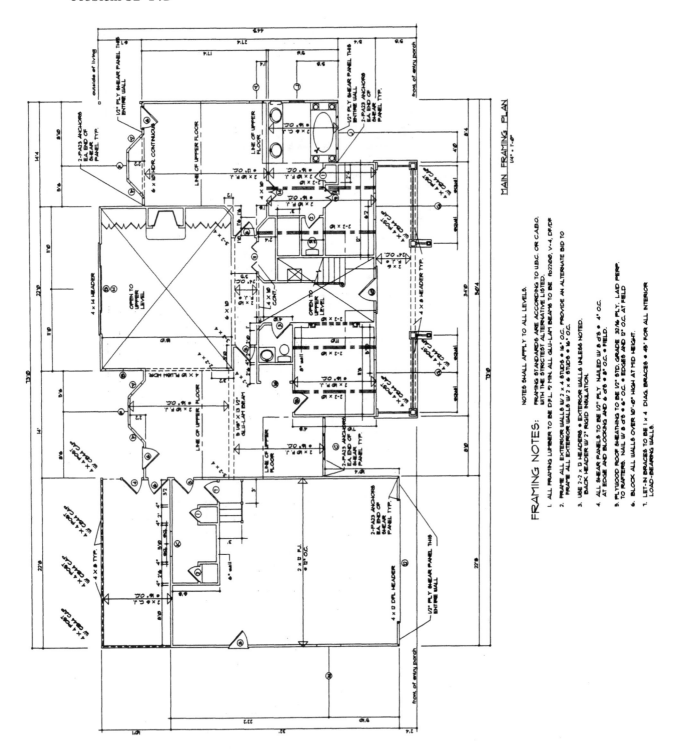

© 2011 Cengage Learning. All Rights Reserved. May not be scanned, copied or duplicated, or posted to a publicly accessible website, in whole or in part.

Problem 32-15A

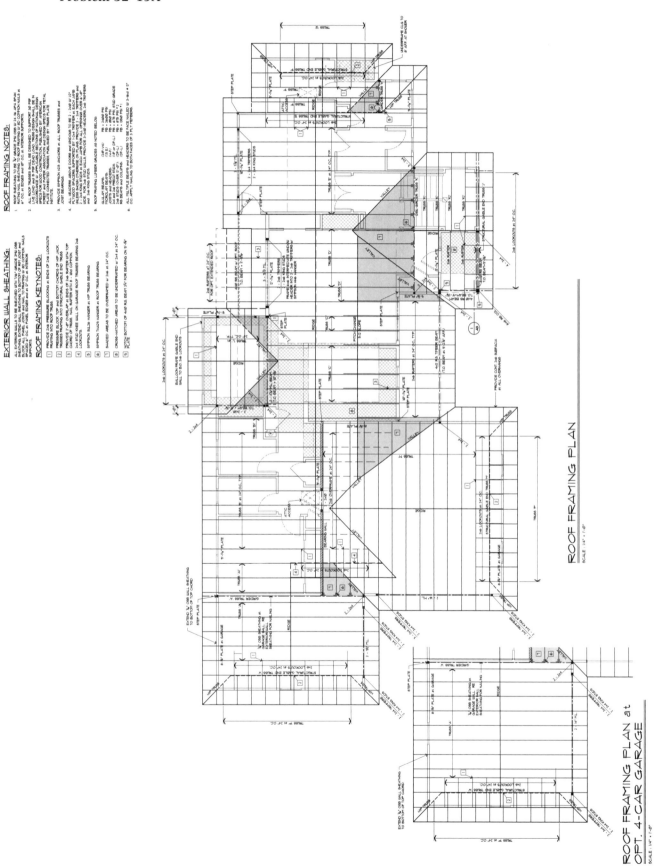

ROOF FRAMING PLAN
SCALE: 1/4" = 1'-0"

ROOF FRAMING PLAN at
OPT. 4-CAR GARAGE
SCALE: 1/4" = 1'-0"

© 2011 Cengage Learning. All Rights Reserved. May not be scanned, copied or duplicated, or posted to a publicly accessible website, in whole or in part.

Problem 32–15B

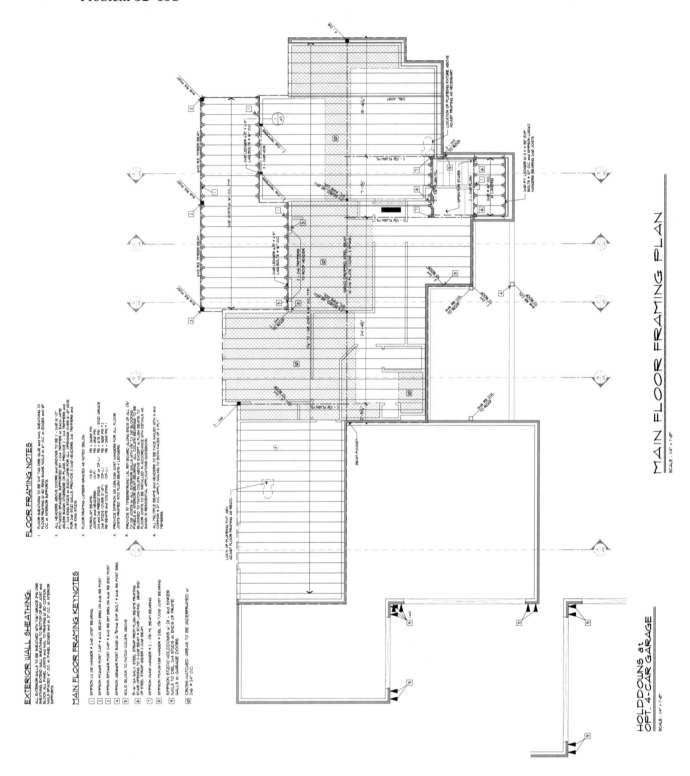

Problem 32–16A

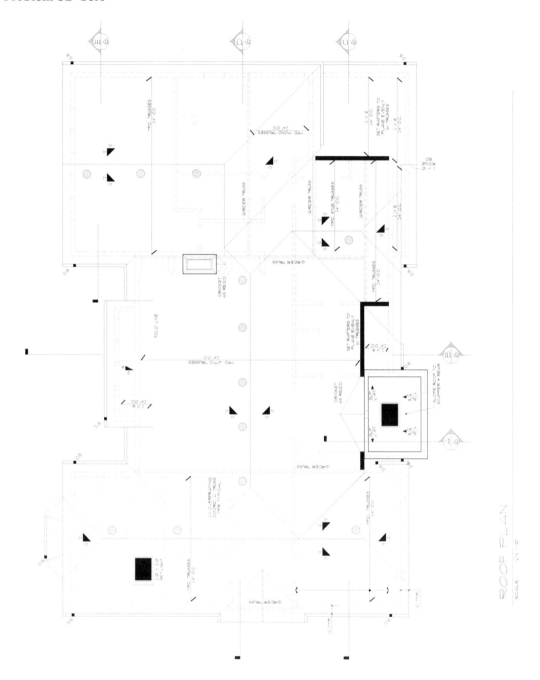

© 2011 Cengage Learning. All Rights Reserved. May not be scanned, copied or duplicated, or posted to a publicly accessible website, in whole or in part.

Problem 32–16B

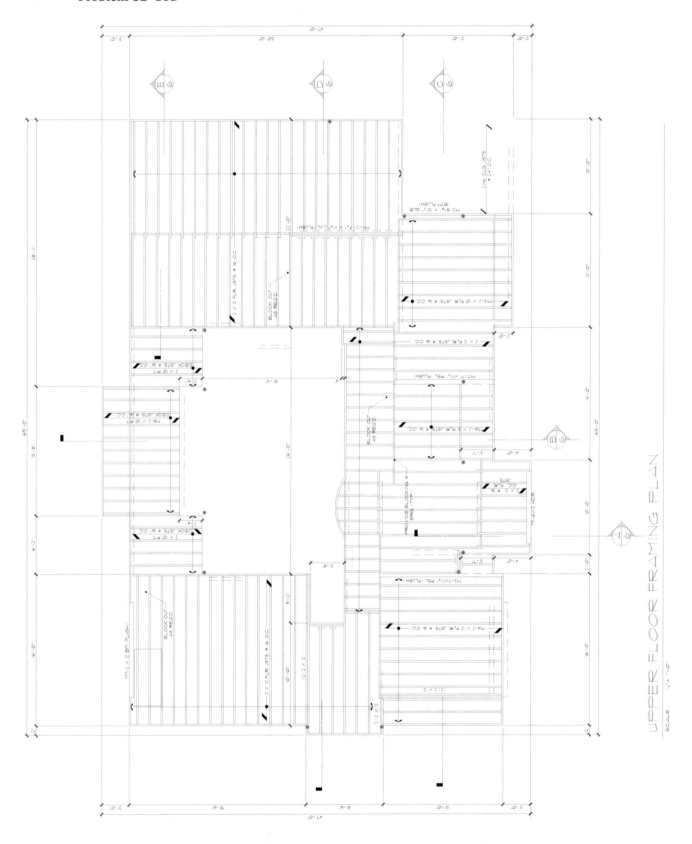

UPPER FLOOR FRAMING PLAN

SCALE: 1/4" = 1'-0"

© 2011 Cengage Learning. All Rights Reserved. May not be scanned, copied or duplicated, or posted to a publicly accessible website, in whole or in part.

Problem 32–16C

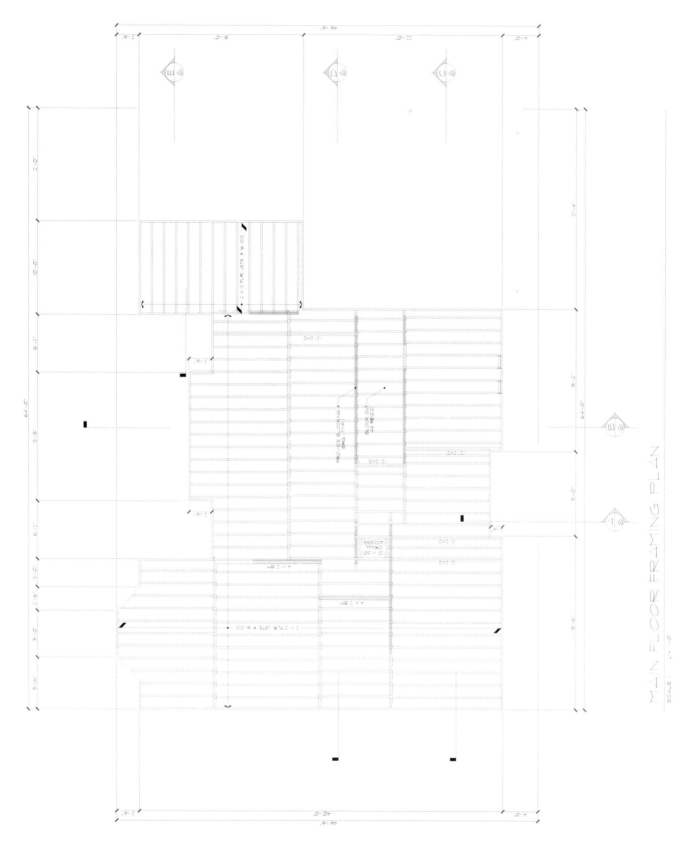

© 2011 Cengage Learning. All Rights Reserved. May not be scanned, copied or duplicated, or posted to a publicly accessible website, in whole or in part.

Problem 32–17

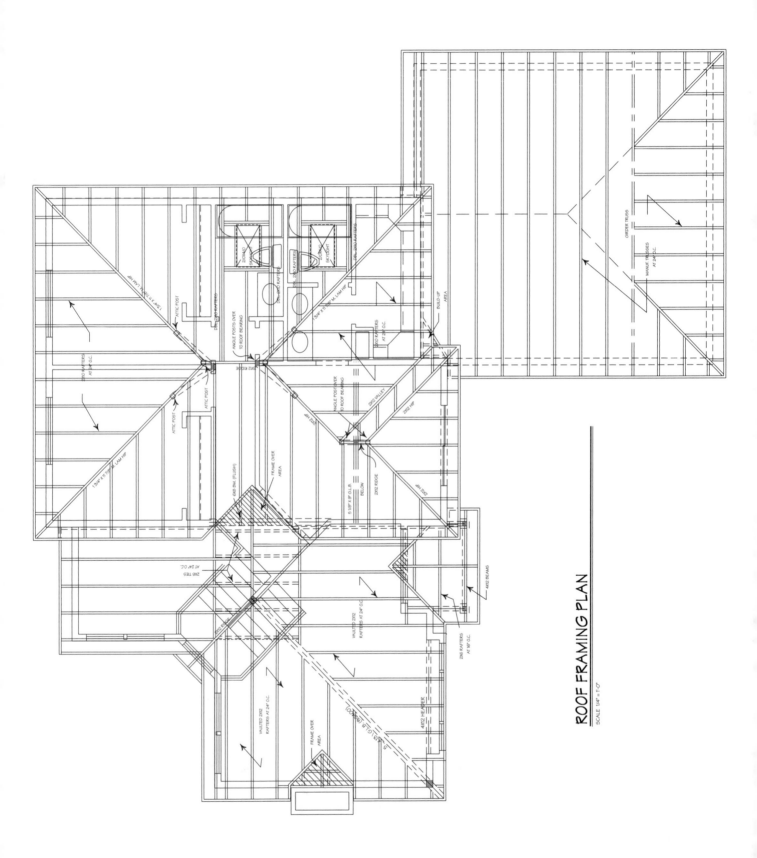

ROOF FRAMING PLAN
SCALE 1/4" = 1'-0"

© 2011 Cengage Learning. All Rights Reserved. May not be scanned, copied or duplicated, or posted to a publicly accessible website, in whole or in part.

32–18   The framing information for this problem has been displayed on the floor plan. See solution for Problem 18–18.

32–19   The framing information for this problem has been displayed on the floor plan. See solution for Problem 18–19.

32–20   The framing information for this problem has been displayed on the floor plan. See solution for Problem 18–20.

32–21   The framing information for this problem has been displayed on the floor plan. See solution for Problem 18–21.

Problem 32–22

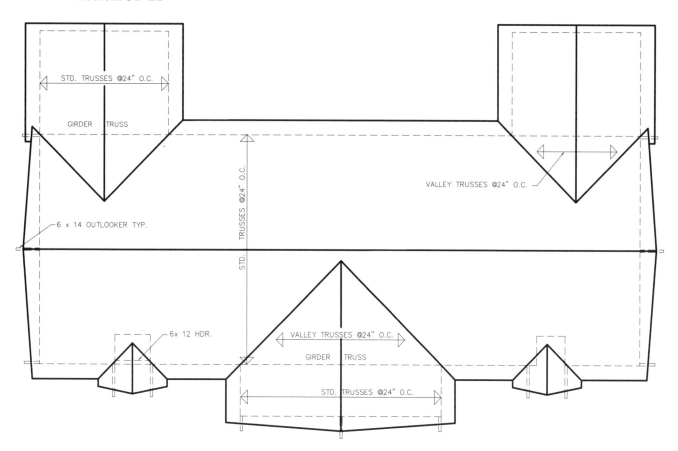

ROOF FRAMING PLAN

© 2011 Cengage Learning. All Rights Reserved. May not be scanned, copied or duplicated, or posted to a publicly accessible website, in whole or in part.

© 2011 Cengage Learning. All Rights Reserved. May not be scanned, copied or duplicated, or posted to a publicly accessible website, in whole or in part.

SECTION 9
Foundation Plans

CHAPTER 33
FOUNDATION SYSTEMS

OBJECTIVES

When students have completed this chapter, they will:

- List and describe soil considerations that affect foundation design.
- List characteristics of different types of foundations.
- List common materials used for foundations.
- List a minimum of ten foundation components.
- List and describe how a foundation can be considered green and determine how to obtain LEED credits for the foundation materials.

TEST ANSWERS

1. The footing and stem wall
2. The type of footing material, soil bearing value, number of stories to be supported
3. Gravity, flooding, wind, seismic, freezing
4. The texture of the soil will affect how much the soil will compact. The tendency to compact will affect the size of the foundation.
5. Poured concrete, concrete blocks, stone
6. To resist tension in the concrete
7. On sloping lots to reduce wall height and save material
8. 16" wide × 8" or 12" deep depending on the height of the structure to be supported
9. Soil-bearing capacity, strength of concrete, load
10. Full-height retaining—anchored at top and bottom of wall
    Partial-height retaining—anchored at bottom of wall only

© 2011 Cengage Learning. All Rights Reserved. May not be scanned, copied or duplicated, or posted to a publicly accessible website, in whole or in part.

CHAPTER 33 PROBLEM SOLUTIONS

Problem 33–1

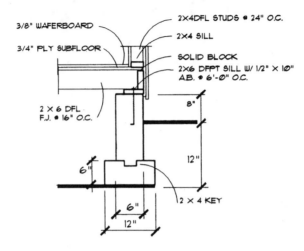

Problem 33–2

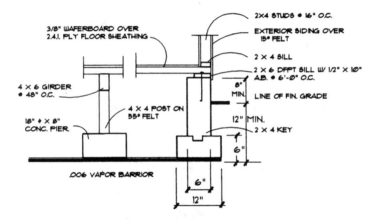

Problem 33–3

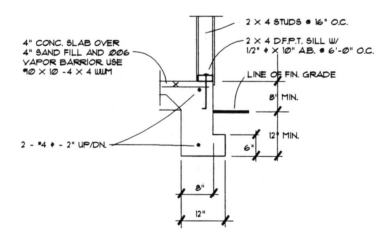

© 2011 Cengage Learning. All Rights Reserved. May not be scanned, copied or duplicated, or posted to a publicly accessible website, in whole or in part.

Problem 33–4

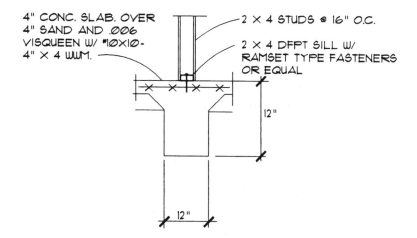

4" CONC. SLAB. OVER
4" SAND AND .006
VISQUEEN W/ #10X10-
4" X 4 WWM.

2 X 4 STUDS @ 16" O.C.

2 X 4 DFPT SILL W/
RAMSET TYPE FASTENERS
OR EQUAL

12"

12"

Problem 33–5

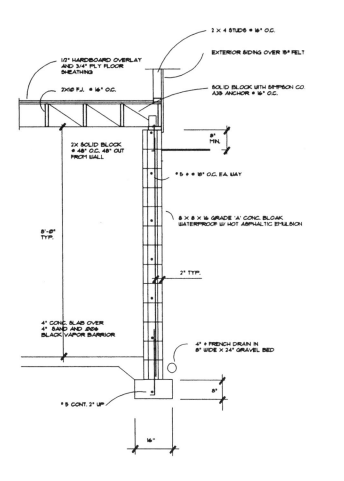

2 X 4 STUDS @ 16" O.C.

EXTERIOR SIDING OVER 15# FELT

1/2" HARDBOARD OVERLAY
AND 3/4" PLY FLOOR
SHEATHING

SOLID BLOCK WITH SIMPSON CO.
A35 ANCHOR @ 16" O.C.

2X10 F.J. @ 16" O.C.

8"
MIN.

2X SOLID BLOCK
@ 48" O.C. 48" OUT
FROM WALL

#5 @ 18" O.C. EA. WAY

8 X 8 X 16 GRADE 'A' CONC. BLOAK
WATERPROOF W/ HOT ASPHALTIC EMULSION

8'-0"
TYP.

2" TYP.

4" CONC. SLAB OVER
4" SAND AND .006
BLACK VAPOR BARRIER

4" ⌀ FRENCH DRAIN IN
8" WIDE X 24" GRAVEL BED

#5 CONT. 2" UP

8"

16"

© 2011 Cengage Learning. All Rights Reserved. May not be scanned, copied or duplicated, or posted to a publicly accessible website, in whole or in part.

Problem 33–6

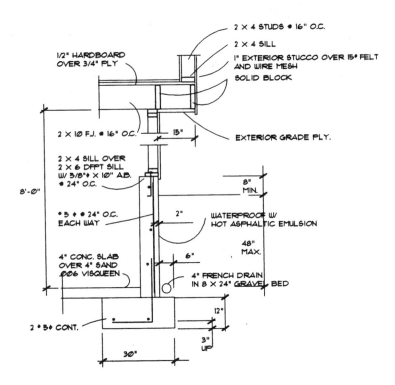

1/2" HARDBOARD
OVER 3/4" PLY

2 × 4 STUDS ● 16" O.C.

2 × 4 SILL

1" EXTERIOR STUCCO OVER 15# FELT
AND WIRE MESH

SOLID BLOCK

2 × 10 F.J. ● 16" O.C.

15"

EXTERIOR GRADE PLY.

2 × 4 SILL OVER
2 × 6 DFPT SILL
W/ 3/8"● × 10" A.B.
● 24" O.C.

8'-0"

8"
MIN.

● 5 ● 24" O.C.
EACH WAY

2"

WATERPROOF W/
HOT ASPHALTIC EMULSION

48"
MAX.

4" CONC. SLAB
OVER 4" SAND
.006 VISQUEEN

6"

4" FRENCH DRAIN
IN 8 × 24" GRAVEL BED

12"

2 ● 5● CONT.

3"
UP

30"

CHAPTER 34
FLOOR SYSTEMS AND FOUNDATION SUPPORT

OBJECTIVES

When students have completed this chapter, they will:

- List, describe, and draw components of an on-grade foundation.
- List, describe, and draw components of joist floor systems.
- List, describe, and draw components of a post-and-beam floor system.
- List, describe, and draw components of a floor constructed of combined methods.
- Describe materials that constitute a green floor system.

TEST ANSWERS

1. Because it is built on the ground with no crawl space
2. 3 1/2"
3. To help control cracking
4. 4"
5. 0.006
6. 18" from the bottom of the floor, 12" from the bottom of the beams
7. To provide support to floor joists or other floor loads
8. They can either rest on the sill or be hung from a ledger.
9. In a pocket notched into the concrete or with a metal hanger
10. 48" O.C. with piers spaced at 8" O.C.

© 2011 Cengage Learning. All Rights Reserved. May not be scanned, copied or duplicated, or posted to a publicly accessible website, in whole or in part.

CHAPTER 34 PROBLEM SOLUTIONS

Chapter 34 of the textbook contains no problems.

CHAPTER 35
FOUNDATION PLAN LAYOUT

OBJECTIVES

When students have completed this chapter, they will:

- Describe line type, line weight, and line scales used on foundation plans.
- Draw, dimension, label, and evaluate a foundation plan with a joist floor system.
- Draw, dimension, label, and evaluate a concrete slab foundation.
- Draw, dimension, label, and evaluate a foundation plan using combined floor systems.
- Draw, dimension, label, and evaluate a foundation with a post-and-beam floor system.
- Draw, dimension, label, and evaluate a piling foundation with a joist floor system.

TEST ANSWERS

1. Typically drawn at the same scale as the floor plan
2. Outline of the slab

   Stem walls and openings in the stem wall

   Bearing wall locations

   Changes in floor evaluation or sloping areas

   Footings and piers

   Underslab heating and air-conditioning (HVAC) equipment
3. Overall size of the slab

   Jogs in the foundation shape

   Openings in the stem walls

   Interior footings locations

   Fireplace locations

   Heating and plumbing materials

   Lateral bracing locations

© 2011 Cengage Learning. All Rights Reserved. May not be scanned, copied or duplicated, or posted to a publicly accessible website, in whole or in part.

4. a. An arrow represents the direction of span and spacing.

   b. An arrow is drawn from bearing point to bearing point.

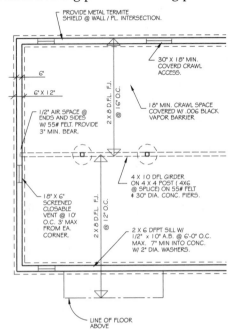

   c. When floor joists extend past the foundation wall, the length should be shown.

5. 8'-4"

6. None. When the door opening is above a wood floor, no opening needs to be provided.

7. Thin dashed lines

8.

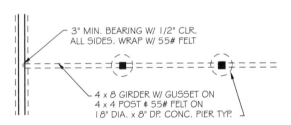

9. Thin lines

10. When the floor plan is traced, errors in the floor plan will be reproduced. If the drafter is not aware of these mistakes, they may make the plan difficult to build.

© 2011 Cengage Learning. All Rights Reserved. May not be scanned, copied or duplicated, or posted to a publicly accessible website, in whole or in part.

CHAPTER 35 PROBLEM SOLUTIONS

Problem 35–1

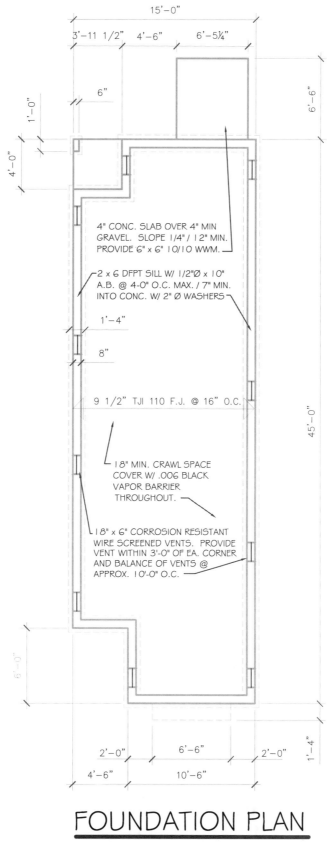

4" CONC. SLAB OVER 4" MIN
GRAVEL. SLOPE 1/4" / 12" MIN.
PROVIDE 6" x 6" 10/10 WWM.

2 x 6 DFPT SILL W/ 1/2"Ø x 10"
A.B. @ 4-0" O.C. MAX. / 7" MIN.
INTO CONC. W/ 2" Ø WASHERS

9 1/2" TJI 110 F.J. @ 16" O.C.

18" MIN. CRAWL SPACE
COVER W/ .006 BLACK
VAPOR BARRIER
THROUGHOUT.

18" x 6" CORROSION RESISTANT
WIRE SCREENED VENTS. PROVIDE
VENT WITHIN 3'-0" OF EA. CORNER
AND BALANCE OF VENTS @
APPROX. 10'-0" O.C.

FOUNDATION PLAN

1/4" ━━━━━━━ 1'-0"

© 2011 Cengage Learning. All Rights Reserved. May not be scanned, copied or duplicated, or posted to a publicly accessible website, in whole or in part.

Problem 35–2

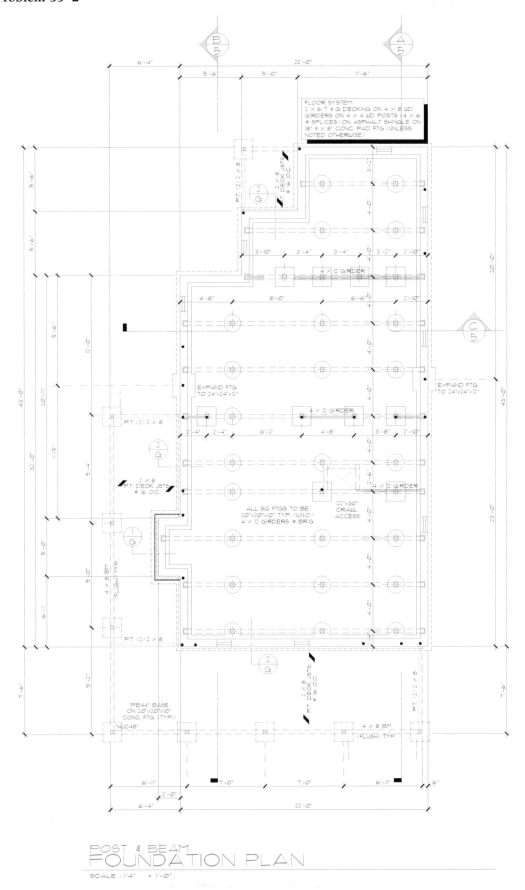

FLOOR SYSTEM:
2 × 6 T & G DECKING ON 4 × 8 WD
GIRDERS ON 4 × 4 WD POSTS (4 × 6
@ SPLICES) ON ASPHALT SHINGLE ON
18" ø × 8" CONC. PAD FTG (UNLESS
NOTED OTHERWISE)

4 × 12 GIRDER

EXPAND FTG.
TO 24"×24"×12"

EXPAND FTG.
TO 24"×24"×12"

ALL SQ. FTGS TO BE
20"×20"×10" TYP. (U.N.O.)
4 × 12 GIRDERS @ BR'G

22"×30'
CRAWL
ACCESS

4 × 12 GIRDER

'PB44' BASE
ON 20"×20"×10"
CONC. FTG. (TYP.)

'HUC48'

4 × 8 BM
(FLUSH) TYP.

POST & BEAM
FOUNDATION PLAN
SCALE : 1/4" = 1'-0"

© 2011 Cengage Learning. All Rights Reserved. May not be scanned, copied or duplicated, or posted to a publicly accessible website, in whole or in part.

Problem 35–3

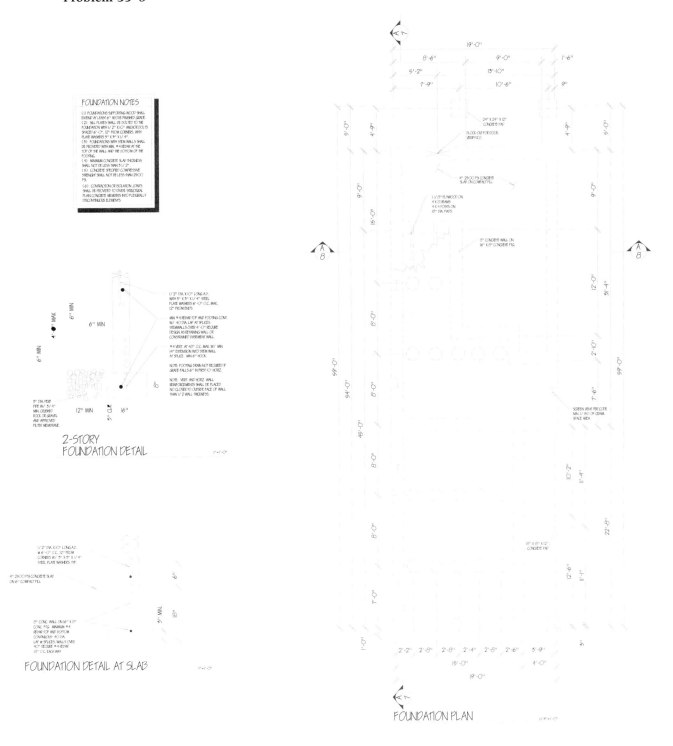

FOUNDATION NOTES

2-STORY
FOUNDATION DETAIL

FOUNDATION DETAIL AT SLAB

FOUNDATION PLAN

© 2011 Cengage Learning. All Rights Reserved. May not be scanned, copied or duplicated, or posted to a publicly accessible website, in whole or in part.

Problem 35–4

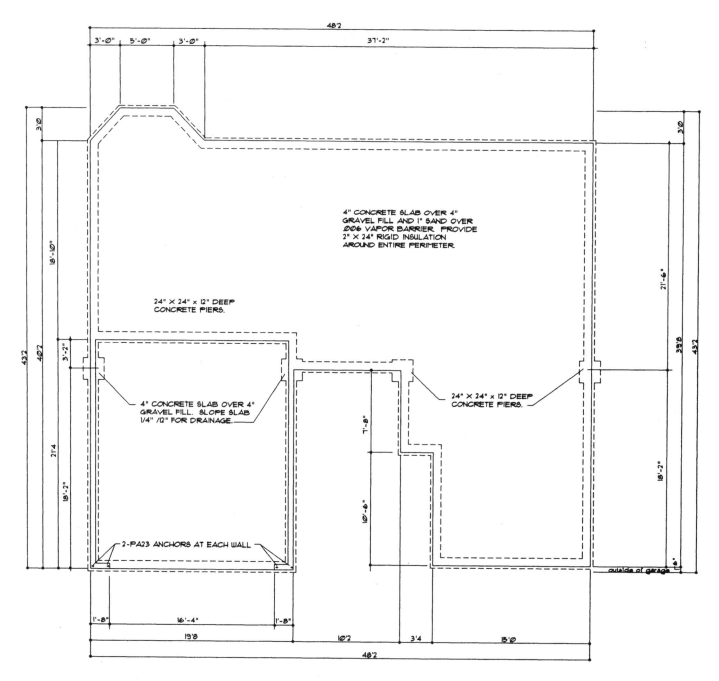

FOUNDATION PLAN
1/4" = 1'-0"

CONCRETE NOTES:
SEE UPPER FRAMING PLAN
FOR ALL FRAMING SPECIFICATIONS

1. EXTEND FOOTINGS 12" MIN. INTO NATURAL SOIL.

2. PROVIDE 4" ∅ FOUNDATION DRAIN AROUND PERIMETER OF FOUNDATION AND SLOPE TO DRAIN
AWAY FROM FOUNDATION. DO NOT CONNECT RAIN DRAINS TO FOUNDATION DRAINS.

3. CONCRETE EXPOSED TO WEATHER TO BE 3000 P.S.I.
CONCRETE NOT EXPOSED TO WEATHER TO BE 2500 P.S.I.
CONCRETE GARAGE SLABS TO BE 2500 P.S.I.
ALL CONCRETE COMPRESSIVE STRENGTH MINIMUMS TO BE AT 28 DAYS.

4. ALL MUDSILLS TO BE 2 x 4 D.F.P.T. W/ ½"∅ X 10" A.B. @ 6'-0" O.C. MAX.
PROVIDE A MINIMUM OF TWO A.B. FOR EA. PLATE. EXTEND 7" MINIMUM INTO CONCRETE
AND PROVIDE 2" ∅ WASHERS. BOLTS TO BE 12" MAX. FROM CORNERS.

5. SLOPE ALL GRADES AWAY FROM FOUNDATION
FOR 60" MINIMUM.

© 2011 Cengage Learning. All Rights Reserved. May not be scanned, copied or duplicated, or posted to a publicly accessible website, in whole or in part.

Problem 35–5

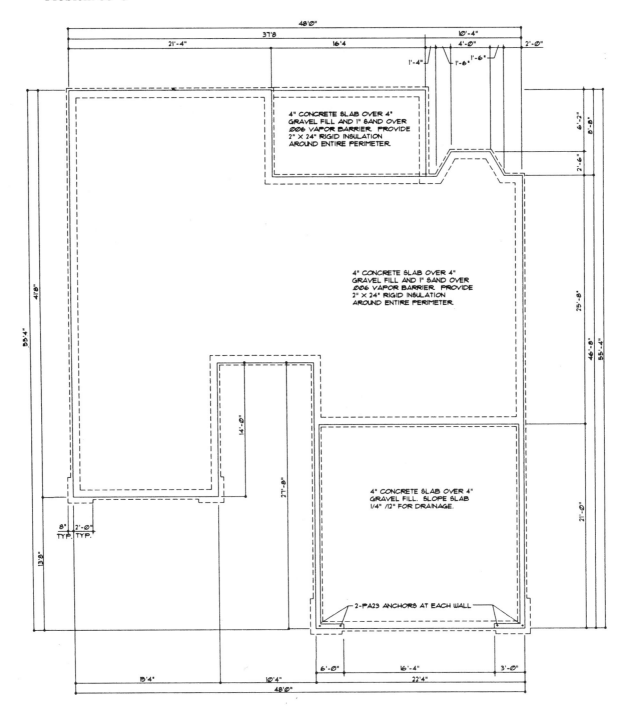

FOUNDATION PLAN
1/4" = 1'-0"

CONCRETE NOTES: SEE UPPER FRAMING PLAN FOR ALL FRAMING SPECIFICATIONS

1. EXTEND FOOTINGS 12" MIN. INTO NATURAL SOIL.

2. PROVIDE 4" ◊ FOUNDATION DRAIN AROUND PERIMETER OF FOUNDATION AND SLOPE TO DRAIN AWAY FROM FOUNDATION. DO NOT CONNECT RAIN DRAINS TO FOUNDATION DRAINS.

3. CONCRETE EXPOSED TO WEATHER TO BE 3000 P.S.I.
CONCRETE NOT EXPOSED TO WEATHER TO BE 2500 P.S.I.
CONCRETE GARAGE SLABS TO BE 2500 P.S.I.
ALL CONCRETE COMPRESSIVE STRENGTH MINIMUMS TO BE AT 28 DAYS.

4. ALL MUDSILLS TO BE 2 x 4 D.F.P.T. W/ ½"◊ X 10" A.B. @ 6'-0" O.C. MAX.
PROVIDE A MINIMUM OF TWO A.B. FOR EA. PLATE. EXTEND 7" MINIMUM INTO CONCRETE AND PROVIDE 2" ◊ WASHERS. BOLTS TO BE 12" MAX. FROM CORNERS.

5. SLOPE ALL GRADES AWAY FROM FOUNDATION FOR 60" MINIMUM.

© 2011 Cengage Learning. All Rights Reserved. May not be scanned, copied or duplicated, or posted to a publicly accessible website, in whole or in part.

Problem 35–6

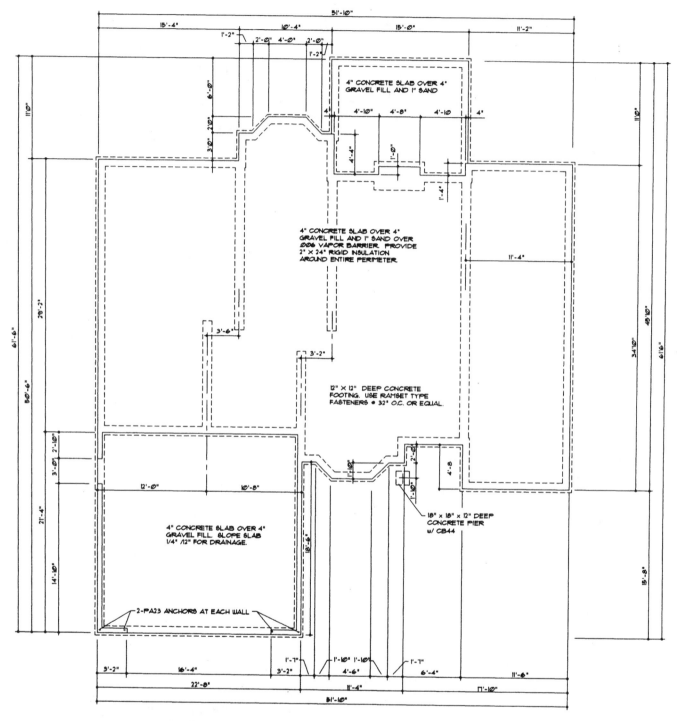

FOUNDATION PLAN
1/4" = 1'0"

CONCRETE NOTES: SEE UPPER FRAMING PLAN FOR ALL FRAMING SPECIFICATIONS

1. EXTEND FOOTINGS 12" MIN. INTO NATURAL SOIL.

2. PROVIDE 4" ∅ FOUNDATION DRAIN AROUND PERIMETER OF FOUNDATION AND SLOPE TO DRAIN AWAY FROM FOUNDATION. DO NOT CONNECT RAIN DRAINS TO FOUNDATION DRAINS.

3. CONCRETE EXPOSED TO WEATHER TO BE 3000 P.S.I.
   CONCRETE NOT EXPOSED TO WEATHER TO BE 2500 P.S.I.
   CONCRETE GARAGE SLABS TO BE 2500 P.S.I.
   ALL CONCRETE COMPRESSIVE STRENGTH MINIMUMS TO BE AT 28 DAYS.

4. ALL MUDSILLS TO BE 2 x 4 D.F.P.T. W/ ½" ∅ X 10" A.B. @ 6'-0" O.C. MAX.
   PROVIDE A MINIMUM OF TWO A.B. FOR EA. PLATE. EXTEND 7" MINIMUM INTO CONCRETE AND PROVIDE 2" ∅ WASHERS. BOLTS TO BE 12" MAX. FROM CORNERS.

5. SLOPE ALL GRADES AWAY FROM FOUNDATION FOR 60" MINIMUM.

© 2011 Cengage Learning. All Rights Reserved. May not be scanned, copied or duplicated, or posted to a publicly accessible website, in whole or in part.

Problem 35–7

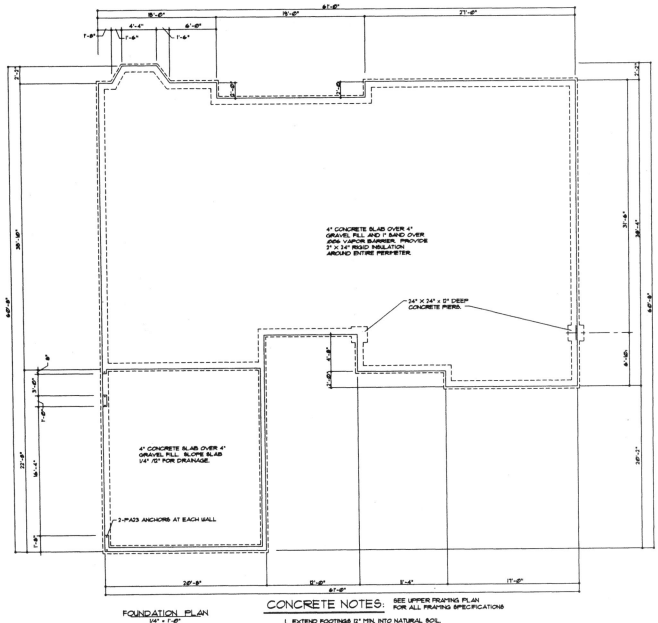

FOUNDATION PLAN
1/4" = 1'-0"

CONCRETE NOTES: SEE UPPER FRAMING PLAN
FOR ALL FRAMING SPECIFICATIONS

1. EXTEND FOOTINGS 12" MIN. INTO NATURAL SOIL.

2. PROVIDE 4" ⏀ FOUNDATION DRAIN AROUND PERIMETER OF FOUNDATION AND SLOPE TO DRAIN
   AWAY FROM FOUNDATION. DO NOT CONNECT RAIN DRAINS TO FOUNDATION DRAINS.

3. CONCRETE EXPOSED TO WEATHER TO BE 3000 P.S.I.
   CONCRETE NOT EXPOSED TO WEATHER TO BE 2500 P.S.I.
   CONCRETE GARAGE SLABS TO BE 2500 P.S.I.
   ALL CONCRETE COMPRESSIVE STRENGTH MINIMUMS TO BE AT 28 DAYS.

4. ALL MUDSILLS TO BE 2 x 4 D.F.P.T. W/ ½"⏀ x 10" A.B. @ 6'-0" O.C. MAX.
   PROVIDE A MINIMUM OF TWO A.B. FOR EA. PLATE. EXTEND 7" MINIMUM INTO CONCRETE
   AND PROVIDE 2" ⏀ WASHERS. BOLTS TO BE 12" MAX. FROM CORNERS.

5. SLOPE ALL GRADES AWAY FROM FOUNDATION
   FOR 60" MINIMUM.

© 2011 Cengage Learning. All Rights Reserved. May not be scanned, copied or duplicated, or posted to a publicly accessible website, in whole or in part.

Problem 35–8

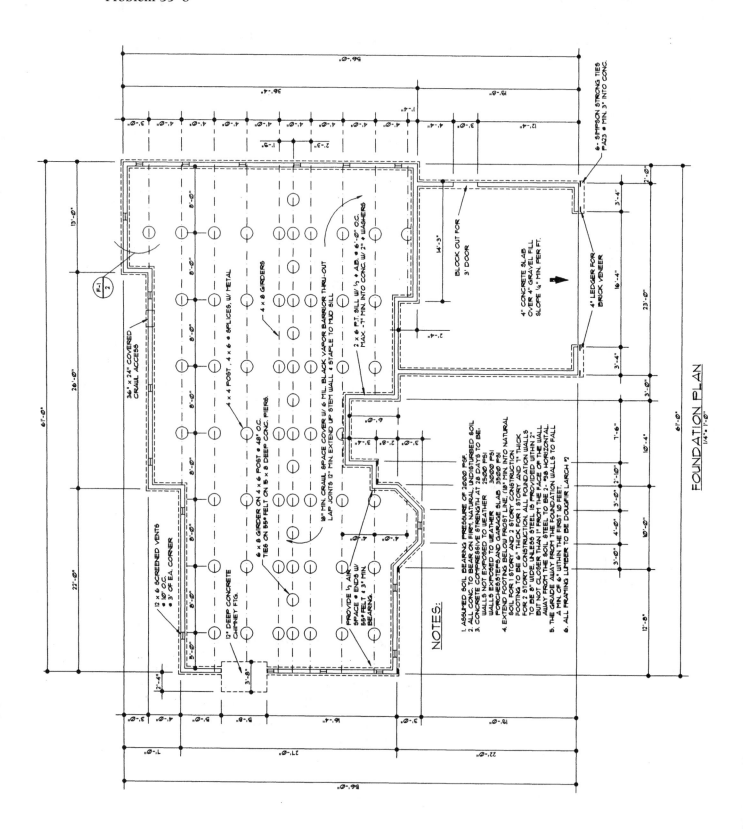

FOUNDATION PLAN
1/4" = 1'-0"

NOTES:
1. ASSUMED SOIL BEARING PRESSURE OF 2000 PSF.
2. ALL CONC. TO BEAR ON FIRM, NATURAL, UNDISTURBED SOIL.
3. CONCRETE COMPRESSIVE STRENGTH AT 28 DAYS TO BE:
   WALLS NOT EXPOSED TO WEATHER   2500 PSI
   WALLS EXPOSED TO WEATHER   3000 PSI
   PORCHES, STEPS AND GARAGE SLAB   3500 PSI
4. EXTEND FOOTINGS BELOW FROST LINE, 18" MIN. INTO NATURAL
   SOIL FOR 1 STORY AND 2 STORY CONSTRUCTION
   FOOTING TO BE 6" THICK FOR 1 STORY AND 11" THICK
   FOR 2 STORY CONSTRUCTION. ALL FOUNDATION WALLS
   TO BE 8" WIDE UNLESS STEEL IS PROVIDED WITHIN 2"
   BUT NOT CLOSER THAN 1" FROM THE FACE OF THE WALL
5. THE GRADE AWAY FROM THE FOUNDATION WALLS TO FALL
   A MIN. OF 6" WITHIN THE FIRST 10 FEET.
6. ALL FRAMING LUMBER TO BE DOUGFIR LARCH 2

© 2011 Cengage Learning. All Rights Reserved. May not be scanned, copied or duplicated, or posted to a publicly accessible website, in whole or in part.

Problem 35–9

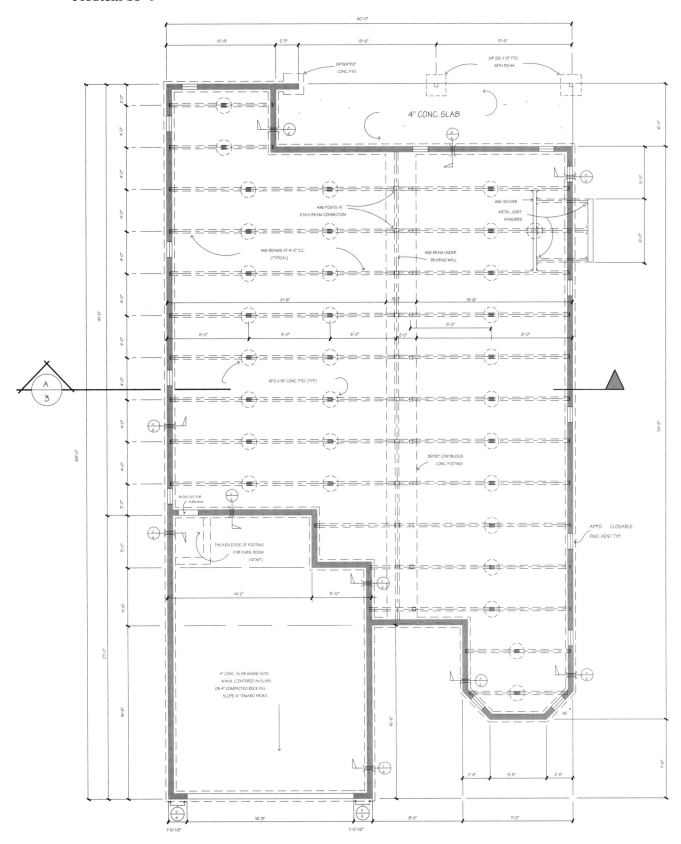

FOUNDATION PLAN

SCALE 1/4" = 1'-0"

© 2011 Cengage Learning. All Rights Reserved. May not be scanned, copied or duplicated, or posted to a publicly accessible website, in whole or in part.

Problem 35–10

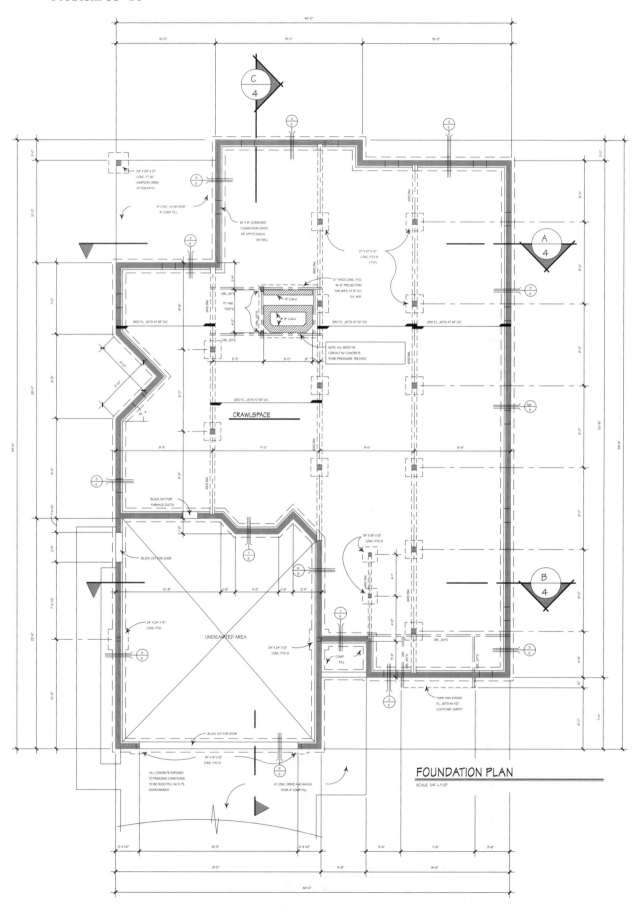

CRAWLSPACE

UNEXCAVATED AREA

FOUNDATION PLAN

SCALE 1/4" = 1'-0"

© 2011 Cengage Learning. All Rights Reserved. May not be scanned, copied or duplicated, or posted to a publicly accessible website, in whole or in part.

Problem 35–11

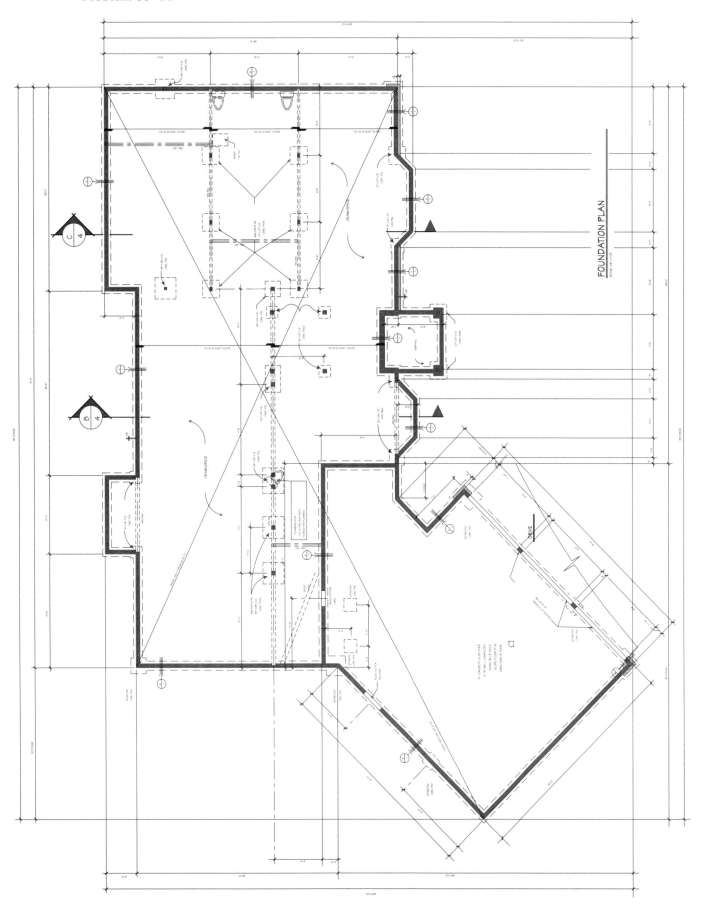

© 2011 Cengage Learning. All Rights Reserved. May not be scanned, copied or duplicated, or posted to a publicly accessible website, in whole or in part.

Problem 35–12

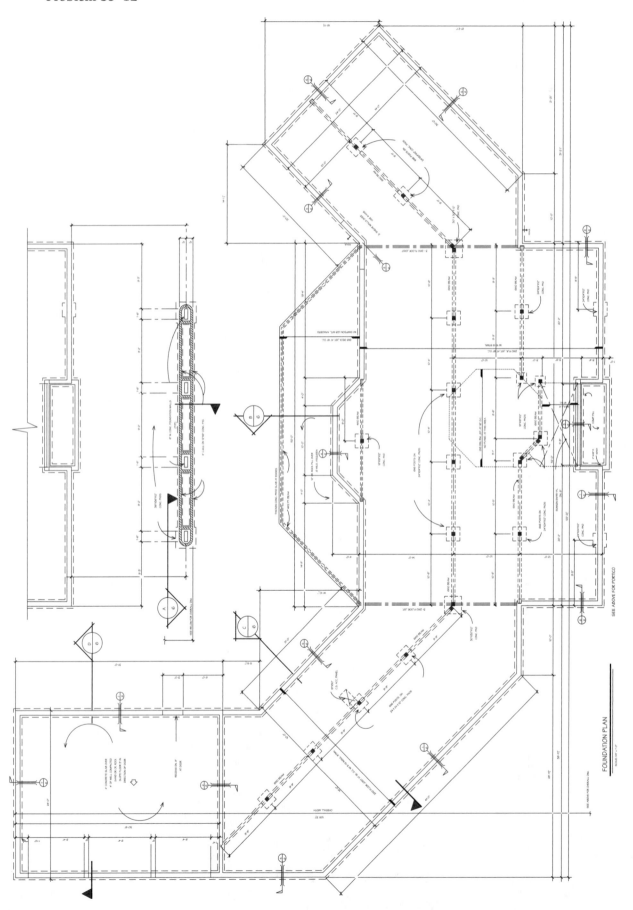

© 2011 Cengage Learning. All Rights Reserved. May not be scanned, copied or duplicated, or posted to a publicly accessible website, in whole or in part.

Problem 35–13

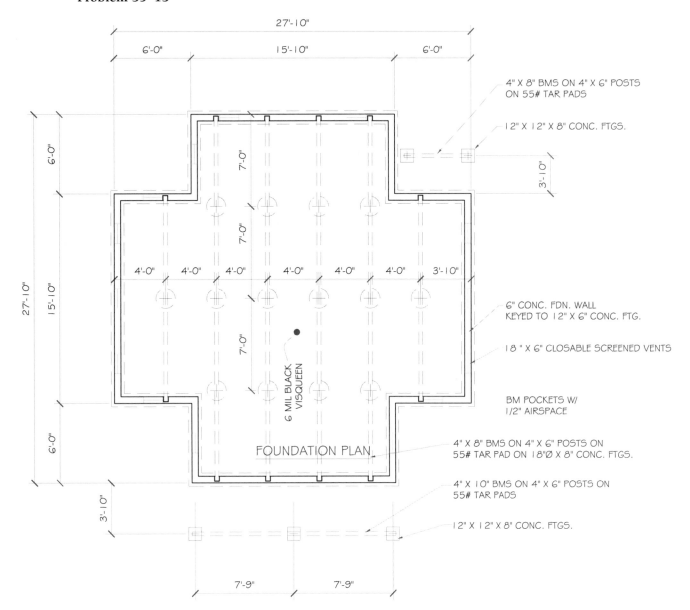

4" X 8" BMS ON 4" X 6" POSTS
ON 55# TAR PADS

12" X 12" X 8" CONC. FTGS.

6" CONC. FDN. WALL
KEYED TO 12" X 6" CONC. FTG.

18 " X 6" CLOSABLE SCREENED VENTS

BM POCKETS W/
1/2" AIRSPACE

4" X 8" BMS ON 4" X 6" POSTS ON
55# TAR PAD ON 18"Ø X 8" CONC. FTGS.

4" X 10" BMS ON 4" X 6" POSTS ON
55# TAR PADS

12" X 12" X 8" CONC. FTGS.

6 MIL BLACK VISQUEEN

FOUNDATION PLAN

© 2011 Cengage Learning. All Rights Reserved. May not be scanned, copied or duplicated, or posted to a publicly accessible website, in whole or in part.

Problem 35–14

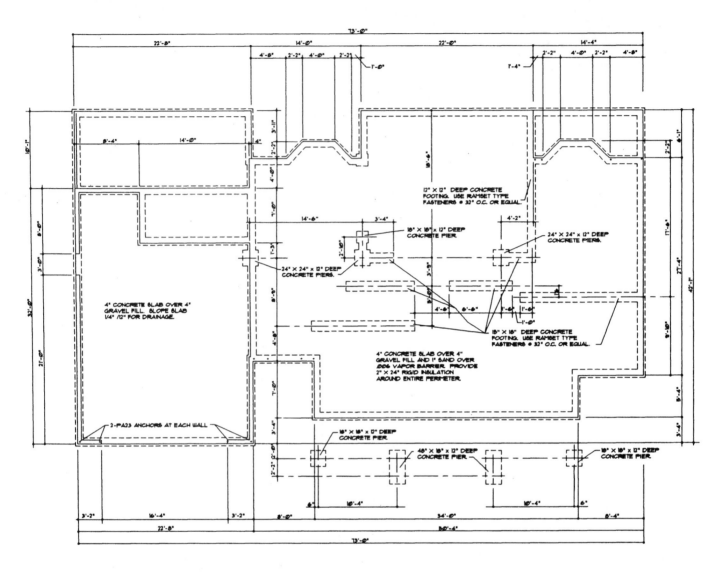

FOUNDATION PLAN
1/4" = 1'-0"

CONCRETE NOTES: SEE UPPER FRAMING PLAN
FOR ALL FRAMING SPECIFICATIONS

1. EXTEND FOOTINGS 12" MIN. INTO NATURAL SOIL.

2. PROVIDE 4" ∅ FOUNDATION DRAIN AROUND PERIMETER OF FOUNDATION AND SLOPE TO DRAIN
AWAY FROM FOUNDATION. DO NOT CONNECT RAIN DRAINS TO FOUNDATION DRAINS.

3. CONCRETE EXPOSED TO WEATHER TO BE 3000 P.S.I.
CONCRETE NOT EXPOSED TO WEATHER TO BE 2500 P.S.I.
CONCRETE GARAGE SLABS TO BE 2500 P.S.I.
ALL CONCRETE COMPRESSIVE STRENGTH MINIMUMS TO BE AT 28 DAYS.

4. ALL MUDSILLS TO BE 2 x 4 D.F.P.T. W/ ½"∅ x 10" A.B. @ 6'-0" O.C. MAX.
PROVIDE A MINIMUM OF TWO A.B. FOR EA. PLATE. EXTEND 7" MINIMUM INTO CONCRETE
AND PROVIDE 2" ∅ WASHERS. BOLTS TO BE 12" MAX. FROM CORNERS.

5. SLOPE ALL GRADES AWAY FROM FOUNDATION
FOR 60" MINIMUM.

© 2011 Cengage Learning. All Rights Reserved. May not be scanned, copied or duplicated, or posted to a publicly accessible website, in whole or in part.

Problem 35–15

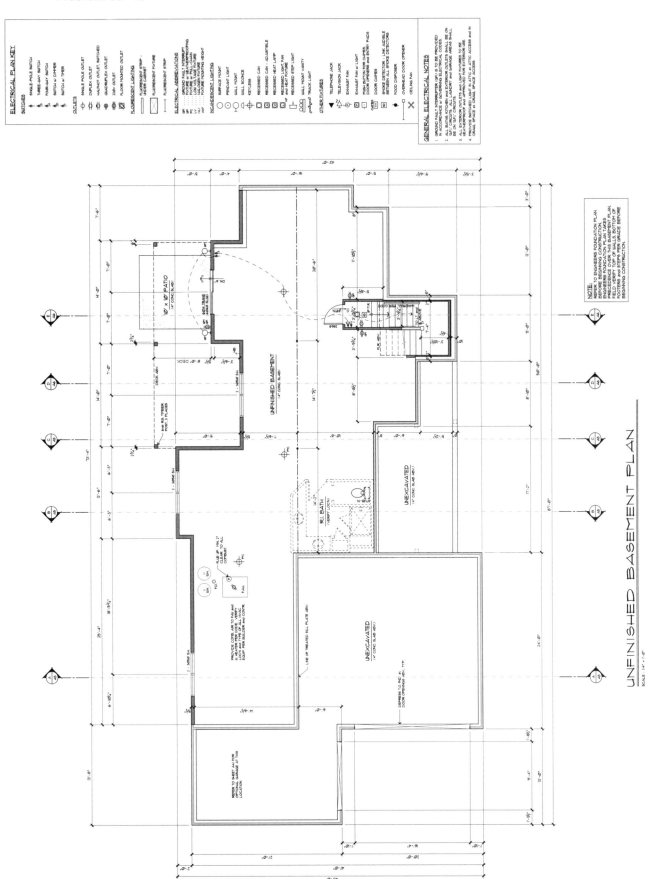

UNFINISHED BASEMENT PLAN

SCALE 1/4" = 1'-0"

© 2011 Cengage Learning. All Rights Reserved. May not be scanned, copied or duplicated, or posted to a publicly accessible website, in whole or in part.

Problem 35–16

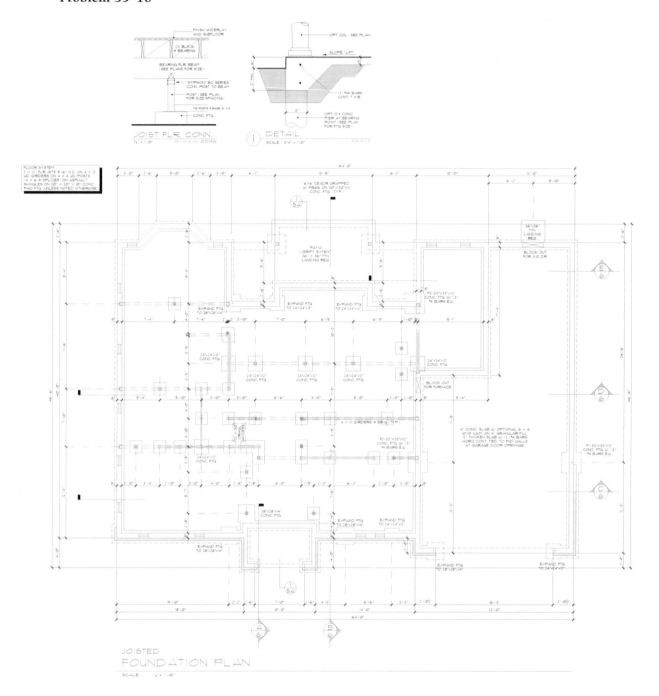

JOIST FLR. CONN.

DETAIL
SCALE 3/4" = 1'-0"

JOISTED
FOUNDATION PLAN
SCALE 1/2" = 1'-0"

© 2011 Cengage Learning. All Rights Reserved. May not be scanned, copied or duplicated, or posted to a publicly accessible website, in whole or in part.

Problem 35–17

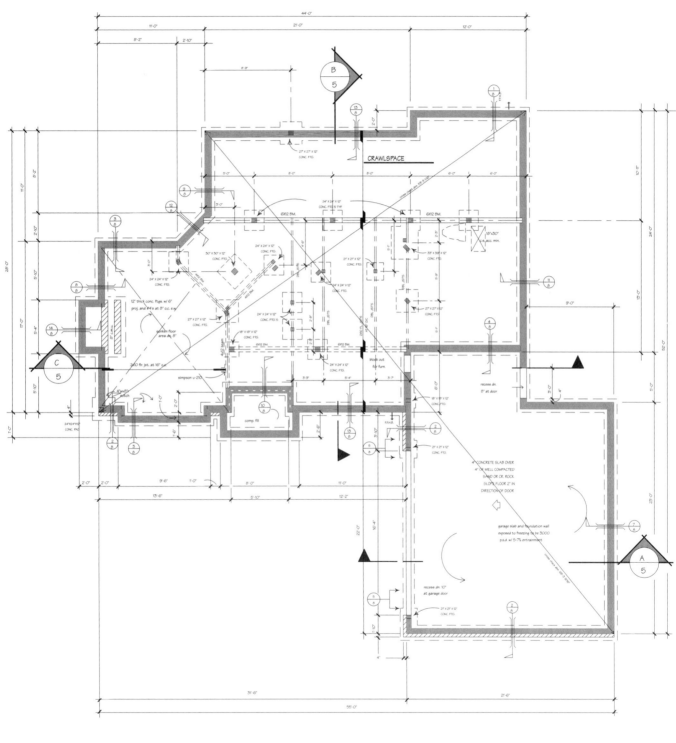

FOUNDATION PLAN
SCALE 1/4" = 1'-0"

© 2011 Cengage Learning. All Rights Reserved. May not be scanned, copied or duplicated, or posted to a publicly accessible website, in whole or in part.

Problem 35–18

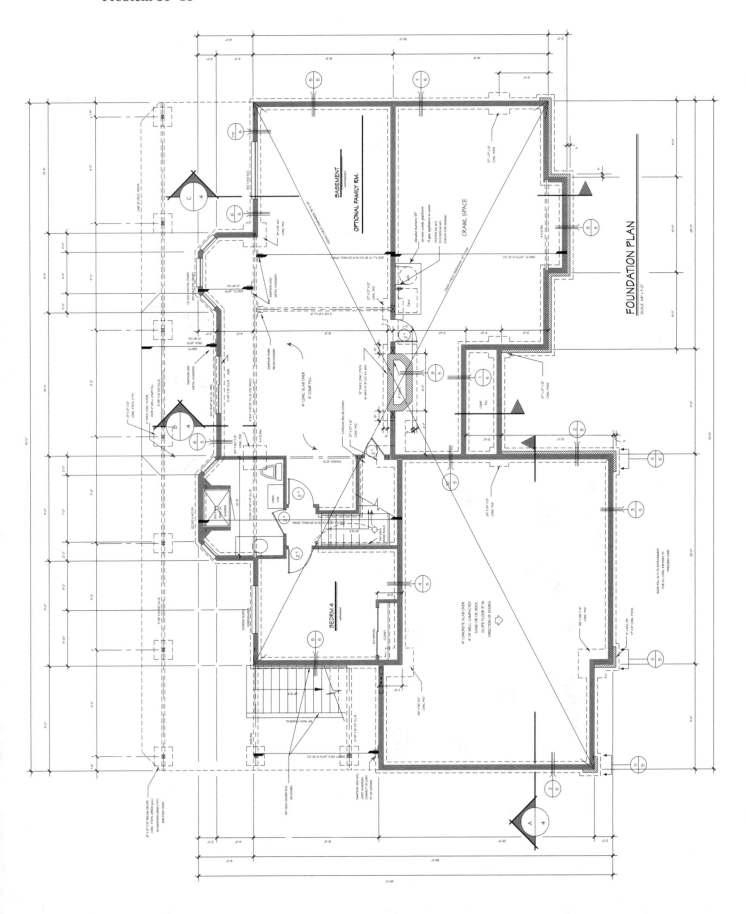

© 2011 Cengage Learning. All Rights Reserved. May not be scanned, copied or duplicated, or posted to a publicly accessible website, in whole or in part.

Problem 35–19

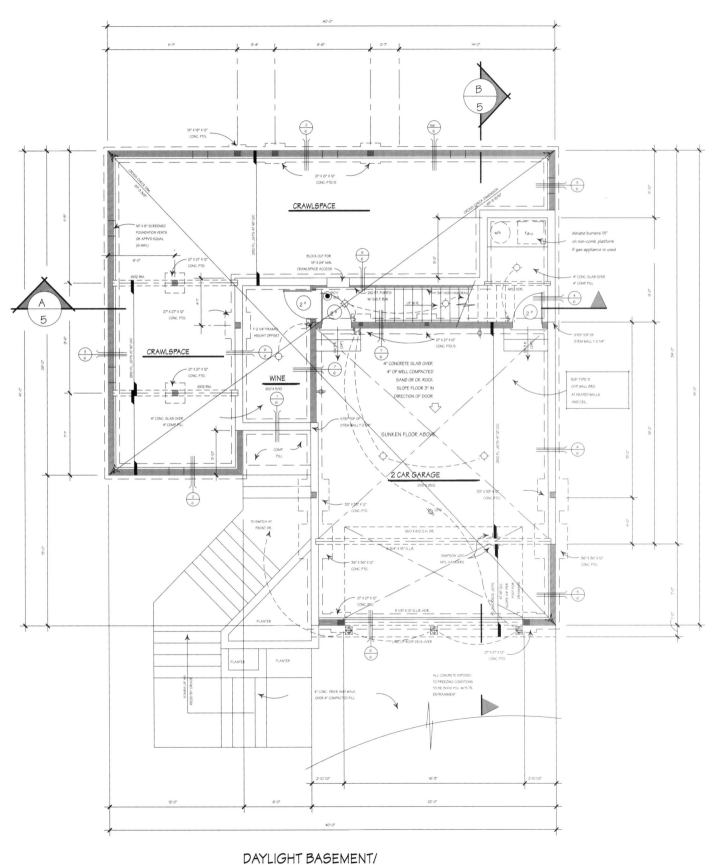

DAYLIGHT BASEMENT/
FOUNDATION PLAN

SCALE 1/4" = 1'-0"   FIN. BSMT. 21 SQ. FT.

© 2011 Cengage Learning. All Rights Reserved. May not be scanned, copied or duplicated, or posted to a publicly accessible website, in whole or in part.

Problem 35–20

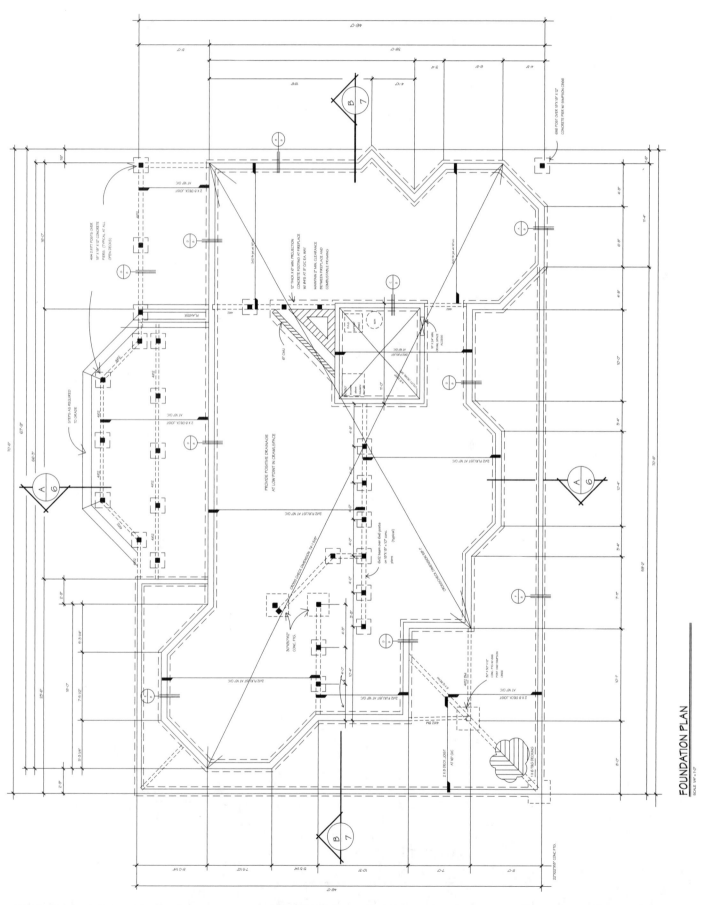

FOUNDATION PLAN
SCALE 1/4" = 1'-0"

© 2011 Cengage Learning. All Rights Reserved. May not be scanned, copied or duplicated, or posted to a publicly accessible website, in whole or in part.

Problem 35–21

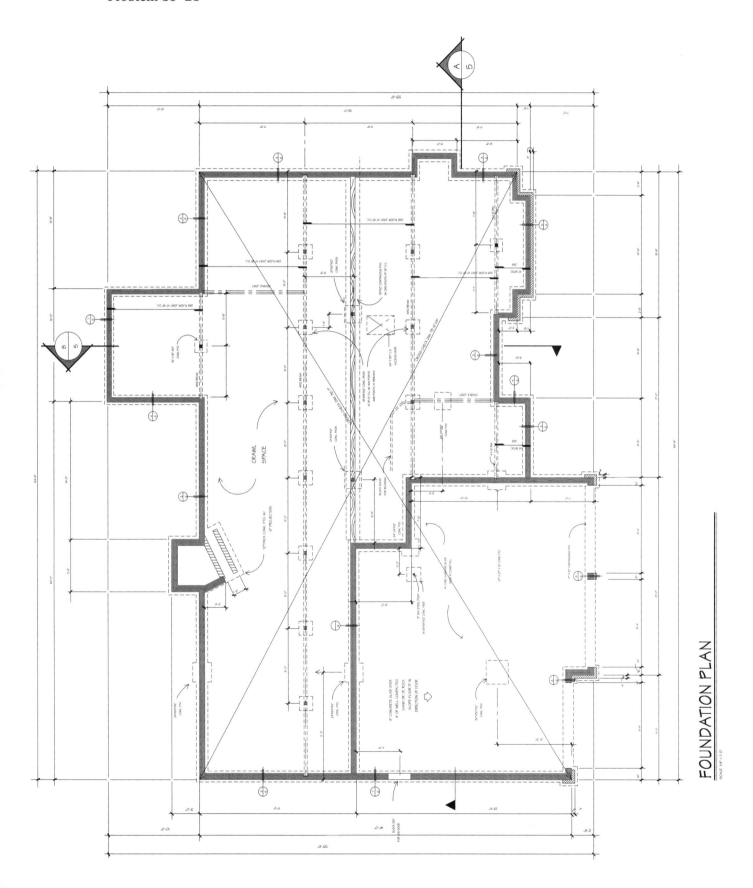

FOUNDATION PLAN

SCALE 1/4" = 1'-0"

© 2011 Cengage Learning. All Rights Reserved. May not be scanned, copied or duplicated, or posted to a publicly accessible website, in whole or in part.

Problem 35–22

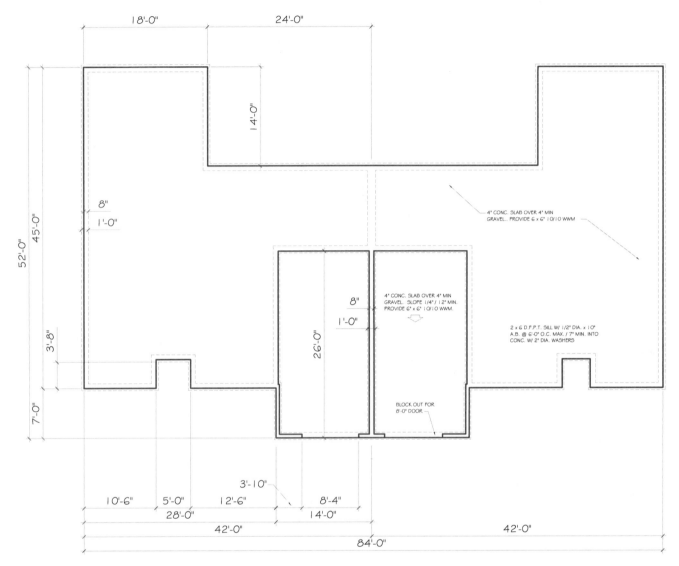

FOUNDATION PLAN

1/4" ========= 1'-0"

NOTE: ALL TEXT & DIMENSIONS
ARE TYPICAL BOTH SIDES

GENERAL CONCRETE NOTES:

1. EXTEND 1 STORY FOOTINGS 12" MIN. INTO NATURAL SOIL.

2. PROVIDE 4" Ø FND. DRAIN AROUND PERIMETER OF FND. AND SLOPE TO DRAIN
   AWAY FROM FND. DO NOT CONNECT RAIN DRAINS TO FOUNDATION DRAINS.

3. CONCRETE EXPOSED TO WEATHER TO BE 3000 P.S.I.
   CONCRETE NOT EXPOSED TO WEATHER TO BE 2500 P.S.I.
   CONCRETE GARAGE SLABS TO BE 2500 P.S.I.
   ALL CONCRETE COMPRESSIVE STRENGTH MINIMUMS TO BE AT 28 DAYS.

4. ALL MUDSILLS TO BE DFPT W/ 1/2" Ø x 10" A.B. (SEE PLAN FOR SPACING).
   PROVIDE A MINIMUM OF TWO A.B. FOR EA. PLATE W/ ONE BOLT LOCATED NOT MORE
   THAN 12" OR MORE THAN 7 BOLT DIAMETERS FROM EACH END OF EACH PLATE PIECE.
   PROVIDE 2" Ø WAHERS AT EACH BOLT.

5. SLOPE ALL GRADES AWAY FROM FOUNDATION FOR 60" MINIMUM.

© 2011 Cengage Learning. All Rights Reserved. May not be scanned, copied or duplicated, or posted to a publicly accessible website, in whole or in part.

SECTION 10

Wall Sections and Details

CHAPTER 36
SECTIONING BASICS

OBJECTIVES

When students have completed this chapter, they will:

- Explain the relationship of the viewing plan shown on the floor plan and the resulting section.
- Describe drawing methods for five different types of sections.
- Know common scales that each type of section is typically drawn at.
- Know how, and be able to represent various building materials using methods appropriate to the drawing scale.
- Demonstrate appropriate methods for placing annotation and dimensions on each type of section drawing.

TEST ANSWERS

1. A section that cuts through the entire structure using either transverse or longitudinal methods
2. To supplement a full section, showing a typical construction
3. A drawing of a typical item such as a footing or a chimney that has minor variations from job to job that is used to save time
4. Floor, framing, foundation, grading, and roof plans
5. 3/8" = 1'-0"
6. The amount of information to be placed in the drawing, the complexity of the drawing, available space
7. The cutting plane shows where an imaginary cut is made in the structure to allow the internal parts to be seen. The cutting plane on the framing plan shows which way the section is being viewed.
8. Either toward the top or the left side of the plan
9. A supplemental section that will not need to show much detail other than the shape of the structure
10. Size of the drawing material, size of the project, the purpose of the drawing, and the amount of space for the placement of the drawing

CHAPTER 36 PROBLEM SOLUTIONS

Chapter 36 of the textbook contains no problems.

© 2011 Cengage Learning. All Rights Reserved. May not be scanned, copied or duplicated, or posted to a publicly accessible website, in whole or in part.

CHAPTER 37
SECTION LAYOUT

OBJECTIVES

When students have completed this chapter, they will:

- Evaluate what sections need to be drawn to describe the structure.
- Lay out the structural elements of a section showing a concrete slab floor with the finish line quality used to draw a section.
- Draw nonstructural members using approperiate line quality.
- Be familiar with dimensions and lettering techniques used to complete a section.
- Evaluate his or her work for quality and accuracy.

TEST ANSWERS

1. a. A rafter is the inclined roof support member used to support the weight of the roofing material.
   b. A roof component, typically premanufactured away from the job site, consisting of top and bottom chords, which are tied together with web members
   c. Horizontal ceiling support members used to resist the outward thrust of the rafters
   d. Horizontal support members, typically placed in the upper one-third of the attic to resist the outward thrust of the rafters.
   e. A wall member that is not full height, often called a cripple
   f. The joist that runs perpendicular to the floor joists at their ends to provide a nailing surface for the siding, and to keep the floor joist from rolling over
   g. The top and bottom members of a truss, which would correspond to a rafter or ceiling joist in stick construction
   h. A covering applied in sheets, typically 4' × 8', to floors, walls, and roofs

2.

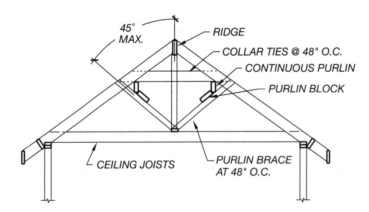

45° MAX.
RIDGE
COLLAR TIES @ 48" O.C.
CONTINUOUS PURLIN
PURLIN BLOCK
CEILING JOISTS
PURLIN BRACE AT 48" O.C.

3. a. 2 × 6
   b. 88 5/8" or 92 5/8"
   c. 1/2" × 4' × 8' sheets
   d. 3/8" × 4' × 8' or 1/2" × 4' × 8' sheets
   e. 2 × 6s, 2 × 8s or 1 1/8" plywood decking
   f. 3/8"

© 2011 Cengage Learning. All Rights Reserved. May not be scanned, copied or duplicated, or posted to a publicly accessible website, in whole or in part.

4. 3/8" = 1'-0" best for full sections

     1/4" = 1'-0" good for partial sections

     1/8" = 1'-0" good for showing the shape of a structure

5. a. evaluate needs

     b. layout the section

     c. finished quality lines (darken all structural members)

     d. draw all finishing materials

     e. dimension

     f. lettering notes

     g. evaluate your work

6. Foundation details, chimney construction, standard connections

CHAPTER 37 PROBLEM SOLUTIONS

Chapter 37 of the textbook contains no problems.

CHAPTER 38
ALTERNATIVE LAYOUT TECHNIQUES

OBJECTIVES

When students have completed this chapter, they will:

*   Be able to draw the components required for floor joists, post-and-beam, and basement foundations systems.
*   Be able to draw the components required to draw stick and vaulted roof systems.

TEST ANSWERS

1. Drawing should be similar to the right portion of Figure 38–11 in the text.
2. 2" (1/8" Ply)
3. Thick lines
4. Very bold lines
5. 0.006
6. 6" IRC. (8" for most lending institutions)
7. 8"
8. Seismic zone and the wall height
9. Solid block 48" O.C.– 48" out from wall where floor joists are parallel to the wall
10. See Figure 28–47 in the text.

© 2011 Cengage Learning. All Rights Reserved. May not be scanned, copied or duplicated, or posted to a publicly accessible website, in whole or in part.

11.
1. Roof sheathing
2. Top chord
3. Baffles
4. Hurricane tie
5. Solid blocking
6. Fascia
7. Gutter
8. Studs
9. Sheathing

10. Siding
11. Insulation
12. Sill
13. Mudsill
14. Finish grade
15. Key way
16. Foundation
17. Vapor barrier
18. Insulation

19. Sheetrock
20. Top plates
21. Interior finish
22. Anchor bolt
23. Floor sheathing
24. Floor decking
25. Crawl space

12.
1. Rafter
2. Plywood sheathing
3. Baffle
4. Solid blocking
5. Eave
6. Insulation (or studs)
7. Exterior sheathing
8. Exterior siding
9. Sill

10. Rim joist or blocking
11. Mudsill
12. Stemwall
13. Finish grade
14. Key way
15. Footing
16. Insulation
17. Ceiling joists
18. Finish ceiling

19. Top plates
20. Interior wall finish
21. Studs (or insulation)
22. Hardboard overlay
23. Floor sheathing or sub floor
24. Floor joists
25. Insulation
26. Vapor barrier

CHAPTER 38 PROBLEM SOLUTIONS

Students should use the information from the floor plan, roof plan, foundation plan, framing plans, and the elevations for the residence started in Chapter 18 to draw the appropriate sections. Student solutions will vary, but should resemble the following solutions.

38–4, 38–5, 38–6, 38–7, and 38–14 The solutions provided can be used to provide for concrete slab or joist foundations for several framing methods for the wall and roof. Student solutions will vary depending on climatic conditions, but should resemble the drawings shown on the following pages.

© 2011 Cengage Learning. All Rights Reserved. May not be scanned, copied or duplicated, or posted to a publicly accessible website, in whole or in part.

Problem 38–1A

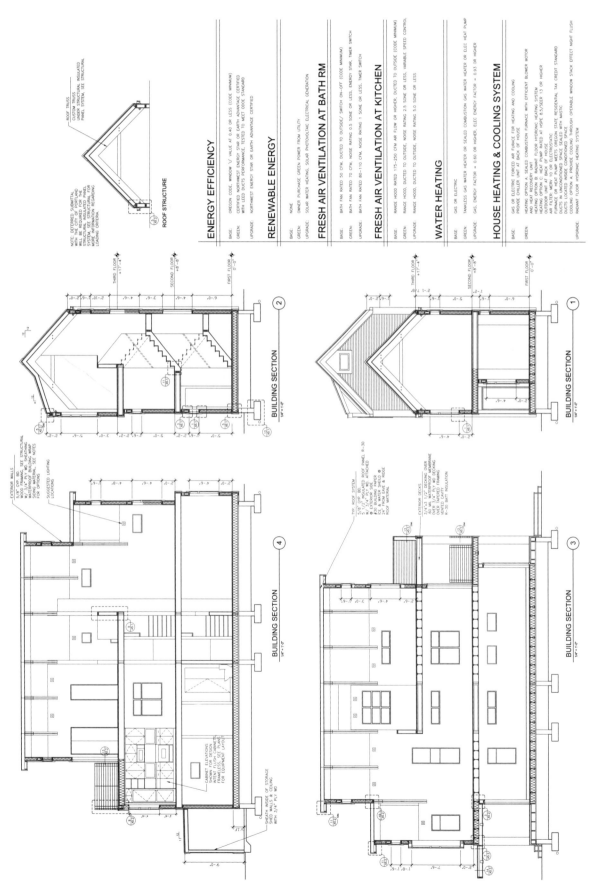

© 2011 Cengage Learning. All Rights Reserved. May not be scanned, copied or duplicated, or posted to a publicly accessible website, in whole or in part.

Problem 38–1B

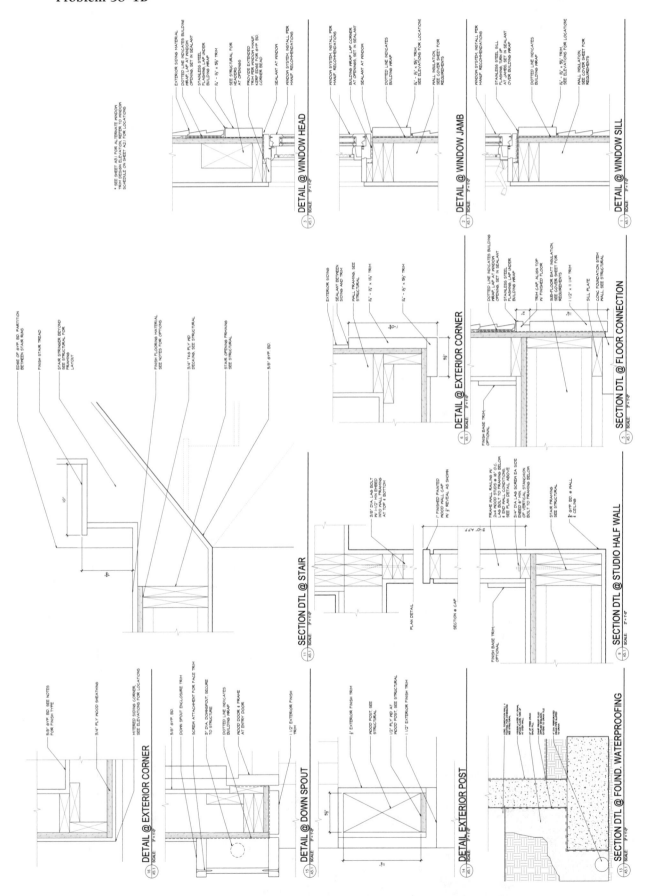

© 2011 Cengage Learning. All Rights Reserved. May not be scanned, copied or duplicated, or posted to a publicly accessible website, in whole or in part.

Problem 38–1C

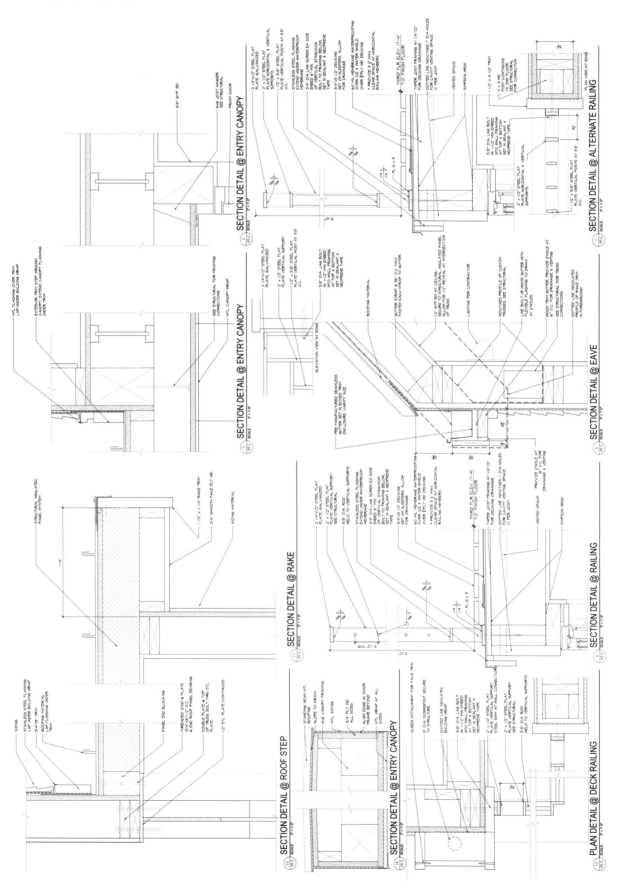

© 2011 Cengage Learning. All Rights Reserved. May not be scanned, copied or duplicated, or posted to a publicly accessible website, in whole or in part.

Problem 38–2A

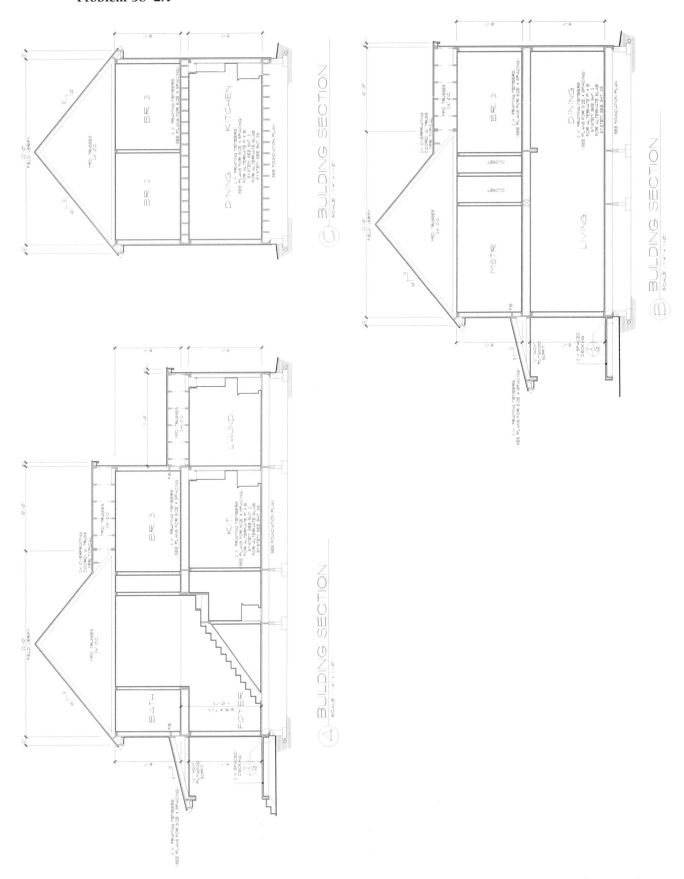

© 2011 Cengage Learning. All Rights Reserved. May not be scanned, copied or duplicated, or posted to a publicly accessible website, in whole or in part.

Problem 38–2B

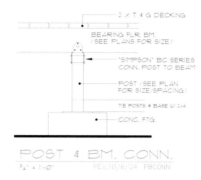

2 × T & G DECKING

BEARING FLR. BM.
(SEE PLANS FOR SIZE)

'SIMPSON' BC SERIES
CONN. POST TO BEAM

POST (SEE PLAN
FOR SIZE/SPACING)

TIE POSTS @ BASE W/ 2×4

CONC. FTG.

POST & BM. CONN.

³⁄₄" = 1'-0"   REV.10/6/04   PBCONN

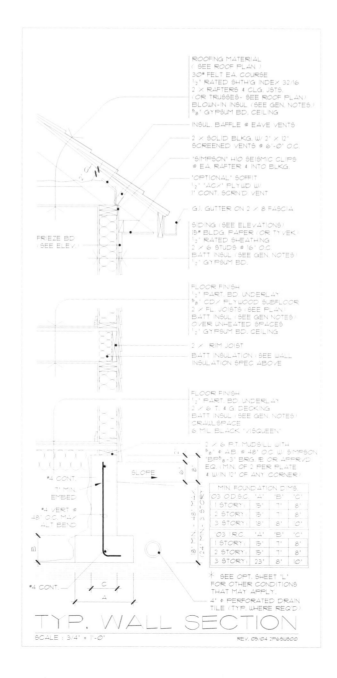

ROOFING MATERIAL
(SEE ROOF PLAN)
30# FELT EA. COURSE
½" RATED SHTH'G INDEX 32/16
2 × RAFTERS & CLG. JSTS.
(OR TRUSSES- SEE ROOF PLAN)
BLOWN-IN INSUL (SEE GEN. NOTES)
⅝" GYPSUM BD. CEILING

INSUL. BAFFLE @ EAVE VENTS

2 × SOLID BLKG. W/ 2" × 12"
SCREENED VENTS @ 6'-0" O.C.

'SIMPSON' H10 SEISMIC CLIPS
@ EA. RAFTER & INTO BLKG.

'OPTIONAL' SOFFIT
½" 'ACX' PLYWD W/
1" CONT. SCRN'D VENT

G.I. GUTTER ON 2 × 8 FASCIA

SIDING (SEE ELEVATIONS)
15# BLDG. PAPER (OR TYVEK)
½" RATED SHEATHING
2 × 6 STUDS @ 16" O.C.
BATT INSUL (SEE GEN. NOTES)
½" GYPSUM BD.

FREIZE BD
(SEE ELEV.)

FLOOR FINISH
½" PART. BD. UNDERLAY
⅝" CDX PLYWOOD SUBFLOOR
2 × FL JOISTS (SEE PLAN)
BATT INSUL (SEE GEN NOTES)
OVER UNHEATED SPACES
½" GYPSUM BD. CEILING

2 × RIM JOIST

BATT INSULATION (SEE WALL
INSULATION SPEC ABOVE

FLOOR FINISH
½" PART. BD. UNDERLAY
2 × 6 T. & G. DECKING
BATT INSUL (SEE GEN. NOTES)
CRAWLSPACE
6 MIL BLACK 'VISQUEEN'

2 × 6 P.T. MUDSILL WITH
⅝" Ø AB @ 48" O.C. W/ SIMPSON
'BP⅝-3' BRG. PL OR APPR'D
EQ. (MIN. OF 2 PER PLATE
& W/IN 12" OF ANY CORNER)

SLOPE

#4 CONT.
7" MIN.
EMBED

#4 VERT @
48" O.C. MAX
ALT. BEND

#4 CONT.

MIN. FOUNDATION DIM'S.			
03 O.D.S.C.	'A'	'B'	'C'
1 STORY	15"	7"	8"
2 STORY	15"	7"	8"
3 STORY	18"	8"	10"

03 IRC.	'A'	'B'	'C'
1 STORY	15"	7"	8"
2 STORY	15"	7"	8"
3 STORY	23"	8"	10"

✳ SEE OPT. SHEET 'L'
FOR OTHER CONDITIONS
THAT MAY APPLY.

4" Ø PERFORATED DRAIN
TILE (TYP. WHERE REQ'D)

TYP. WALL SECTION

SCALE : 3/4" = 1'-0"   REV. 05/04 2P6BU800

© 2011 Cengage Learning. All Rights Reserved. May not be scanned, copied or duplicated, or posted to a publicly accessible website, in whole or in part.

Problem 38–3A

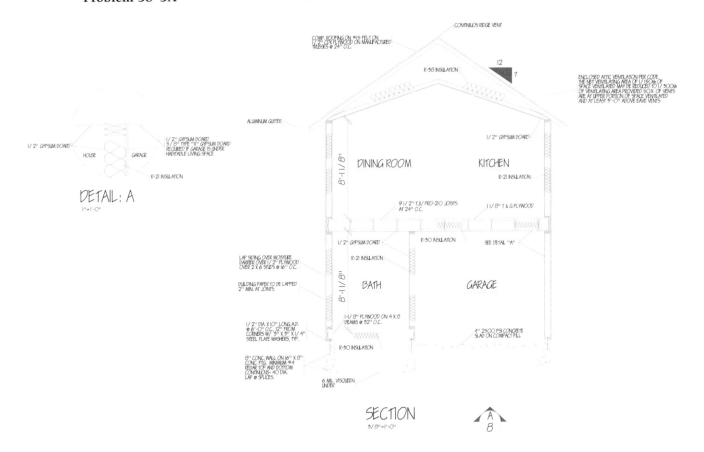

DETAIL: A

1"=1'-0"

1/2" GYPSUM BOARD

HOUSE   GARAGE

R-21 INSULATION

1/2" GYPSUM BOARD
5/8" TYPE "X" GYPSUM BOARD
REQUIRED IF GARAGE IS UNDER
HABITABLE LIVING SPACE

CONTINUOUS RIDGE VENT

COMP. ROOFING ON #15 FELT ON
1/2" CDX PLYWOOD ON MANUFACTURED
TRUSSES @ 24" O.C.

R-38 INSULATION

12
7

ENCLOSED ATTIC VENTILATION PER CODE.
THE NET VENTILATING AREA OF 1/150th OF
SPACE VENTILATED MAY BE REDUCED TO 1/300th
OF VENTILATING AREA PROVIDED 50% OF VENTS
ARE AT UPPER PORTION OF SPACE VENTILATED
AND AT LEAST 3'-0" ABOVE EAVE VENTS

ALUMINUM GUTTER

1/2" GYPSUM BOARD

DINING ROOM   KITCHEN

R-21 INSULATION

8'-11/8"

9 1/2" TJI PRO-210 JOISTS
AT 24" O.C.

1 1/8" T & G PLYWOOD

1/2" GYPSUM BOARD

R-30 INSULATION

SEE DETAIL "A"

LAP SIDING OVER MOISTURE
BARRIER OVER 1/2" PLYWOOD
OVER 2 X 6 STUDS @ 16" O.C.

BUILDING PAPER TO BE LAPPED
2" MIN. AT JOINTS.

R-21 INSULATION

BATH   GARAGE

8'-11/8"

1/2" DIA. X 10" LONG A.B.
@ 6'-0" O.C. 12" FROM
CORNERS W/ 3" X 3" X 1/4"
STEEL PLATE WASHERS, TYP.

1 1/8" PLYWOOD ON 4 X 8
BEAMS @ 32" O.C.

4" 2500 PSI CONCRETE
SLAB ON COMPACT FILL

8" CONC. WALL ON 16" X 8"
CONC. FTG. MINIMUM #4
REBAR TOP AND BOTTOM
CONTINUOUS. 40 DIA.
LAP @ SPLICES.

R-30 INSULATION

6 MIL. VISQUEEN
UNDER

SECTION

3/8"=1'-0"

A
8

© 2011 Cengage Learning. All Rights Reserved. May not be scanned, copied or duplicated, or posted to a publicly accessible website, in whole or in part.

Problem 38–3B

© 2011 Cengage Learning. All Rights Reserved. May not be scanned, copied or duplicated, or posted to a publicly accessible website, in whole or in part.

Problems 38–4, 38–5, 38–6, 38–7, and 38–14

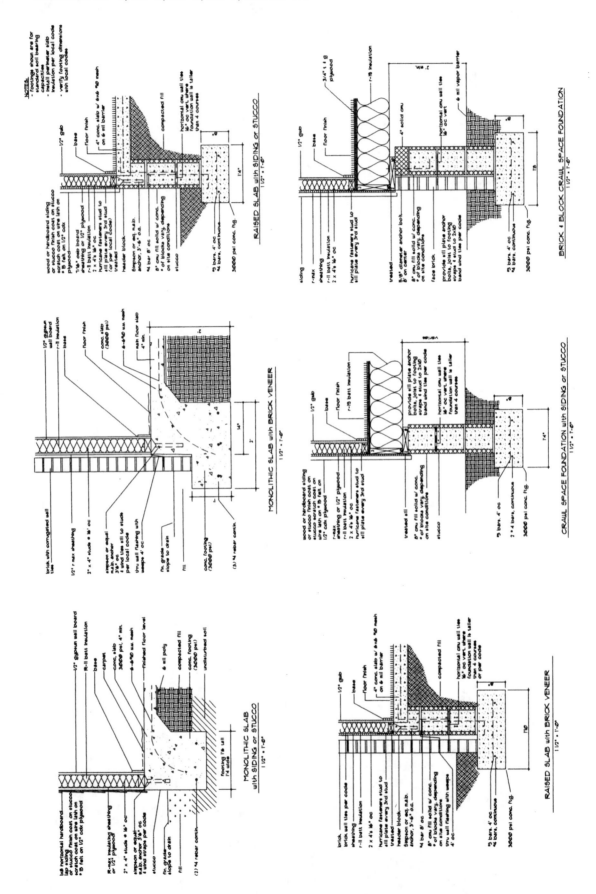

© 2011 Cengage Learning. All Rights Reserved. May not be scanned, copied or duplicated, or posted to a publicly accessible website, in whole or in part.

Problems 38–4, 38–5, 38–6, 38–7, and 38–14

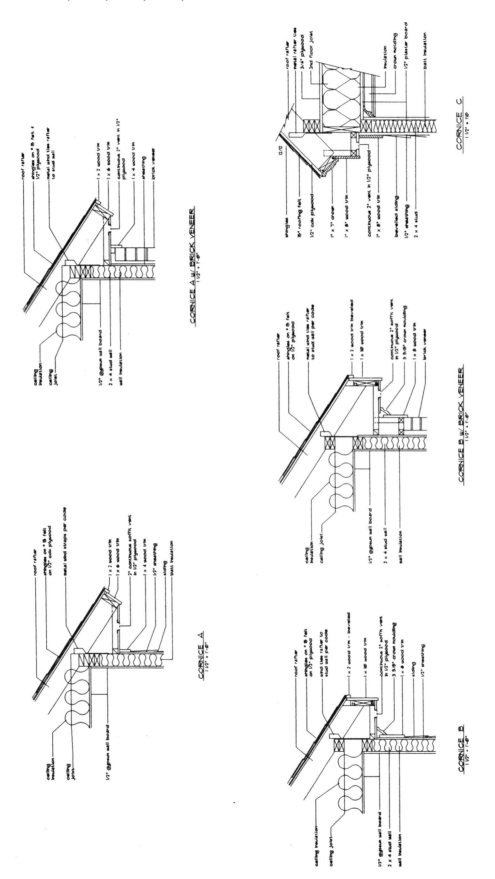

© 2011 Cengage Learning. All Rights Reserved. May not be scanned, copied or duplicated, or posted to a publicly accessible website, in whole or in part.

Problem 38–8

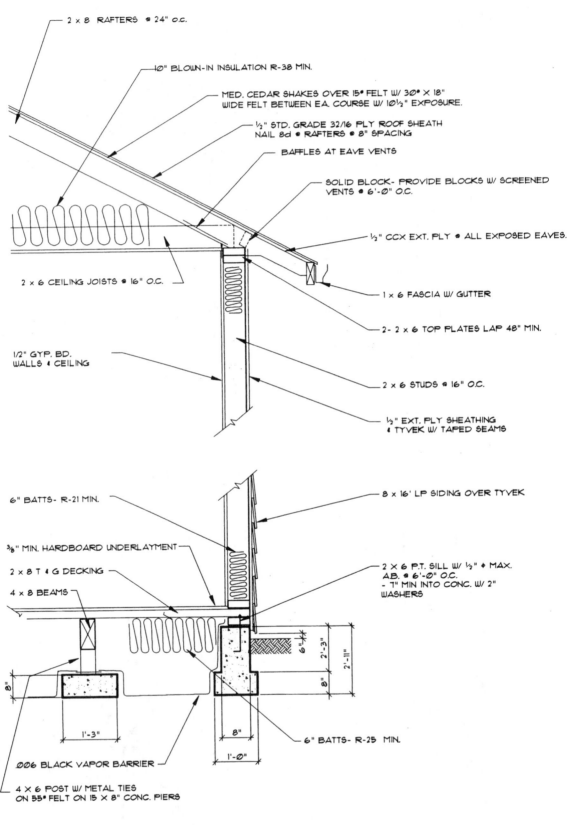

2 x 8 RAFTERS @ 24" o.c.

10" BLOWN-IN INSULATION R-38 MIN.

MED. CEDAR SHAKES OVER 15# FELT W/ 30° X 18" WIDE FELT BETWEEN EA. COURSE W/ 10½" EXPOSURE.

½" STD. GRADE 32/16 PLY ROOF SHEATH NAIL 8d @ RAFTERS @ 8" SPACING

BAFFLES AT EAVE VENTS

SOLID BLOCK- PROVIDE BLOCKS W/ SCREENED VENTS @ 6'-0" O.C.

½" CCX EXT. PLY @ ALL EXPOSED EAVES.

2 x 6 CEILING JOISTS @ 16" O.C.

1 x 6 FASCIA W/ GUTTER

2- 2 x 6 TOP PLATES LAP 48" MIN.

½" GYP. BD. WALLS & CEILING

2 x 6 STUDS @ 16" O.C.

½" EXT. PLY SHEATHING & TYVEK W/ TAPED SEAMS

6" BATTS- R-21 MIN.

8 x 16' LP SIDING OVER TYVEK

⅜" MIN. HARDBOARD UNDERLAYMENT

2 x 8 T & G DECKING

4 x 8 BEAMS

2 X 6 P.T. SILL W/ ½" ∅ MAX. A.B. @ 6'-0" O.C. - 7" MIN INTO CONC. W/ 2" WASHERS

6"

2'-3"

2'-11"

8"

8"

8"

1'-3"

8"

6" BATTS- R-25 MIN.

1'-0"

.006 BLACK VAPOR BARRIER

4 X 6 POST W/ METAL TIES ON 55# FELT ON 15 X 8" CONC. PIERS

F / 1 P-1 / 2 **DETAILS**

SCALE ¼" = 1'

© 2011 Cengage Learning. All Rights Reserved. May not be scanned, copied or duplicated, or posted to a publicly accessible website, in whole or in part.

Problem 38–9

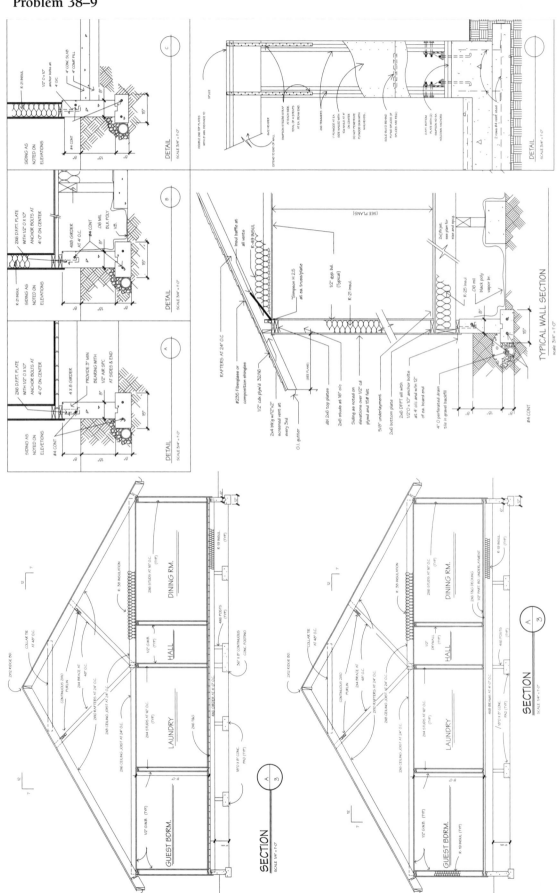

© 2011 Cengage Learning. All Rights Reserved. May not be scanned, copied or duplicated, or posted to a publicly accessible website, in whole or in part.

Problem 38–10

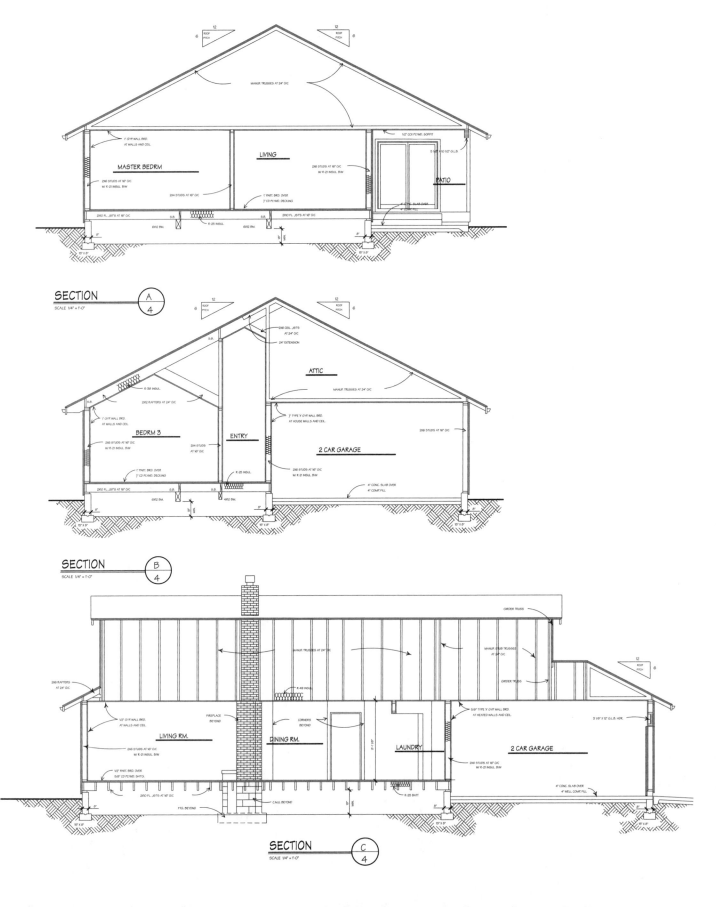

© 2011 Cengage Learning. All Rights Reserved. May not be scanned, copied or duplicated, or posted to a publicly accessible website, in whole or in part.

Problem 38–11A

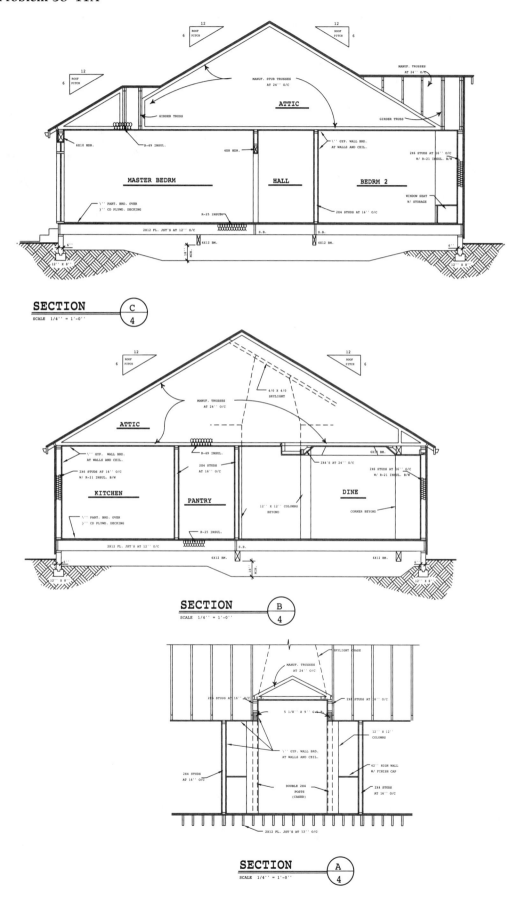

SECTION C / 4
SCALE 1/4'' = 1'-0''

SECTION B / 4
SCALE 1/4'' = 1'-0''

SECTION A / 4
SCALE 1/4'' = 1'-0''

© 2011 Cengage Learning. All Rights Reserved. May not be scanned, copied or duplicated, or posted to a publicly accessible website, in whole or in part.

Problem 38–11B

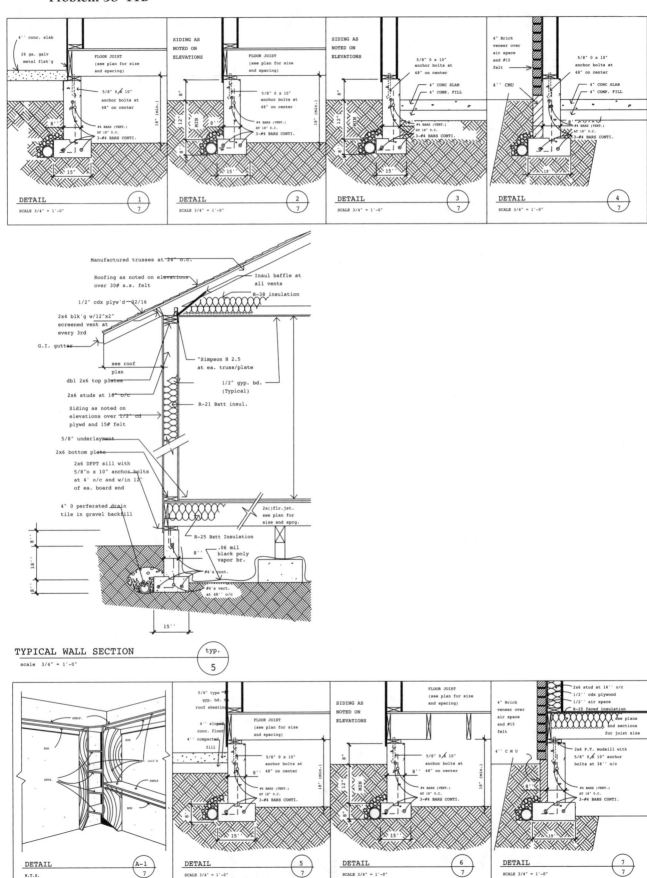

DETAIL 1/7 SCALE 3/4" = 1'-0"

DETAIL 2/7 SCALE 3/4" = 1'-0"

DETAIL 3/7 SCALE 3/4" = 1'-0"

DETAIL 4/7 SCALE 3/4" = 1'-0"

TYPICAL WALL SECTION typ. 5 scale 3/4" = 1'-0"

DETAIL A-1/7 N.T.S.

DETAIL 5/7 SCALE 3/4" = 1'-0"

DETAIL 6/7 SCALE 3/4" = 1'-0"

DETAIL 7/7 SCALE 3/4" = 1'-0"

© 2011 Cengage Learning. All Rights Reserved. May not be scanned, copied or duplicated, or posted to a publicly accessible website, in whole or in part.

Problem 38–12A

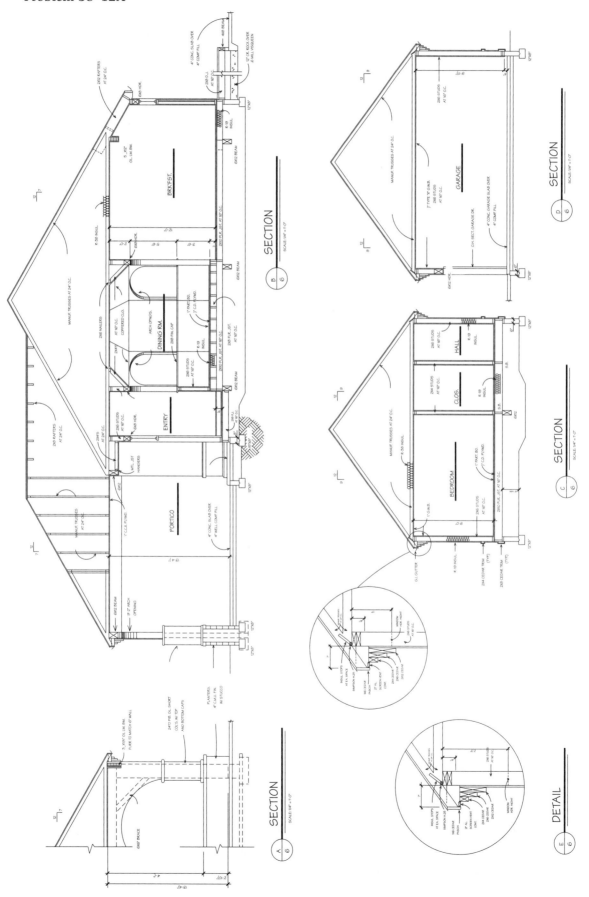

© 2011 Cengage Learning. All Rights Reserved. May not be scanned, copied or duplicated, or posted to a publicly accessible website, in whole or in part.

Problem 38–12B

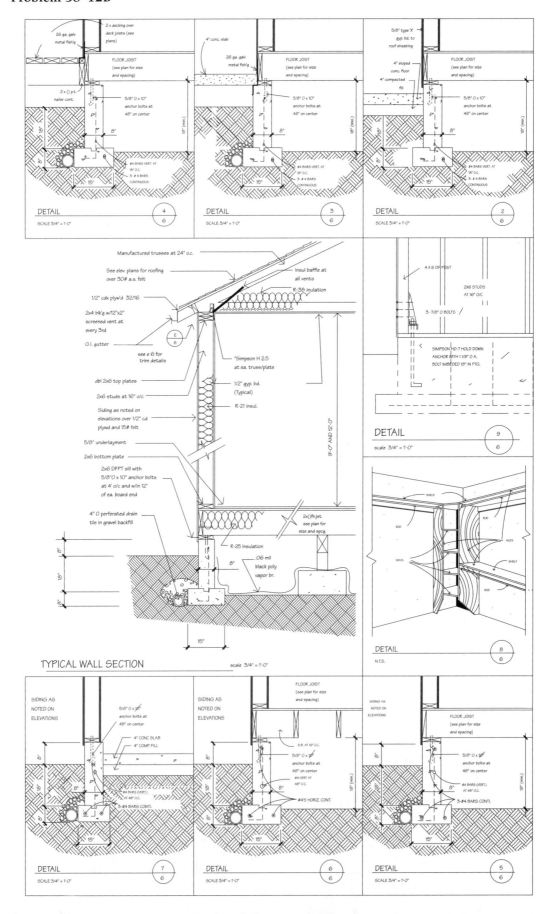

© 2011 Cengage Learning. All Rights Reserved. May not be scanned, copied or duplicated, or posted to a publicly accessible website, in whole or in part.

Problem 38–13A

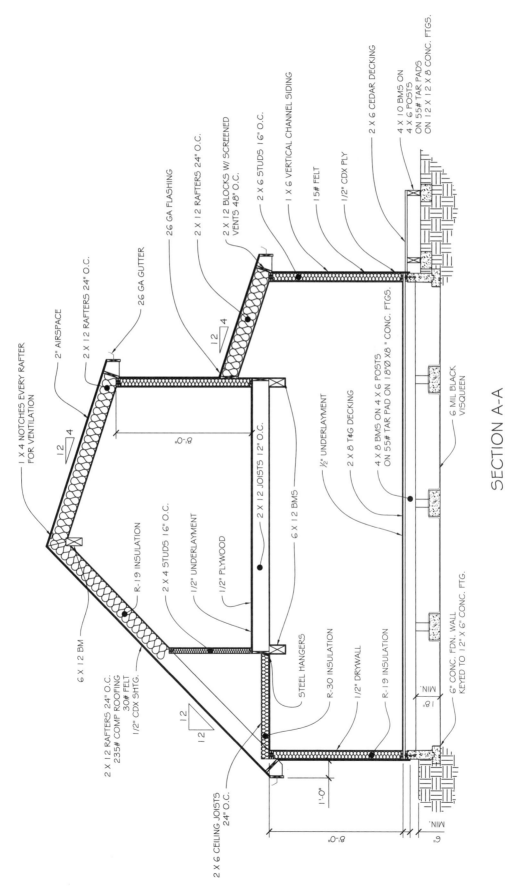

SECTION A-A

© 2011 Cengage Learning. All Rights Reserved. May not be scanned, copied or duplicated, or posted to a publicly accessible website, in whole or in part.

Problem 38–13B

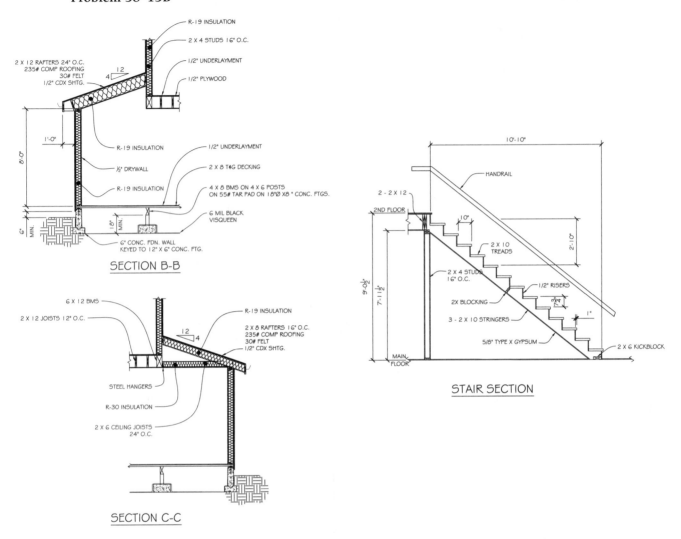

2 X 12 RAFTERS 24" O.C.
235# COMP ROOFING
30# FELT
1/2" CDX SHTG.

R-19 INSULATION

2 X 4 STUDS 16" O.C.

1/2" UNDERLAYMENT

1/2" PLYWOOD

12
4

1'-0"

8'-0"

6"
MIN.

R-19 INSULATION

½" DRYWALL

R-19 INSULATION

18" MIN.

6" CONC. FDN. WALL
KEYED TO 12" X 6" CONC. FTG.

1/2" UNDERLAYMENT

2 X 8 T&G DECKING

4 X 8 BMS ON 4 X 6 POSTS
ON 55# TAR PAD ON 18"Ø X8 " CONC. FTGS.

6 MIL BLACK
VISQUEEN

SECTION B-B

6 X 12 BMS

2 X 12 JOISTS 12" O.C.

12
4

R-19 INSULATION

2 X 8 RAFTERS 16" O.C.
235# COMP ROOFING
30# FELT
1/2" CDX SHTG.

STEEL HANGERS

R-30 INSULATION

2 X 6 CEILING JOISTS
24" O.C.

SECTION C-C

10'-10"

HANDRAIL

2 - 2 X 12

2ND FLOOR

10"

2 X 10
TREADS

2'-0"

9'-0"

7'-11½"

2 X 4 STUDS
16" O.C.

1/2" RISERS

2X BLOCKING

3 - 2 X 10 STRINGERS

1"

5/8" TYPE X GYPSUM

2 X 6 KICKBLOCK

MAIN
FLOOR

STAIR SECTION

Problem 38–14   See solution presented earlier in this chapter with Problem 38–4.

© 2011 Cengage Learning. All Rights Reserved. May not be scanned, copied or duplicated, or posted to a publicly accessible website, in whole or in part.

Problem 38–15A

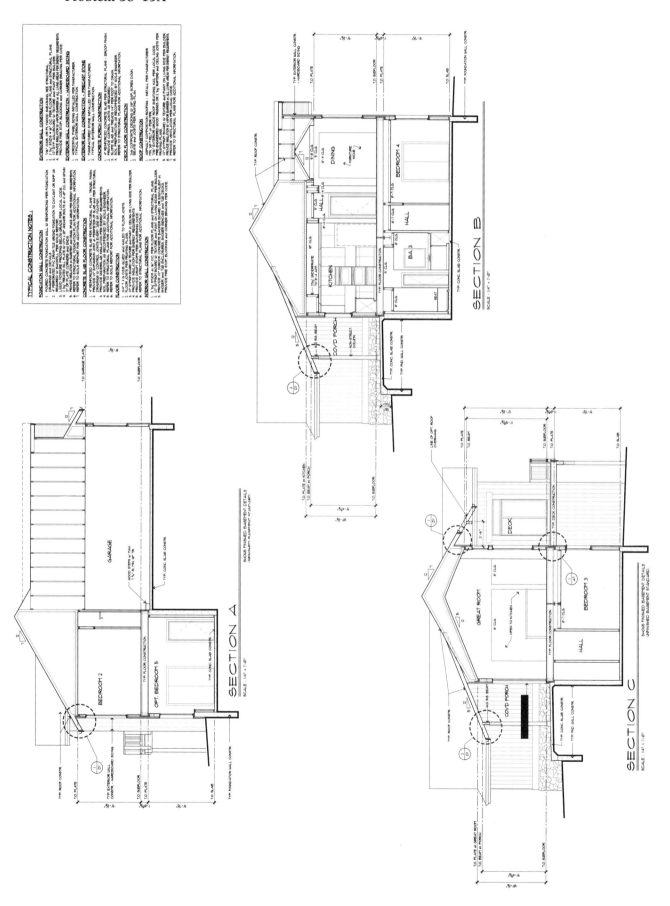

© 2011 Cengage Learning. All Rights Reserved. May not be scanned, copied or duplicated, or posted to a publicly accessible website, in whole or in part.

Problem 38–15B

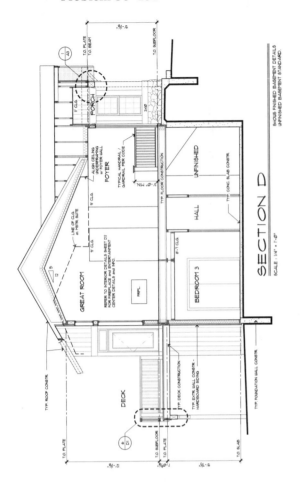

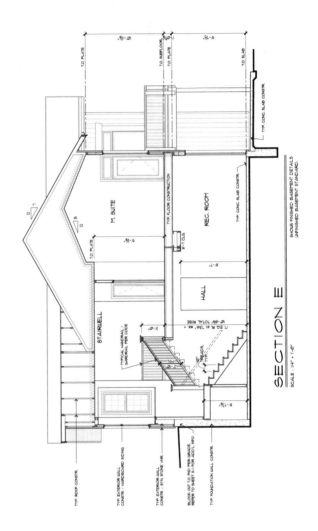

© 2011 Cengage Learning. All Rights Reserved. May not be scanned, copied or duplicated, or posted to a publicly accessible website, in whole or in part.

Problem 38–15C

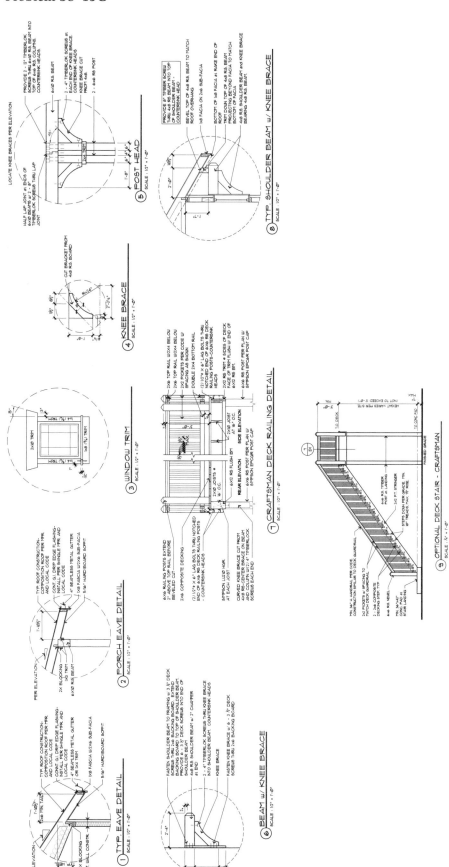

CRAFTSMAN ELEVATION EXTERIOR DETAILS

SCALE: 1/2" = 1'-0"

© 2011 Cengage Learning. All Rights Reserved. May not be scanned, copied or duplicated, or posted to a publicly accessible website, in whole or in part.

Problem 38–16A

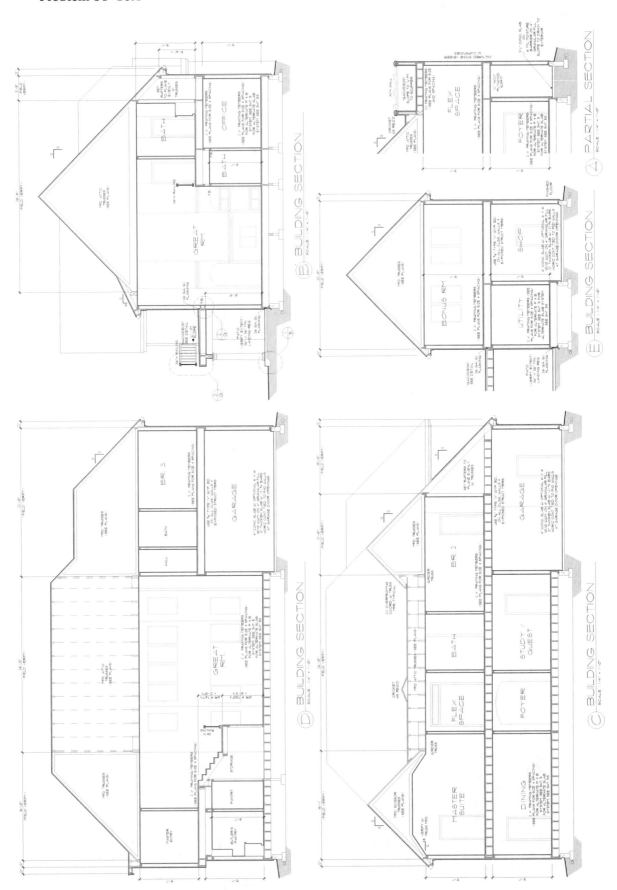

© 2011 Cengage Learning. All Rights Reserved. May not be scanned, copied or duplicated, or posted to a publicly accessible website, in whole or in part.

Problem 38–16B

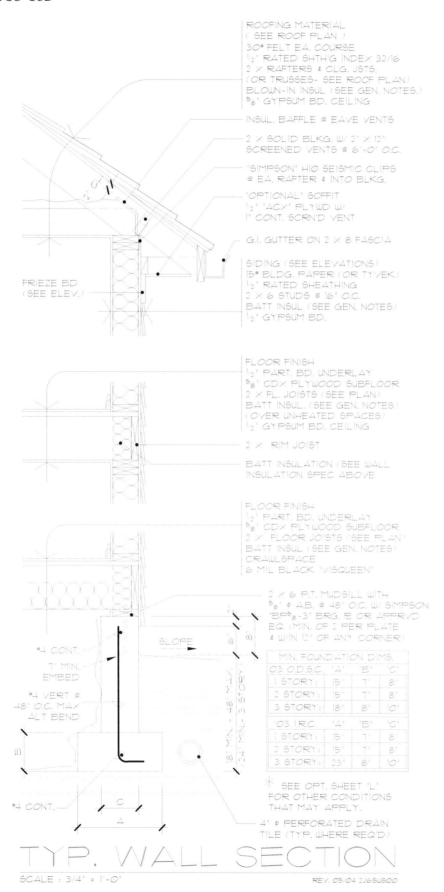

ROOFING MATERIAL
(SEE ROOF PLAN)
30# FELT EA. COURSE
1/2" RATED SHTH'G INDEX 32/16
2 × RAFTERS & CLG. JSTS.
(OR TRUSSES- SEE ROOF PLAN)
BLOWN-IN INSUL (SEE GEN. NOTES.)
5/8" GYPSUM BD. CEILING

INSUL. BAFFLE @ EAVE VENTS

2 × SOLID BLKG. W/ 2" × 12"
SCREENED VENTS @ 6'-0" O.C.

"SIMPSON" H10 SEISMIC CLIPS
@ EA. RAFTER & INTO BLKG.

"OPTIONAL" SOFFIT
1/2" "ACX" PLYWD W/
1" CONT. SCRN'D VENT

G.I. GUTTER ON 2 × 8 FASCIA

SIDING (SEE ELEVATIONS)
15# BLDG. PAPER (OR TYVEK)
1/2" RATED SHEATHING
2 × 6 STUDS @ 16" O.C.
BATT INSUL (SEE GEN. NOTES)
1/2" GYPSUM BD.

FRIEZE BD
(SEE ELEV.)

FLOOR FINISH
1/2" PART. BD. UNDERLAY
5/8" CDX PLYWOOD SUBFLOOR
2 × FL. JOISTS (SEE PLAN)
BATT INSUL. (SEE GEN. NOTES)
(OVER UNHEATED SPACES)
1/2" GYPSUM BD. CEILING

2 × RIM JOIST

BATT INSULATION (SEE WALL
INSULATION SPEC ABOVE

FLOOR FINISH
1/2" PART. BD. UNDERLAY
5/8" CDX PLYWOOD SUBFLOOR
2 × FLOOR JOISTS (SEE PLAN)
BATT INSUL (SEE GEN. NOTES)
CRAWLSPACE
6 MIL BLACK "VISQUEEN"

2 × 6 P.T. MUDSILL WITH
5/8" Φ A.B. @ 48" O.C. W/ SIMPSON
"BP5/8-3" BRG. PL OR APPR'VD
EQ. (MIN. OF 2 PER PLATE
& W/IN 12" OF ANY CORNER)

#4 CONT.
7" MIN.
EMBED

#4 VERT @
48" O.C. MAX
ALT BEND

SLOPE

#4 CONT.

MIN. FOUNDATION DIMS.			
'03 O.D.S.C.	"A"	"B"	"C"
1 STORY:	15"	7"	8"
2 STORY:	15"	7"	8"
3 STORY:	18"	8"	10"
'03 I.R.C.	"A"	"B"	"C"
1 STORY:	15"	7"	8"
2 STORY:	15"	7"	8"
3 STORY:	23"	8"	10"

✳ SEE OPT. SHEET "L"
FOR OTHER CONDITIONS
THAT MAY APPLY.

4" Φ PERFORATED DRAIN
TILE (TYP. WHERE REQ'D)

TYP. WALL SECTION

SCALE : 3/4" = 1'-0"   REV. 05/04 2J6SW600

© 2011 Cengage Learning. All Rights Reserved. May not be scanned, copied or duplicated, or posted to a publicly accessible website, in whole or in part.

Problem 38–17A

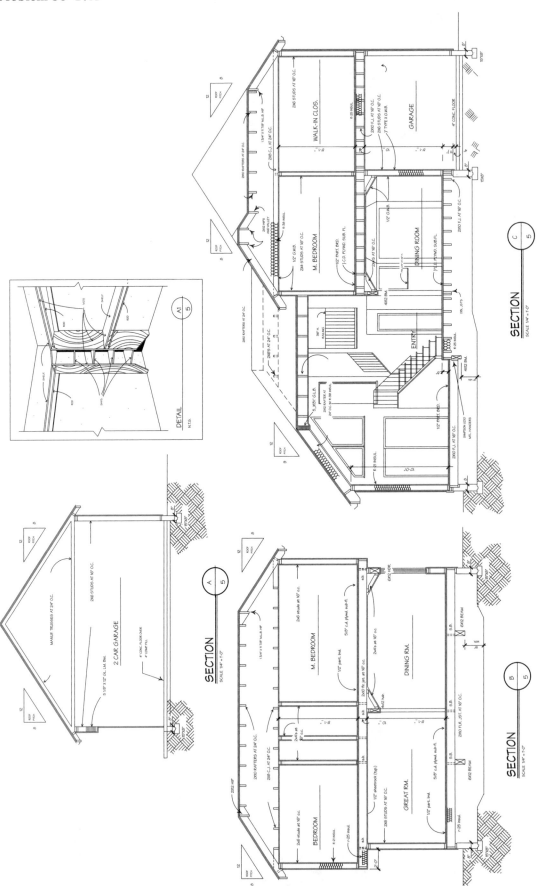

© 2011 Cengage Learning. All Rights Reserved. May not be scanned, copied or duplicated, or posted to a publicly accessible website, in whole or in part.

Problem 38–17B

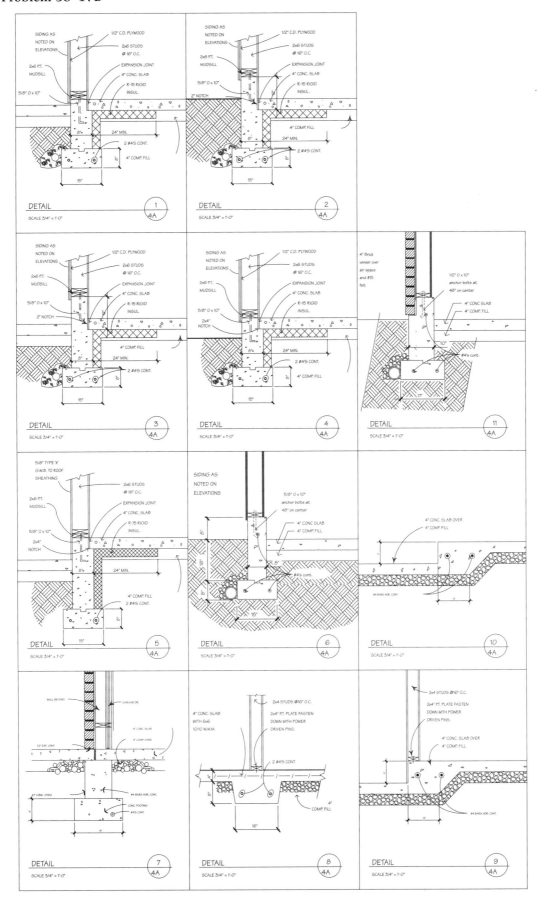

© 2011 Cengage Learning. All Rights Reserved. May not be scanned, copied or duplicated, or posted to a publicly accessible website, in whole or in part.

Problem 38–17C

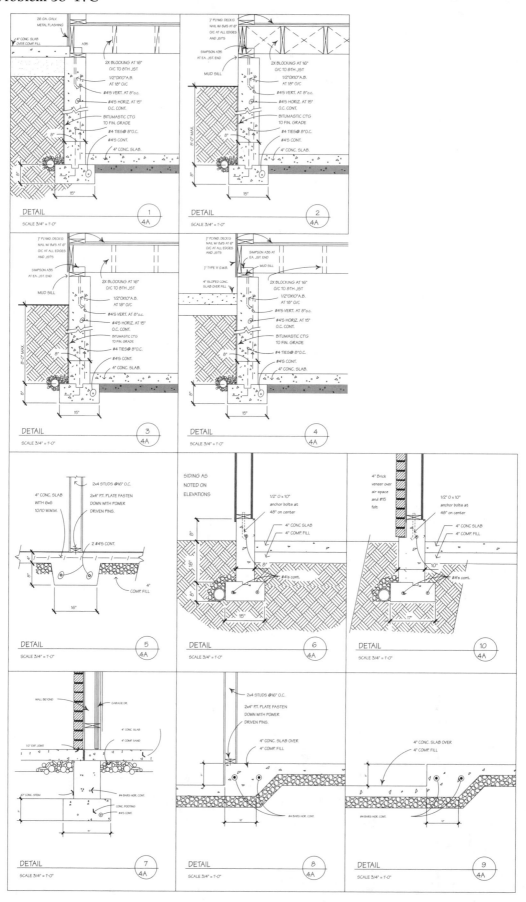

© 2011 Cengage Learning. All Rights Reserved. May not be scanned, copied or duplicated, or posted to a publicly accessible website, in whole or in part.

Problem 38–17D

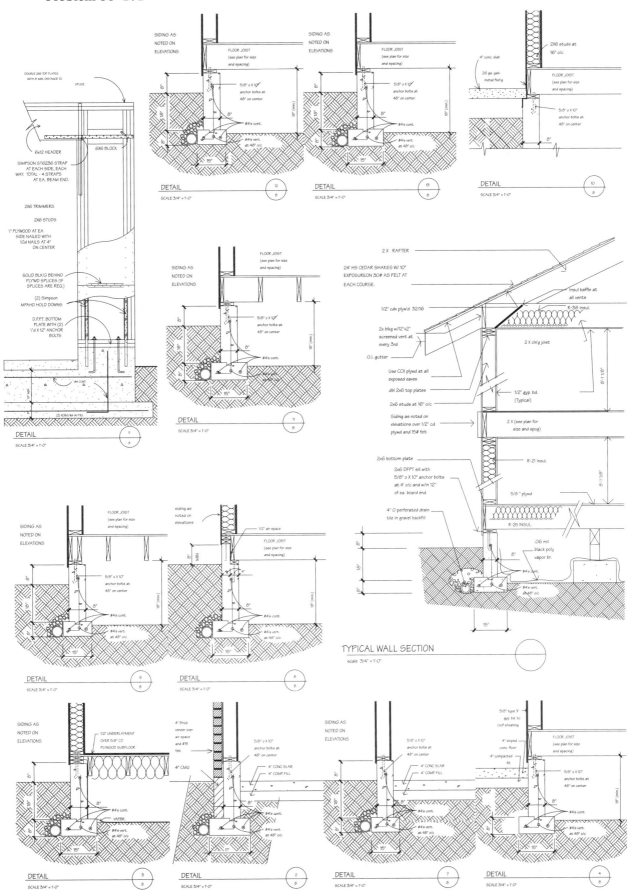

© 2011 Cengage Learning. All Rights Reserved. May not be scanned, copied or duplicated, or posted to a publicly accessible website, in whole or in part.

Problem 38–18A

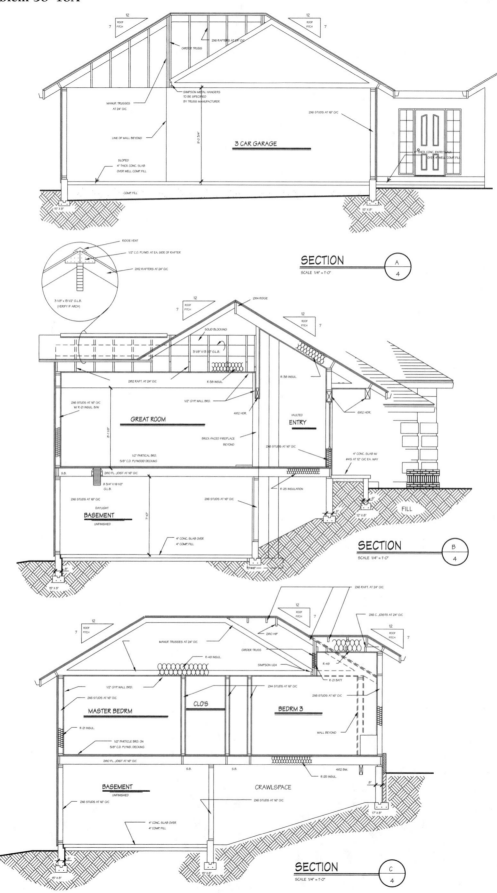

SECTION — A / 4
SCALE 1/4" = 1'-0"

SECTION — B / 4
SCALE 1/4" = 1'-0"

SECTION — C / 4
SCALE 1/4" = 1'-0"

© 2011 Cengage Learning. All Rights Reserved. May not be scanned, copied or duplicated, or posted to a publicly accessible website, in whole or in part.

Problem 38–18B

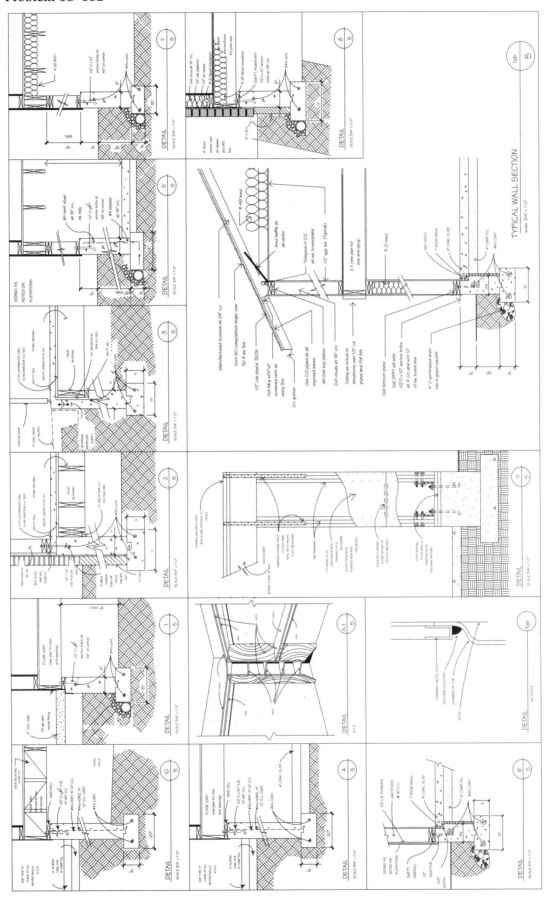

© 2011 Cengage Learning. All Rights Reserved. May not be scanned, copied or duplicated, or posted to a publicly accessible website, in whole or in part.

Problem 38–19A

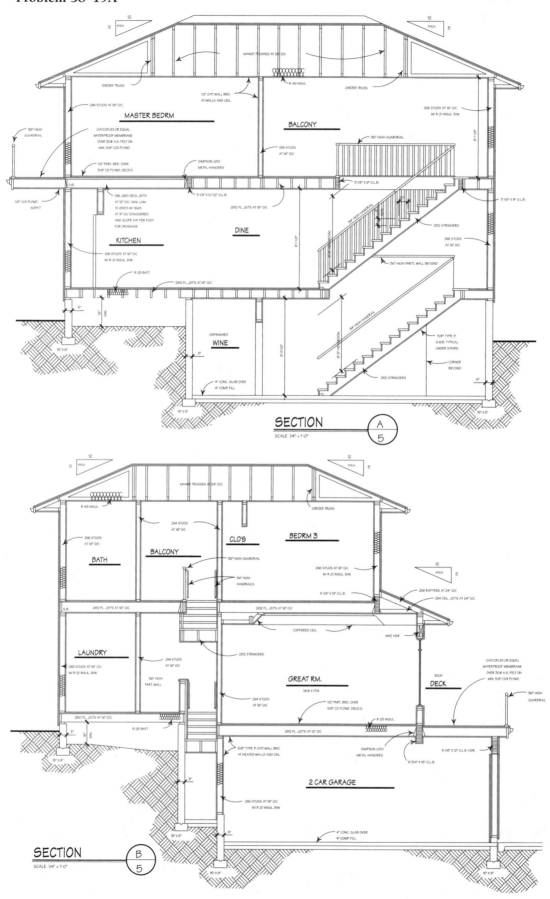

© 2011 Cengage Learning. All Rights Reserved. May not be scanned, copied or duplicated, or posted to a publicly accessible website, in whole or in part.

Problem 38–19B

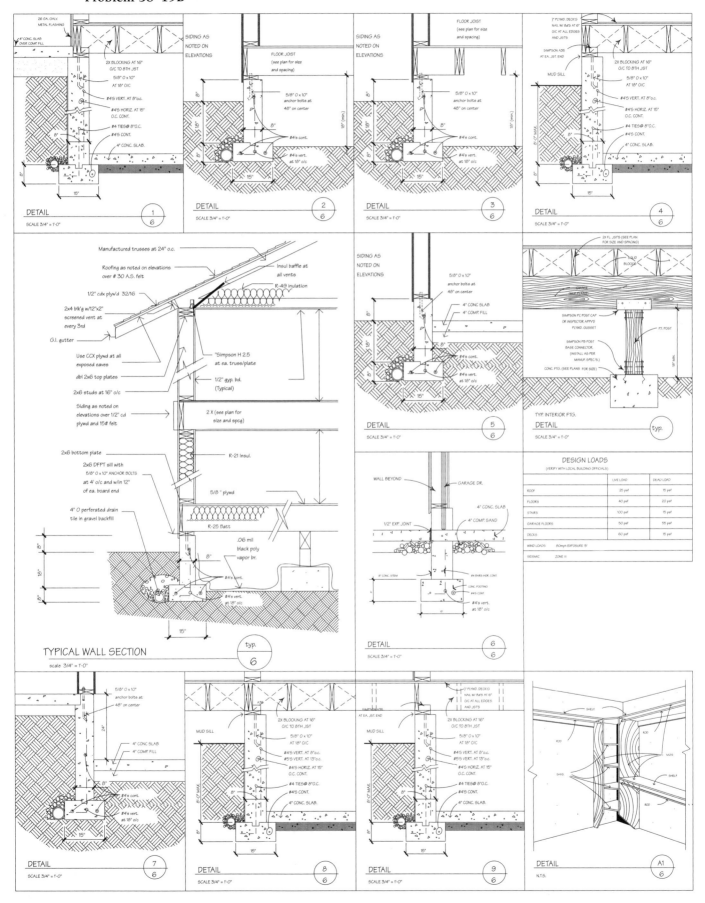

DESIGN LOADS
(VERIFY WITH LOCAL BUILDING OFFICIALS)

	LIVE LOAD	DEAD LOAD
ROOF	25 psf	15 psf
FLOORS	40 psf	20 psf
STAIRS	100 psf	15 psf
GARAGE FLOORS	50 psf	55 psf
DECKS	60 psf	15 psf
WIND LOADS	80mph EXPOSURE 'B'	
SEISMIC	ZONE III	

© 2011 Cengage Learning. All Rights Reserved. May not be scanned, copied or duplicated, or posted to a publicly accessible website, in whole or in part.

Problem 38–20A

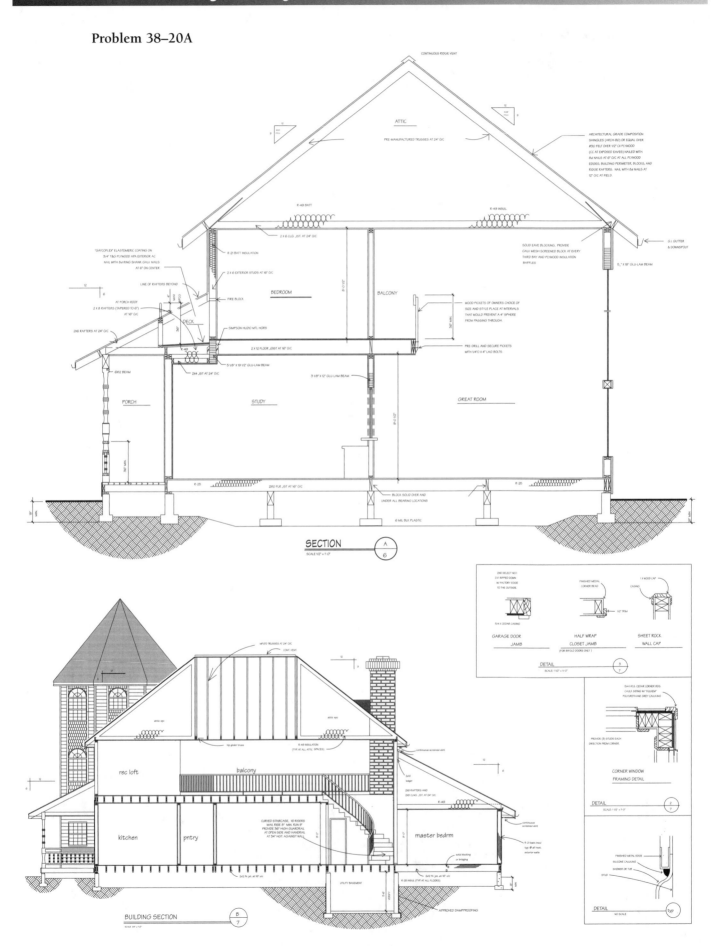

SECTION

BUILDING SECTION

DETAIL

GARAGE DOOR JAMB

HALF WRAP CLOSET JAMB

SHEET ROCK WALL CAP

CORNER WINDOW FRAMING DETAIL

© 2011 Cengage Learning. All Rights Reserved. May not be scanned, copied or duplicated, or posted to a publicly accessible website, in whole or in part.

Problem 38–20B

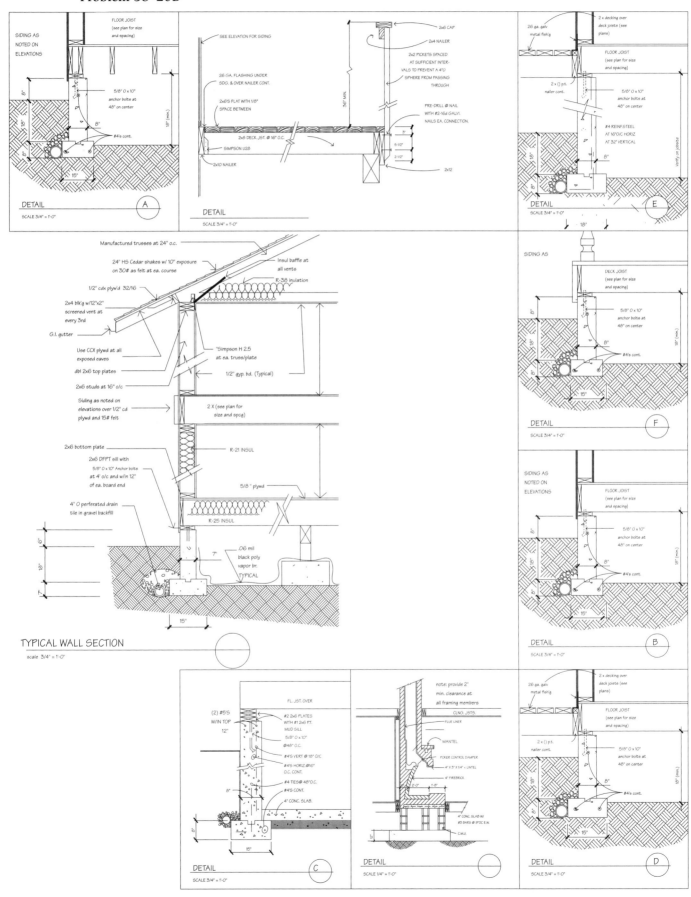

© 2011 Cengage Learning. All Rights Reserved. May not be scanned, copied or duplicated, or posted to a publicly accessible website, in whole or in part.

Problem 38–21A

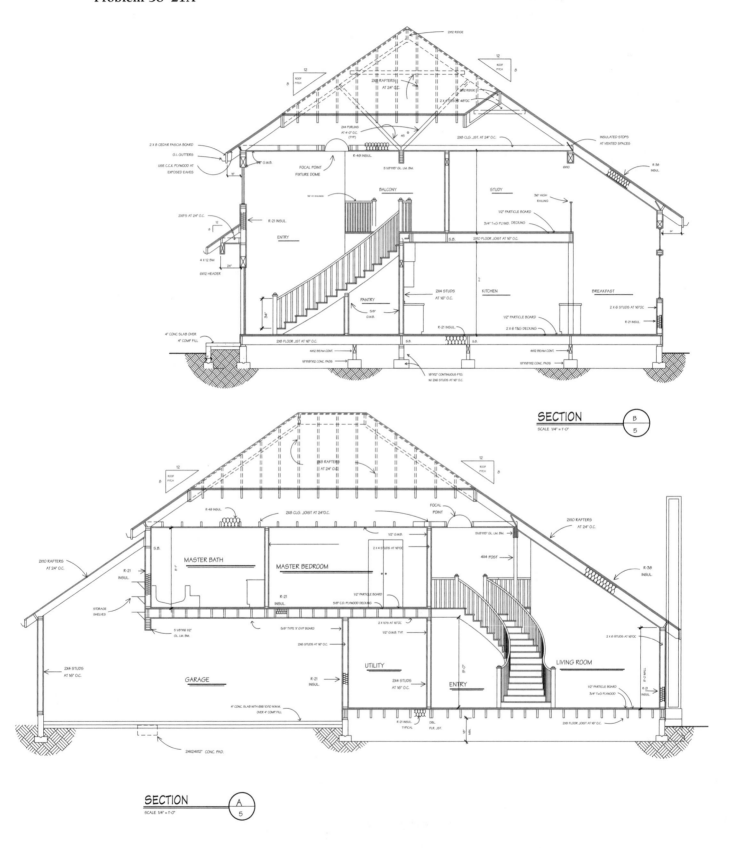

SECTION ⃝B/5
SCALE 1/4" = 1'-0"

SECTION ⃝A/5
SCALE 1/4" = 1'-0"

© 2011 Cengage Learning. All Rights Reserved. May not be scanned, copied or duplicated, or posted to a publicly accessible website, in whole or in part.

Problem 38–21B

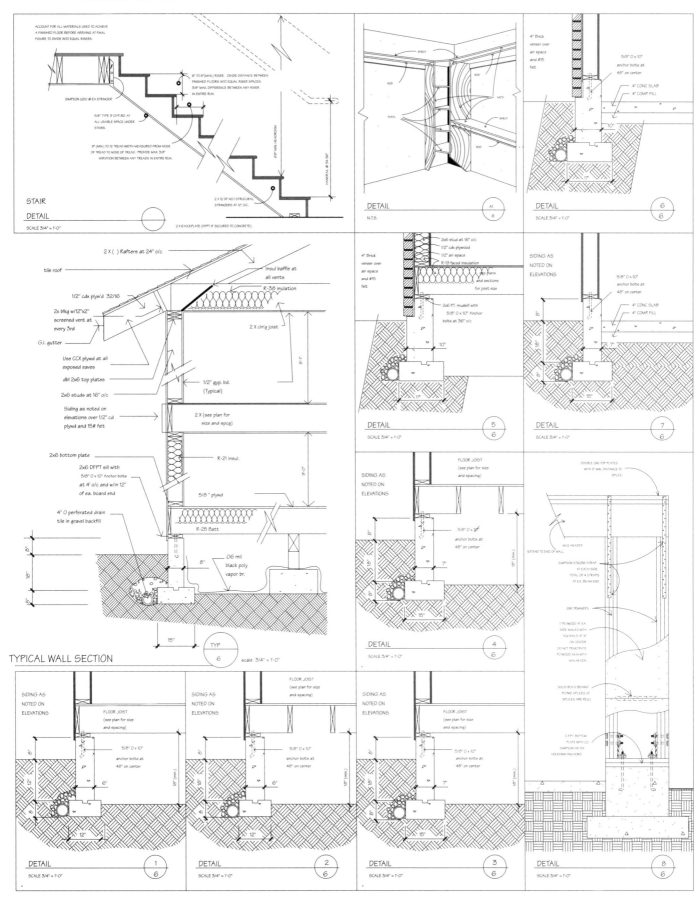

© 2011 Cengage Learning. All Rights Reserved. May not be scanned, copied or duplicated, or posted to a publicly accessible website, in whole or in part.

Problem 38–22

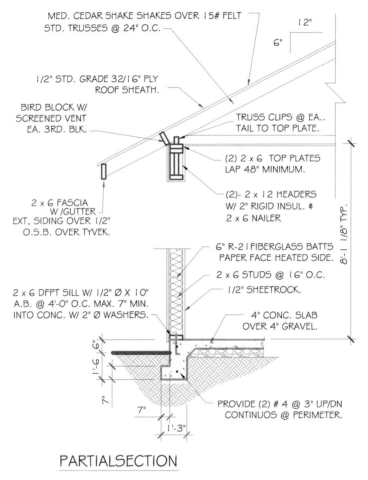

MED. CEDAR SHAKE SHAKES OVER 15# FELT
STD. TRUSSES @ 24" O.C.

12"

6"

1/2" STD. GRADE 32/16" PLY
ROOF SHEATH.

BIRD BLOCK W/
SCREENED VENT
EA. 3RD. BLK.

TRUSS CLIPS @ EA..
TAIL TO TOP PLATE.

(2) 2 x 6 TOP PLATES
LAP 48" MINIMUM.

(2)- 2 x 12 HEADERS
W/ 2" RIGID INSUL. &
2 x 6 NAILER

2 x 6 FASCIA
W /GUTTER
EXT, SIDING OVER 1/2"
O.S.B. OVER TYVEK.

8'- 1 1/8" TYP.

6" R-21 FIBERGLASS BATTS
PAPER FACE HEATED SIDE.

2 x 6 STUDS @ 16" O.C.

1/2" SHEETROCK.

2 x 6 DFPT SILL W/ 1/2" Ø X 10"
A.B. @ 4'-0" O.C. MAX. 7" MIN.
INTO CONC. W/ 2" Ø WASHERS.

4" CONC. SLAB
OVER 4" GRAVEL.

6"

1'-6"

7"

7"

1'-3"

PROVIDE (2) # 4 @ 3" UP/DN
CONTINUOS @ PERIMETER.

PARTIALSECTION

SCALE 1/2" = 1'-0"

© 2011 Cengage Learning. All Rights Reserved. May not be scanned, copied or duplicated, or posted to a publicly accessible website, in whole or in part.

Supplemental Drawing 38–1

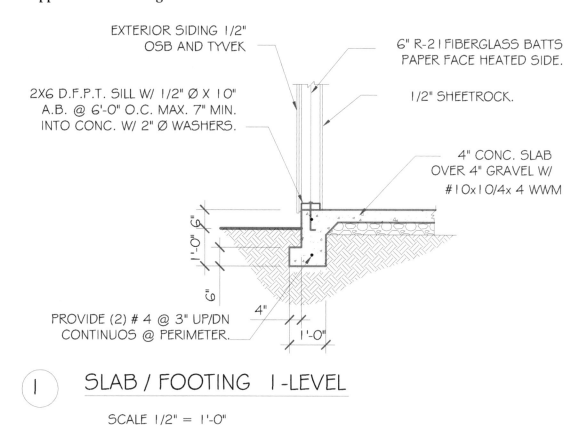

EXTERIOR SIDING 1/2"
OSB AND TYVEK

6" R-21 FIBERGLASS BATTS
PAPER FACE HEATED SIDE.

1/2" SHEETROCK.

2X6 D.F.P.T. SILL W/ 1/2" Ø X 10"
A.B. @ 6'-0" O.C. MAX. 7" MIN.
INTO CONC. W/ 2" Ø WASHERS.

4" CONC. SLAB
OVER 4" GRAVEL W/
#10x10/4x 4 WWM

6"

1'-0"

6"

4"

1'-0"

PROVIDE (2) # 4 @ 3" UP/DN
CONTINUOS @ PERIMETER.

① SLAB / FOOTING 1-LEVEL

SCALE 1/2" = 1'-0"

© 2011 Cengage Learning. All Rights Reserved. May not be scanned, copied or duplicated, or posted to a publicly accessible website, in whole or in part.

Supplemental Drawing 38–2

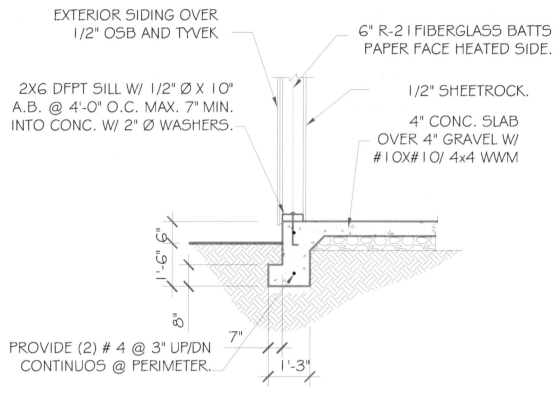

EXTERIOR SIDING OVER
1/2" OSB AND TYVEK

6" R-21 FIBERGLASS BATTS
PAPER FACE HEATED SIDE.

2X6 DFPT SILL W/ 1/2" Ø X 10"
A.B. @ 4'-0" O.C. MAX. 7" MIN.
INTO CONC. W/ 2" Ø WASHERS.

1/2" SHEETROCK.

4" CONC. SLAB
OVER 4" GRAVEL W/
#10X#10/ 4x4 WWM

6"

1'-6"

8"

7"

1'-3"

PROVIDE (2) # 4 @ 3" UP/DN
CONTINUOS @ PERIMETER.

(2) SLAB / FOOTING

SCALE 1/2" = 1'-0"

© 2011 Cengage Learning. All Rights Reserved. May not be scanned, copied or duplicated, or posted to a publicly accessible website, in whole or in part.

Supplemental Drawing 38–3

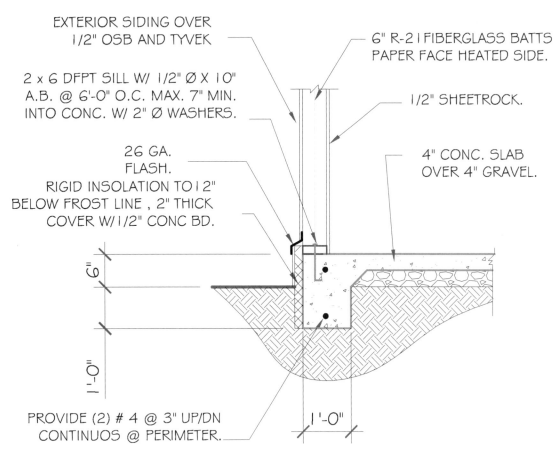

EXTERIOR SIDING OVER
1/2" OSB AND TYVEK

2 x 6 DFPT SILL W/ 1/2" Ø X 10"
A.B. @ 6'-0" O.C. MAX. 7" MIN.
INTO CONC. W/ 2" Ø WASHERS.

26 GA.
FLASH.
RIGID INSOLATION TO 12"
BELOW FROST LINE , 2" THICK
COVER W/1/2" CONC BD.

6"

1'-0"

PROVIDE (2) # 4 @ 3" UP/DN
CONTINUOS @ PERIMETER.

6" R-21 FIBERGLASS BATTS
PAPER FACE HEATED SIDE.

1/2" SHEETROCK.

4" CONC. SLAB
OVER 4" GRAVEL.

1'-0"

③ INSULATED FOOTING.

SCALE 1/2" = 1' -0"

© 2011 Cengage Learning. All Rights Reserved. May not be scanned, copied or duplicated, or posted to a publicly accessible website, in whole or in part.

Supplemental Drawing 38–4A

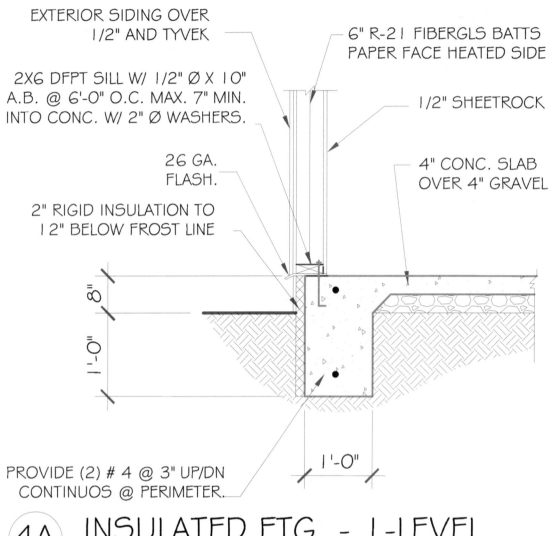

EXTERIOR SIDING OVER
1/2" AND TYVEK

6" R-21 FIBERGLS BATTS
PAPER FACE HEATED SIDE

2X6 DFPT SILL W/ 1/2" Ø X 10"
A.B. @ 6'-0" O.C. MAX. 7" MIN.
INTO CONC. W/ 2" Ø WASHERS.

1/2" SHEETROCK

26 GA.
FLASH.

4" CONC. SLAB
OVER 4" GRAVEL

2" RIGID INSULATION TO
12" BELOW FROST LINE

8"

1'-0"

PROVIDE (2) # 4 @ 3" UP/DN
CONTINUOS @ PERIMETER.

1'-0"

4A   INSULATED FTG. - 1-LEVEL

SCALE 1/2" = 1'-0"

© 2011 Cengage Learning. All Rights Reserved. May not be scanned, copied or duplicated, or posted to a publicly accessible website, in whole or in part.

Supplemental Drawing 38–4B

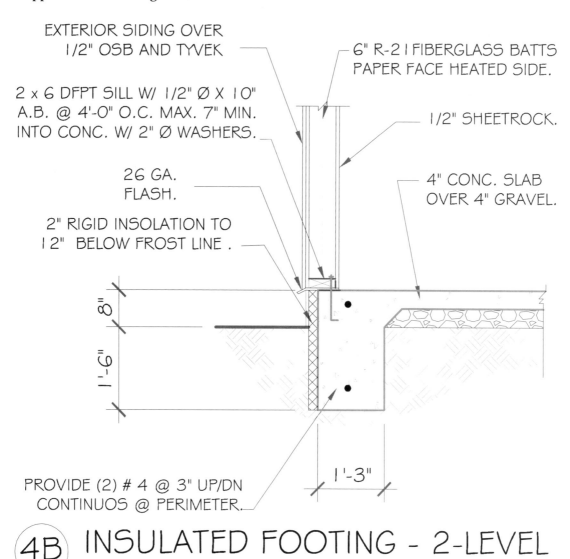

EXTERIOR SIDING OVER
1/2" OSB AND TYVEK

6" R-21 FIBERGLASS BATTS
PAPER FACE HEATED SIDE.

2 x 6 DFPT SILL W/ 1/2" Ø X 10"
A.B. @ 4'-0" O.C. MAX. 7" MIN.
INTO CONC. W/ 2" Ø WASHERS.

1/2" SHEETROCK.

26 GA.
FLASH.

4" CONC. SLAB
OVER 4" GRAVEL.

2" RIGID INSOLATION TO
12" BELOW FROST LINE .

8"

1'-6"

1'-3"

PROVIDE (2) # 4 @ 3" UP/DN
CONTINUOS @ PERIMETER.

(4B) INSULATED FOOTING - 2-LEVEL

SCALE 1/2" = 1'-0"

© 2011 Cengage Learning. All Rights Reserved. May not be scanned, copied or duplicated, or posted to a publicly accessible website, in whole or in part.

Supplemental Drawing 38–5

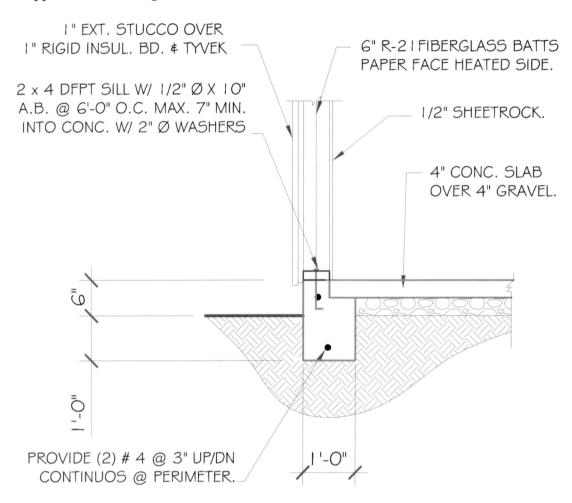

1" EXT. STUCCO OVER
1" RIGID INSUL. BD. & TYVEK

2 x 4 DFPT SILL W/ 1/2" Ø X 10"
A.B. @ 6'-0" O.C. MAX. 7" MIN.
INTO CONC. W/ 2" Ø WASHERS

6" R-21 FIBERGLASS BATTS
PAPER FACE HEATED SIDE.

1/2" SHEETROCK.

4" CONC. SLAB
OVER 4" GRAVEL.

6"

1'-0"

PROVIDE (2) # 4 @ 3" UP/DN
CONTINUOS @ PERIMETER.

1'-0"

⑤ SLAB W/ INSULATED FOOTING.

SCALE 1/2" = 1'-0"

© 2011 Cengage Learning. All Rights Reserved. May not be scanned, copied or duplicated, or posted to a publicly accessible website, in whole or in part.

Supplemental Drawing 38–6

2 x 6 DFPT SILL W/ 1/2" Ø X 10"
A.B. @ 6'-0" O.C. MAX. 7" MIN.
INTO CONC. W/ 2" Ø WASHERS.

1/2" SHEETROCK

4" CONC. SLAB
w/ 4 x 4-10 x 10
WWW OVER 4"
GRAVEL.

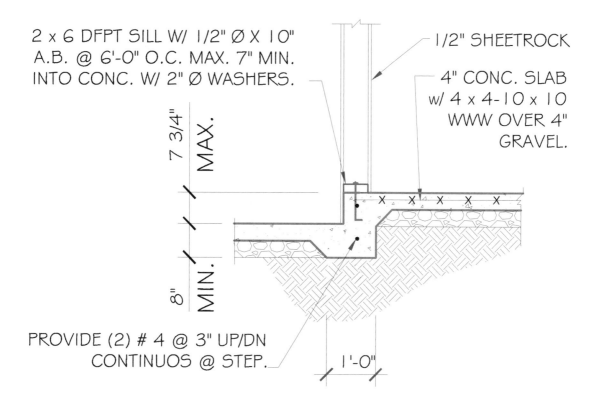

7 3/4" MAX.

8" MIN.

PROVIDE (2) # 4 @ 3" UP/DN
CONTINUOS @ STEP.

1'-0"

(6) SLAB STEP

SCALE 1/2" = 1'-0"

© 2011 Cengage Learning. All Rights Reserved. May not be scanned, copied or duplicated, or posted to a publicly accessible website, in whole or in part.

Supplemental Drawing 38–7

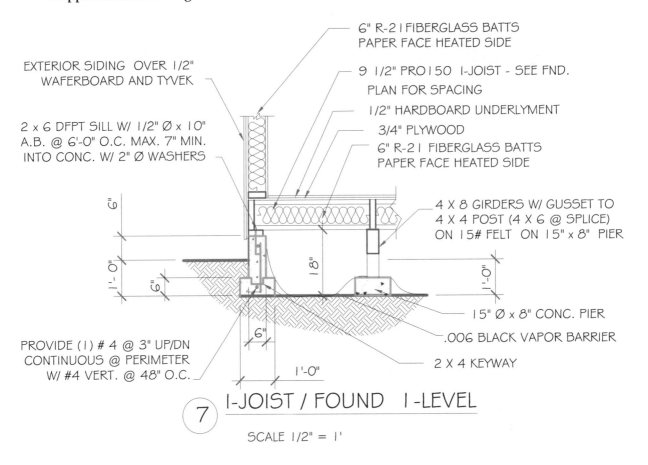

6" R-21 FIBERGLASS BATTS
PAPER FACE HEATED SIDE

9 1/2" PRO150 I-JOIST - SEE FND.
PLAN FOR SPACING

1/2" HARDBOARD UNDERLYMENT

3/4" PLYWOOD

6" R-21 FIBERGLASS BATTS
PAPER FACE HEATED SIDE

EXTERIOR SIDING OVER 1/2"
WAFERBOARD AND TYVEK

2 x 6 DFPT SILL W/ 1/2" Ø x 10"
A.B. @ 6'-0" O.C. MAX. 7" MIN.
INTO CONC. W/ 2" Ø WASHERS

4 X 8 GIRDERS W/ GUSSET TO
4 X 4 POST (4 X 6 @ SPLICE)
ON 15# FELT ON 15" x 8" PIER

15" Ø x 8" CONC. PIER

.006 BLACK VAPOR BARRIER

2 X 4 KEYWAY

PROVIDE (1) # 4 @ 3" UP/DN
CONTINUOUS @ PERIMETER
W/ #4 VERT. @ 48" O.C.

6"

1'-0"

6"

6"

8"

1'-0"

1'-0"

⑦ I-JOIST / FOUND 1-LEVEL

SCALE 1/2" = 1'

© 2011 Cengage Learning. All Rights Reserved. May not be scanned, copied or duplicated, or posted to a publicly accessible website, in whole or in part.

Supplemental Drawing 38–8

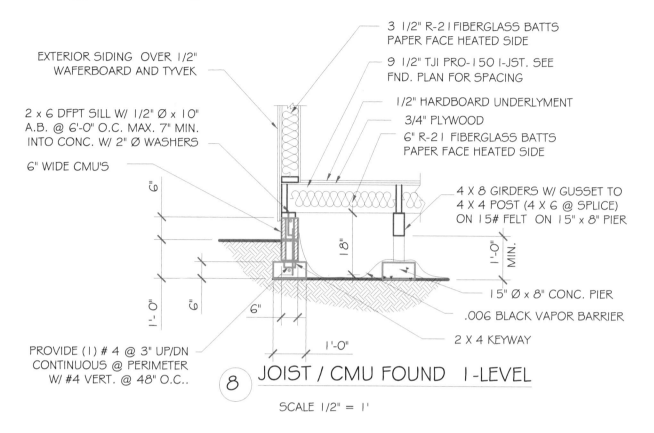

EXTERIOR SIDING OVER 1/2"
WAFERBOARD AND TYVEK

2 x 6 DFPT SILL W/ 1/2" Ø x 10"
A.B. @ 6'-0" O.C. MAX. 7" MIN.
INTO CONC. W/ 2" Ø WASHERS

6" WIDE CMU'S

3 1/2" R-21 FIBERGLASS BATTS
PAPER FACE HEATED SIDE

9 1/2" TJI PRO-150 I-JST. SEE
FND. PLAN FOR SPACING

1/2" HARDBOARD UNDERLYMENT

3/4" PLYWOOD

6" R-21 FIBERGLASS BATTS
PAPER FACE HEATED SIDE

4 X 8 GIRDERS W/ GUSSET TO
4 X 4 POST (4 X 6 @ SPLICE)
ON 15# FELT ON 15" x 8" PIER

15" Ø x 8" CONC. PIER

.006 BLACK VAPOR BARRIER

2 X 4 KEYWAY

PROVIDE (1) # 4 @ 3" UP/DN
CONTINUOUS @ PERIMETER
W/ #4 VERT. @ 48" O.C..

6"

6"

6"

1'-0"

18"

1'-0" MIN.

1'-0"

⑧ JOIST / CMU FOUND 1-LEVEL

SCALE 1/2" = 1'

© 2011 Cengage Learning. All Rights Reserved. May not be scanned, copied or duplicated, or posted to a publicly accessible website, in whole or in part.

Supplemental Drawing 38–9

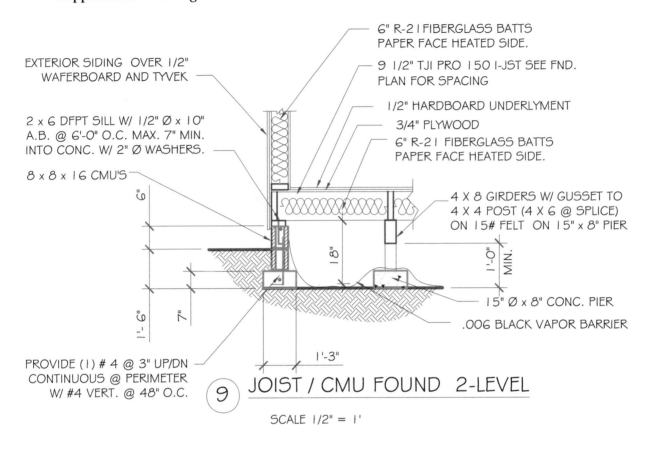

EXTERIOR SIDING OVER 1/2"
WAFERBOARD AND TYVEK

2 x 6 DFPT SILL W/ 1/2" Ø x 10"
A.B. @ 6'-0" O.C. MAX. 7" MIN.
INTO CONC. W/ 2" Ø WASHERS.

8 x 8 x 16 CMU'S

6"

1'-6"

7"

PROVIDE (1) # 4 @ 3" UP/DN
CONTINUOUS @ PERIMETER
W/ #4 VERT. @ 48" O.C.

6" R-21 FIBERGLASS BATTS
PAPER FACE HEATED SIDE.

9 1/2" TJI PRO 150 I-JST SEE FND.
PLAN FOR SPACING

1/2" HARDBOARD UNDERLYMENT

3/4" PLYWOOD

6" R-21 FIBERGLASS BATTS
PAPER FACE HEATED SIDE.

4 X 8 GIRDERS W/ GUSSET TO
4 X 4 POST (4 X 6 @ SPLICE)
ON 15# FELT ON 15" x 8" PIER

18"

1'-0"
MIN.

15" Ø x 8" CONC. PIER

.006 BLACK VAPOR BARRIER

1'-3"

⑨ JOIST / CMU FOUND 2-LEVEL

SCALE 1/2" = 1'

© 2011 Cengage Learning. All Rights Reserved. May not be scanned, copied or duplicated, or posted to a publicly accessible website, in whole or in part.

Supplemental Drawing 38–10

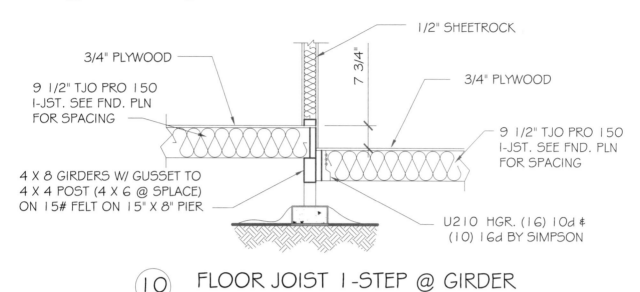

3/4" PLYWOOD

9 1/2" TJO PRO 150
I-JST. SEE FND. PLN
FOR SPACING

4 X 8 GIRDERS W/ GUSSET TO
4 X 4 POST (4 X 6 @ SPLACE)
ON 15# FELT ON 15" X 8" PIER

1/2" SHEETROCK

7 3/4"

3/4" PLYWOOD

9 1/2" TJO PRO 150
I-JST. SEE FND. PLN
FOR SPACING

U210 HGR. (16) 10d &
(10) 16d BY SIMPSON

(10) FLOOR JOIST 1-STEP @ GIRDER

SCALE 1/2" = 1'-0"

© 2011 Cengage Learning. All Rights Reserved. May not be scanned, copied or duplicated, or posted to a publicly accessible website, in whole or in part.

Supplemental Drawing 38–11

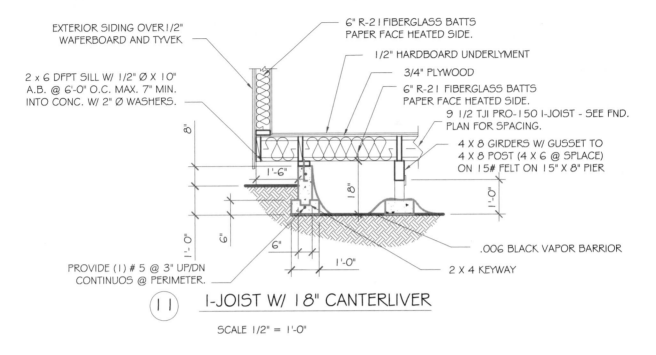

EXTERIOR SIDING OVER 1/2"
WAFERBOARD AND TYVEK

2 x 6 DFPT SILL W/ 1/2" Ø X 10"
A.B. @ 6'-0" O.C. MAX. 7" MIN.
INTO CONC. W/ 2" Ø WASHERS.

6" R-21 FIBERGLASS BATTS
PAPER FACE HEATED SIDE.

1/2" HARDBOARD UNDERLYMENT

3/4" PLYWOOD

6" R-21 FIBERGLASS BATTS
PAPER FACE HEATED SIDE.

9 1/2 TJI PRO-150 I-JOIST - SEE FND.
PLAN FOR SPACING.

4 X 8 GIRDERS W/ GUSSET TO
4 X 8 POST (4 X 6 @ SPLACE)
ON 15# FELT ON 15" X 8" PIER

.006 BLACK VAPOR BARRIOR

2 X 4 KEYWAY

PROVIDE (1) # 5 @ 3" UP/DN
CONTINUOS @ PERIMETER.

8"

1'-6"

1'-0"

6"

6"

1'-0"

18"

1'-0"

⑪ I-JOIST W/ 18" CANTERLIVER

SCALE 1/2" = 1'-0"

© 2011 Cengage Learning. All Rights Reserved. May not be scanned, copied or duplicated, or posted to a publicly accessible website, in whole or in part.

Supplemental Drawing 38–12

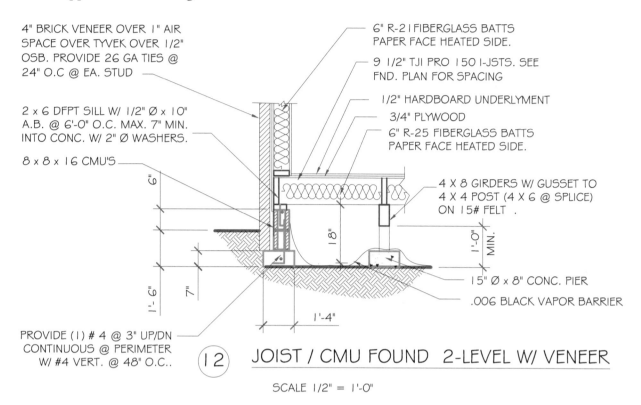

4" BRICK VENEER OVER 1" AIR
SPACE OVER TYVEK OVER 1/2"
OSB. PROVIDE 26 GA TIES @
24" O.C @ EA. STUD

2 x 6 DFPT SILL W/ 1/2" Ø x 10"
A.B. @ 6'-0" O.C. MAX. 7" MIN.
INTO CONC. W/ 2" Ø WASHERS.

8 x 8 x 16 CMU'S

PROVIDE (1) # 4 @ 3" UP/DN
CONTINUOUS @ PERIMETER
W/ #4 VERT. @ 48" O.C..

6" R-21 FIBERGLASS BATTS
PAPER FACE HEATED SIDE.

9 1/2" TJI PRO 150 I-JSTS. SEE
FND. PLAN FOR SPACING

1/2" HARDBOARD UNDERLYMENT

3/4" PLYWOOD

6" R-25 FIBERGLASS BATTS
PAPER FACE HEATED SIDE.

4 X 8 GIRDERS W/ GUSSET TO
4 X 4 POST (4 X 6 @ SPLICE)
ON 15# FELT .

15" Ø x 8" CONC. PIER

.006 BLACK VAPOR BARRIER

6"

1'-6"

9"

7"

8"

1'-0" MIN.

1'-4"

(12) JOIST / CMU FOUND 2-LEVEL W/ VENEER

SCALE 1/2" = 1'-0"

© 2011 Cengage Learning. All Rights Reserved. May not be scanned, copied or duplicated, or posted to a publicly accessible website, in whole or in part.

Supplemental Drawing 38–13

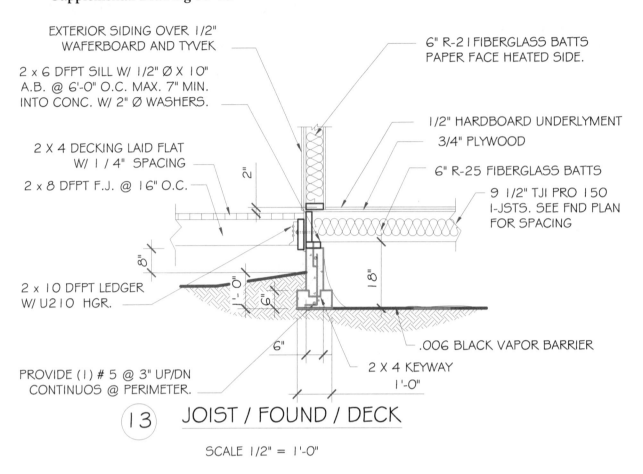

EXTERIOR SIDING OVER 1/2"
WAFERBOARD AND TYVEK

2 x 6 DFPT SILL W/ 1/2" Ø X 10"
A.B. @ 6'-0" O.C. MAX. 7" MIN.
INTO CONC. W/ 2" Ø WASHERS.

2 X 4 DECKING LAID FLAT
W/ 1 / 4" SPACING

2 x 8 DFPT F.J. @ 16" O.C.

2 x 10 DFPT LEDGER
W/ U210 HGR.

PROVIDE (1) # 5 @ 3" UP/DN
CONTINUOS @ PERIMETER.

6" R-21 FIBERGLASS BATTS
PAPER FACE HEATED SIDE.

1/2" HARDBOARD UNDERLYMENT

3/4" PLYWOOD

6" R-25 FIBERGLASS BATTS

9 1/2" TJI PRO 150
I-JSTS. SEE FND PLAN
FOR SPACING

.006 BLACK VAPOR BARRIER

2 X 4 KEYWAY

1'-0"

2"

8"

1'-0"

6"

18"

6"

⑬ JOIST / FOUND / DECK

SCALE 1/2" = 1'-0"

© 2011 Cengage Learning. All Rights Reserved. May not be scanned, copied or duplicated, or posted to a publicly accessible website, in whole or in part.

Supplemental Drawing 38–14

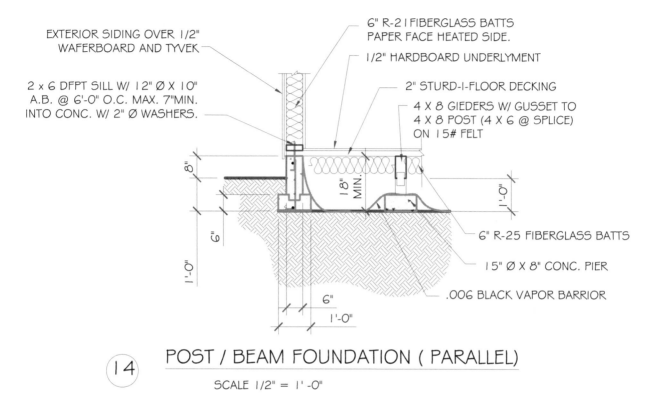

EXTERIOR SIDING OVER 1/2"
WAFERBOARD AND TYVEK

2 x 6 DFPT SILL W/ 12" Ø X 10"
A.B. @ 6'-0" O.C. MAX. 7"MIN.
INTO CONC. W/ 2" Ø WASHERS.

6" R-21 FIBERGLASS BATTS
PAPER FACE HEATED SIDE.

1/2" HARDBOARD UNDERLYMENT

2" STURD-I-FLOOR DECKING

4 X 8 GIEDERS W/ GUSSET TO
4 X 8 POST (4 X 6 @ SPLICE)
ON 15# FELT

6" R-25 FIBERGLASS BATTS

15" Ø X 8" CONC. PIER

.006 BLACK VAPOR BARRIOR

8"

18" MIN.

1'-0"

6"

1'-0"

6"

1'-0"

(14) POST / BEAM FOUNDATION (PARALLEL)

SCALE 1/2" = 1'-0"

© 2011 Cengage Learning. All Rights Reserved. May not be scanned, copied or duplicated, or posted to a publicly accessible website, in whole or in part.

Supplemental Drawing 38–15

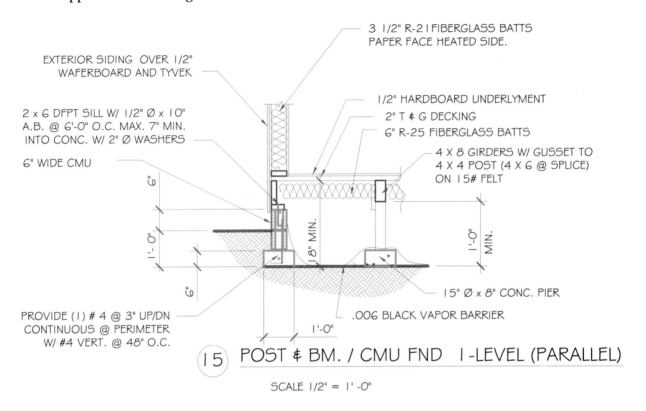

3 1/2" R-21 FIBERGLASS BATTS
PAPER FACE HEATED SIDE.

EXTERIOR SIDING OVER 1/2"
WAFERBOARD AND TYVEK

2 x 6 DFPT SILL W/ 1/2" Ø x 10"
A.B. @ 6'-0" O.C. MAX. 7" MIN.
INTO CONC. W/ 2" Ø WASHERS

6" WIDE CMU

1/2" HARDBOARD UNDERLYMENT
2" T & G DECKING
6" R-25 FIBERGLASS BATTS

4 X 8 GIRDERS W/ GUSSET TO
4 X 4 POST (4 X 6 @ SPLICE)
ON 15# FELT

6"

1'-0"

18" MIN.

1'-0" MIN.

6"

PROVIDE (1) # 4 @ 3" UP/DN
CONTINUOUS @ PERIMETER
W/ #4 VERT. @ 48" O.C.

15" Ø x 8" CONC. PIER

.006 BLACK VAPOR BARRIER

1'-0"

$\widehat{15}$ POST & BM. / CMU FND 1-LEVEL (PARALLEL)

SCALE 1/2" = 1'-0"

© 2011 Cengage Learning. All Rights Reserved. May not be scanned, copied or duplicated, or posted to a publicly accessible website, in whole or in part.

Supplemental Drawing 38–16

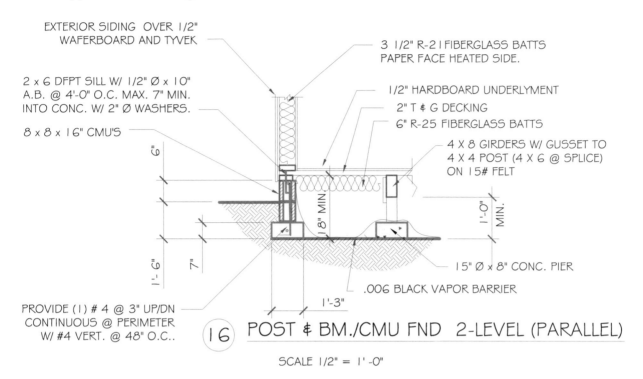

EXTERIOR SIDING OVER 1/2"
WAFERBOARD AND TYVEK

3 1/2" R-21 FIBERGLASS BATTS
PAPER FACE HEATED SIDE.

2 x 6 DFPT SILL W/ 1/2" Ø x 10"
A.B. @ 4'-0" O.C. MAX. 7" MIN.
INTO CONC. W/ 2" Ø WASHERS.

1/2" HARDBOARD UNDERLYMENT

2" T & G DECKING

6" R-25 FIBERGLASS BATTS

8 x 8 x 16" CMU'S

4 X 8 GIRDERS W/ GUSSET TO
4 X 4 POST (4 X 6 @ SPLICE)
ON 15# FELT

6"

18" MIN.

1'-0" MIN.

1'-6"

7"

15" Ø x 8" CONC. PIER

.006 BLACK VAPOR BARRIER

PROVIDE (1) # 4 @ 3" UP/DN
CONTINUOUS @ PERIMETER
W/ #4 VERT. @ 48" O.C..

1'-3"

16 POST & BM./CMU FND 2-LEVEL (PARALLEL)

SCALE 1/2" = 1'-0"

© 2011 Cengage Learning. All Rights Reserved. May not be scanned, copied or duplicated, or posted to a publicly accessible website, in whole or in part.

Supplemental Drawing 38–17

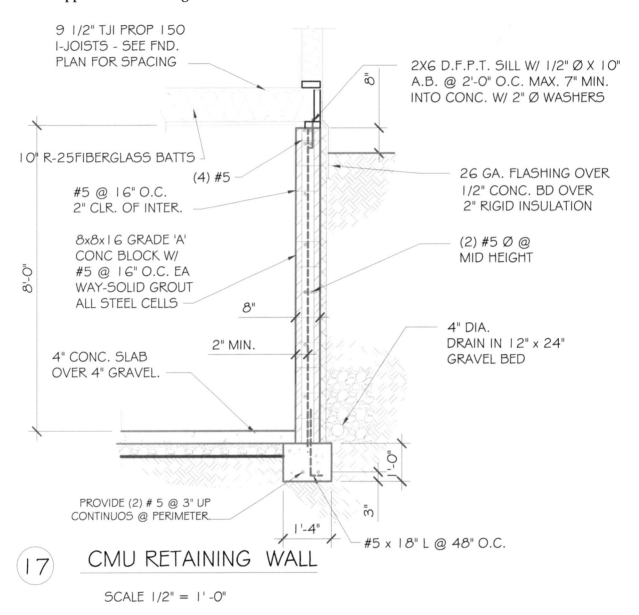

9 1/2" TJI PROP 150
I-JOISTS - SEE FND.
PLAN FOR SPACING

2X6 D.F.P.T. SILL W/ 1/2" Ø X 10"
A.B. @ 2'-0" O.C. MAX. 7" MIN.
INTO CONC. W/ 2" Ø WASHERS

8"

10" R-25FIBERGLASS BATTS

(4) #5

26 GA. FLASHING OVER
1/2" CONC. BD OVER
2" RIGID INSULATION

#5 @ 16" O.C.
2" CLR. OF INTER.

8x8x16 GRADE 'A'
CONC BLOCK W/
#5 @ 16" O.C. EA
WAY-SOLID GROUT
ALL STEEL CELLS

(2) #5 Ø @
MID HEIGHT

8'-0"

8"

4" DIA.
DRAIN IN 12" x 24"
GRAVEL BED

2" MIN.

4" CONC. SLAB
OVER 4" GRAVEL.

1'-0"

3"

PROVIDE (2) # 5 @ 3" UP
CONTINUOS @ PERIMETER.

1'-4"

#5 x 18" L @ 48" O.C.

(17) CMU RETAINING WALL

SCALE 1/2" = 1'-0"

© 2011 Cengage Learning. All Rights Reserved. May not be scanned, copied or duplicated, or posted to a publicly accessible website, in whole or in part.

Supplemental Drawing 38–18

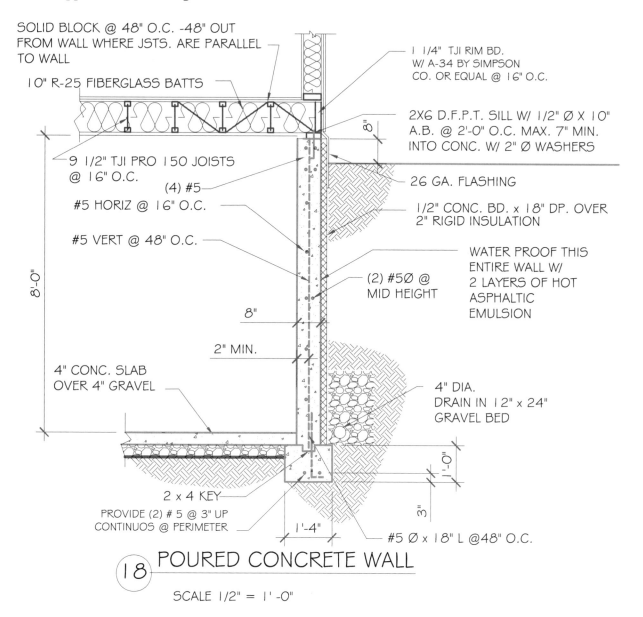

SOLID BLOCK @ 48" O.C. -48" OUT
FROM WALL WHERE JSTS. ARE PARALLEL
TO WALL

10" R-25 FIBERGLASS BATTS

1 1/4" TJI RIM BD.
W/ A-34 BY SIMPSON
CO. OR EQUAL @ 16" O.C.

2X6 D.F.P.T. SILL W/ 1/2" Ø X 10"
A.B. @ 2'-0" O.C. MAX. 7" MIN.
INTO CONC. W/ 2" Ø WASHERS

9 1/2" TJI PRO 150 JOISTS
@ 16" O.C.

26 GA. FLASHING

(4) #5

#5 HORIZ @ 16" O.C.

1/2" CONC. BD. x 18" DP. OVER
2" RIGID INSULATION

#5 VERT @ 48" O.C.

WATER PROOF THIS
ENTIRE WALL W/
2 LAYERS OF HOT
ASPHALTIC
EMULSION

(2) #5Ø @
MID HEIGHT

8"

2" MIN.

4" CONC. SLAB
OVER 4" GRAVEL

4" DIA.
DRAIN IN 12" x 24"
GRAVEL BED

8'-0"

1'-0"

3"

2 x 4 KEY

PROVIDE (2) # 5 @ 3" UP
CONTINUOS @ PERIMETER

1'-4"

#5 Ø x 18" L @48" O.C.

(18) POURED CONCRETE WALL

SCALE 1/2" = 1'-0"

© 2011 Cengage Learning. All Rights Reserved. May not be scanned, copied or duplicated, or posted to a publicly accessible website, in whole or in part.

Supplemental Drawing 38–19

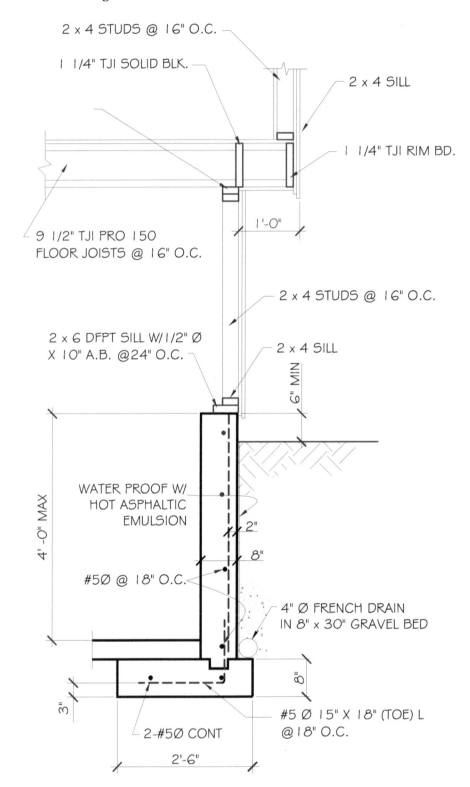

2 x 4 STUDS @ 16" O.C.

1 1/4" TJI SOLID BLK.

2 x 4 SILL

1 1/4" TJI RIM BD.

9 1/2" TJI PRO 150
FLOOR JOISTS @ 16" O.C.

1'-0"

2 x 4 STUDS @ 16" O.C.

2 x 6 DFPT SILL W/1/2" Ø
X 10" A.B. @24" O.C.

2 x 4 SILL

6" MIN

4'-0" MAX

WATER PROOF W/
HOT ASPHALTIC
EMULSION

2"

8"

#5Ø @ 18" O.C.

4" Ø FRENCH DRAIN
IN 8" x 30" GRAVEL BED

8"

3"

2-#5Ø CONT

#5 Ø 15" X 18" (TOE) L
@ 18" O.C.

2'-6"

(19) 48" RETAINING WALL

SCALE 1/2" = 1'-0"

© 2011 Cengage Learning. All Rights Reserved. May not be scanned, copied or duplicated, or posted to a publicly accessible website, in whole or in part.

Supplemental Drawing 38–20

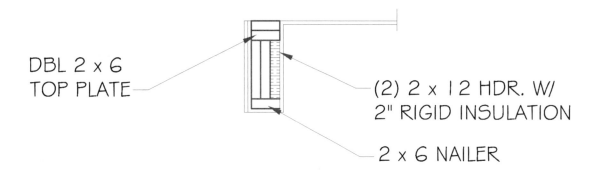

DBL 2 x 6
TOP PLATE

(2) 2 x 12 HDR. W/
2" RIGID INSULATION

2 x 6 NAILER

(20) <u>(2) 2 x 12 HDR</u>
SCALE 1/2" = 1'-0"

© 2011 Cengage Learning. All Rights Reserved. May not be scanned, copied or duplicated, or posted to a publicly accessible website, in whole or in part.

Supplemental Drawing 38–21

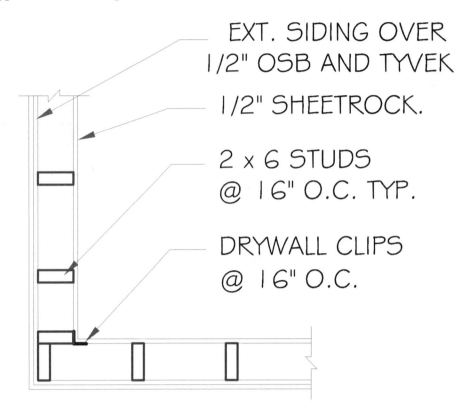

EXT. SIDING OVER
1/2" OSB AND TYVEK

1/2" SHEETROCK.

2 x 6 STUDS
@ 16" O.C. TYP.

DRYWALL CLIPS
@ 16" O.C.

$\left(21\right)$ 2 STUD EXT. CORNER

SCALE 1/2" = 1'-0"

© 2011 Cengage Learning. All Rights Reserved. May not be scanned, copied or duplicated, or posted to a publicly accessible website, in whole or in part.

Supplemental Drawing 38–22

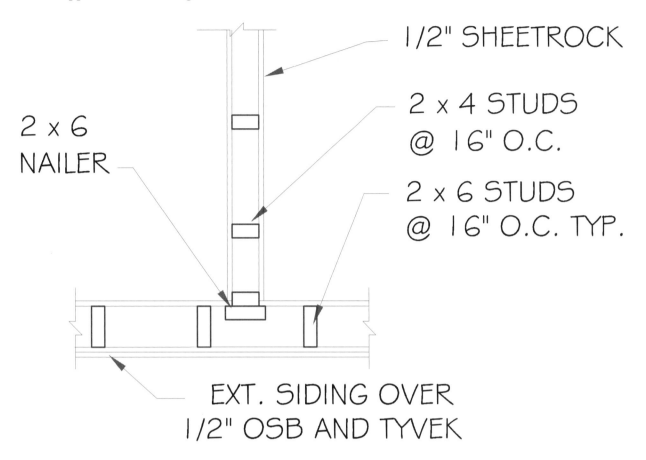

1/2" SHEETROCK

2 x 4 STUDS
@ 16" O.C.

2 x 6 STUDS
@ 16" O.C. TYP.

2 x 6
NAILER

EXT. SIDING OVER
1/2" OSB AND TYVEK

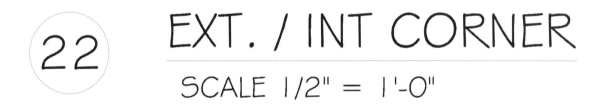

22 EXT. / INT CORNER

SCALE 1/2" = 1'-0"

© 2011 Cengage Learning. All Rights Reserved. May not be scanned, copied or duplicated, or posted to a publicly accessible website, in whole or in part.

Supplemental Drawing 38–23

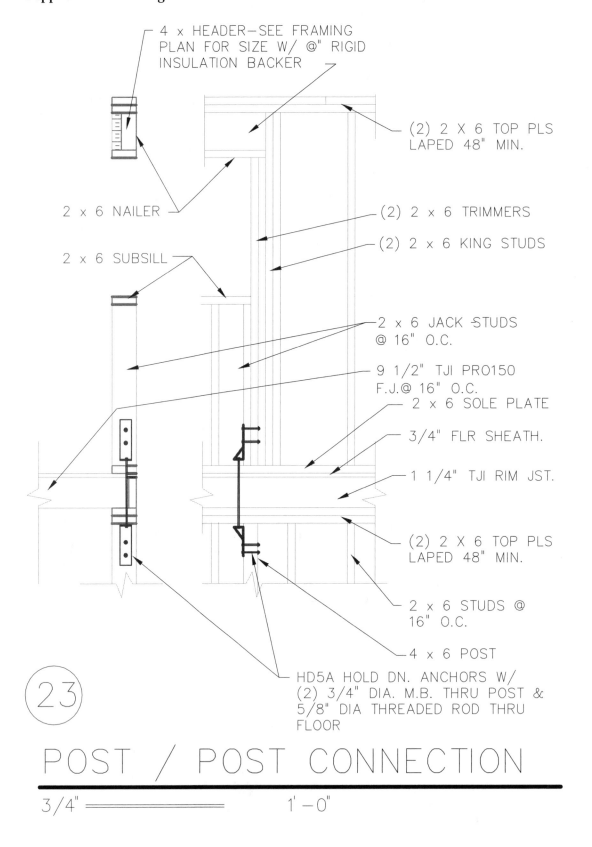

4 x HEADER—SEE FRAMING PLAN FOR SIZE W/ @" RIGID INSULATION BACKER

(2) 2 X 6 TOP PLS LAPED 48" MIN.

2 x 6 NAILER

(2) 2 x 6 TRIMMERS

(2) 2 x 6 KING STUDS

2 x 6 SUBSILL

2 x 6 JACK STUDS @ 16" O.C.

9 1/2" TJI PRO150 F.J.@ 16" O.C.

2 x 6 SOLE PLATE

3/4" FLR SHEATH.

1 1/4" TJI RIM JST.

(2) 2 X 6 TOP PLS LAPED 48" MIN.

2 x 6 STUDS @ 16" O.C.

4 x 6 POST

HD5A HOLD DN. ANCHORS W/ (2) 3/4" DIA. M.B. THRU POST & 5/8" DIA THREADED ROD THRU FLOOR

(23)

POST / POST CONNECTION

3/4" ══════════ 1'–0"

© 2011 Cengage Learning. All Rights Reserved. May not be scanned, copied or duplicated, or posted to a publicly accessible website, in whole or in part.

Supplemental Drawing 38–24

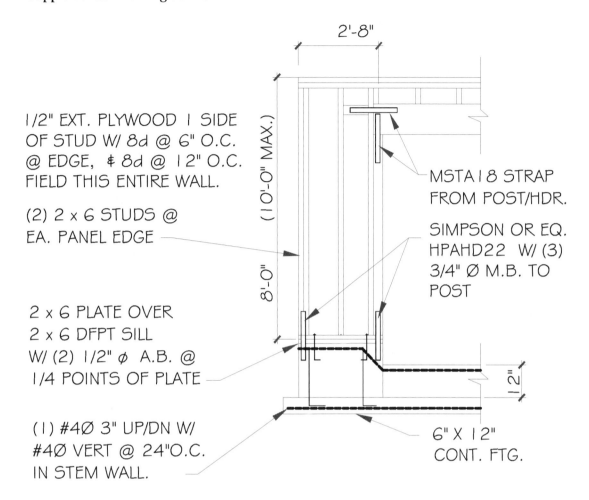

1/2" EXT. PLYWOOD 1 SIDE
OF STUD W/ 8d @ 6" O.C.
@ EDGE, & 8d @ 12" O.C.
FIELD THIS ENTIRE WALL.

(2) 2 x 6 STUDS @
EA. PANEL EDGE

2 x 6 PLATE OVER
2 x 6 DFPT SILL
W/ (2) 1/2" ∅ A.B. @
1/4 POINTS OF PLATE

(1) #4∅ 3" UP/DN W/
#4∅ VERT @ 24"O.C.
IN STEM WALL.

2'-8"

(10'-0" MAX.)

8'-0"

MSTA18 STRAP
FROM POST/HDR.

SIMPSON OR EQ.
HPAHD22 W/ (3)
3/4" ∅ M.B. TO
POST

12"

6" X 12"
CONT. FTG.

(24) **ALT. BRACED WALL PANEL**

© 2011 Cengage Learning. All Rights Reserved. May not be scanned, copied or duplicated, or posted to a publicly accessible website, in whole or in part.

Supplemental Drawing 38–25

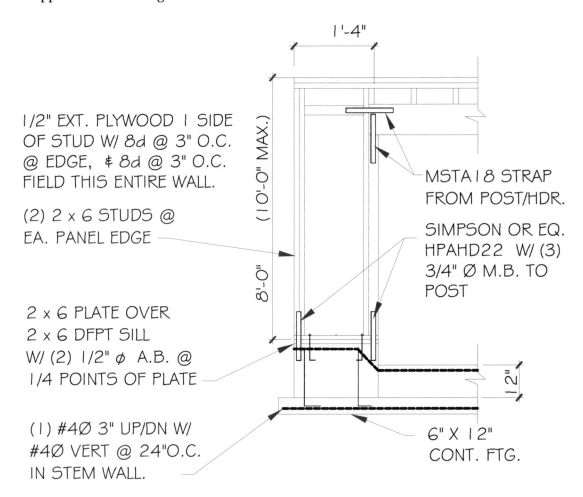

1/2" EXT. PLYWOOD 1 SIDE
OF STUD W/ 8d @ 3" O.C.
@ EDGE, & 8d @ 3" O.C.
FIELD THIS ENTIRE WALL.

(2) 2 x 6 STUDS @
EA. PANEL EDGE

2 x 6 PLATE OVER
2 x 6 DFPT SILL
W/ (2) 1/2" ⌀ A.B. @
1/4 POINTS OF PLATE

(1) #4⌀ 3" UP/DN W/
#4⌀ VERT @ 24"O.C.
IN STEM WALL.

1'-4"

(10'-0" MAX.)

8'-0"

MSTA18 STRAP
FROM POST/HDR.

SIMPSON OR EQ.
HPAHD22 W/ (3)
3/4" ⌀ M.B. TO
POST

12"

6" X 12"
CONT. FTG.

25   A. B. W. P. A. O.

© 2011 Cengage Learning. All Rights Reserved. May not be scanned, copied or duplicated, or posted to a publicly accessible website, in whole or in part.

Supplemental Drawing 38–26

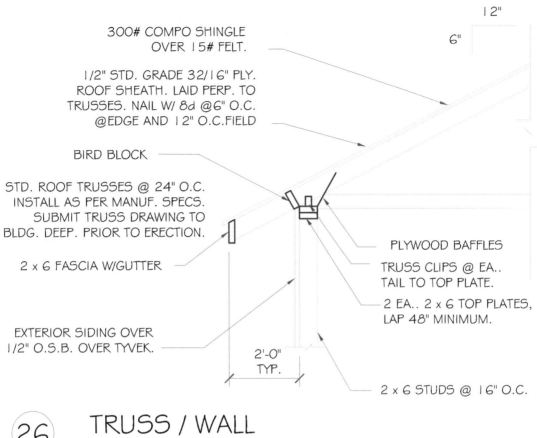

300# COMPO SHINGLE
OVER 15# FELT.

1/2" STD. GRADE 32/16" PLY.
ROOF SHEATH. LAID PERP. TO
TRUSSES. NAIL W/ 8d @6" O.C.
@EDGE AND 12" O.C.FIELD

BIRD BLOCK

STD. ROOF TRUSSES @ 24" O.C.
INSTALL AS PER MANUF. SPECS.
SUBMIT TRUSS DRAWING TO
BLDG. DEEP. PRIOR TO ERECTION.

2 x 6 FASCIA W/GUTTER

EXTERIOR SIDING OVER
1/2" O.S.B. OVER TYVEK.

12"

6"

PLYWOOD BAFFLES

TRUSS CLIPS @ EA..
TAIL TO TOP PLATE.

2 EA.. 2 x 6 TOP PLATES,
LAP 48" MINIMUM.

2 x 6 STUDS @ 16" O.C.

2'-0"
TYP.

(26) **TRUSS / WALL**

SCALE 1/2" = 1'-0"

© 2011 Cengage Learning. All Rights Reserved. May not be scanned, copied or duplicated, or posted to a publicly accessible website, in whole or in part.

Supplemental Drawing 38–27

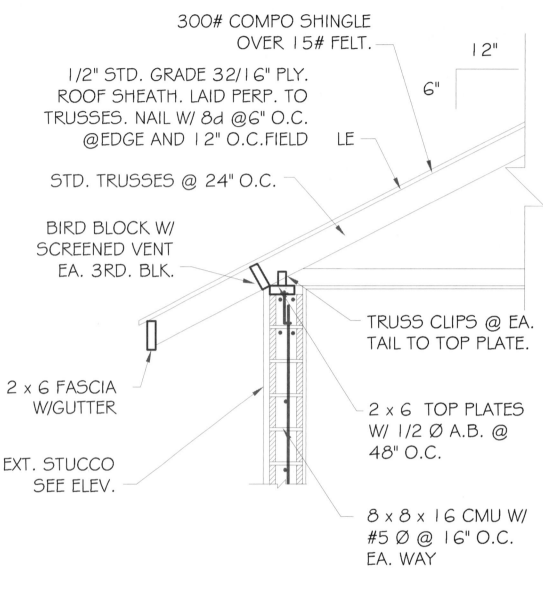

300# COMPO SHINGLE
OVER 15# FELT.

1/2" STD. GRADE 32/16" PLY.
ROOF SHEATH. LAID PERP. TO
TRUSSES. NAIL W/ 8d @6" O.C.
@EDGE AND 12" O.C.FIELD

12"

6"

LE

STD. TRUSSES @ 24" O.C.

BIRD BLOCK W/
SCREENED VENT
EA. 3RD. BLK.

TRUSS CLIPS @ EA.
TAIL TO TOP PLATE.

2 x 6 FASCIA
W/GUTTER

2 x 6 TOP PLATES
W/ 1/2 Ø A.B. @
48" O.C.

EXT. STUCCO
SEE ELEV.

8 x 8 x 16 CMU W/
#5 Ø @ 16" O.C.
EA. WAY

27 TRUSS / CMU WALL

SCALE 1/2" = 1'-0"

© 2011 Cengage Learning. All Rights Reserved. May not be scanned, copied or duplicated, or posted to a publicly accessible website, in whole or in part.

Supplemental Drawing 38–28

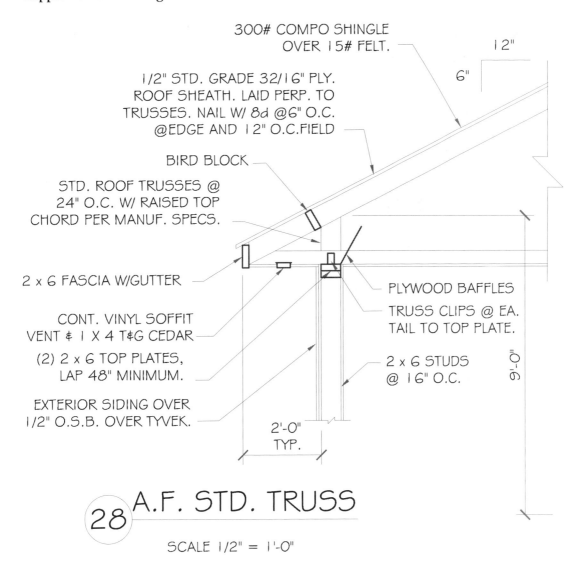

300# COMPO SHINGLE
OVER 15# FELT.

12"

6"

1/2" STD. GRADE 32/16" PLY.
ROOF SHEATH. LAID PERP. TO
TRUSSES. NAIL W/ 8d @6" O.C.
@EDGE AND 12" O.C.FIELD

BIRD BLOCK

STD. ROOF TRUSSES @
24" O.C. W/ RAISED TOP
CHORD PER MANUF. SPECS.

2 x 6 FASCIA W/GUTTER

PLYWOOD BAFFLES

TRUSS CLIPS @ EA.
TAIL TO TOP PLATE.

CONT. VINYL SOFFIT
VENT & 1 X 4 T&G CEDAR

(2) 2 x 6 TOP PLATES,
LAP 48" MINIMUM.

2 x 6 STUDS
@ 16" O.C.

9'-0"

EXTERIOR SIDING OVER
1/2" O.S.B. OVER TYVEK.

2'-0"
TYP.

28 **A.F. STD. TRUSS**

SCALE 1/2" = 1'-0"

© 2011 Cengage Learning. All Rights Reserved. May not be scanned, copied or duplicated, or posted to a publicly accessible website, in whole or in part.

Supplemental Drawing 38–29

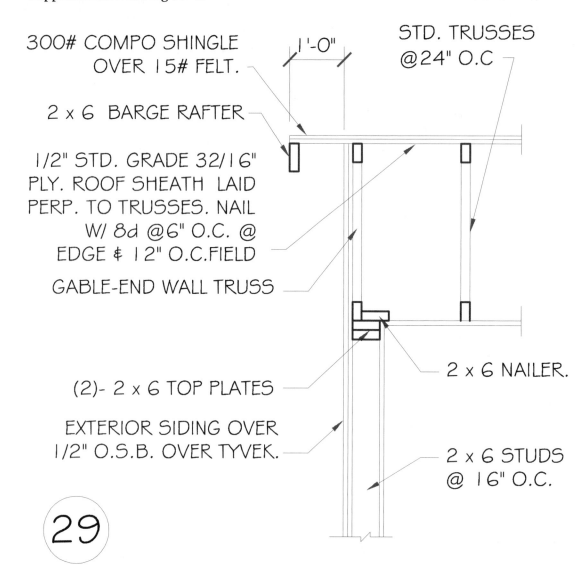

300# COMPO SHINGLE OVER 15# FELT.

1'-0"

STD. TRUSSES @24" O.C

2 x 6 BARGE RAFTER

1/2" STD. GRADE 32/16" PLY. ROOF SHEATH LAID PERP. TO TRUSSES. NAIL W/ 8d @6" O.C. @ EDGE & 12" O.C.FIELD

GABLE-END WALL TRUSS

2 x 6 NAILER.

(2)- 2 x 6 TOP PLATES

EXTERIOR SIDING OVER 1/2" O.S.B. OVER TYVEK.

2 x 6 STUDS @ 16" O.C.

29

TRUSS / GABLE-END WALL

SCALE 1/2" = 1'-0"

© 2011 Cengage Learning. All Rights Reserved. May not be scanned, copied or duplicated, or posted to a publicly accessible website, in whole or in part.

Supplemental Drawing 38–30

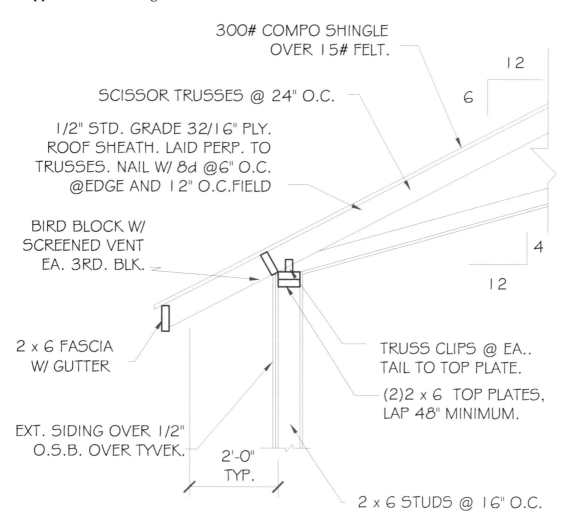

300# COMPO SHINGLE
OVER 15# FELT.

12

6

SCISSOR TRUSSES @ 24" O.C.

1/2" STD. GRADE 32/16" PLY.
ROOF SHEATH. LAID PERP. TO
TRUSSES. NAIL W/ 8d @6" O.C.
@EDGE AND 12" O.C.FIELD

4

12

BIRD BLOCK W/
SCREENED VENT
EA. 3RD. BLK.

2 x 6 FASCIA
W/ GUTTER

TRUSS CLIPS @ EA..
TAIL TO TOP PLATE.

(2)2 x 6 TOP PLATES,
LAP 48" MINIMUM.

EXT. SIDING OVER 1/2"
O.S.B. OVER TYVEK.

2'-0"
TYP.

2 x 6 STUDS @ 16" O.C.

30 SCISSOR TRUSS / PLATE

SCALE 1/2" = 1'-0"

© 2011 Cengage Learning. All Rights Reserved. May not be scanned, copied or duplicated, or posted to a publicly accessible website, in whole or in part.

Supplemental Drawing 38–31

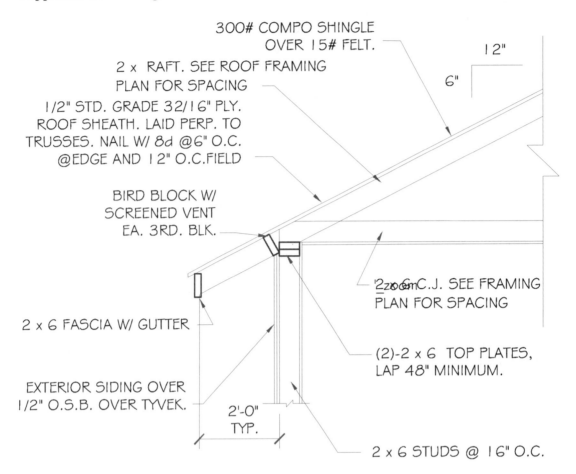

300# COMPO SHINGLE
OVER 15# FELT.

2 x RAFT. SEE ROOF FRAMING
PLAN FOR SPACING

1/2" STD. GRADE 32/16" PLY.
ROOF SHEATH. LAID PERP. TO
TRUSSES. NAIL W/ 8d @6" O.C.
@EDGE AND 12" O.C.FIELD

BIRD BLOCK W/
SCREENED VENT
EA. 3RD. BLK.

2 x 6 FASCIA W/ GUTTER

EXTERIOR SIDING OVER
1/2" O.S.B. OVER TYVEK.

12"

6"

2 x 6 C.J. SEE FRAMING
PLAN FOR SPACING

(2)-2 x 6 TOP PLATES,
LAP 48" MINIMUM.

2'-0"
TYP.

2 x 6 STUDS @ 16" O.C.

(31) RAFTER/WALL - EXPOSED EAVE

SCALE 1/2" = 1'-0"

© 2011 Cengage Learning. All Rights Reserved. May not be scanned, copied or duplicated, or posted to a publicly accessible website, in whole or in part.

Supplemental Drawing 38–32

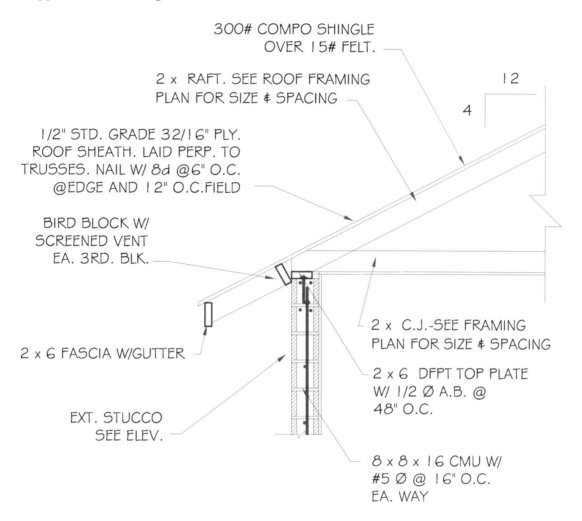

300# COMPO SHINGLE
OVER 15# FELT.

2 x RAFT. SEE ROOF FRAMING
PLAN FOR SIZE & SPACING

1/2" STD. GRADE 32/16" PLY.
ROOF SHEATH. LAID PERP. TO
TRUSSES. NAIL W/ 8d @6" O.C.
@EDGE AND 12" O.C.FIELD

BIRD BLOCK W/
SCREENED VENT
EA. 3RD. BLK.

2 x 6 FASCIA W/GUTTER

EXT. STUCCO
SEE ELEV.

12

4

2 x C.J.-SEE FRAMING
PLAN FOR SIZE & SPACING

2 x 6 DFPT TOP PLATE
W/ 1/2 Ø A.B. @
48" O.C.

8 x 8 x 16 CMU W/
#5 Ø @ 16" O.C.
EA. WAY

32 RAFTERS W/ CMU WALL

SCALE 1/2" = 1'-0"

© 2011 Cengage Learning. All Rights Reserved. May not be scanned, copied or duplicated, or posted to a publicly accessible website, in whole or in part.

Supplemental Drawing 38–33

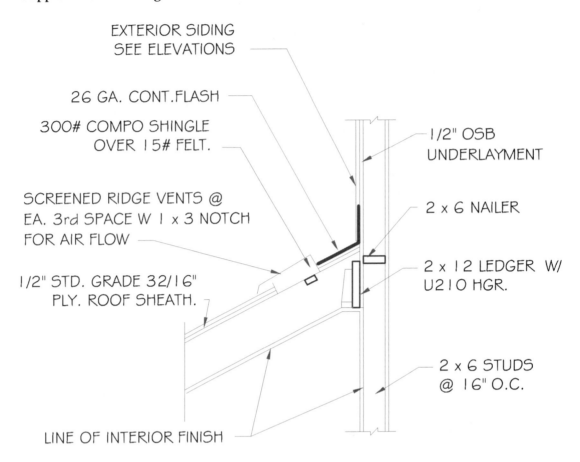

EXTERIOR SIDING
SEE ELEVATIONS

26 GA. CONT.FLASH

300# COMPO SHINGLE
OVER 15# FELT.

SCREENED RIDGE VENTS @
EA. 3rd SPACE W 1 x 3 NOTCH
FOR AIR FLOW

1/2" STD. GRADE 32/16"
PLY. ROOF SHEATH.

LINE OF INTERIOR FINISH

1/2" OSB
UNDERLAYMENT

2 x 6 NAILER

2 x 12 LEDGER W/
U210 HGR.

2 x 6 STUDS
@ 16" O.C.

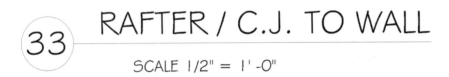

(33) RAFTER / C.J. TO WALL

SCALE 1/2" = 1'-0"

© 2011 Cengage Learning. All Rights Reserved. May not be scanned, copied or duplicated, or posted to a publicly accessible website, in whole or in part.

Supplemental Drawing 38–34

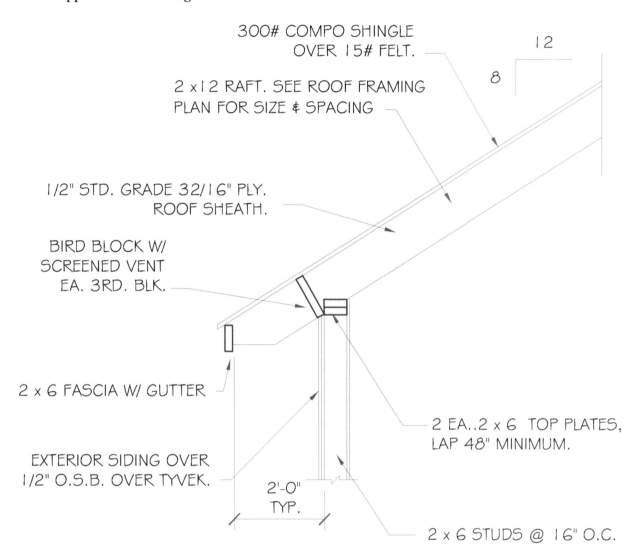

300# COMPO SHINGLE
OVER 15# FELT.

2 x 12 RAFT. SEE ROOF FRAMING
PLAN FOR SIZE & SPACING

12

8

1/2" STD. GRADE 32/16" PLY.
ROOF SHEATH.

BIRD BLOCK W/
SCREENED VENT
EA. 3RD. BLK.

2 x 6 FASCIA W/ GUTTER

2 EA..2 x 6 TOP PLATES,
LAP 48" MINIMUM.

EXTERIOR SIDING OVER
1/2" O.S.B. OVER TYVEK.

2'-0"
TYP.

2 x 6 STUDS @ 16" O.C.

34 RAFTER /C.J. /WALL: EXP. EAVE

SCALE 1/2" = 1'-0"

© 2011 Cengage Learning. All Rights Reserved. May not be scanned, copied or duplicated, or posted to a publicly accessible website, in whole or in part.

Supplemental Drawing 38–35

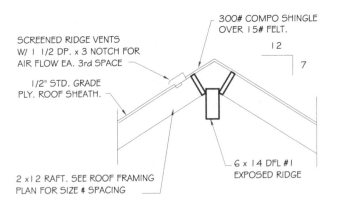

300# COMPO SHINGLE OVER 15# FELT.

12
7

SCREENED RIDGE VENTS W/ 1 1/2 DP. x 3 NOTCH FOR AIR FLOW EA. 3rd SPACE

1/2" STD. GRADE PLY. ROOF SHEATH.

6 x 14 DFL #1 EXPOSED RIDGE

2 x 12 RAFT. SEE ROOF FRAMING PLAN FOR SIZE & SPACING

35 RAFTER /C.J. / EXP. RIDGE

SCALE 1/2" = 1'-0"

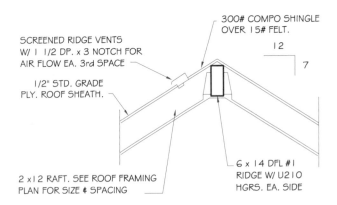

300# COMPO SHINGLE OVER 15# FELT.

12
7

SCREENED RIDGE VENTS W/ 1 1/2 DP. x 3 NOTCH FOR AIR FLOW EA. 3rd SPACE

1/2" STD. GRADE PLY. ROOF SHEATH.

6 x 14 DFL #1 RIDGE W/ U210 HGRS. EA. SIDE

2 x 12 RAFT. SEE ROOF FRAMING PLAN FOR SIZE & SPACING

35 RAFTER /C.J. / RIDGE

SCALE 1/2" = 1'-0"

© 2011 Cengage Learning. All Rights Reserved. May not be scanned, copied or duplicated, or posted to a publicly accessible website, in whole or in part.

CHAPTER 39
STAIR CONSTRUCTION AND LAYOUT

OBJECTIVES

When students have completed this chapter, they will:

- Determine stair rise and run.
- List, define, and locate ten stair components.
- Lay out; draw, using the proper line type and quality; and letter multiple types of stairs.

TEST ANSWERS

1. The horizontal member of the stair where the foot is placed as the stairs are used
2. 6'–8"
3. 7 3/4" IRC
4. The stringer or stair jack
5. 4" maximum
6. A guardrail is a railing placed around an opening for the stairs. A handrail is the inclined rail that can be used as the stairs are used.
7. 10' × 12" = 120" divided by the maximum rise equals 120/7.75 = 15.48 = 16 risers
8. Typical stair drawings are shown in Figures 39–4, 14, 17, and 18 of the text.
9. 9' × 12 = 108 rise

    108 ÷ 7.75 = 13.9 risers = 14/13 treads

    13 × 10" = 130" = 10.8' run
10. 3 × 12"

CHAPTER 39 PROBLEM SOLUTIONS

This chapter has no specific drawing problems. For a complete set of plans, a stair section should be drawn. Although solutions will vary greatly depending on the materials used and the code that is followed, the following drawings can be used as a guideline:

The stair drawings for the home in Problem 18–1 is contained in the sections and details provided for solution 38–1A.

The solution for the home in Problem 18–2 is contained in the sections and details provided for solution 38–2A and would resemble Figure 39–12.

The solution for the home in Problem 18–3 would resemble Figure 39–12.

Home plans 18–4 through 18–12 do not require drawings for stairs.

The stair drawings for the home in Problem 18–13 is contained in the sections and details provided for solution 38–13B.

The solution for the home in Problem 18–14 would resemble Figure 39–12 and Figure 39–21B.

The solution for the home in Problem 18–15 is contained in the sections and details provided for solution 38–15A and 15B and would resemble Figure 39–12 and Figure 39–21A.

The solution for the home in Problem 18–16 is contained in the sections and details provided for solution 38–16A and would resemble Figure 39–20.

The solution for the home in Problem 18–17 is contained in the sections and details provided for solution 38–17A and would resemble Figure 39–20.

© 2011 Cengage Learning. All Rights Reserved. May not be scanned, copied or duplicated, or posted to a publicly accessible website, in whole or in part.

The solution for the home in Problem 18–18 would resemble Figure 39–18 and Figure 39–21B.

The solution for the home in Problem 18–19 is contained in the sections and details provided for solution 38–19A and would resemble Figure 39–12.

The solution for the home in Problem 18–20 is contained in the sections and details provided for solution 38–20A and would resemble Figure 39–12.

The solution for the home in Problem 18–21 is contained in the sections and details provided for solution 38–21A and would resemble Figure 39–12.

Home plan 18–22 does not require drawings for stairs.

CHAPTER 40
FIREPLACE CONSTRUCTION AND LAYOUT

OBJECTIVES

When students have completed this chapter, they will:

- Identify and describe common fireplace components.
- Draw, label, and dimension a fireplace section using CADD or manual methods.
- Draw, label, and dimension a fireplace elevation using CADD or manual methods.

TEST ANSWERS

1. The damper prevents heat from escaping up the chimney when the fireplace is not in use.
2. The firebox and the chimney
3. 36" × 26"
4. 44" × 26" = 1144 sq in. Flue size is generally required to equal either 1/8 or 1/10 of the fireplace opening.
5. 13 × 17 oval
6. Bold object lines represent the outline of the masonry, and thin parallel lines at a 45-degree angle represent the masonry.
7. To detail the front face showing such items as the size of the fireplace opening, mantle size and location, hearth height, and face material
8. Because of the repetitive nature of chimney construction, a stock detail can be used to show common construction material.
9. Anchors should be placed at each floor and ceiling level.
10. 16" min. < 6 sq ft/20" ≥ 6 sq ft.

CHAPTER 40 PROBLEM SOLUTIONS

Home Problems 18–1, 18–3, 18–4, 18–5, 18–6, 18–7, 18–11, 18–19 and 18–22 require no fireplace drawings.

Home Problems 18–8, 18–10, 18–12, 18–20, and 18–21 each have a masonry fireplace and would need a drawing similar to Figure 40–18 or Figure 40–23.

Home Problems 18–9, 18–13, 18–14, 18–15, 18–16, 18–17, 18–18 each have a self-venting fireplace or zero-clearance fireplace and would require no fireplace drawings.

© 2011 Cengage Learning. All Rights Reserved. May not be scanned, copied or duplicated, or posted to a publicly accessible website, in whole or in part.

SECTION

Presentation Drawings and Renderings

CHAPTER 41
PRESENTATION DRAWINGS

OBJECTIVES

When students have completed this chapter, they will:
- Be familiar with common types of presentation drawings.
- List and describe common media used for presentation drawings.
- Be familiar with drawing methods used for presentation drawings.

TEST ANSWERS

1. Presentation drawings are used to show basic design concepts from the design team to the owner or other interested persons. They are often a very valuable part of public hearings and marketing programs.

2. Information on presentation drawings is usually presented in less structural detail and in a more artistic fashion.

3. The artistic ability of the drafter, the type of drawing to be done, and the client.

4. Renderings—artistic presentation of the structure as it will appear in a natural setting

    Elevations—similar information as found on the working elevations with the addition of shade, plants, people, and automobiles

    Floor Plan—room relationships, furniture layout, traffic flow

    Site Plan—similar information to the plat plan but a more artistic method is used

    Sections—floors and ceiling levels, vertical relationships, sun angle

5. Renderings

6. Sketch paper, vellum, mylar, illustration board

7. Vellum mounted on illustration board

8. Colored pencils, felt tip pens, water colors, pastels

9. A similar scale to the floor plan

10. 1/4" = 1'-0" or 1/8" = 1'-0"

© 2011 Cengage Learning. All Rights Reserved. May not be scanned, copied or duplicated, or posted to a publicly accessible website, in whole or in part.

CHAPTER 41 PROBLEM SOLUTIONS

To complete the requirements of this chapter, students are required to develop a presentation package for the home they started in Chapter 18. Solutions for the projects will vary widely, but should reflect the minimum requested in the project standards.

CHAPTER 41
PRESENTATION DRAWINGS
PERSPECTIVE DRAWING TECHNIQUES

OBJECTIVES

When students have completed this chapter, they will:

- Be familiar with three types of perspective drawings.
- Describe six terms common to perspective drawings.
- Lay out a structure using two-point drawing methods.
- Lay out a room using the one-point drawing method.

TEST ANSWERS

S1–1. One- and two-point perspectives

S1–2. On the horizon line at the vanishing points

S1–3. Movement in any direction will affect the size of the structure. As the SP is moved toward the PP, the structure will be smaller. As it is moved away from the PP, it will become larger. As the SP is moved to the left of the THL, the left side of the structure will be accented. As the SP is moved to the right of the THL, the right surface of the structure is accented.

S1–4. Interior surfaces and courtyards

S1–5.

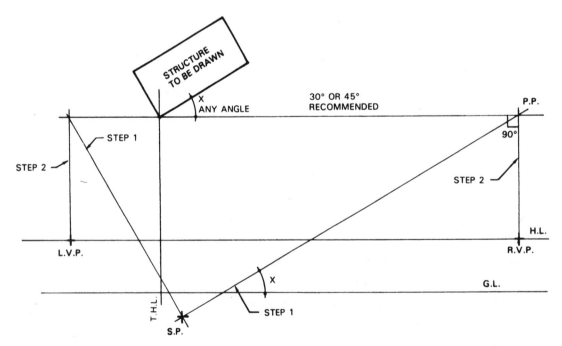

S1–6. The floor plan affects the height of the drawing and the amount of surface area that will be shown.

S1–7. Heights are projected from the elevation to the true height line.

S1–8. Typically used for drawing very tall buildings

© 2011 Cengage Learning. All Rights Reserved. May not be scanned, copied or duplicated, or posted to a publicly accessible website, in whole or in part.

S1–9. A floor plan with the outline of the roof shape and an elevation

S1–10. The ground line

CHAPTER 41–S1 PROBLEM SOLUTIONS

Problem S1–1

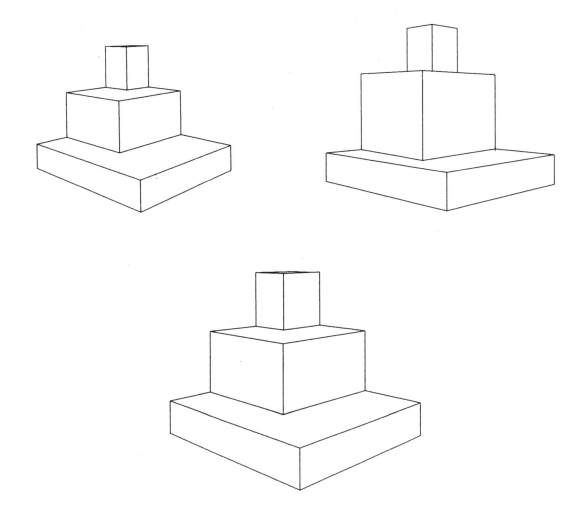

© 2011 Cengage Learning. All Rights Reserved. May not be scanned, copied or duplicated, or posted to a publicly accessible website, in whole or in part.

Problem S1–2

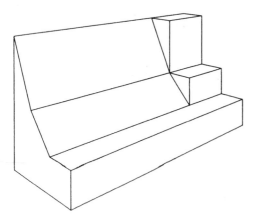

Problem S1–4

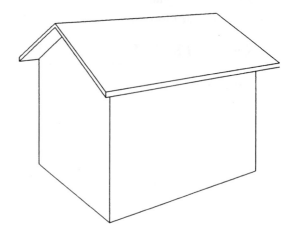

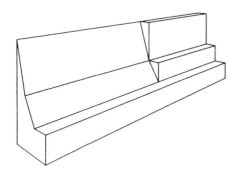

Problem S1–3   Solutions will vary greatly.

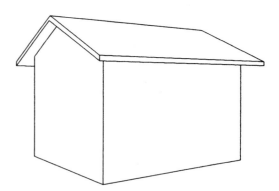

Problem S1–5

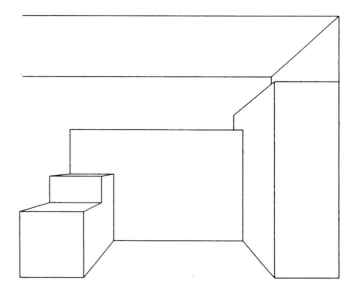

© 2011 Cengage Learning. All Rights Reserved. May not be scanned, copied or duplicated, or posted to a publicly accessible website, in whole or in part.

Problem S1–6

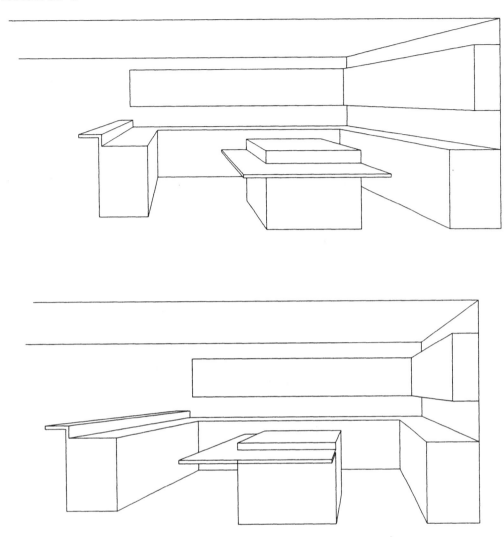

NOTE: *The drawing possibilities for solutions to Problems 41–7 and 41–8 are unlimited. As student solutions are examined, look for lines that do not converge to the same vanishing point.*

CHAPTER 41
PRESENTATION DRAWINGS
RENDERING METHODS FOR PERSPECTIVE
DRAWINGS

OBJECTIVES

When students have completed this chapter, they will:

- Calculate how shades and shadows are cast.
- Identify and represent methods used to represent texture in perspective drawings.
- Identify common types of entourage.
- Use common methods to render a one- or two-point perspective.

© 2011 Cengage Learning. All Rights Reserved. May not be scanned, copied or duplicated, or posted to a publicly accessible website, in whole or in part.

TEST ANSWERS

S2–1. a. A vertical wall will cast a shadow on a horizontal surface in the direction that the light rays are traveling.

b. A shadow on a plane caused by a surface parallel to the plane will cast a shadow that is parallel to the surface.

S2–2.

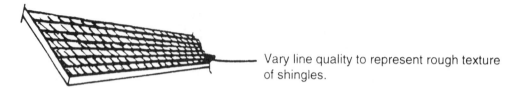

Vary line quality to represent rough texture of shingles.

S2–3. Lots of practice, a scrap book of renderings by professionals, and careful observation of materials in their natural state

S2–4. 30, 45, or 50 degrees. These angles are locked in on a standard drafting machine as the head is rotated and will save time by not having to hunt for these degrees.

S2–5. The light source will need to be moved so that light rays are no longer parallel to the picture plane.

S2–6. Ground cover, trees, people, and cars. Helps create an attractive, realistic drawing.

S2–7. a. Only use to help show the location, scale, and usage of the structure.

b. Draw with only enough detail to illustrate the desired material or object.

c. Never obscure the structure.

S2–8. Examples will vary greatly. Glass can be left clear, may have an outdoor scene drawn in the window, ink wash, or may be rendered solid black with small areas of white to indicate reflection. Examples should reflect methods shown throughout the chapter.

S2–9.

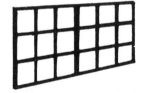

S2–10. Types of balance to be used are:

Areas of contrast

Placement of the structure

Placement and type of entourage

CHAPTER 41–S2 PROBLEM SOLUTIONS

NOTE: The drawing possibilities for solutions to Problems S2–1 and S2–2 are unlimited. As student solutions are re-examined, look for lines that do not converge to the same vanishing point. Students must also be careful to keep materials in the background from obstructing materials in the foreground. Shade and shadows should be used to accent changes of planes and not as a means of obscuring the structure. Shadows should originate from the same light sources. Materials should be clearly distinguished and proportioned.

© 2011 Cengage Learning. All Rights Reserved. May not be scanned, copied or duplicated, or posted to a publicly accessible website, in whole or in part.

CHAPTER 42
BUILDING CODES AND COMMERCIAL DESIGN

OBJECTIVES

When students have completed this chapter, they will:

- Describe how building codes relate to commercial structures.
- Identify and determine occupancy groups.
- Determine required separation ratings between mixed ratings.
- Determine type of construction.
- Determine basic allowable floor area and maximum height.
- Identify minimum egress and access requirements.

TEST ANSWERS

1. Group B
2. 1-hour rating. (R.3/U)
3. 3 levels
4. 8,500 sq ft
5. 1 hr fire resistance is required.
6. 1-hour rating
7. 3 stories for type V construction, and 4 stories for types II & III
8. B; V-A.; 3 levels; 18,000 sq ft; 30 per sq ft at basement and 60 per sq ft at other floor
9. A 10-unit apartment building is an R-2.
10. A clothing store is type M.
11. A 1-hour rating is required for a type III-A floor.
12. The building would be an H-2 occupancy. With a III-B rating the building can be 1 level high and 7,000 sq ft.
13. A building with an M occupancy can be within 5' of the property line if the walls are made of 2-hr. materials.
14. 500 sq ft.
15. The maximum occupant load is 50

© 2011 Cengage Learning. All Rights Reserved. May not be scanned, copied or duplicated, or posted to a publicly accessible website, in whole or in part.

CHAPTER 42 PROBLEM SOLUTIONS

Chapter 42 of the textbook contains no problems.

CHAPTER 43
COMMON COMMERCIAL CONSTRUCTION MATERIALS

OBJECTIVES

When students have completed this chapter, they will:

- Identify common uses for wood, timber, and engineered lumber in commercial structures.
- Identify common uses for concrete blocks in commercial construction.
- Describe common uses for poured concrete in commercial construction.
- Identify common uses for steel in commercial structures.
- Identify three types of common connection methods used on commercial structures.

TEST ANSWERS

1. If covered with two layers of 5/8" type 'x' gyp. bd. on each side or two layers of type 'x' on the interior side and 1" of stucco or plaster over one layer of type 'x' gyp. bd. on the exterior side

2. Usually the cost and labor involved will not fit within the residential budget.

3. Beams are typically placed at about 20 to 30 feet apart. Purlins are then used to span between these beams. Joists are then used to span between the purlins.

4. Glu-lam = between 2000 and 2400; DFL #1 = 1350

5. Because the wood will char but not burn through; a steel beam will deform in fires

6. Structural or engineering drawings and shop drawings

7. By placing steel cables held in tension in the concrete forms prior to placing the concrete. The concrete is then allowed to harden around the steel, which places the beam in compression.

8. Exposed metal flanges are typically welded to a column or to the flange of another panel.

9. Up to four stories in height

10.

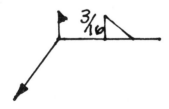

11. #4 = 1/2", #8 = 1", #14 = 1 3/4"

12. A nested joist is a steel joist encased around another joist.

13. Rigid frames are connected by bolts and welded connections.

14. The size of the member to be connected, the bolt diameter, length, spacing, and washer size

15. Common nails are most typically used for construction.

16. Steel is represented by a solid circle in end view and is not represented on the floor plan.

17. Anchor bolt, carriage bolt, high strength, machine bolt

18. 8d nails are 2 1/2" long.

© 2011 Cengage Learning. All Rights Reserved. May not be scanned, copied or duplicated, or posted to a publicly accessible website, in whole or in part.

19. Centered in the wall above grade, and 2" from the side opposite the soil for below grade walls.

20. The approximate joist depth, the series designation, and the chord size and spacing are normally given when an open-web joist is specified.

21. 3-8d connect a rafter to a top plate. 8d common are used to nail 3/4" plywood to joists.

22. See Figure 43–60.

23. Each is a nailing term. *Field* nails are the nails placed in the middle of a piece of plywood. *Edge* nails are the nails placed at the edge of individual pieces of plywood. *Boundary* nails are placed at the edge of an area of plywood.

24. W, S, M, and C shapes are often used for steel frames.

25. The stud size, style, gage, and manufacturer should be specified for steel studs.

26. To help spread loads evenly across material to avoid crushing, and to resist uplift

27. Smooth rebar is used when expansion is needed, and deformed bars are used to bond to concrete.

28. The manufacturer, type of decking, depth, and gage should be specified in the project manual and sections and details.

29. Weld symbol will be similar to Figure 43–55.

30. A continuous beam can have an X, a noncontinuous beam has a diagonal line between corners, and a glu-lam has horizontal lines placed at 1 1/2" to represent the laminations.

31. Butt, lap, Tee, outside corner, and edge joint

32. The symbol should resemble Figure 43–58c.

33. Steel shapes are bolted for a temporary connection and welded for final placement.

34. Laminated beams are used for their appearance, strength, fire resistance, and wide variety of shapes.

35. Poured concrete walls are represented by pairs of bold parallel lines. Concrete block walls are represented by pairs of bold parallel lines with 45° cross-hatching.

36. The reinforcement is #6 (round) bars placed at 8" O.C. each way at the top and bottom of the pier.

37. The symbol should resemble Figure 43–60c.

38. 3 1/8", 5 1/8", 6 3/4", 8 3/4" and 10 3/4" are the common widths for glu-lam beams.

39. Student answers will vary.

40. Codes include the IBC, or a modified version of the IBC specific to country or state requirements.

CHAPTER 43 PROBLEM SOLUTIONS

Chapter 43 of the textbook contains no drawing problems.

CHAPTER 44
COMMERCIAL CONSTRUCTION PROJECTS

OBJECTIVES

When students have completed this chapter, they will:

- Describe common office practice typically used to draw commercial projects.
- Identify common types of commercial drawings.

TEST ANSWERS

1. Architect, Engineering, Designer/Drafter

2. Sweet's catalogs (vendor catalogs), building codes

© 2011 Cengage Learning. All Rights Reserved. May not be scanned, copied or duplicated, or posted to a publicly accessible website, in whole or in part.

3. A plan showing the location, starting point, and type of material used to form the ceiling. The plan will also show light panels and ceiling-mounted heat registers.

4. By state law, commercial calculations are required to be signed by a licensed architect or engineer. In residential drafting, engineer's calcs are used to determine sizes of retaining walls and seismic and wind loads. In commercial drafting, calcs are provided for the entire structure.

5. Plumbing plan shows how sewer and fresh water will be routed; schematic plumbing diagrams

6. As a reference drawing showing basic shape with several details drawn at a larger scale to provide more detail, or as several partial sections

7. Grading plans showing existing and finished soil contours, and a landscape plan showing planting and watering methods

8. Statement of the problem, mathematical formula, and written specification. The problem will help the drafter find the material in question. The math work will not be of use to the drafter. The solution must be specified in the plans by the drafter in its correct form, which may require the drafter to do research in vendor catalogs.

9. Site, grading, and landscaping

10. The slab-on-grade plan shows the concrete floor. The foundation plan shows the support system, which is placed below the grade.

11. The architectural drawings are the floor plan, enlarged floor plans, roof plan, reflected ceiling plan, interior elevations, elevations, sections, exterior details, interior details, and vertical circulation drawings.

12. A floor plan, an enlarged floor plan, and a reference plan

13. A floor plan is the result of passing a cutting plane through a building and looking down. The reflected ceiling plan is the result of looking up.

14. The finished floor lines, match lines, grid line markers, elevation (height) symbols, section markers, and detail markers

15. To protect the structure from fire from surrounding buildings, and to hide HVAC equipment

16. This type of information is typically found on the roof plan or details related to the roof plan.

17. Elevations can be specified with dimensions, or by an elevation symbol.

18. Wall sections are used to show the construction of one specific area. A full section will show general information about a specific area.

19. Common symbols include grid markers, elevation markers, section markers, details and room names, and numbers.

20. Notes on a detail will be much more specific than the generic notes placed on a section.

21. Interior elevations can be referenced to the floor plan with titles such as East wall, or by using a reference arrow.

22. Interior elevations are usually placed on the A-500 sheets.

23. Stairs and ramps are governed by the building code and the ADA.

24. Information about the interior finish of an elevator car would typically be in the A-700 drawings.

25. Horizontal and vertical grids are used to divide and reference space on a large building.

26. The framing plan is used to show the size and location of the materials used to form the skeleton of the building.

27. Tables are used to describe beams and columns.

28. Steel elevations are used to show how the structural steel will relate to the architectural members of the structure.

© 2011 Cengage Learning. All Rights Reserved. May not be scanned, copied or duplicated, or posted to a publicly accessible website, in whole or in part.

29. Individual panel elevations are used to show the size, shape, and reinforcing of each panel.

30. North arrow, grid markers, section markers, detail markers, elevation symbols, and schedule reference symbols

CHAPTER 44 PROBLEM SOLUTIONS

Chapter 44 of the textbook contains no problems.

CHAPTER 45
STRUCTURAL DRAFTING

OBJECTIVES

When students have completed this chapter, they will:

- Identify and draw the needed plans to represent the structural portions of a structure separate from a floor plan. This would include:
    1. a floor plan
    2. a framing plan
    3. a roof framing plan
    4. a slab plan
    5. a foundation plan
- Identify, draw, and specify the materials needed to represent the structural considerations in details related to wood, timber, concrete, and steel.

TEST ANSWERS

Chapter 45 contains no written test answers.

© 2011 Cengage Learning. All Rights Reserved. May not be scanned, copied or duplicated, or posted to a publicly accessible website, in whole or in part.

CHAPTER 45 PROBLEM SOLUTIONS

Problem 45–1

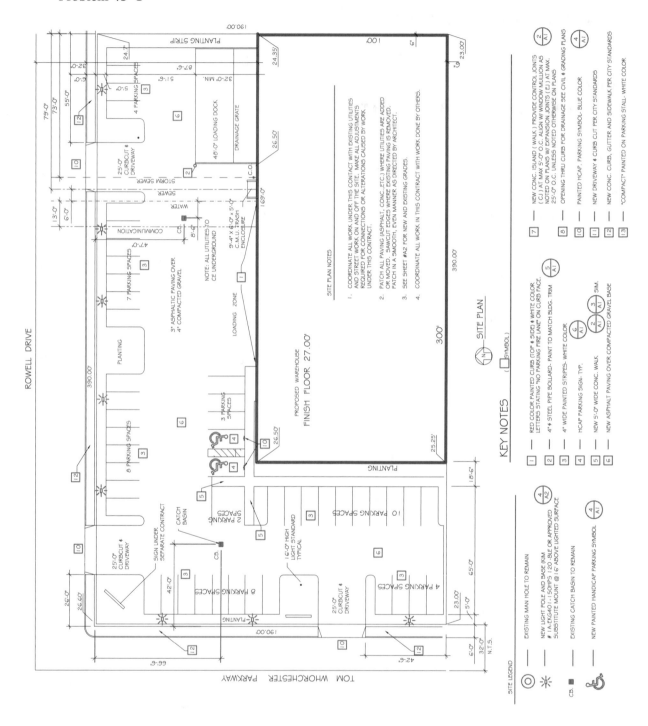

© 2011 Cengage Learning. All Rights Reserved. May not be scanned, copied or duplicated, or posted to a publicly accessible website, in whole or in part.

Problem 45–2

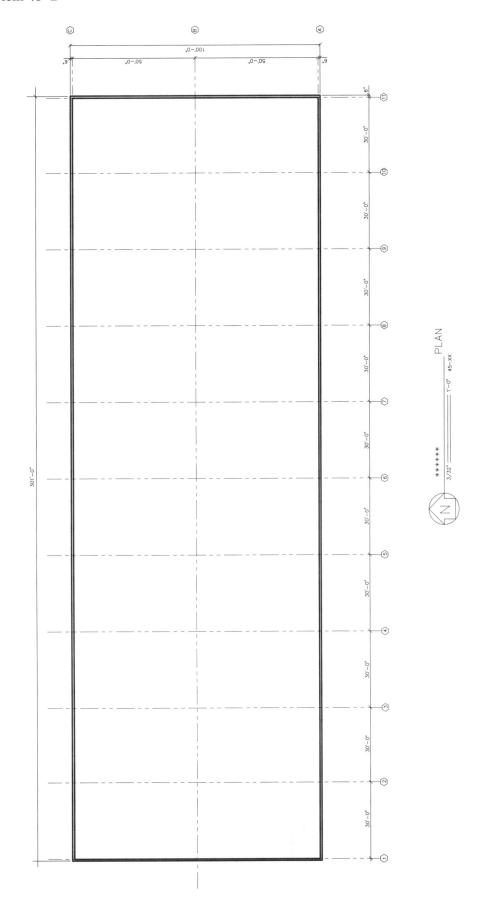

© 2011 Cengage Learning. All Rights Reserved. May not be scanned, copied or duplicated, or posted to a publicly accessible website, in whole or in part.

Problem 45–3A

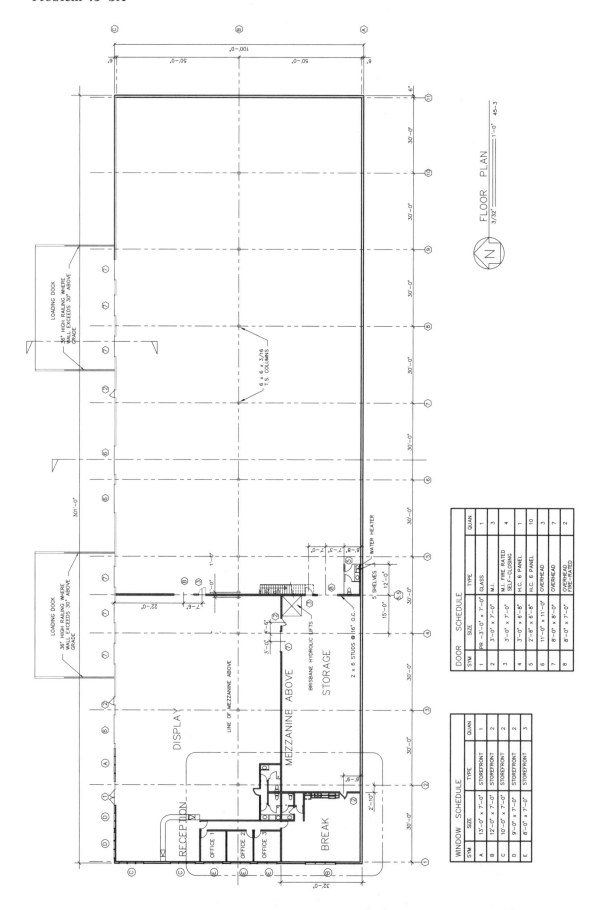

FLOOR PLAN
3/32" = 1'-0"   45-3

N

DOOR SCHEDULE

SYM	SIZE	TYPE	QUAN
1	PR –3'-0" x 7'-0"	GLASS	1
2	3'-0" x 7'-0"	M.I.	3
3	3'-0" x 7'-0"	M.I. FIRE RATED SELF–CLOSING	4
4	3'-0" x 6'-8"	H.C. 6 PANEL	1
5	2'-8" x 6'-8"	H.C. 6 PANEL	10
6	11'-0" x 11'-0"	OVERHEAD	3
7	8'-0" x 8'-0"	OVERHEAD	7
8	8'-0" x 7'-0"	OVERHEAD FIRE–RATED	2

WINDOW SCHEDULE

SYM	SIZE	TYPE	QUAN
A	13'-0" x 7'-0"	STOREFRONT	1
B	12'-0" x 7'-0"	STOREFRONT	2
C	10'-0" x 7'-0"	STOREFRONT	2
D	9'-0" x 7'-0"	STOREFRONT	2
E	8'-0" x 7'-0"	STOREFRONT	3

© 2011 Cengage Learning. All Rights Reserved. May not be scanned, copied or duplicated, or posted to a publicly accessible website, in whole or in part.

Problem 45–3B

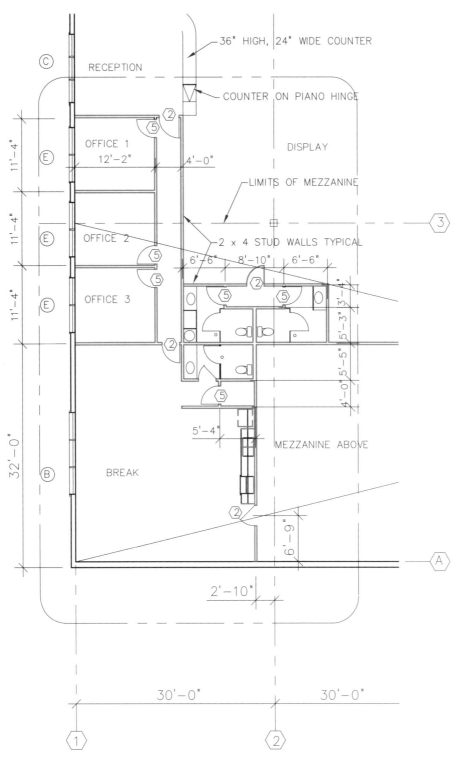

36" HIGH, 24" WIDE COUNTER

RECEPTION

COUNTER ON PIANO HINGE

DISPLAY

OFFICE 1
12'-2"   4'-0"

LIMITS OF MEZZANINE

OFFICE 2

2 x 4 STUD WALLS TYPICAL

6'-6"   8'-10"   6'-6"

OFFICE 3

5'-3" 3'-4"

4'-0" 5'-5"

MEZZANINE ABOVE

5'-4"

BREAK

6'-9"

2'-10"

11'-4"   11'-4"   11'-4"   32'-0"

30'-0"   30'-0"

NOTE: ALL BATHROOMS TO
CONFORM TO ICC/ANSI A117.1−2003

ENLARGED FLOOR PLAN
1/4" ═══════════ 1'-0"   45−3B

© 2011 Cengage Learning. All Rights Reserved. May not be scanned, copied or duplicated, or posted to a publicly accessible website, in whole or in part.

Problem 45–4

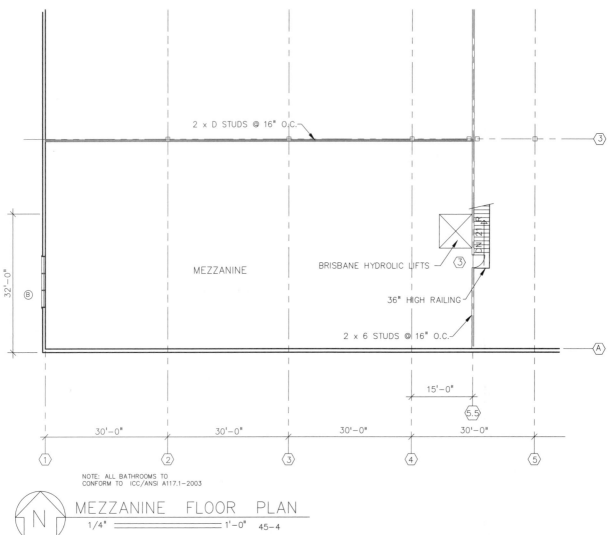

2 x D STUDS @ 16" O.C.

MEZZANINE

BRISBANE HYDROLIC LIFTS

36" HIGH RAILING

2 x 6 STUDS @ 16" O.C.

DN 21 R

32'-0"

15'-0"

30'-0"   30'-0"   30'-0"   30'-0"

NOTE: ALL BATHROOMS TO
CONFORM TO ICC/ANSI A117.1–2003

MEZZANINE   FLOOR   PLAN
1/4" ═══ 1'-0"   45-4

© 2011 Cengage Learning. All Rights Reserved. May not be scanned, copied or duplicated, or posted to a publicly accessible website, in whole or in part.

Problem 45–5

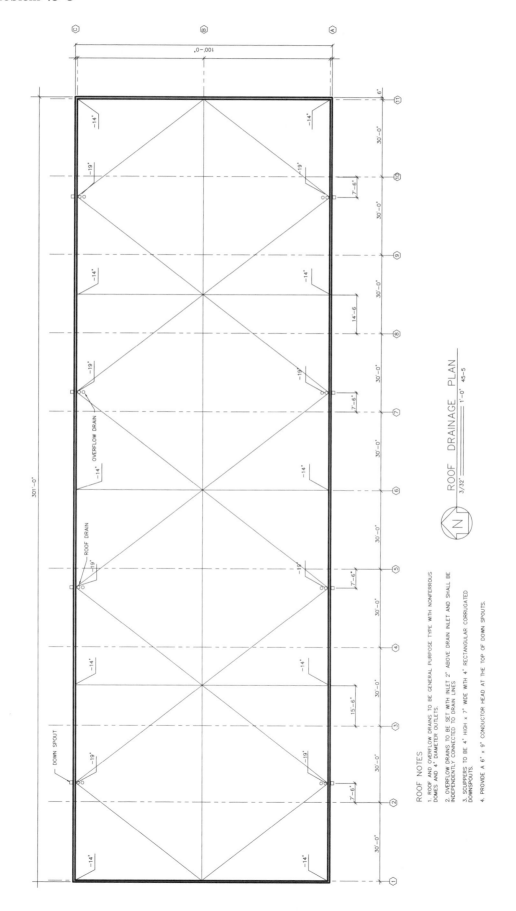

ROOF DRAINAGE PLAN
3/32" = 1'-0"   45–5

ROOF NOTES

1. ROOF AND OVERFLOW DRAINS TO BE GENERAL PURPOSE TYPE WITH NONFERROUS DOMES AND 4" DIAMETER OUTLETS.

2. OVERFLOW DRAINS TO BE SET WITH INLET 2" ABOVE DRAIN INLET AND SHALL BE INDEPENDENTLY CONNECTED TO DRAIN LINES

3. SCUPPERS TO BE 4" HIGH x 7" WIDE WITH 4" RECTANGULAR CORRUGATED DOWNSPOUTS.

4. PROVIDE A 6" x 9" CONDUCTOR HEAD AT THE TOP OF DOWN SPOUTS.

© 2011 Cengage Learning. All Rights Reserved. May not be scanned, copied or duplicated, or posted to a publicly accessible website, in whole or in part.

Problem 45–6A

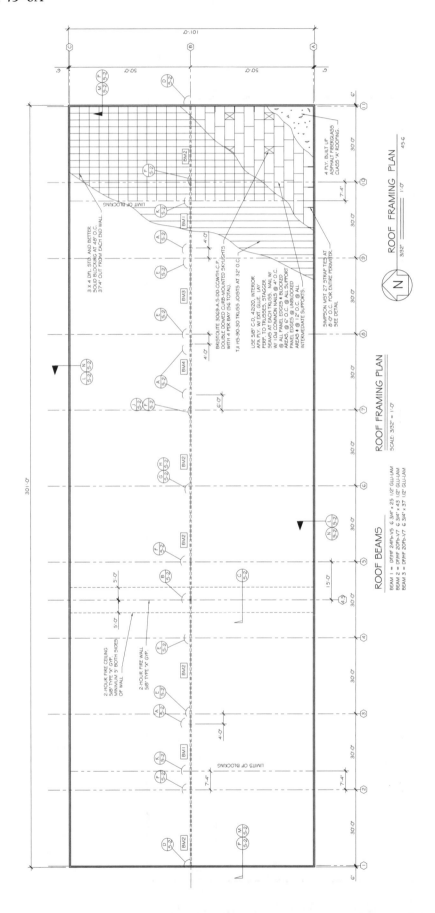

© 2011 Cengage Learning. All Rights Reserved. May not be scanned, copied or duplicated, or posted to a publicly accessible website, in whole or in part.

Problem 45–7

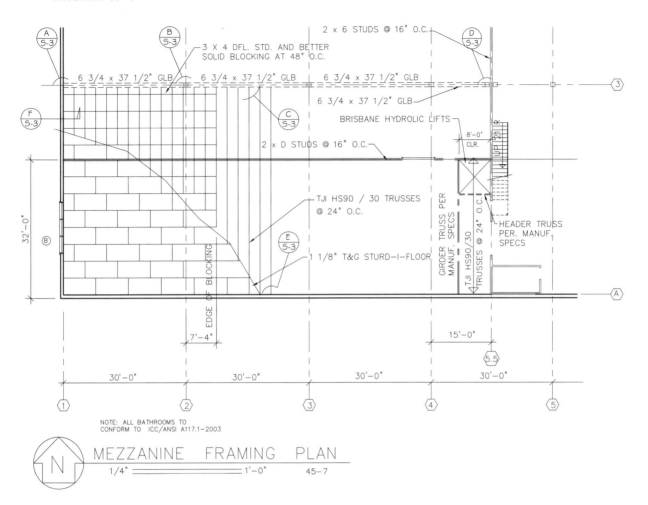

2 × 6 STUDS @ 16" O.C.

3 X 4 DFL. STD. AND BETTER
SOLID BLOCKING AT 48" O.C.

6 3/4 x 37 1/2" GLB   6 3/4 x 37 1/2" GLB   6 3/4 x 37 1/2" GLB

6 3/4 x 37 1/2" GLB

BRISBANE HYDROLIC LIFTS

8'-0"
CLR.

2 x D STUDS @ 16" O.C.

TJI HS90 / 30 TRUSSES
@ 24" O.C.

HEADER TRUSS
PER. MANUF.
SPECS

GIRDER TRUSS PER
MANUF. SPECS

TJI HS90/30
TRUSSES @ 24" O.C.

EDGE OF BLOCKING

1 1/8" T&G STURD-I-FLOOR

32'-0"

7'-4"

15'-0"

5.5

30'-0"   30'-0"   30'-0"   30'-0"

① ② ③ ④ ⑤

NOTE: ALL BATHROOMS TO
CONFORM TO ICC/ANSI A117.1–2003

MEZZANINE FRAMING PLAN
1/4" = 1'-0"   45-7

© 2011 Cengage Learning. All Rights Reserved. May not be scanned, copied or duplicated, or posted to a publicly accessible website, in whole or in part.

Problem 45–8

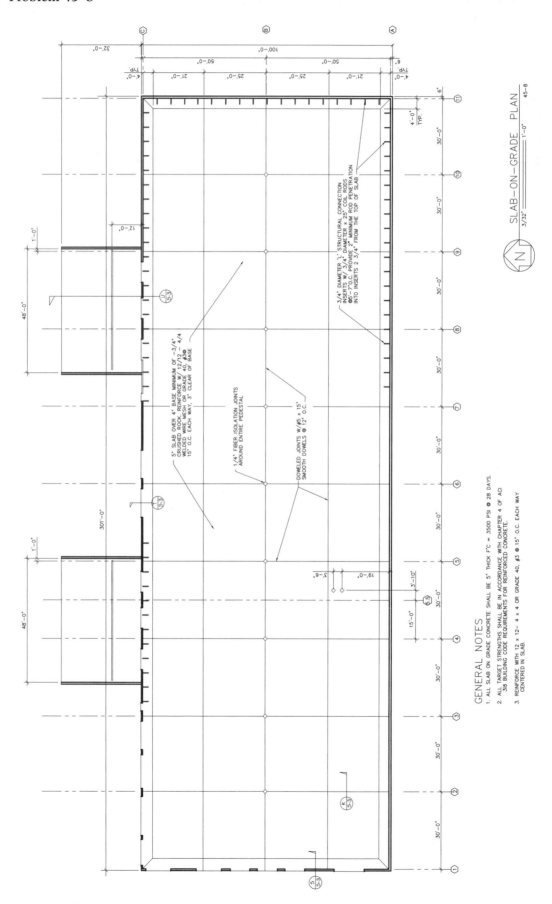

© 2011 Cengage Learning. All Rights Reserved. May not be scanned, copied or duplicated, or posted to a publicly accessible website, in whole or in part.

Problem 45–9

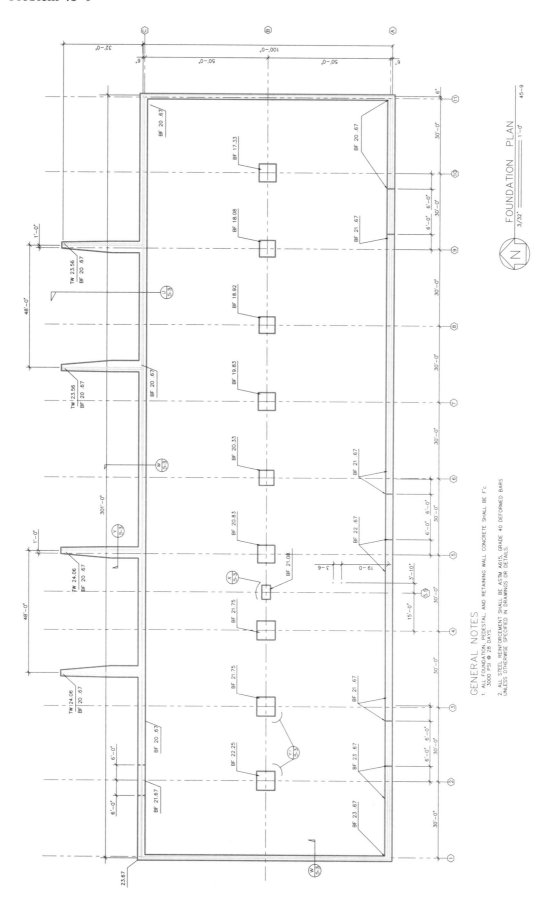

FOUNDATION PLAN
3/32" = 1'-0"   45-9

GENERAL NOTES
1. ALL FOUNDATION, PEDESTAL, AND RETAINING WALL CONCRETE SHALL BE F'c
   3000 PSI @ 28 DAYS.

2. ALL STEEL REINFORCEMENT SHALL BE ASTM A615, GRADE 40 DEFORMED BARS
   UNLESS OTHERWISE SPECIFIED IN DRAWINGS OR DETAILS.

© 2011 Cengage Learning. All Rights Reserved. May not be scanned, copied or duplicated, or posted to a publicly accessible website, in whole or in part.

Problem 45–10 Details A–F

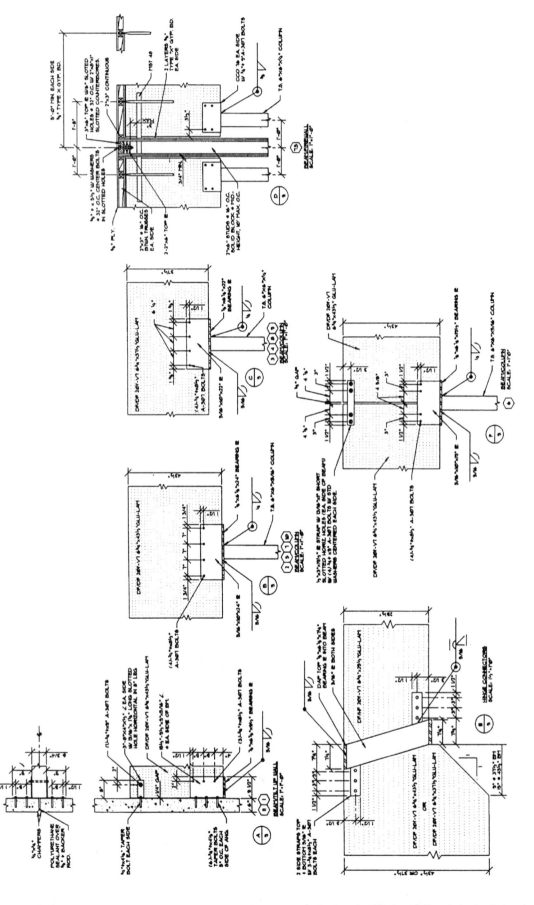

© 2011 Cengage Learning. All Rights Reserved. May not be scanned, copied or duplicated, or posted to a publicly accessible website, in whole or in part.

Problem 45–10 Detail G and Problem 45–11A and B Details H–P

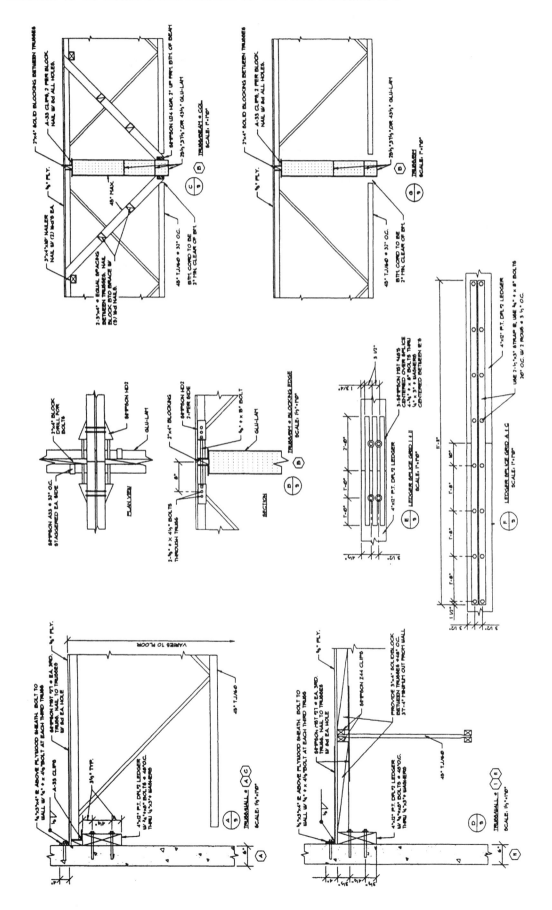

© 2011 Cengage Learning. All Rights Reserved. May not be scanned, copied or duplicated, or posted to a publicly accessible website, in whole or in part.

Problem 45–12 Floor Details

A—Beam to Concrete Wall: The solution for this detail should resemble the drawing created from sketch 45–10D with adjustments made for the beam size.

B—Beam to Column: The solution for this detail should resemble the drawing created from sketch 45–10E with adjustments made for the beam size.

C—Truss to Beam: The solution for this detail should resemble the drawing created from sketch 45–11A with adjustments made for the truss and beam sizes.

D—Beam to Column at Wood Wall: The solution for this detail should resemble the drawing created from sketch 45-10B with adjustments made for the columns and beam size. The detail should reflect each column extending to the roof level, with the floor beam only placed on the west side of the wall.

E—Truss to Wall Ledger, Perpendicular: The solution for this detail should resemble the drawing created from sketch 45–12N with adjustments made for the truss size.

E—Truss to Wall Ledger, Parallel: The solution for this detail should resemble the drawing created from sketch 45–12P with adjustments made for the truss size.

© 2011 Cengage Learning. All Rights Reserved. May not be scanned, copied or duplicated, or posted to a publicly accessible website, in whole or in part.

Problem 45–13

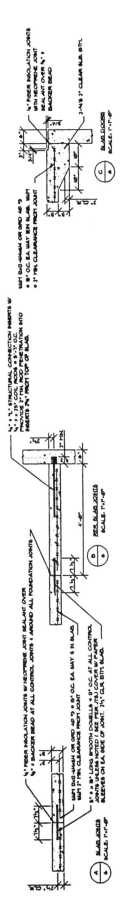

© 2011 Cengage Learning. All Rights Reserved. May not be scanned, copied or duplicated, or posted to a publicly accessible website, in whole or in part.

Problem 45–14

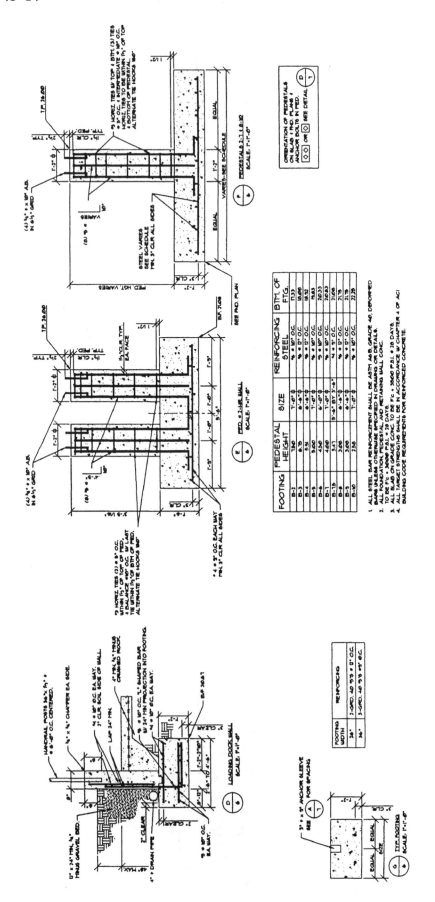

© 2011 Cengage Learning. All Rights Reserved. May not be scanned, copied or duplicated, or posted to a publicly accessible website, in whole or in part.

Problem 45–15

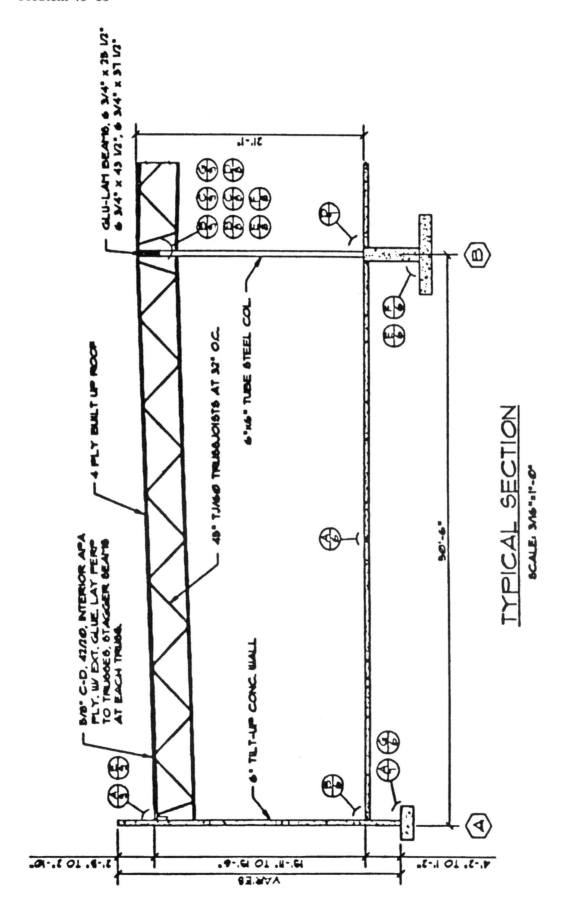

GLU-LAM BEAMS, 6 3/4" x 28 1/2"
6 3/4" x 43 1/2", 6 3/4" x 57 1/2"

4 PLY BUILT UP ROOF

5/8" C-D, 47/0, INTERIOR APA
PLY. W/ EXT. GLUE LAY PERP
TO TRUSSES, STAGGER SEAMS
AT EACH TRUSS.

48" TJ/60 TRUSSJOISTS AT 32" O.C.

6"x6" TUBE STEEL COL.

6" TILT-UP CONC. WALL

21'-1"

90'-6"

VARIES

TYPICAL SECTION
SCALE: 3/16"=1'-0"

© 2011 Cengage Learning. All Rights Reserved. May not be scanned, copied or duplicated, or posted to a publicly accessible website, in whole or in part.

Problem 45–16

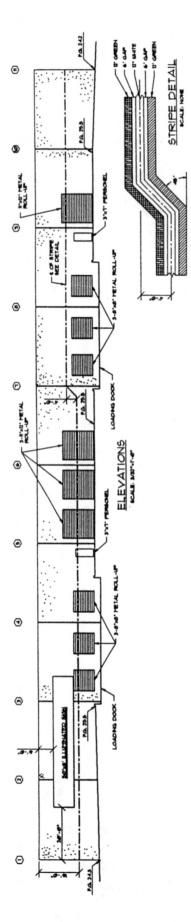

© 2011 Cengage Learning. All Rights Reserved. May not be scanned, copied or duplicated, or posted to a publicly accessible website, in whole or in part.

Problem 45–17

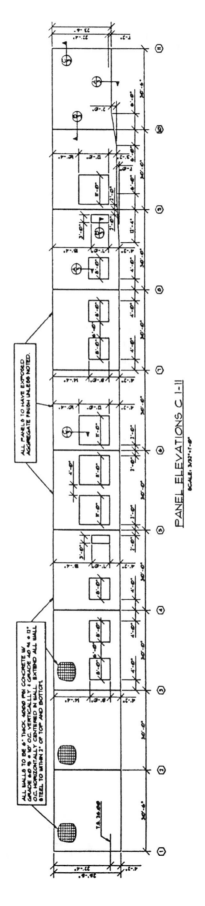

PANEL ELEVATIONS C 1-11

SCALE: 3/32"=1'-0"

© 2011 Cengage Learning. All Rights Reserved. May not be scanned, copied or duplicated, or posted to a publicly accessible website, in whole or in part.

Problem 45–18

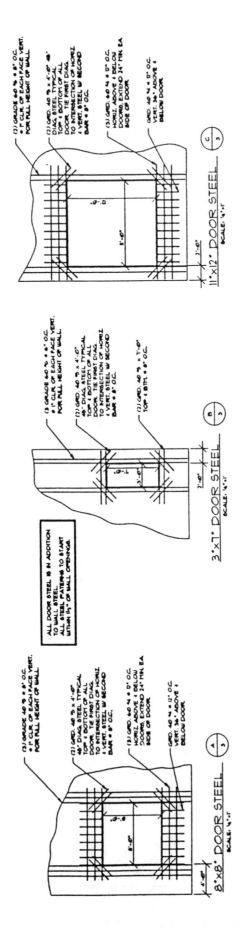

© 2011 Cengage Learning. All Rights Reserved. May not be scanned, copied or duplicated, or posted to a publicly accessible website, in whole or in part.

Problem 45–19

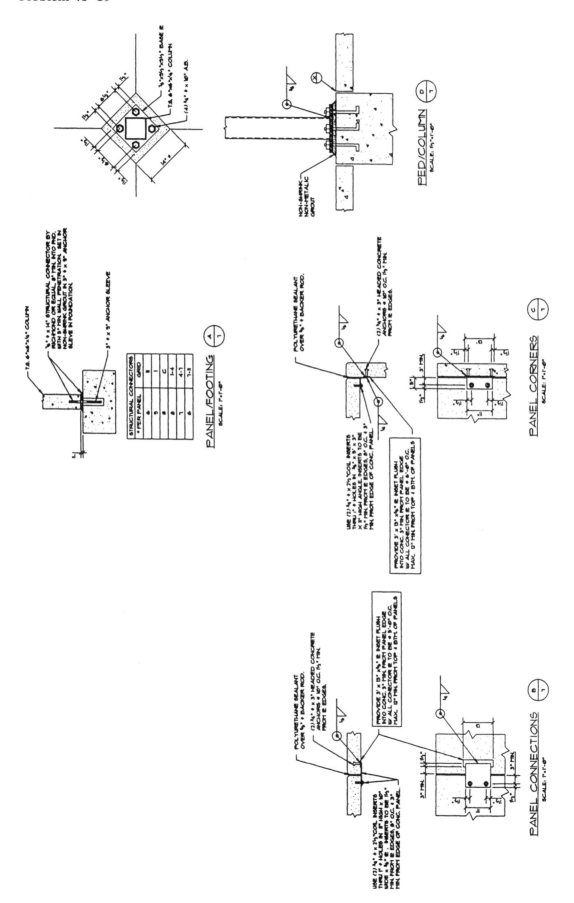

© 2011 Cengage Learning. All Rights Reserved. May not be scanned, copied or duplicated, or posted to a publicly accessible website, in whole or in part.

© 2011 Cengage Learning. All Rights Reserved. May not be scanned, copied or duplicated, or posted to a publicly accessible website, in whole or in part.

PART 2

Solutions to Workbook Problems

© 2011 Cengage Learning. All Rights Reserved. May not be scanned, copied or duplicated, or posted to a publicly accessible website, in whole or in part.

© 2011 Cengage Learning. All Rights Reserved. May not be scanned, copied or duplicated, or posted to a publicly accessible website, in whole or in part.

SECTION

Basic Residential Problems

CHAPTER 1 DRAWING FUNDAMENTALS

© 2011 Cengage Learning. All Rights Reserved. May not be scanned, copied or duplicated, or posted to a publicly accessible website, in whole or in part.

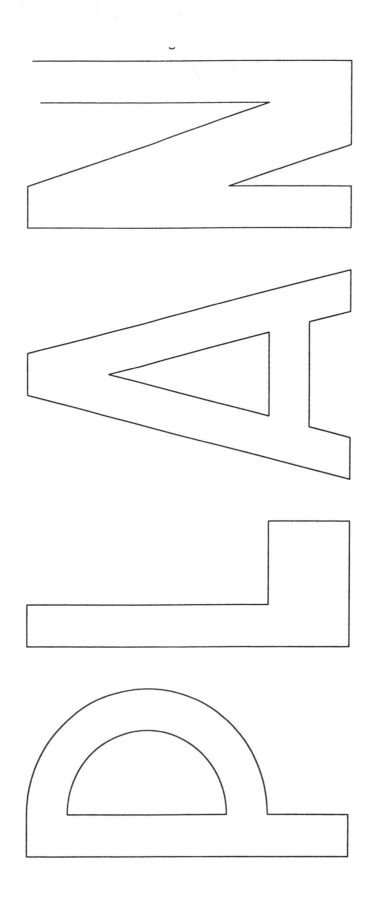

© 2011 Cengage Learning. All Rights Reserved. May not be scanned, copied or duplicated, or posted to a publicly accessible website, in whole or in part.

Problem 1–2

Scale 1/4" = 1'–0" **18'–6"**   1" = 10'–0"   **46"**   1:1 **117.5 mm**

Scale 3/8" = 1'–0" **16'–0"**   1" = 20'–0"   **120'**   1:2 **304.8 mm**

Scale 1/2" = 1'–0" **8'–9"**   1" = 30'–0"   **132'**   1:5 **558.8 mm**

Scale 3/4" = 1'–0" **6'–9"**   1" = 40'–0"   **230'**   1:25 **3238.5 mm**
3.24 m

Scale 1" = 1'–0" **3'–2½"**   1" = 50'–0"   **288'**   1:50 **7302.5 mm**
7.3 m

Scale 1/8" = 1'–0" **25'–8"**   1" = 100'–0"   **320'**   1:75 **60960 mm**
60.9 m

Scale 1 1/2" = 1'–0" **3'–2½"** 1" = 60'–0"   **290'**   1:50 **50 mm**
5 m

Scale 3" = 1'–0" **1'–10"**   1" = 200'–0"   **1100'**   1:5 **698.5 mm**
7 mm

© 2011 Cengage Learning. All Rights Reserved. May not be scanned, copied or duplicated, or posted to a publicly accessible website, in whole or in part.

Problem 1–3   Sketch straight lines between the numbered points below.

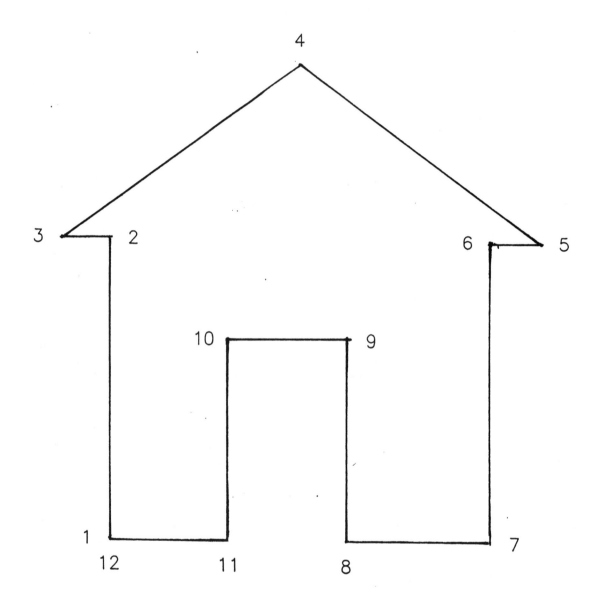

© 2011 Cengage Learning. All Rights Reserved. May not be scanned, copied or duplicated, or posted to a publicly accessible website, in whole or in part.

Problem 1–4

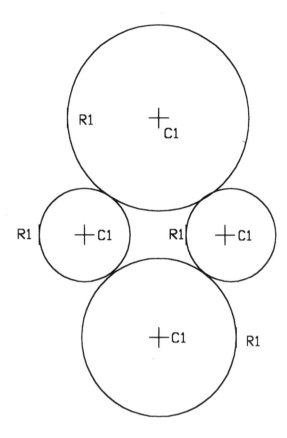

Problem 1–5

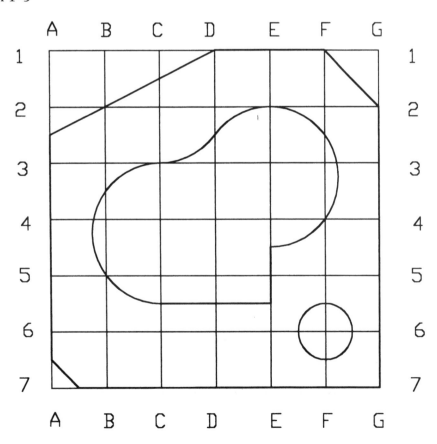

© 2011 Cengage Learning. All Rights Reserved. May not be scanned, copied or duplicated, or posted to a publicly accessible website, in whole or in part.

Problem 1–6

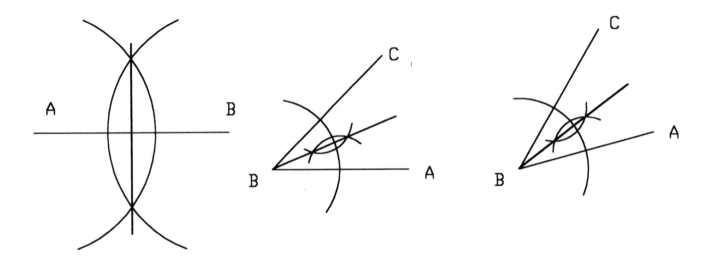

Problem 1–7

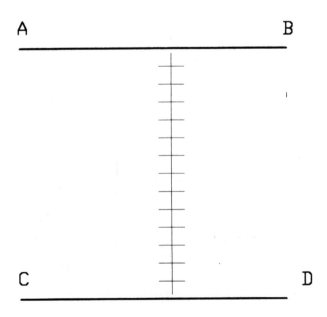

© 2011 Cengage Learning. All Rights Reserved. May not be scanned, copied or duplicated, or posted to a publicly accessible website, in whole or in part.

Problem 1–8

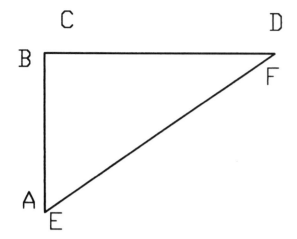

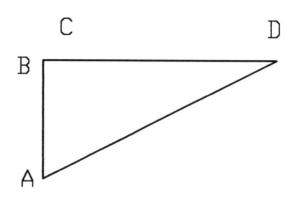

Problem 1–9

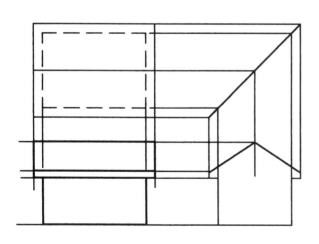

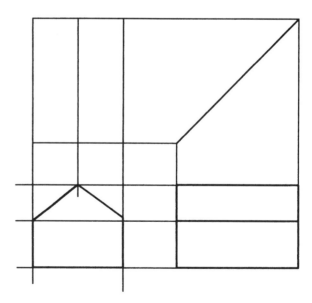

© 2011 Cengage Learning. All Rights Reserved. May not be scanned, copied or duplicated, or posted to a publicly accessible website, in whole or in part.

Problem 1–10   Solutions will vary but should resemble the objects on the problem.

Problem 1–11

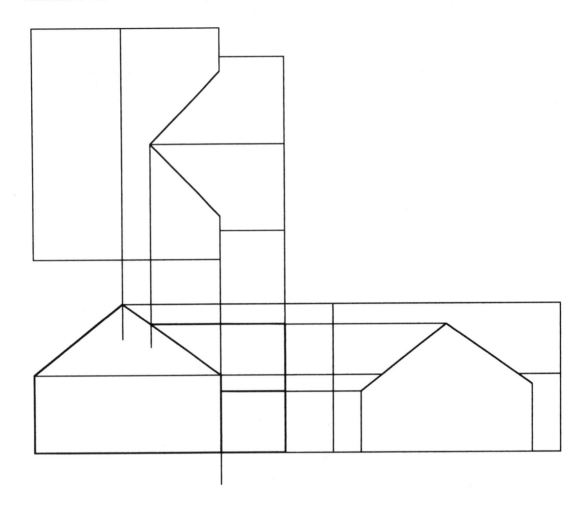

© 2011 Cengage Learning. All Rights Reserved. May not be scanned, copied or duplicated, or posted to a publicly accessible website, in whole or in part.

Problem 1–12

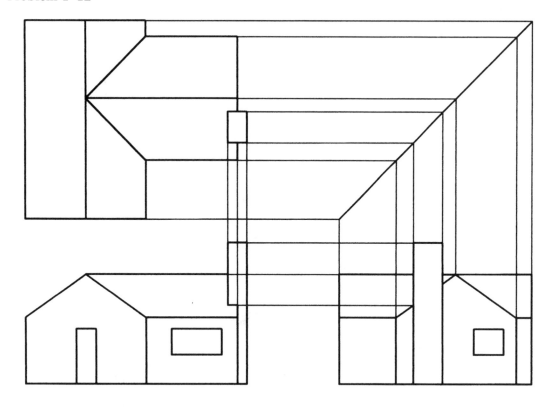

Problem 1–13

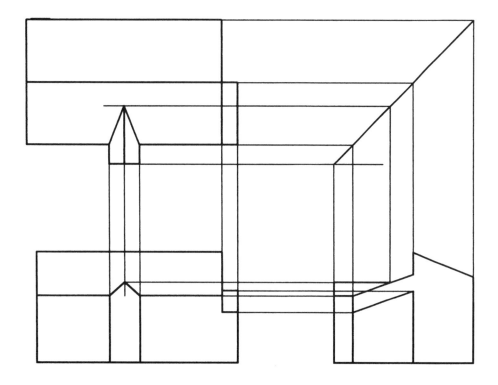

© 2011 Cengage Learning. All Rights Reserved. May not be scanned, copied or duplicated, or posted to a publicly accessible website, in whole or in part.

Problem 1–14

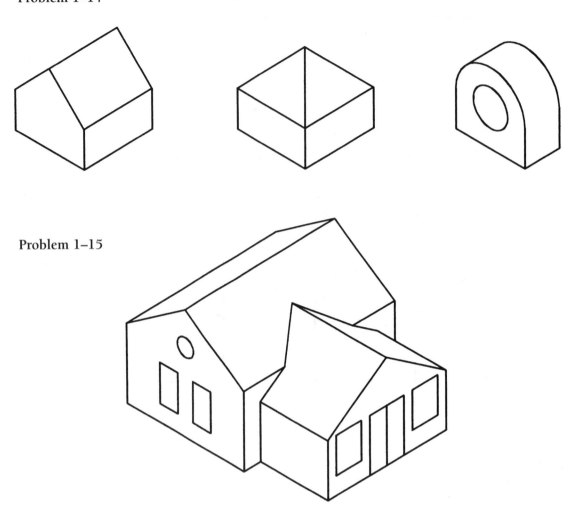

Problem 1–15

Problem 1–16	Answers should resemble the letters in the problem using 1/8" high text.
Problem 1–17	Answers should resemble the paragraphs in the problem.
Problem 1–18	Answers should resemble the paragraphs in the problem.
Problem 1–19	Answers should resemble the letters in the problem using 1/4" high text.
Problem 1–20	Answers should resemble the letters in the problem using the indicated text height.

© 2011 Cengage Learning. All Rights Reserved. May not be scanned, copied or duplicated, or posted to a publicly accessible website, in whole or in part.

CHAPTER 2 SITE PLAN PROJECTS

Problem 2–1

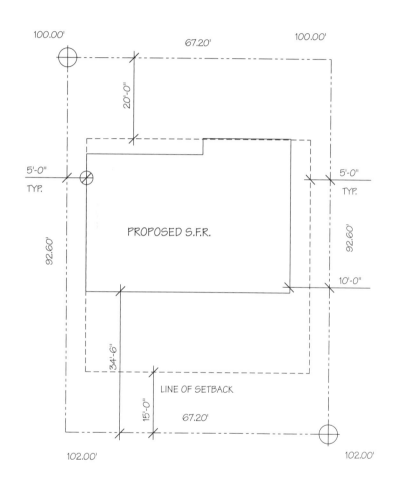

C S.W. LOMA VISTA STREET

100.00'   67.20'   100.00'

20'-0"

5'-0"   PROPOSED S.F.R.   5'-0"
TYP.   TYP.

92.60'   92.60'

                                    10'-0"

34'-6"

LINE OF SETBACK

15'-0"   67.20'

102.00'   102.00'

NORTH

SITE PLAN

LEGAL:

LOT 55, WICHER HEIGHTS NO 2

SW 1/4 SE 1/4 SEC 19 T1S RW

WASHINGTON COUNTY, OR.

Problems 2–2 through 2–10   Solutions should resemble the site provided in the workbook. Exact outcome will vary depending on the footprint of the house that is represented.

© 2011 Cengage Learning. All Rights Reserved. May not be scanned, copied or duplicated, or posted to a publicly accessible website, in whole or in part.

Problem 2–11

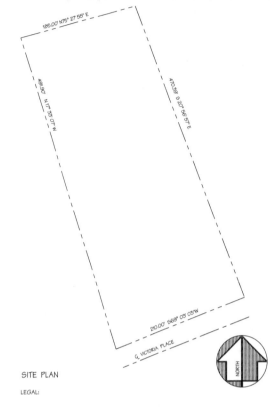

185.00' N75° 27' 55" E

491.90' N 17° 33' 07" W

470.33' S 20° 56' 57" E

210.00' S69° 03' 03"W

G. VICTORIA PLACE

NORTH

SITE PLAN

LEGAL:

STARTING AT THE SOUTHEAST CORNER OF THE PROPERTY,
PROCEED 210.00' S69° 03' 03" W, THENCE 491.90' N17° 33' 07"W,
THENCE 185.89 N75° 27' 55"E, THENCE BACK TO THE TRUE POINT
OF BEGINNING.

Problem 2–12

297.13' S86° 37' 50" E

491.70' N29° 19' 51" W

369.13' S 14° 45' 49" E

158.90'

ASHDOWN CIRCLE

NORTH

SITE PLAN

LEGAL:

STARTING AT THE SOUTHWEST CORNER OF THE PROPERTY,
PROCEED 497.70' N29° 19' 51"W, THENCE 297.13' S86° 37' 50"E,
THENCE 369.13' S 14° 45' 49"S, THENCE BACK TO THE TRUE POINT
OF BEGINNING ON AN ARC 158.90' LONG.

© 2011 Cengage Learning. All Rights Reserved. May not be scanned, copied or duplicated, or posted to a publicly accessible website, in whole or in part.

Problem 2–13

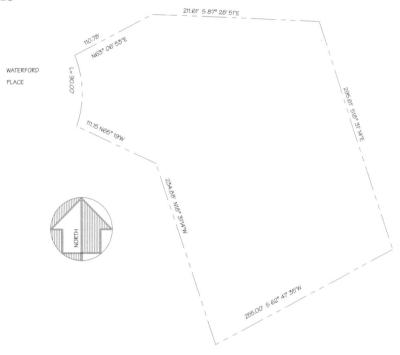

SITE PLAN

BEGINNING AT THE NORTHWEST CORNER, THENCE 110.78' N63° 06' 53"E,
THENCE 211.61' S87° 28' 51"E, THENCE 295.61' S18° 31' 14"E, THENCE
255.00' S62° 47' 35"W, THENCE 234.88' N18° 31' 14"W, THENCE 111.15'
N65° 19'W, THENCE 90.00' ON AN ARC BACK TO THE TRUE POINT OF BEGINNING.

Problem 2–14

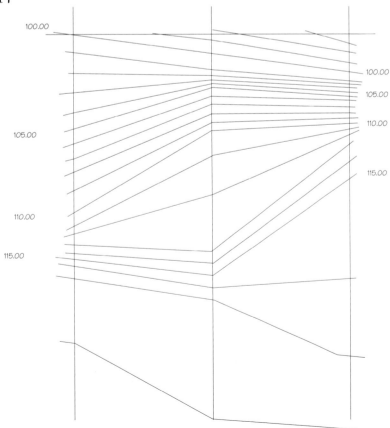

© 2011 Cengage Learning. All Rights Reserved. May not be scanned, copied or duplicated, or posted to a publicly accessible website, in whole or in part.

Problem 2–15

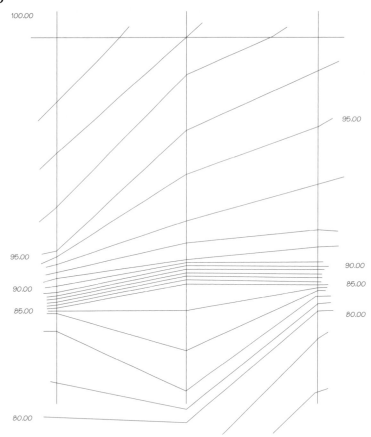

CHAPTER 3 FLOOR PLAN FUNDAMENTALS

Problem 3–1   Solutions will vary, but may resemble the attached kitchen.

© 2011 Cengage Learning. All Rights Reserved. May not be scanned, copied or duplicated, or posted to a publicly accessible website, in whole or in part.

Problem 3–1

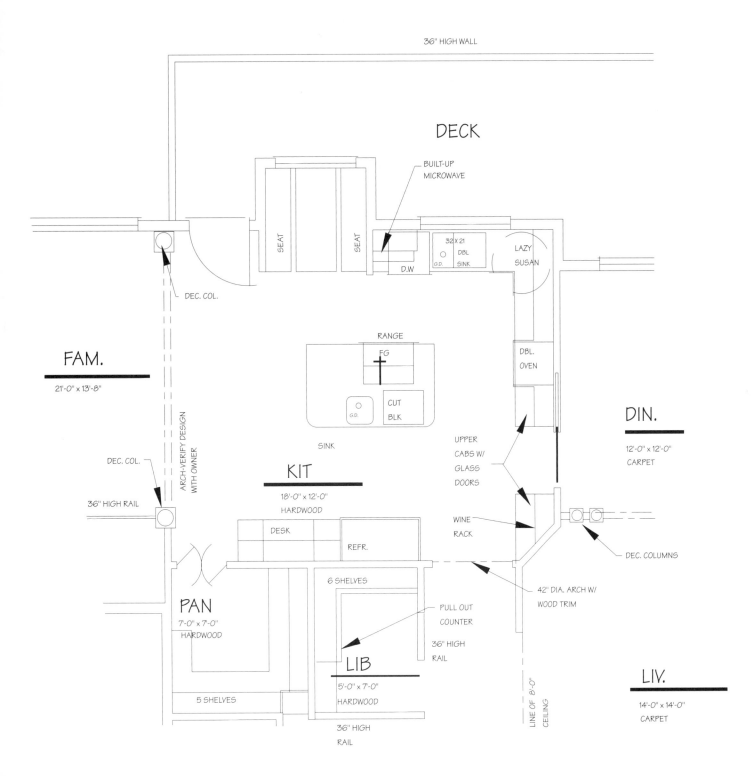

36" HIGH WALL

DECK

BUILT-UP
MICROWAVE

SEAT

SEAT

32 X 21
DBL
SINK

G.D.

D.W

LAZY
SUSAN

DEC. COL.

FAM.

21'-0" x 13'-8"

RANGE

FG

DBL.
OVEN

DEC. COL.

36" HIGH RAIL

ARCH-VERIFY DESIGN
WITH OWNER

CUT
BLK

G.D.

SINK

KIT

18'-0" x 12'-0"
HARDWOOD

UPPER
CABS W/
GLASS
DOORS

DIN.

12'-0" x 12'-0"
CARPET

DESK

REFR.

6 SHELVES

WINE
RACK

DEC. COLUMNS

42" DIA. ARCH W/
WOOD TRIM

PAN

7'-0" x 7'-0"
HARDWOOD

PULL OUT
COUNTER

36" HIGH
RAIL

LIB

5'-0" x 7'-0"
HARDWOOD

LIV.

14'-0" x 14'-0"
CARPET

5 SHELVES

36" HIGH
RAIL

LINE OF 8'-0"
CEILING

© 2011 Cengage Learning. All Rights Reserved. May not be scanned, copied or duplicated, or posted to a publicly accessible website, in whole or in part.

Problem 3–2

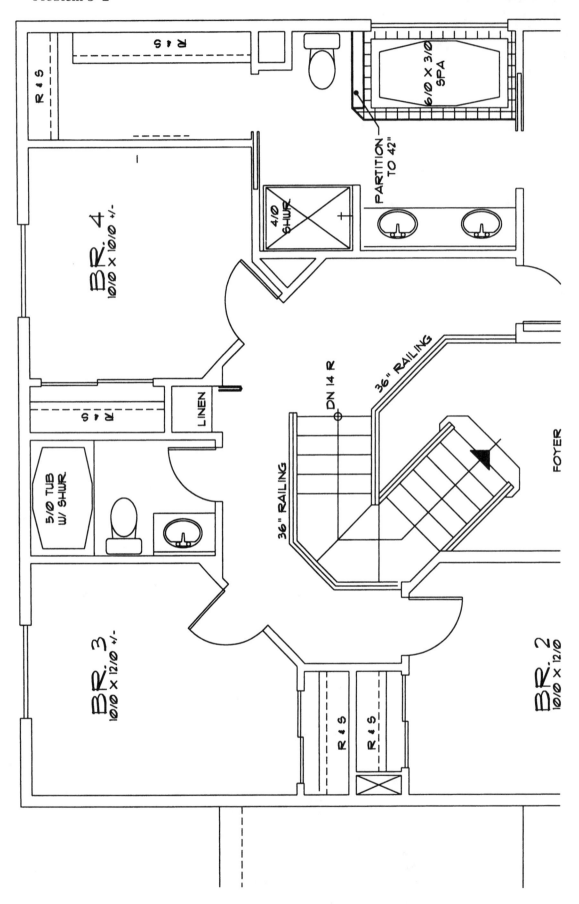

© 2011 Cengage Learning. All Rights Reserved. May not be scanned, copied or duplicated, or posted to a publicly accessible website, in whole or in part.

Problem 3–3

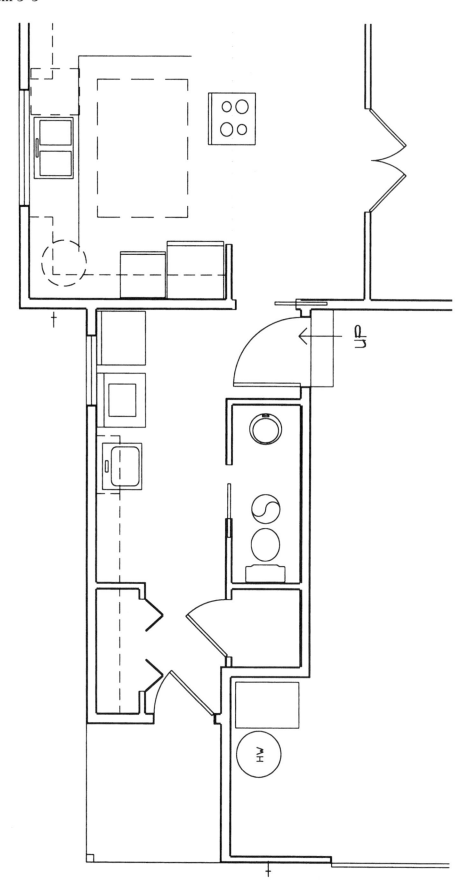

© 2011 Cengage Learning. All Rights Reserved. May not be scanned, copied or duplicated, or posted to a publicly accessible website, in whole or in part.

Problem 3–4

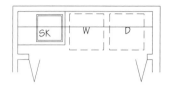

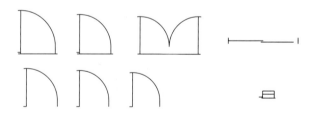

LAUNDRY CHUTE
TO LOWER FLOOR
LINE W/ 26 GA.
METAL

LAUNDRY CHUTE
FROM UPPER BATH.
LINE W/ 26 GA.
METAL

Problem 3–5

APPLIANCES

DOORS / WINDOW

PLUMBING

MISC.

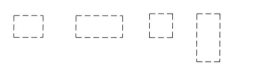

© 2011 Cengage Learning. All Rights Reserved. May not be scanned, copied or duplicated, or posted to a publicly accessible website, in whole or in part.

Problem 3–6   Students are to letter the designated room names and material.

Problem 3–7

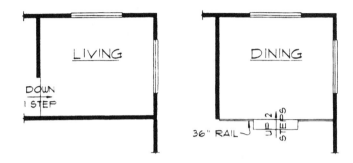

Problem 3–8

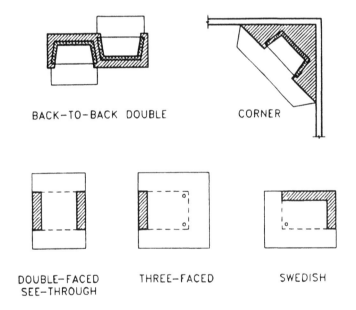

Problem 3–9

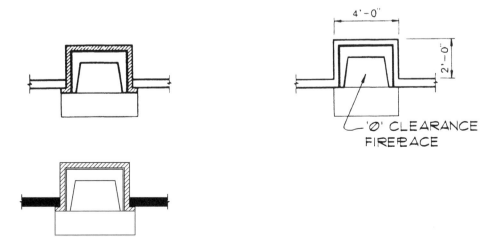

© 2011 Cengage Learning. All Rights Reserved. May not be scanned, copied or duplicated, or posted to a publicly accessible website, in whole or in part.

Problem 3–9 (Continued)

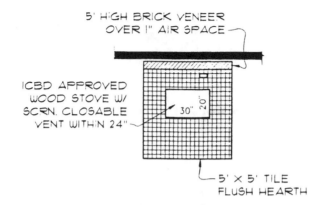

5' HIGH BRICK VENEER OVER 1" AIR SPACE

ICBD APPROVED WOOD STOVE W/ SCRN. CLOSABLE VENT WITHIN 24"

30"
20"

5' X 5' TILE FLUSH HEARTH

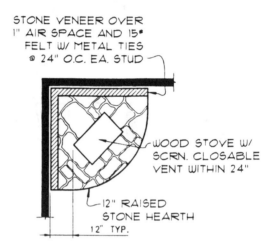

STONE VENEER OVER 1" AIR SPACE AND 15# FELT W/ METAL TIES @ 24" O.C. EA. STUD

WOOD STOVE W/ SCRN. CLOSABLE VENT WITHIN 24"

12" RAISED STONE HEARTH
12" TYP.

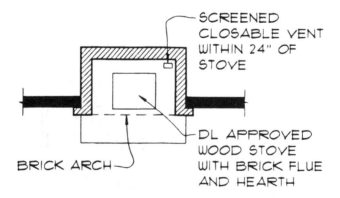

SCREENED CLOSABLE VENT WITHIN 24" OF STOVE

DL APPROVED WOOD STOVE WITH BRICK FLUE AND HEARTH

BRICK ARCH

© 2011 Cengage Learning. All Rights Reserved. May not be scanned, copied or duplicated, or posted to a publicly accessible website, in whole or in part.

Problem 3–10

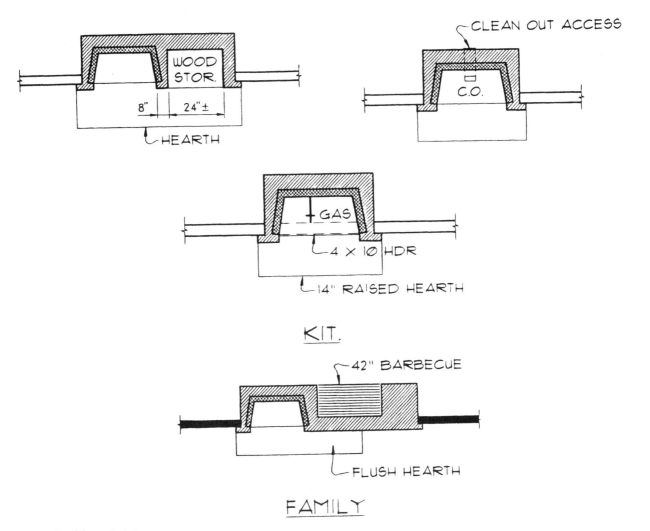

KIT.

FAMILY

Problem 3–11

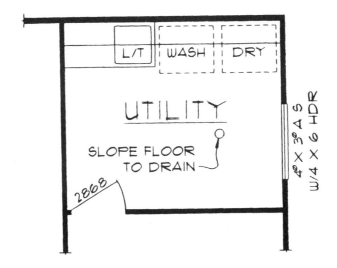

© 2011 Cengage Learning. All Rights Reserved. May not be scanned, copied or duplicated, or posted to a publicly accessible website, in whole or in part.

Problem 3–12

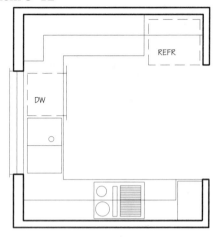

U SHAPE

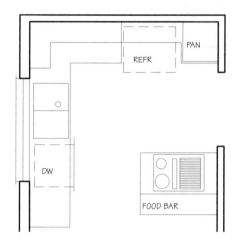

PENINSULA

Problem 3–13

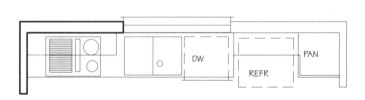

ONE WALL

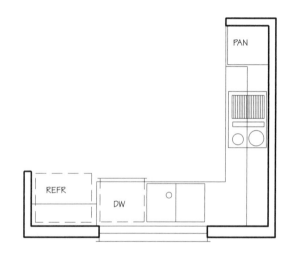

L SHAPE

Problem 3–14

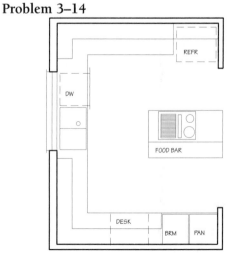

ISLAND

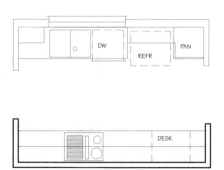

CORRIDOR

© 2011 Cengage Learning. All Rights Reserved. May not be scanned, copied or duplicated, or posted to a publicly accessible website, in whole or in part.

Problem 3–15A and B

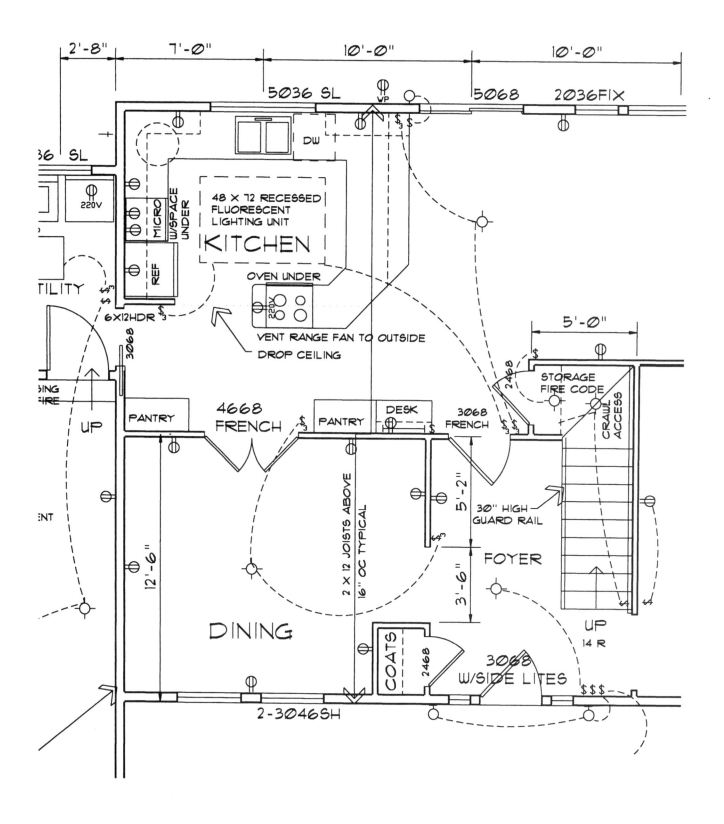

© 2011 Cengage Learning. All Rights Reserved. May not be scanned, copied or duplicated, or posted to a publicly accessible website, in whole or in part.

Problem 3–16

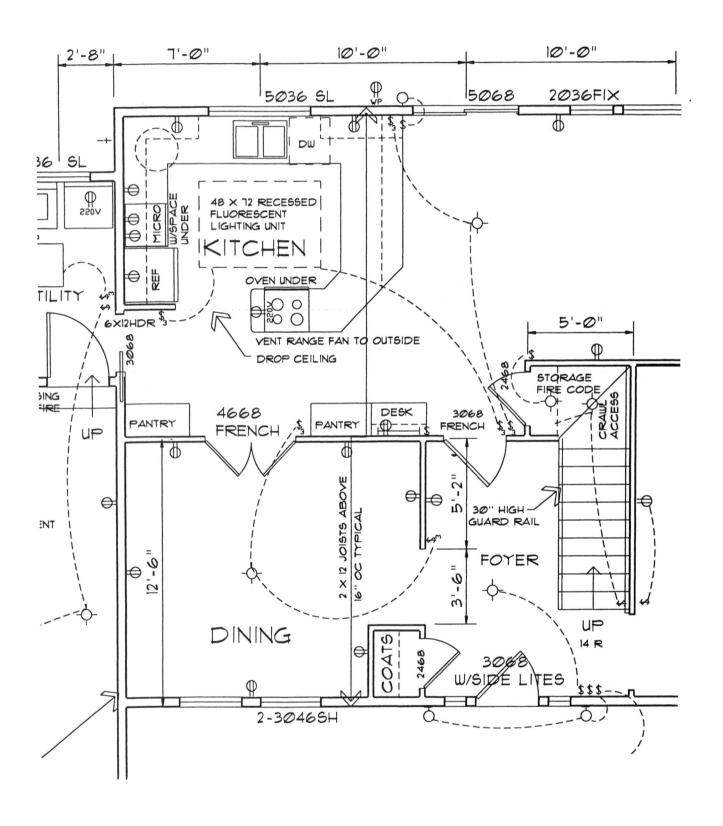

© 2011 Cengage Learning. All Rights Reserved. May not be scanned, copied or duplicated, or posted to a publicly accessible website, in whole or in part.

Problem 3–17

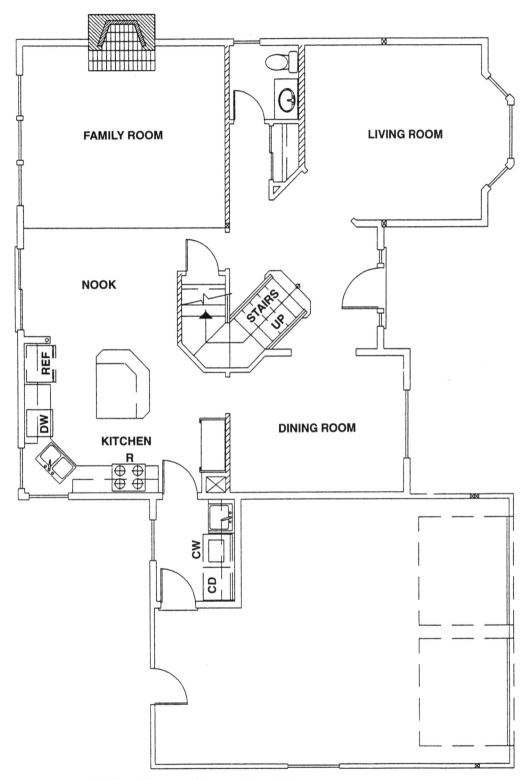

Courtesy of Alan Mascord Design Associates.

© 2011 Cengage Learning. All Rights Reserved. May not be scanned, copied or duplicated, or posted to a publicly accessible website, in whole or in part.

Problem 3–18

PROBLEM 1–8

Au: Problem
here OK?

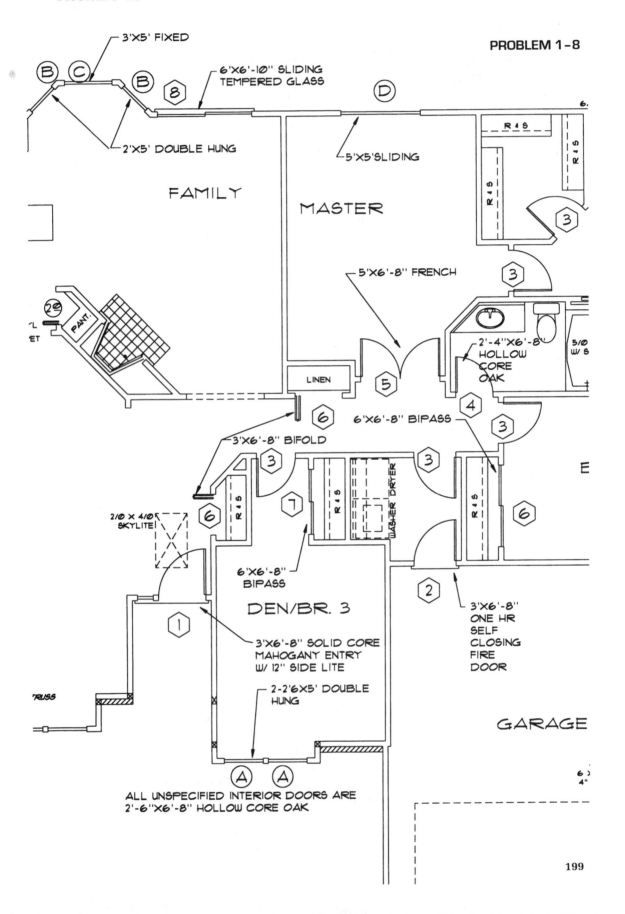

3'X5' FIXED

6'X6'-10" SLIDING
TEMPERED GLASS

2'X5' DOUBLE HUNG

5'X5'SLIDING

FAMILY

MASTER

5'X6'-8" FRENCH

PANT.

2'-4"X6'-8"
HOLLOW
CORE
OAK

LINEN

6'X6'-8" BIPASS

3'X6'-8" BIFOLD

WASHER DRYER

2/0 X 4/0
SKYLITE

6'X6'-8"
BIPASS

DEN/BR. 3

3'X6'-8"
ONE HR
SELF
CLOSING
FIRE
DOOR

3'X6'-8" SOLID CORE
MAHOGANY ENTRY
W/ 12" SIDE LITE

2-2'6X5' DOUBLE
HUNG

TRUSS

GARAGE

ALL UNSPECIFIED INTERIOR DOORS ARE
2'-6"X6'-8" HOLLOW CORE OAK

199

© 2011 Cengage Learning. All Rights Reserved. May not be scanned, copied or duplicated, or posted to a publicly accessible website, in whole or in part.

Problem 3–18 (Continued)

DOOR SCHEDULE

KEY	QTY	SIZE	TYPE
1	1	3'-0" X 6'-8"	SOLID CORE MAHOGANY ENTRY W/ 12" SIDE LITE
2	1	3'-0" X 6'-8"	ONE HOUR SELF CLOSING FIRE
3	5	2'-6" X 6'-8"	HOLLOW CORE OAK
4	1	2'-4" X 6'-8"	HOLLOW CORE OAK
5	1	5'-0" X 6'-8"	FRENCH
6	2	3'-0" X 6'-8"	BIFOLD
7	2	6'-0" X 6'-8"	BIPASS
8	1	6'-0" X 6'-10"	SLIDING TEMPERED GLASS

WINDOW SCHEDULE

KEY	QTY	SIZE	TYPE
A	2	2'-6" X 5'-0"	DOUBLE HUNG
B	2	2'-0" X 5'-0"	DOUBLE HUNG
C	1	3'-0" X 5'-0"	FIXED
D	1	5'-0" X 5'-0"	SLIDING

© 2011 Cengage Learning. All Rights Reserved. May not be scanned, copied or duplicated, or posted to a publicly accessible website, in whole or in part.

Problem 3–19

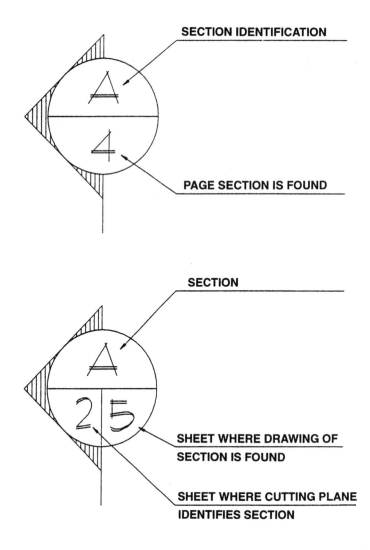

© 2011 Cengage Learning. All Rights Reserved. May not be scanned, copied or duplicated, or posted to a publicly accessible website, in whole or in part.

Problem 3–20

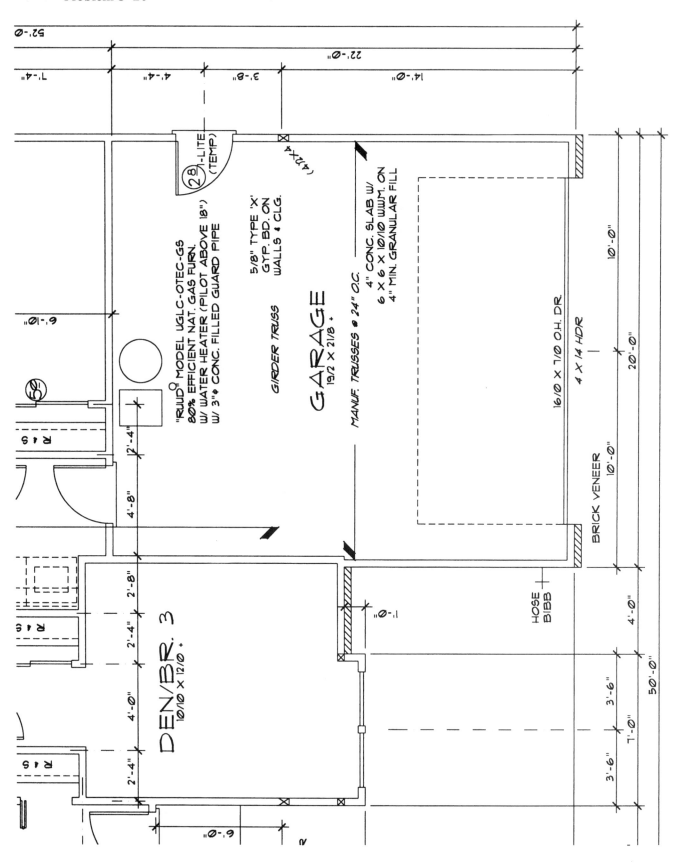

© 2011 Cengage Learning. All Rights Reserved. May not be scanned, copied or duplicated, or posted to a publicly accessible website, in whole or in part.

CHAPTER 4 RESIDENTIAL FLOOR PLAN PROJECTS

Problem 4–1   One-story house

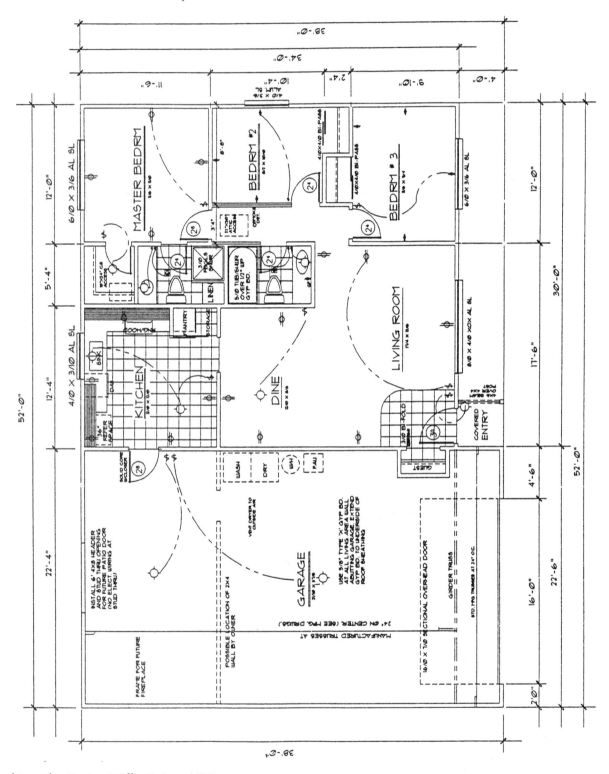

Courtesy of Sunridge Design, Wally Greiner AIBD

© 2011 Cengage Learning. All Rights Reserved. May not be scanned, copied or duplicated, or posted to a publicly accessible website, in whole or in part.

Problem 4–2   One-story house

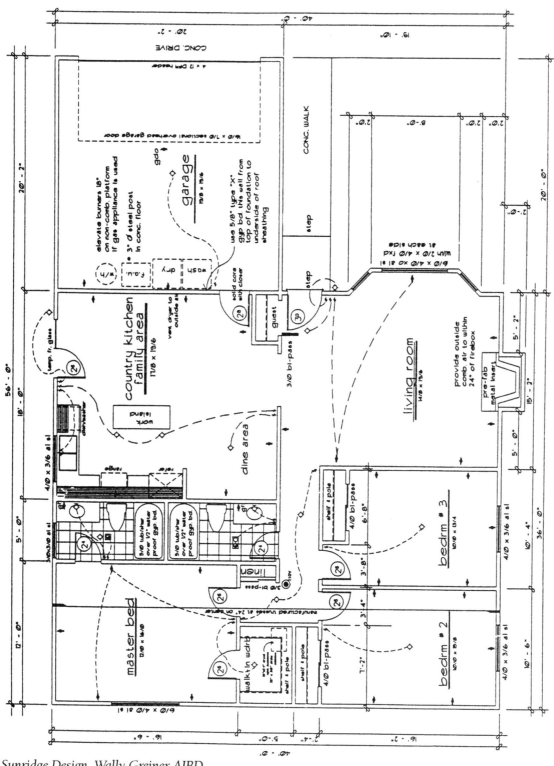

Courtesy of Sunridge Design, Wally Greiner AIBD

© 2011 Cengage Learning. All Rights Reserved. May not be scanned, copied or duplicated, or posted to a publicly accessible website, in whole or in part.

Problem 4–3   One-story house

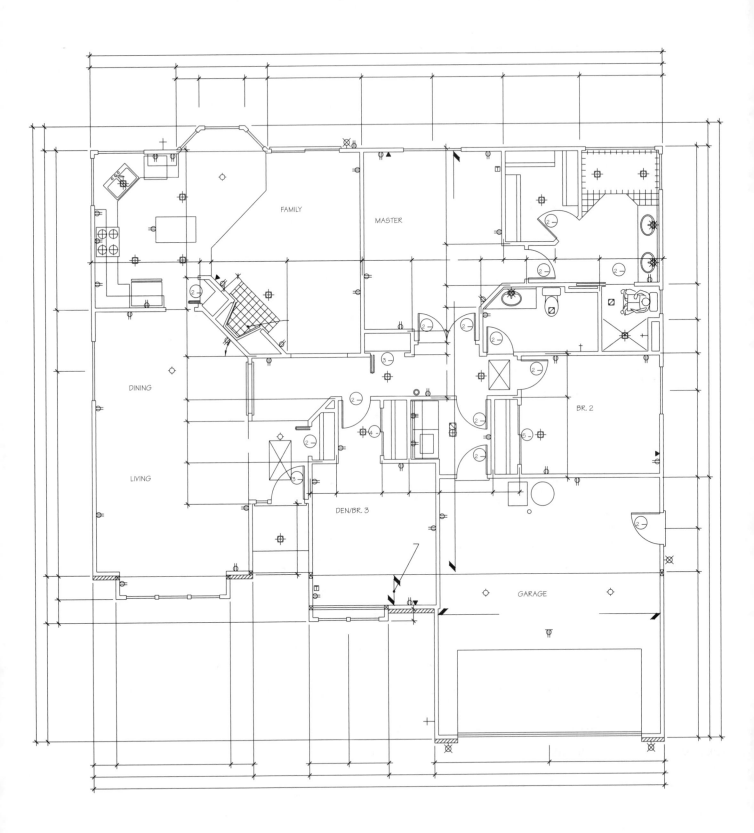

© 2011 Cengage Learning. All Rights Reserved. May not be scanned, copied or duplicated, or posted to a publicly accessible website, in whole or in part.

Problem 4–4   One-story house

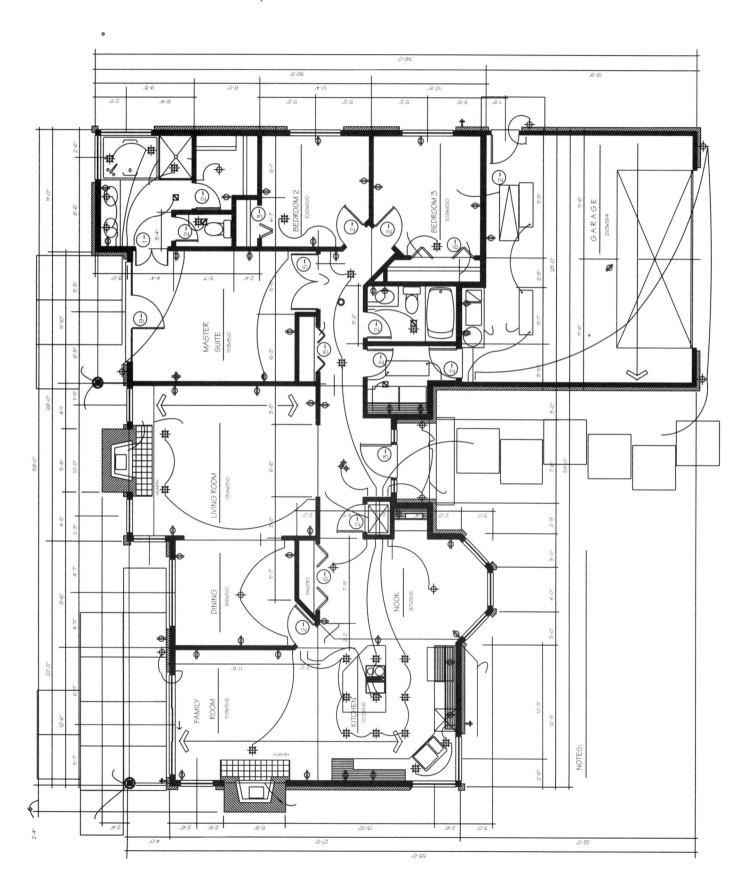

© 2011 Cengage Learning. All Rights Reserved. May not be scanned, copied or duplicated, or posted to a publicly accessible website, in whole or in part.

Problem 4–5   One-story house

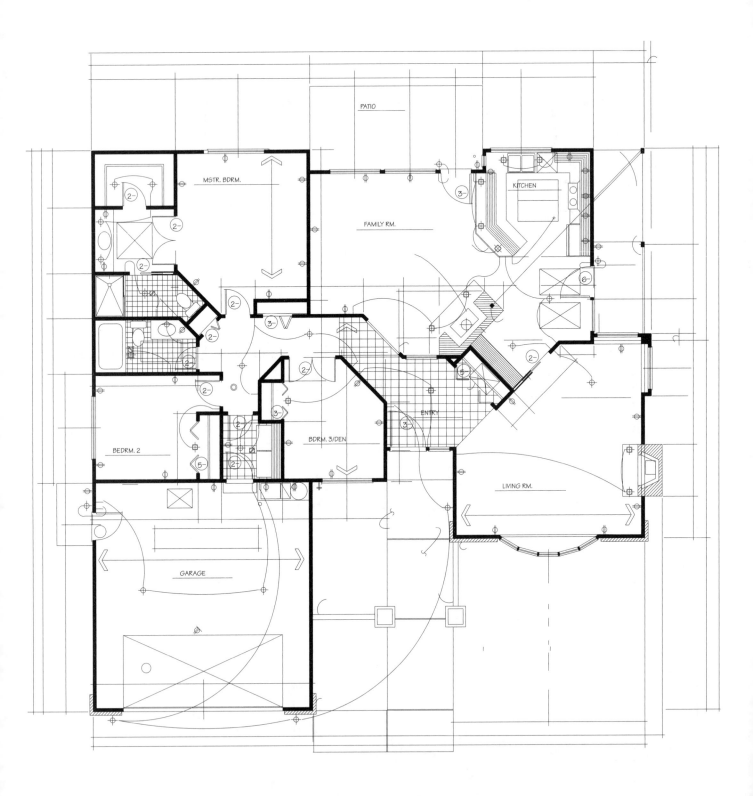

© 2011 Cengage Learning. All Rights Reserved. May not be scanned, copied or duplicated, or posted to a publicly accessible website, in whole or in part.

Problem 4–6   One-story house

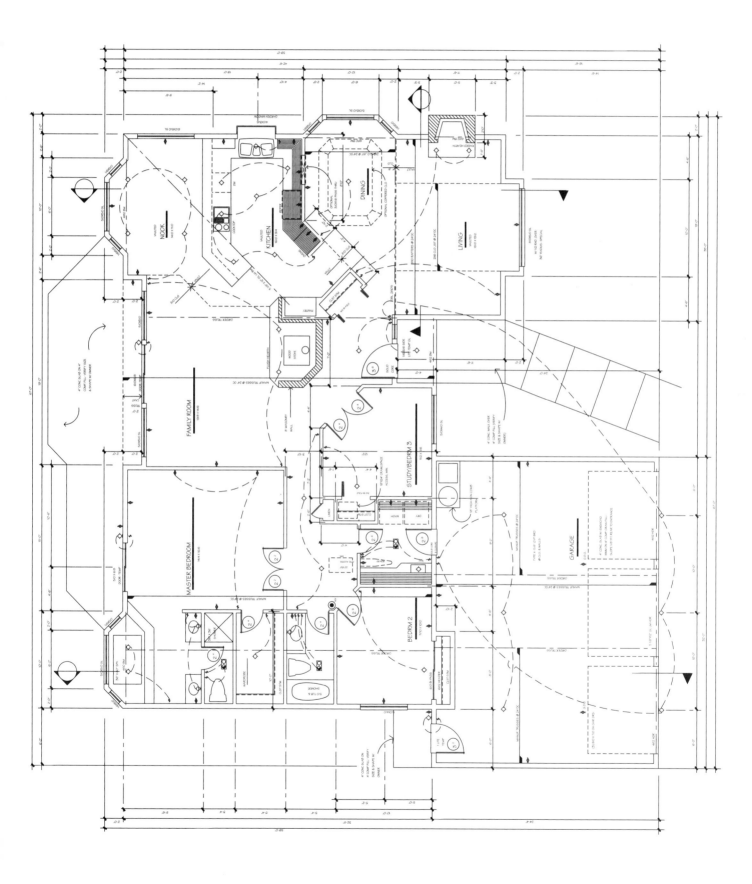

© 2011 Cengage Learning. All Rights Reserved. May not be scanned, copied or duplicated, or posted to a publicly accessible website, in whole or in part.

Problem 4–7   One-story house

© 2011 Cengage Learning. All Rights Reserved. May not be scanned, copied or duplicated, or posted to a publicly accessible website, in whole or in part.

Problem 4–8

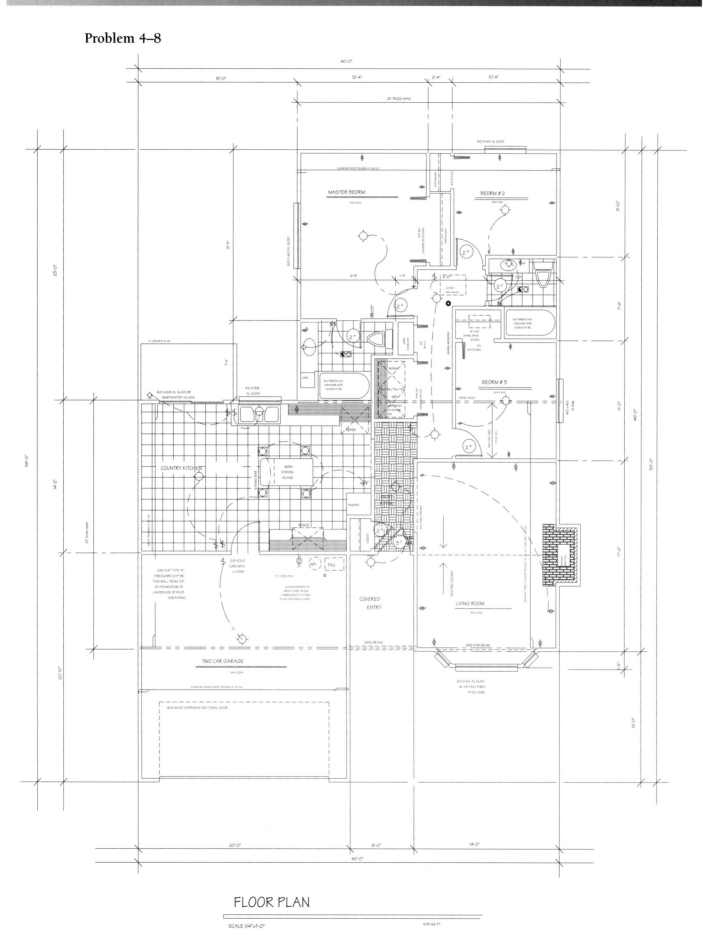

FLOOR PLAN

SCALE 1/4"=1'-0"   1276 SQ. FT.

© 2011 Cengage Learning. All Rights Reserved. May not be scanned, copied or duplicated, or posted to a publicly accessible website, in whole or in part.

Problem 4–9

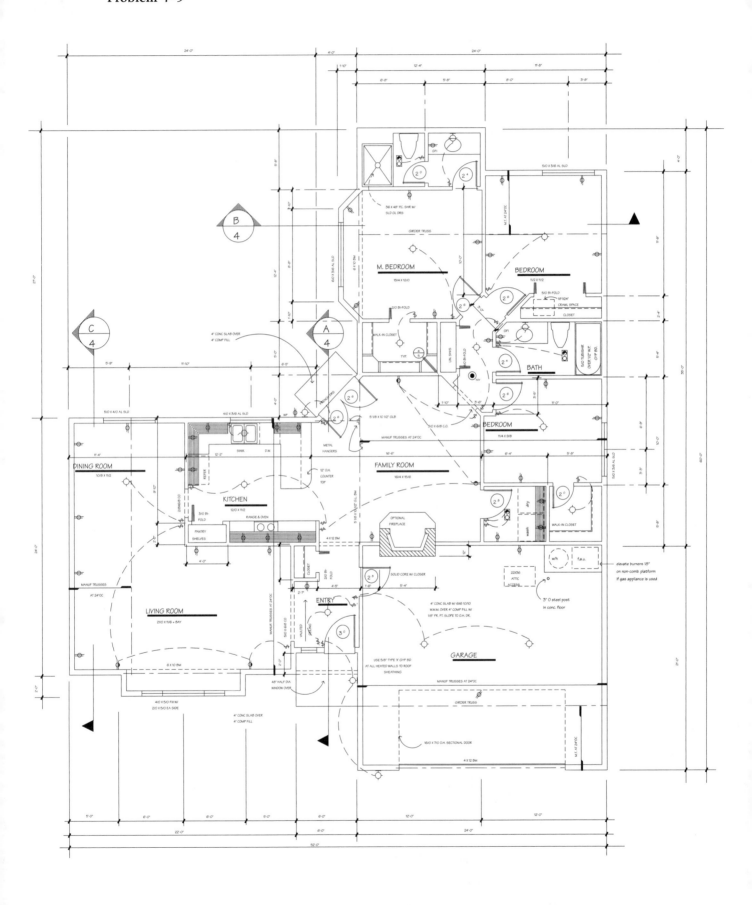

© 2011 Cengage Learning. All Rights Reserved. May not be scanned, copied or duplicated, or posted to a publicly accessible website, in whole or in part.

Problem 4–10

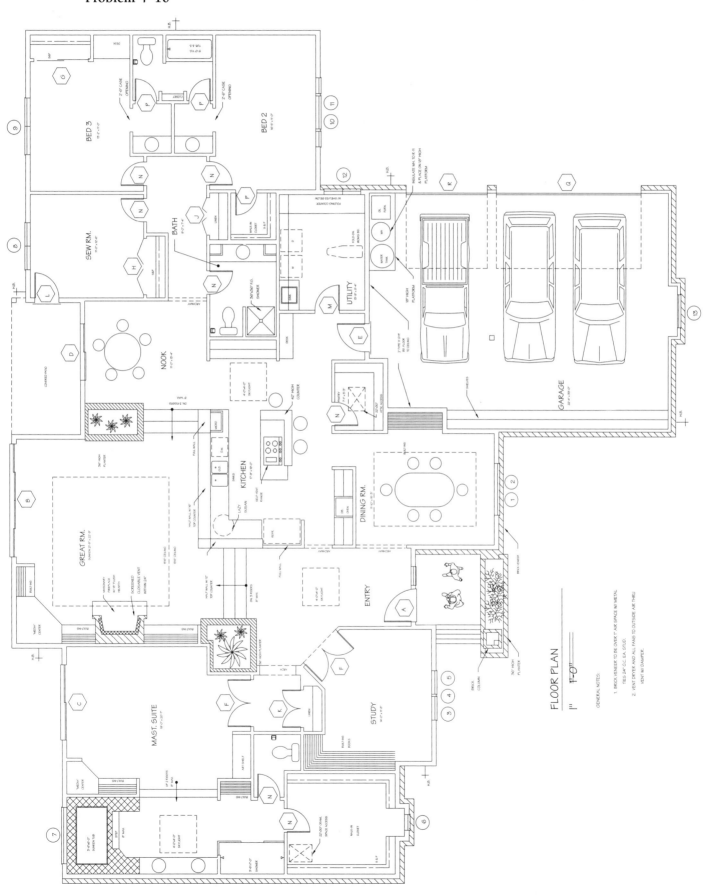

© 2011 Cengage Learning. All Rights Reserved. May not be scanned, copied or duplicated, or posted to a publicly accessible website, in whole or in part.

Problem 4–10 (Continued)

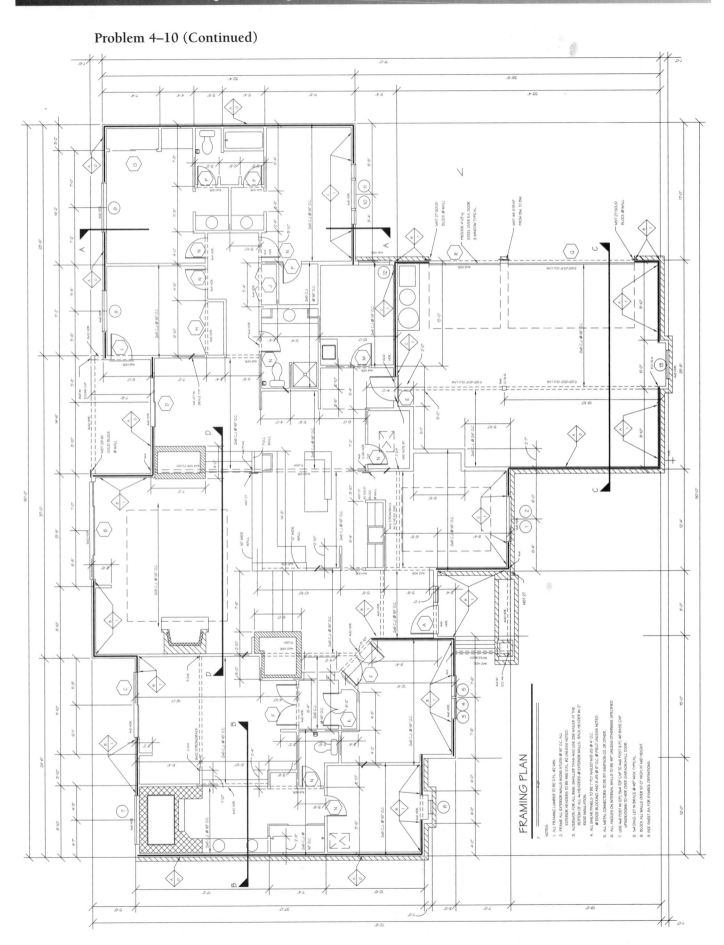

FRAMING PLAN

NOTES:

1. ALL FRAMING LUMBER TO BE D.F.L. #2 MIN.
2. FRAME ALL EXTERIOR WALLS W/2X6 STUDS @ 16" O.C. ALL EXTERIOR HEADERS TO BE 4X12 D.F.L. #2 UNLESS NOTED.
3. ALTERNATE FOR ALL WALLS SMALLER THAN 4X0 USE 1X NAILER AT THE BOTTOM OF ALL HEADERS @ EXTERIOR WALLS. BACK HEADER W/ 2" RIGID INSULATION.
4. ALL SHEAR PANELS TO BE ½" PLY NAILED W/8 d/6 @ 4" O.C.
   ☐ EDGE BLOCKING AND 6 d/8 @ 8" O.C. @ FIELD UNLESS NOTED.
5. ALL METAL CONNECTORS TO BE BY SIMPSON CO. OR OTHER.
6. ALL ANGLES ON INTERNAL WALLS TO BE 45° UNLESS OTHERWISE SPECIFIED.
7. USE 4x6 POST W/ EPC 5&4 TOP CAP TO 4x6 POST & PC 46 BASE CAP UPSIDEDOWN TO HDR. OVER GARAGE/HALL DOOR.
8. 1x4 DIAG. LET IN BRACE @ 45° MAX. TYPICAL.
9. BLOCK ALL WALLS OVER 10'-0" HIGH AT MID HEIGHT.
10. SEE SHEET 6A FOR SYMBOL DEFINITIONS.

© 2011 Cengage Learning. All Rights Reserved. May not be scanned, copied or duplicated, or posted to a publicly accessible website, in whole or in part.

Problem 4–11

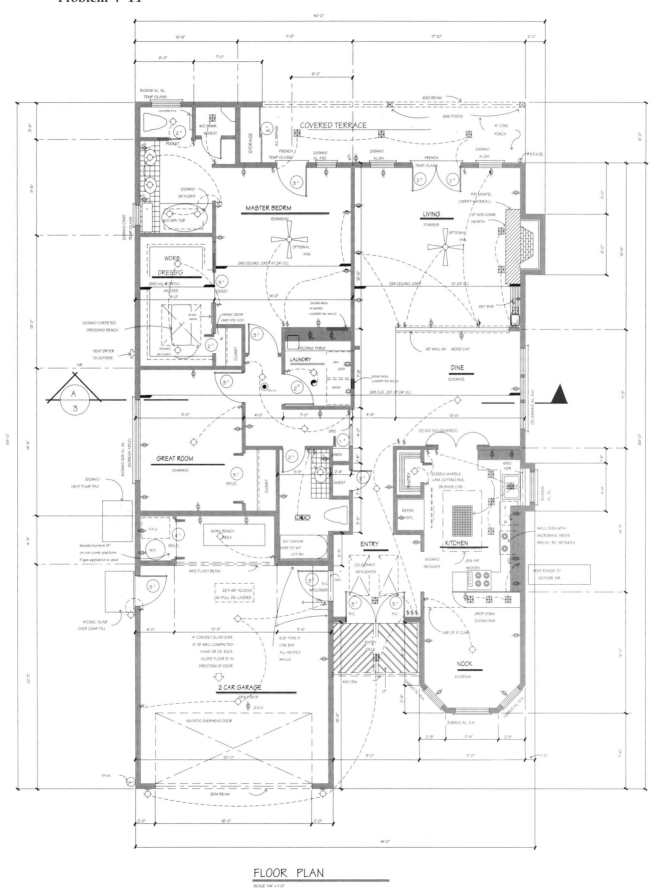

FLOOR PLAN

SCALE 1/4" = 1'-0"

© 2011 Cengage Learning. All Rights Reserved. May not be scanned, copied or duplicated, or posted to a publicly accessible website, in whole or in part.

Problem 4–12

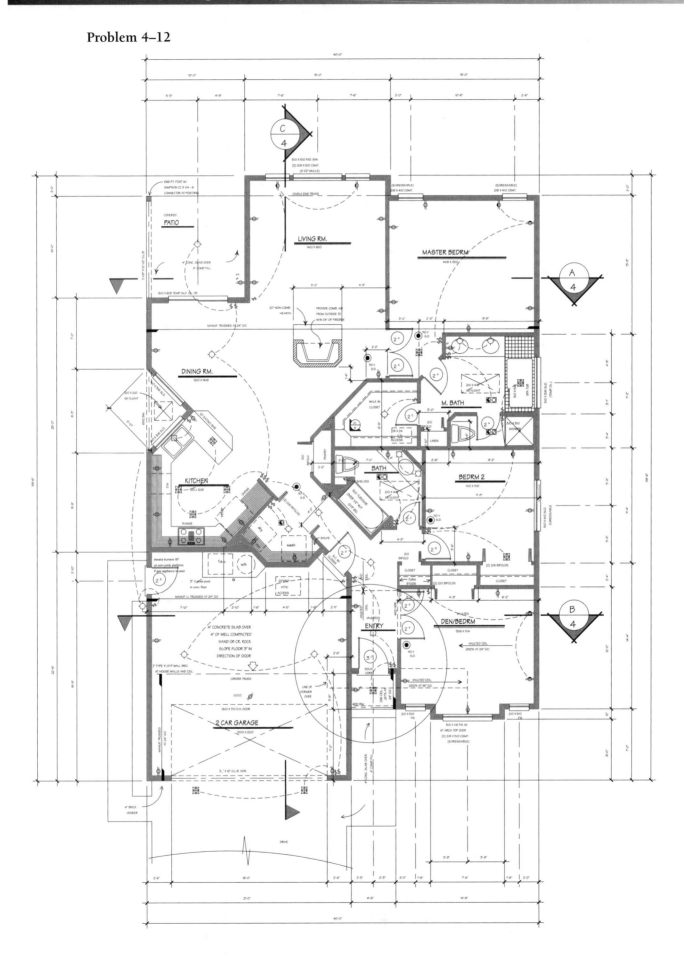

© 2011 Cengage Learning. All Rights Reserved. May not be scanned, copied or duplicated, or posted to a publicly accessible website, in whole or in part.

Problem 4–13

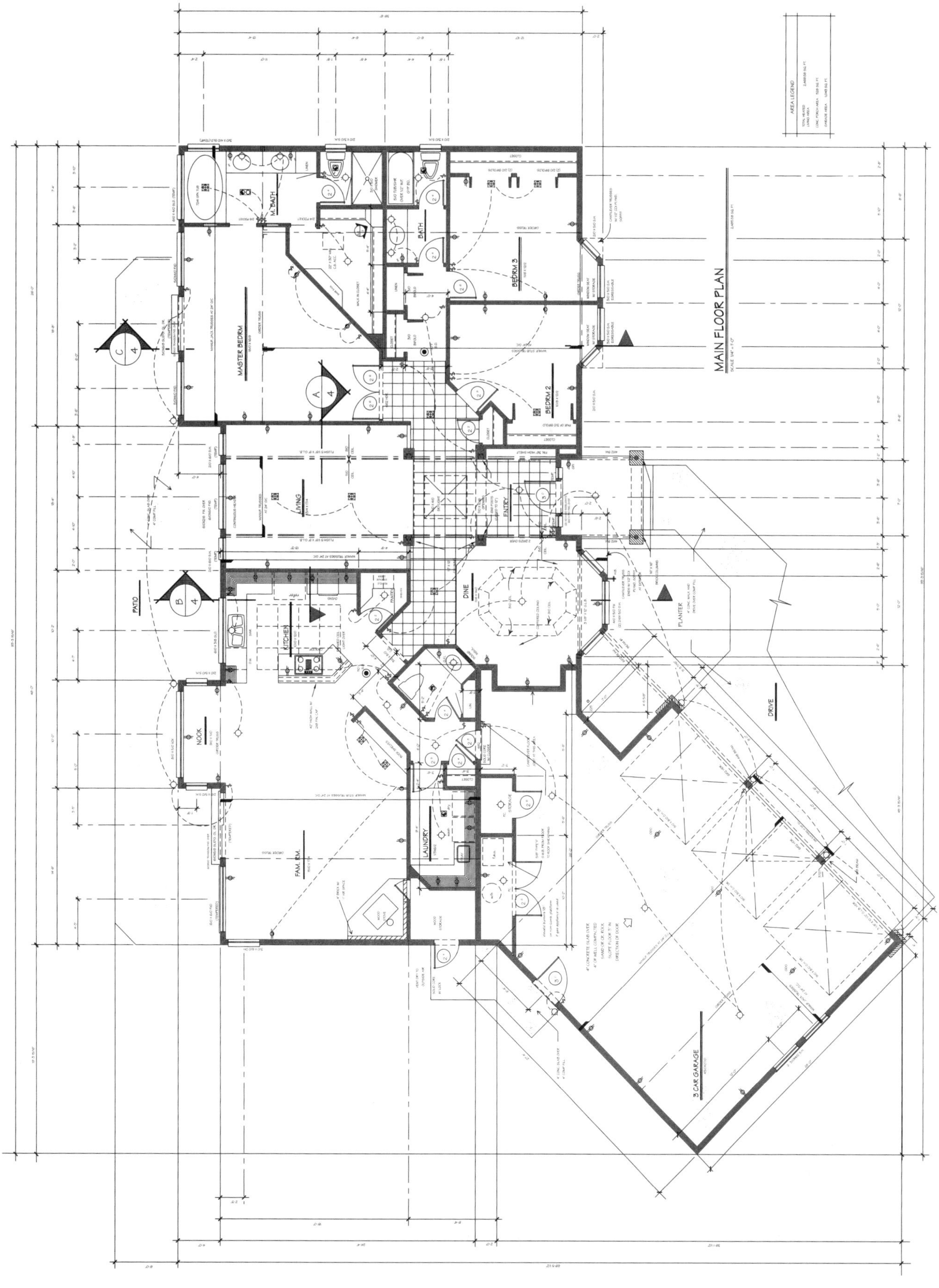

MAIN FLOOR PLAN

© 2011 Cengage Learning. All Rights Reserved. May not be scanned, copied or duplicated, or posted to a publicly accessible website, in whole or in part.

Problem 4–14

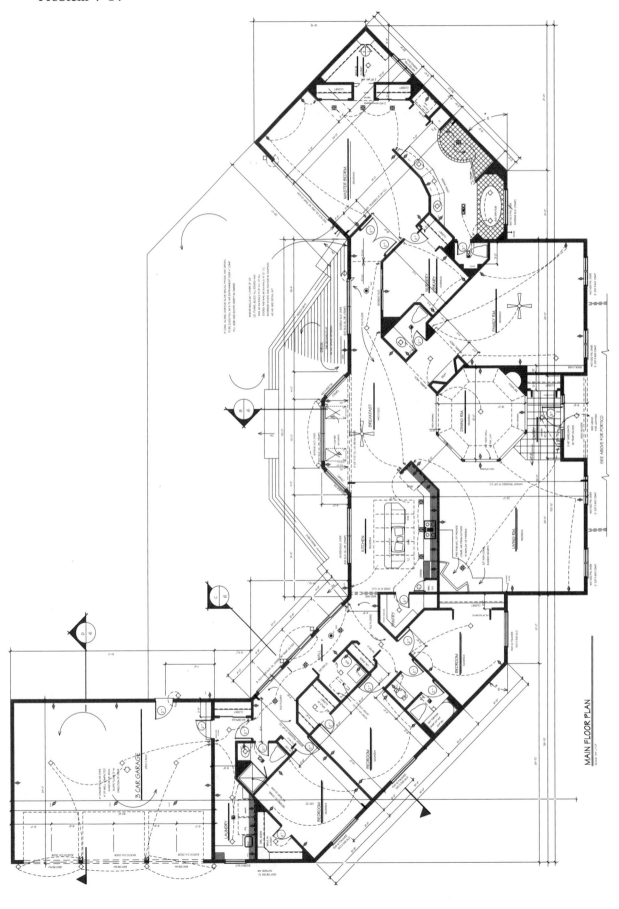

© 2011 Cengage Learning. All Rights Reserved. May not be scanned, copied or duplicated, or posted to a publicly accessible website, in whole or in part.

Problem 4–15A   Two-story house

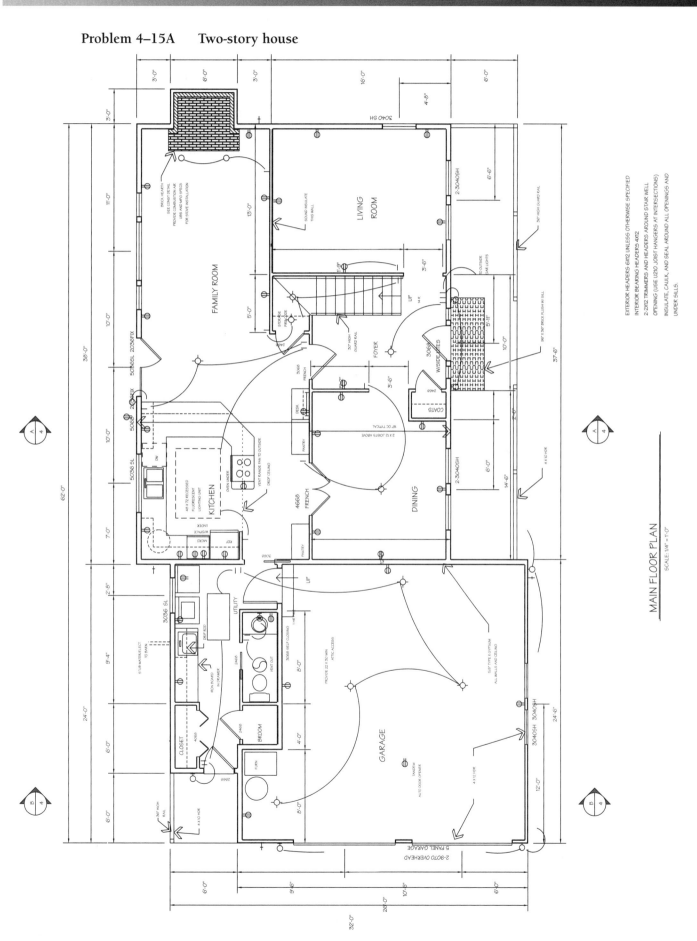

MAIN FLOOR PLAN

SCALE: 1/4" = 1'-0"

© 2011 Cengage Learning. All Rights Reserved. May not be scanned, copied or duplicated, or posted to a publicly accessible website, in whole or in part.

Problem 4–15B   Two-story house

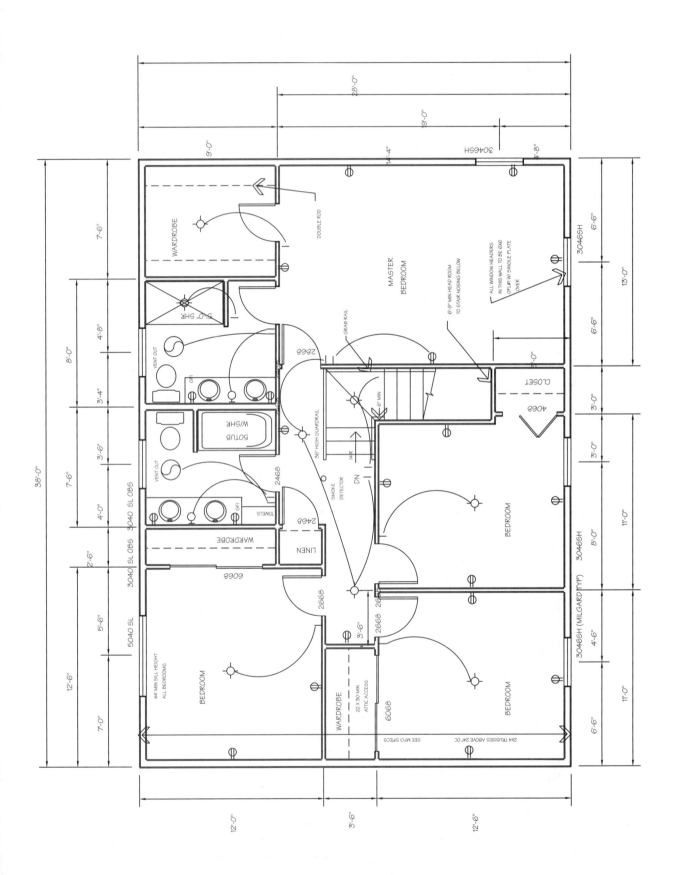

SECOND FLOOR PLAN

SCALE: 1/4" = 1'-0"

© 2011 Cengage Learning. All Rights Reserved. May not be scanned, copied or duplicated, or posted to a publicly accessible website, in whole or in part.

CHAPTER 5 FLOOR PLAN DIMENSIONS

Problem 5–1   Slashes, arrows and dots are enlarged for emphasis. Student drawings should be similar to textbook examples.

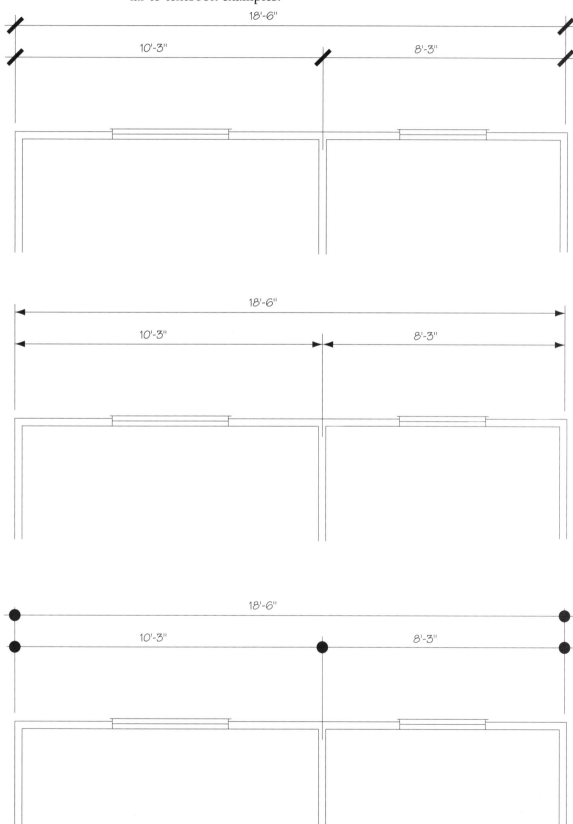

© 2011 Cengage Learning. All Rights Reserved. May not be scanned, copied or duplicated, or posted to a publicly accessible website, in whole or in part.

Problem 5–2

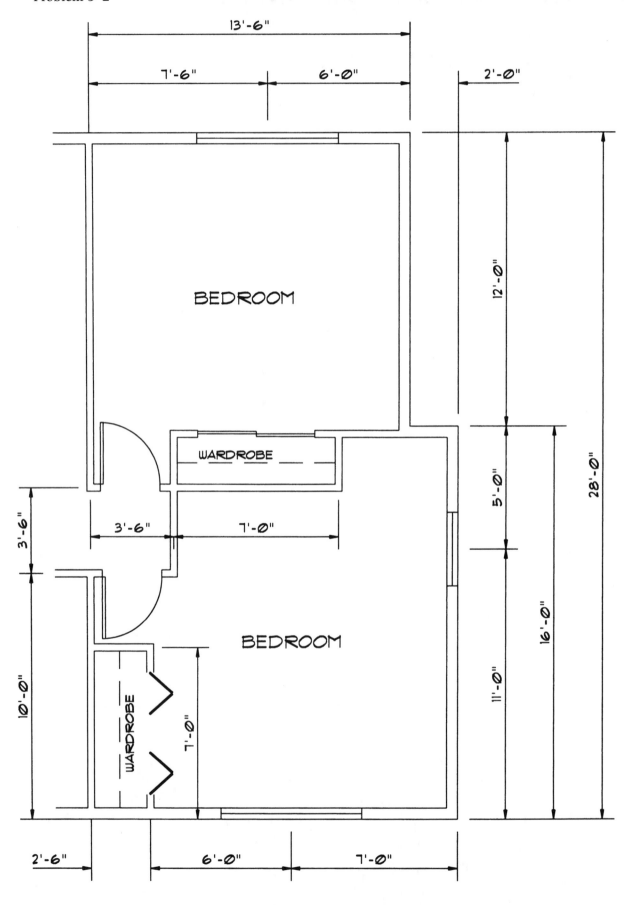

© 2011 Cengage Learning. All Rights Reserved. May not be scanned, copied or duplicated, or posted to a publicly accessible website, in whole or in part.

Problem 5–3

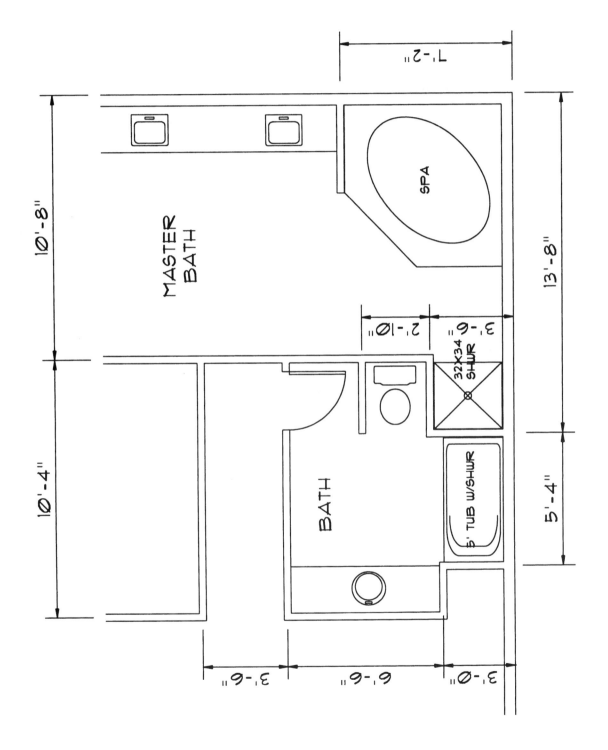

© 2011 Cengage Learning. All Rights Reserved. May not be scanned, copied or duplicated, or posted to a publicly accessible website, in whole or in part.

Problem 5–4

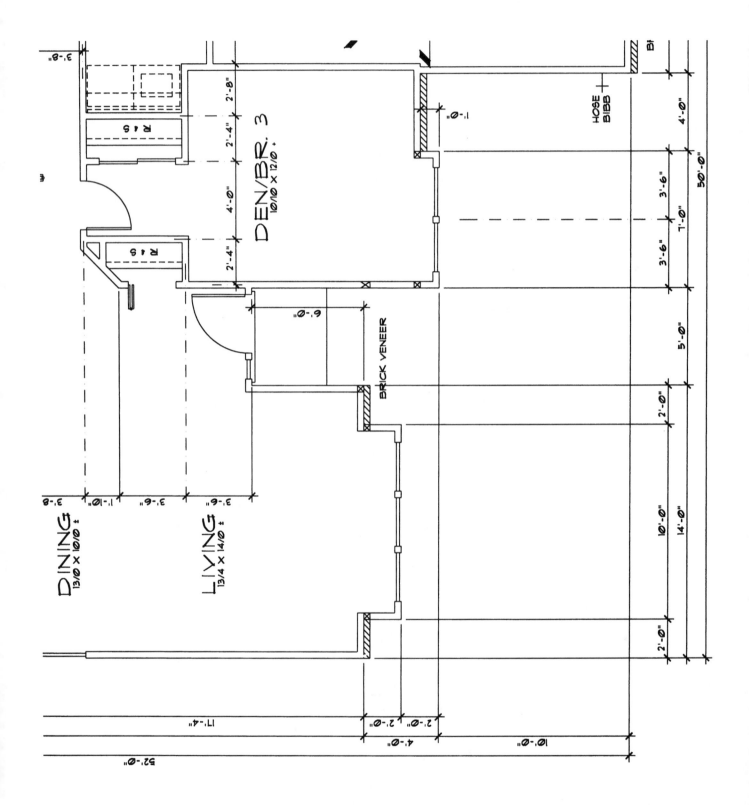

© 2011 Cengage Learning. All Rights Reserved. May not be scanned, copied or duplicated, or posted to a publicly accessible website, in whole or in part.

Problem 5–5 Slashes are enlarged for emphasis. Student drawings should be similar to textbook examples.

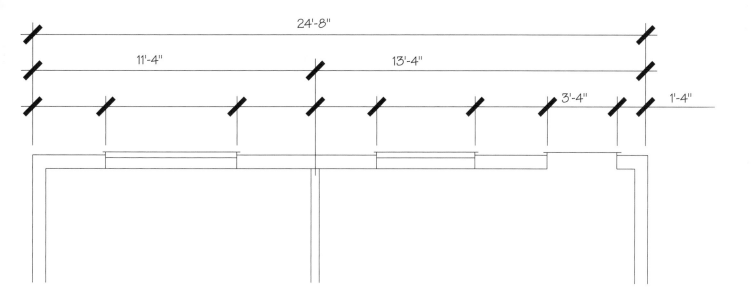

© 2011 Cengage Learning. All Rights Reserved. May not be scanned, copied or duplicated, or posted to a publicly accessible website, in whole or in part.

Problem 5–6

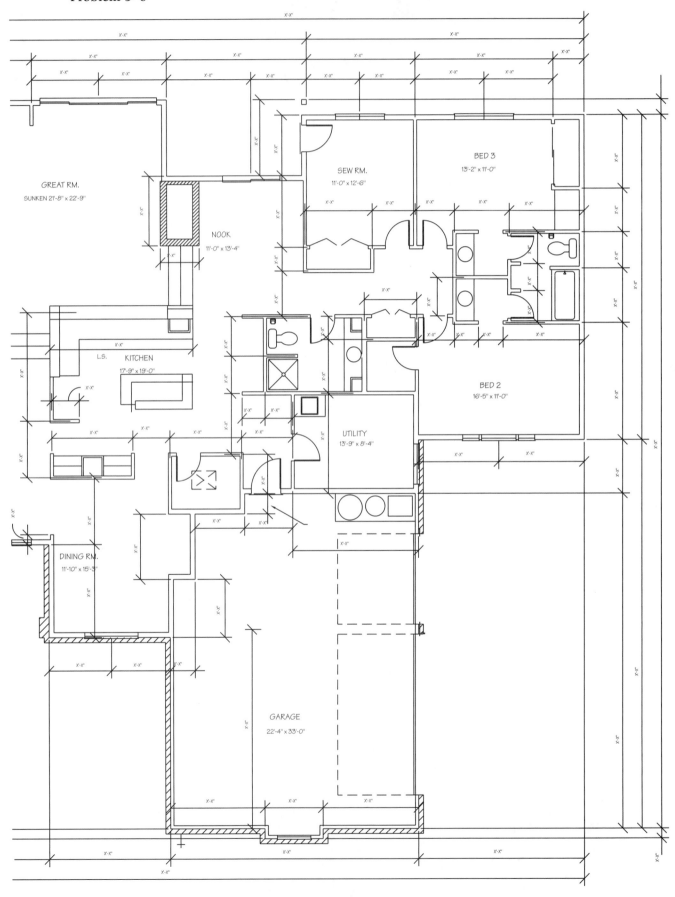

GREAT RM.
SUNKEN 21'-8" x 22'-9"

NOOK
11'-0" x 13'-4"

SEW RM.
11'-0" x 12'-6"

BED 3
13'-2" x 11'-0"

L.S. KITCHEN
17'-9" x 19'-0"

BED 2
16'-5" x 11'-0"

UTILITY
13'-9" x 8'-4"

DINING RM.
11'-10" x 15'-3"

GARAGE
22'-4" x 33'-0"

© 2011 Cengage Learning. All Rights Reserved. May not be scanned, copied or duplicated, or posted to a publicly accessible website, in whole or in part.

Problem 5–7

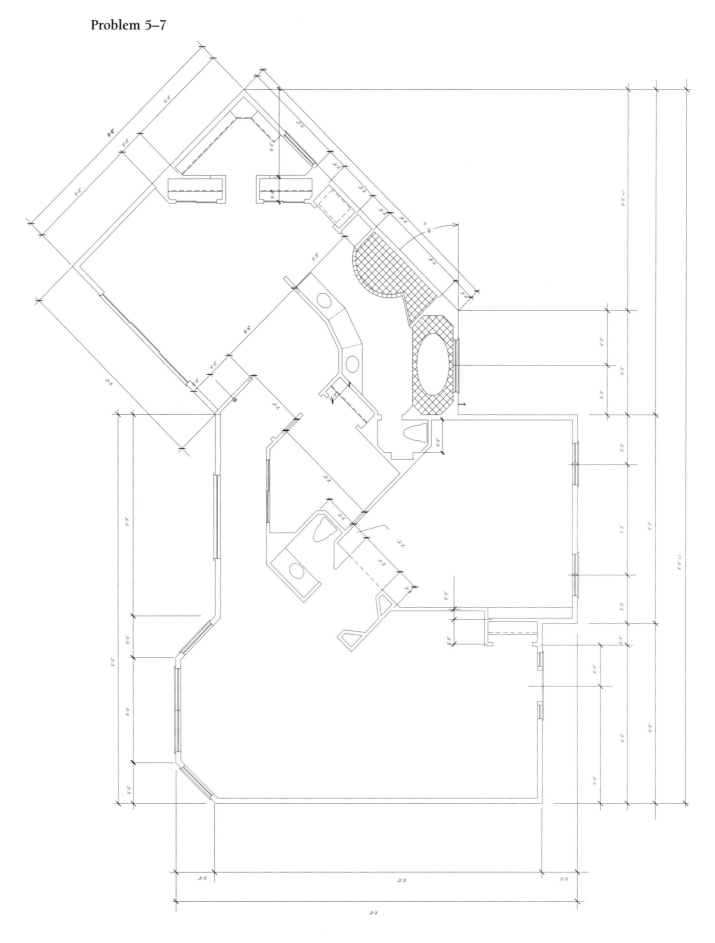

© 2011 Cengage Learning. All Rights Reserved. May not be scanned, copied or duplicated, or posted to a publicly accessible website, in whole or in part.

CHAPTER 6 ELECTRICAL PLANS

Problem 6–1

DUPLEX CONVENIENCE OUTLET

MULTIPLE DUPLEX CONVENIENCE OUTLET

WEATHERPROOF OUTLET 110 VOLTS

GROUND FAULT CIRCUIT INTERUPTER

RANGE OUTLET 220 VOLTS

220 VOLT OUTLET

SPECIAL CONNECTION FOR DISHWASHER, GARBAGE DISPOSAL (GD), HOT WATER HEATER (WH)

SINGLE SPECIAL PURPOSE OUTLET

SINGLE FLOOR OUTLET

FAN

LIGHT

SURFACE MOUNT FIXTURE SQUARE SHAPE

WALL MOUNTED LIGHT

FLUORESCENT LIGHT

TRACK LIGHT OR UNDERCABINET LIGHT

© 2011 Cengage Learning. All Rights Reserved. May not be scanned, copied or duplicated, or posted to a publicly accessible website, in whole or in part.

Problem 6–1 (Continued)

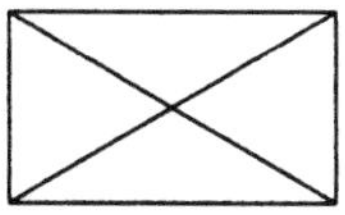

SIMPLIFIED FLUORESCENT LIGHT SURFACE MOUNT

SIMPLIFIED FLUORESCENT LIGHT RECESSED

JUNCTION BOX

CLOCK

RADIO OUTLET

TV OUTLET

SMOKE DETECTOR

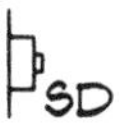

SMOKE DETECTOR WALL MOUNT

INTERCOM OUTLET

BELL

PHONE OUTLET

HEAT, LIGHT, FAN COMBO

SINGLE POLE SWITCH

THREE–WAY SWITCH

FOUR–WAY SWITCH

SWITCH LEG

© 2011 Cengage Learning. All Rights Reserved. May not be scanned, copied or duplicated, or posted to a publicly accessible website, in whole or in part.

Problem 6–2

Problem 6–3

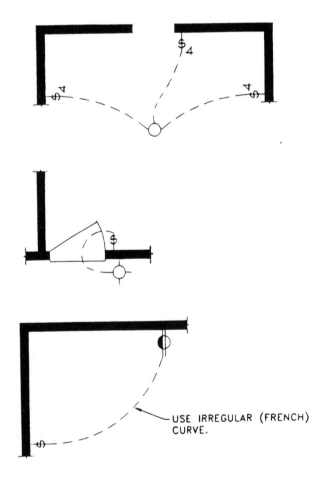

Problem 6–4   No visible solution.

© 2011 Cengage Learning. All Rights Reserved. May not be scanned, copied or duplicated, or posted to a publicly accessible website, in whole or in part.

Problem 6–5

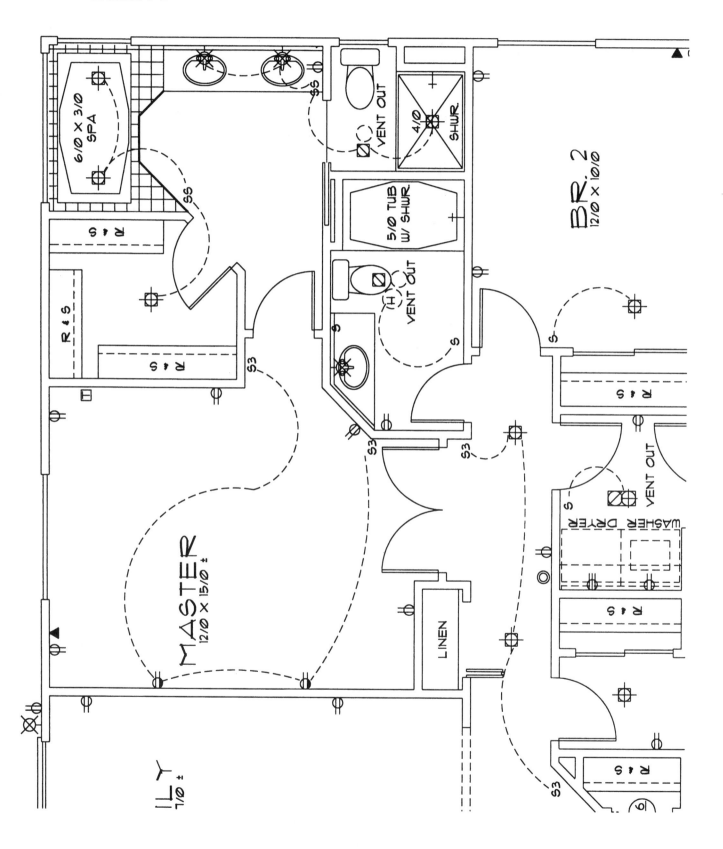

© 2011 Cengage Learning. All Rights Reserved. May not be scanned, copied or duplicated, or posted to a publicly accessible website, in whole or in part.

Problem 6–6

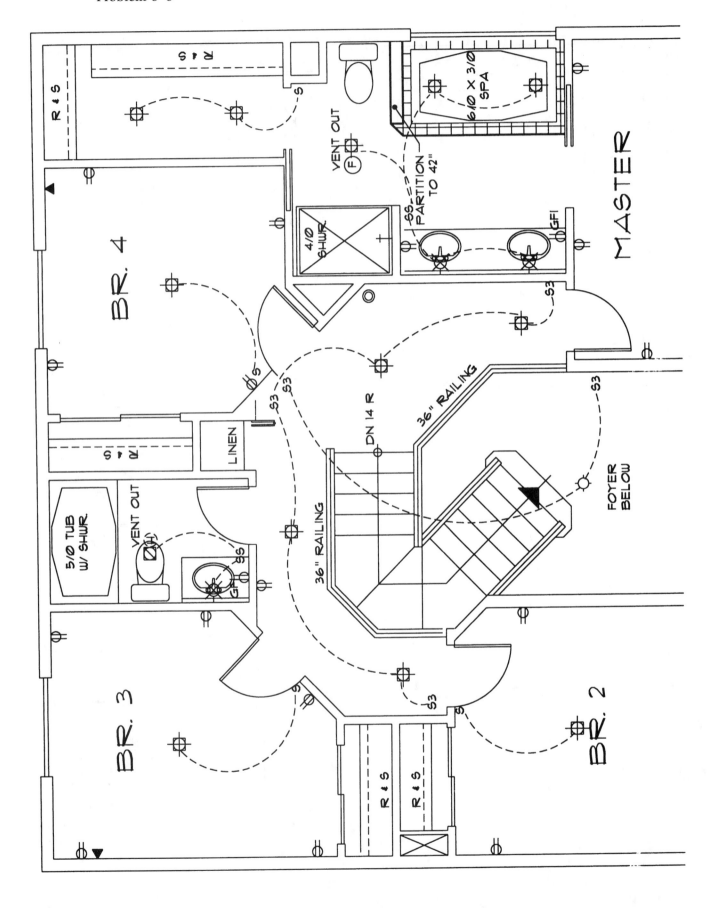

© 2011 Cengage Learning. All Rights Reserved. May not be scanned, copied or duplicated, or posted to a publicly accessible website, in whole or in part.

Problem 6–7

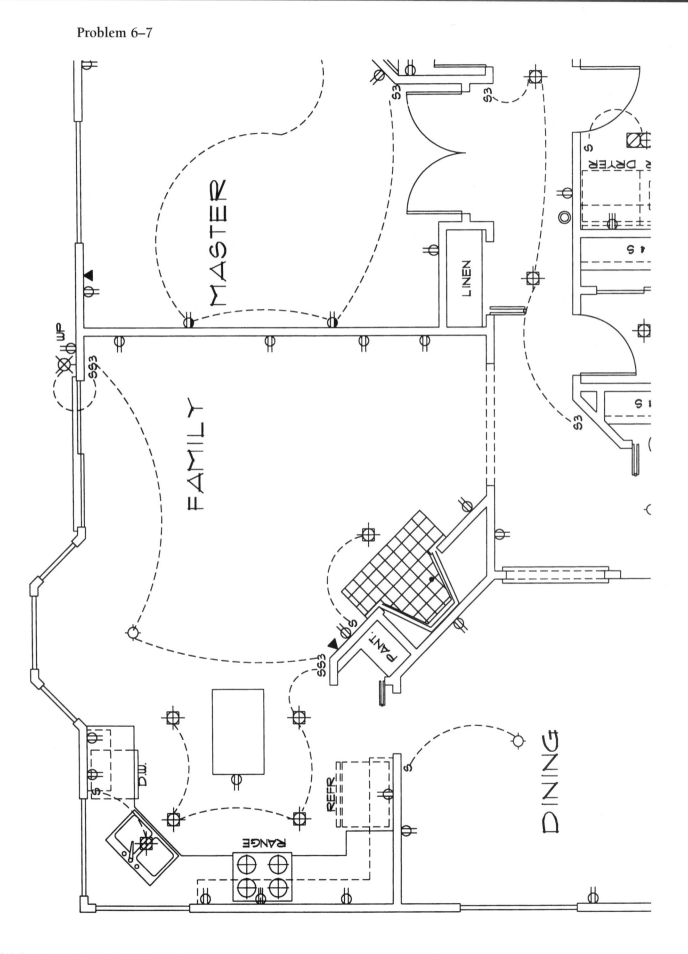

© 2011 Cengage Learning. All Rights Reserved. May not be scanned, copied or duplicated, or posted to a publicly accessible website, in whole or in part.

Problem 6–8

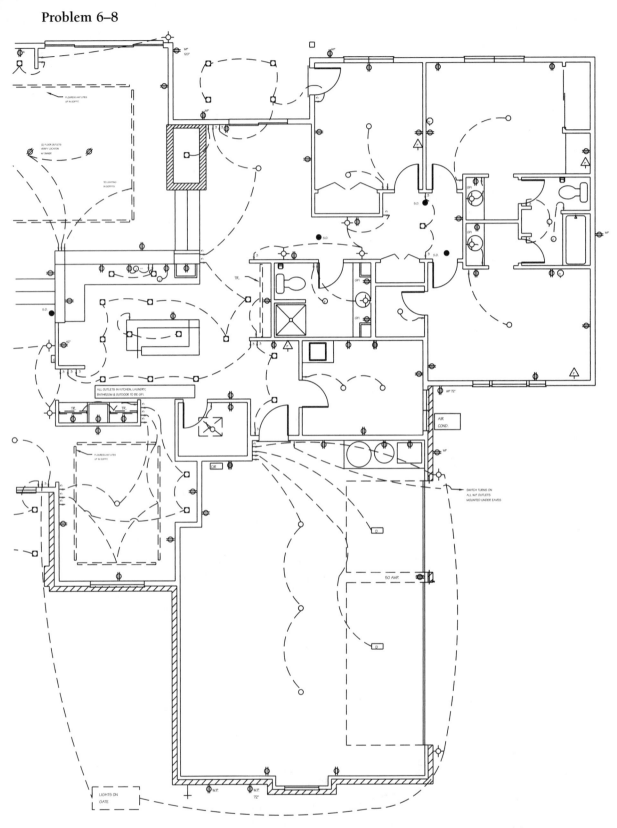

Problem 6–9   Solutions will vary greatly but should resemble examples in Chapter 19 of the text.

Problem 6–10   Solutions will vary greatly depending on the floor plan selected. Floor plans in Solutions Part 4 contain possible layouts.

© 2011 Cengage Learning. All Rights Reserved. May not be scanned, copied or duplicated, or posted to a publicly accessible website, in whole or in part.

CHAPTER 7 PLUMBING AND HVAC DRAWINGS

Problem 7–1

CW–Cold water

HB–Hose bibb–faucet used to attach a hose

HW—Hot water

CO–Clean out–fitting with removable plug to allow access for cleaning

HWR–Hot water return

DS–Downspout–pipe that carries rainwater from gutters of the roof to the ground

Problem 7–2

CB–Catch basin	MH–Manhole	VTR–Vent thru roof
DF–Drinking fountain	WH–Water heater	DW–Dishwasher
BD–Bidget	GD–Garbage disposal	B–Bathtub
WC–Water closet (toilet)	LAV–Lavatory	SH–Shower
S–Sink	U–Urinal	SD–Shower drain
RD–Rain drain	FD–Floor drain	

© 2011 Cengage Learning. All Rights Reserved. May not be scanned, copied or duplicated, or posted to a publicly accessible website, in whole or in part.

CHAPTER 8 ROOF PLANS

PROBLEM 8–1

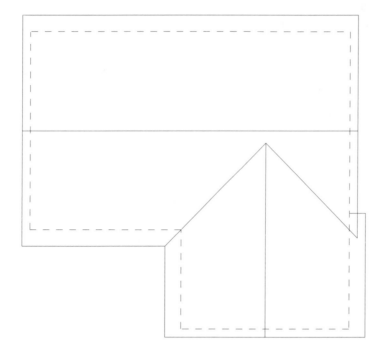

© 2011 Cengage Learning. All Rights Reserved. May not be scanned, copied or duplicated, or posted to a publicly accessible website, in whole or in part.

Problem 8–2

Problem 8–3

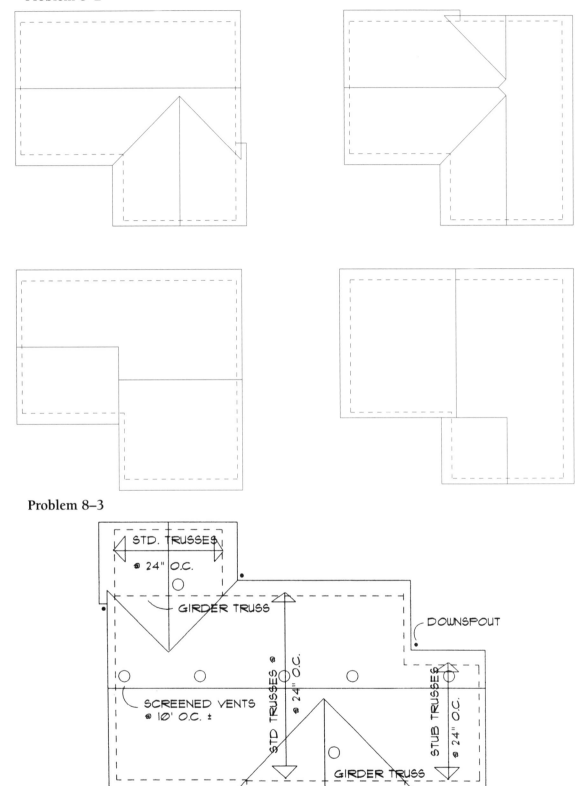

© 2011 Cengage Learning. All Rights Reserved. May not be scanned, copied or duplicated, or posted to a publicly accessible website, in whole or in part.

Problem 8–4

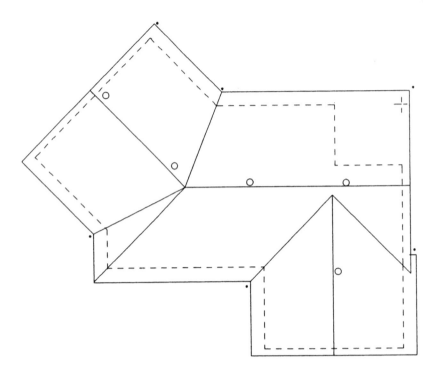

Problem 8–5

© 2011 Cengage Learning. All Rights Reserved. May not be scanned, copied or duplicated, or posted to a publicly accessible website, in whole or in part.

Problem 8–6

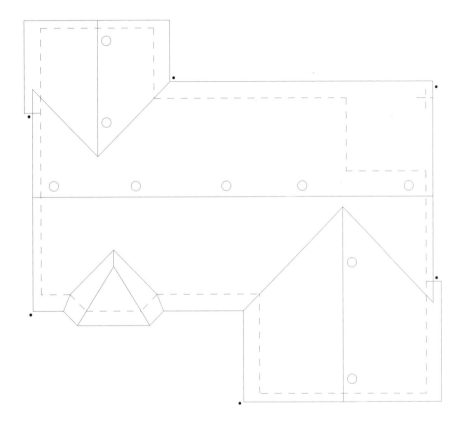

Problem 8–7

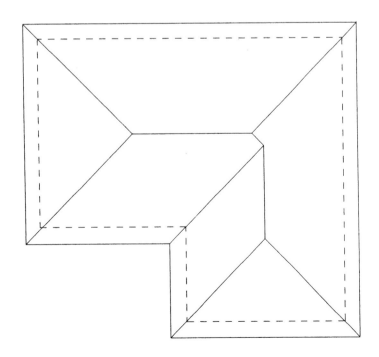

© 2011 Cengage Learning. All Rights Reserved. May not be scanned, copied or duplicated, or posted to a publicly accessible website, in whole or in part.

Problem 8–8

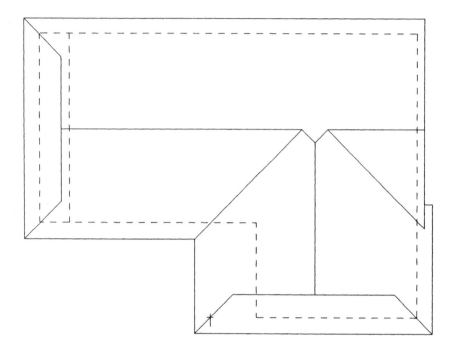

Problem 8–9

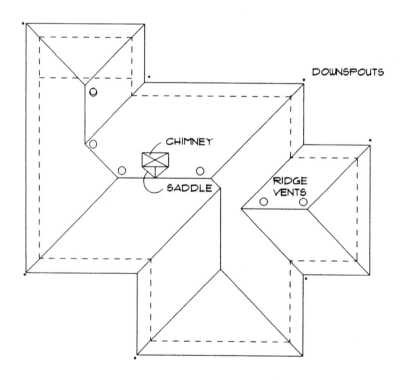

© 2011 Cengage Learning. All Rights Reserved. May not be scanned, copied or duplicated, or posted to a publicly accessible website, in whole or in part.

Problem 8–10

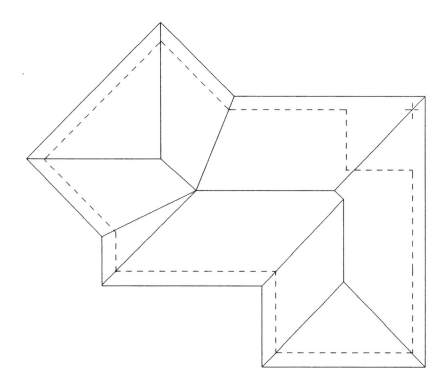

© 2011 Cengage Learning. All Rights Reserved. May not be scanned, copied or duplicated, or posted to a publicly accessible website, in whole or in part.

Problem 8–11

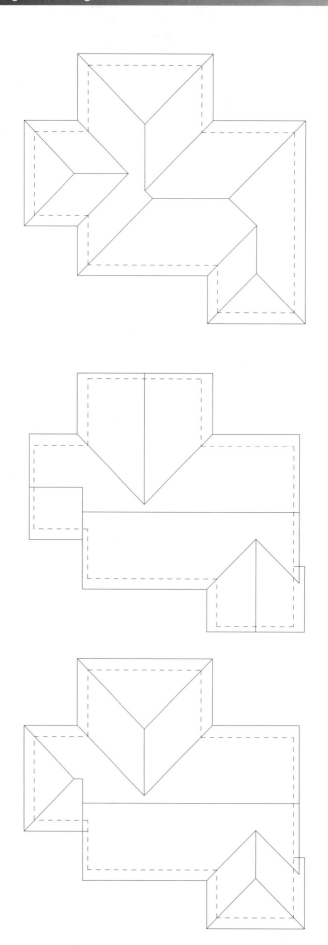

© 2011 Cengage Learning. All Rights Reserved. May not be scanned, copied or duplicated, or posted to a publicly accessible website, in whole or in part.

Problem 8–12

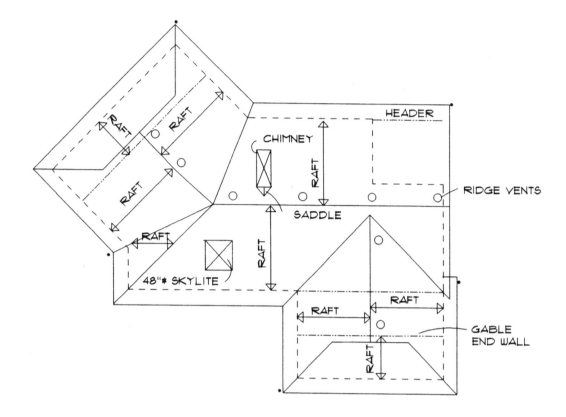

Problem 8–13   Solutions will vary. Possible alternatives for truss and joist framed roofs include the following:

ROOF PLAN

1/8"══════ 1'-0"

ALL FRAMING LUMBER TO BE DFL #2 OR
  BETTER UNLESS NOTED.

SUBMIT TRUSS MANUF. DRAWINGS TO BUILDING
  DEPT. PRIOR TO ERECTION

USE 1/2" 'CCX' EXTERIOR PLY @ ALL
  EXPOSED EAVES

USE 300# COMPO. SHINGLES OVER 15# FELT.

ROOF PLAN

1/8"══════ 1'-0"

ALL FRAMING LUMBER TO BE DFL #2 OR
  BETTER UNLESS NOTED.

ALL RAFTERS TO BE 2 X 6 UNLESS NOTED.
  SEE ATTACHED SCHEDULE FOR SPECIFIC
  SIZES

PROVIDE SCREENED VENTS @ EA. 3rd.
  JOIST SPACE @ ALL ATTIC EAVES.

USE 1/2" 'CCX' EXTERIOR PLY @ ALL
  EXPOSED EAVES

USE MED. CEDAR SHAKES OVER 15# FELT W/
  30# x 18" WIDE FELT BTWN. EA. COURSE. W/
  10 1/2" EXPOSURE.

© 2011 Cengage Learning. All Rights Reserved. May not be scanned, copied or duplicated, or posted to a publicly accessible website, in whole or in part.

Problem 8–14A

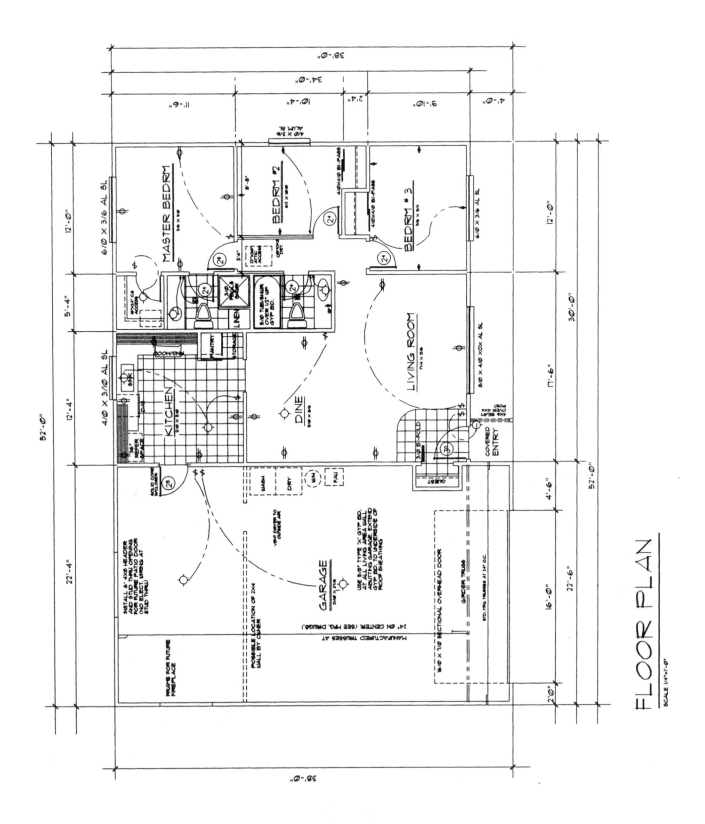

FLOOR PLAN

© 2011 Cengage Learning. All Rights Reserved. May not be scanned, copied or duplicated, or posted to a publicly accessible website, in whole or in part.

Problem 8–14B

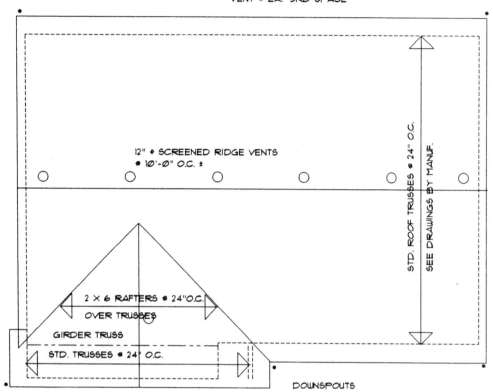

PROVIDE A SCREENED CLOSABLE
VENT @ EA. 3RD SPACE

12" ∅ SCREENED RIDGE VENTS
@ 10'-0" O.C. ±

STD. ROOF TRUSSES @ 24" O.C.

SEE DRAWINGS BY MANUF.

2 X 6 RAFTERS @ 24"O.C.
OVER TRUSSES

GIRDER TRUSS

STD. TRUSSES @ 24' O.C.

DOWNSPOUTS

ROOF PLAN

1/8"   1'-0"

© 2011 Cengage Learning. All Rights Reserved. May not be scanned, copied or duplicated, or posted to a publicly accessible website, in whole or in part.

Problem 8–14C

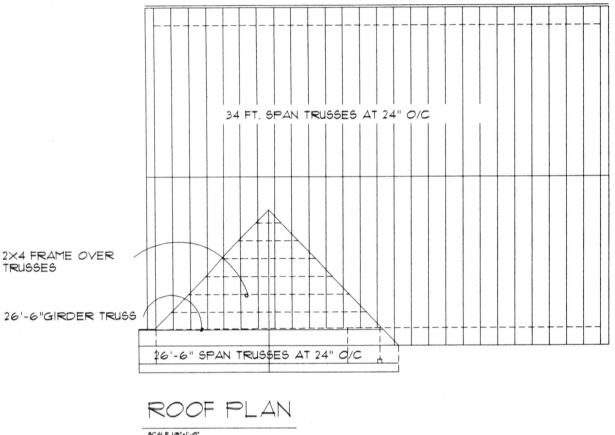

34 FT. SPAN TRUSSES AT 24" O/C

2X4 FRAME OVER TRUSSES

26'-6"GIRDER TRUSS

26'-6" SPAN TRUSSES AT 24" O/C

ROOF PLAN

SCALE 1/8"=1'-0"

© 2011 Cengage Learning. All Rights Reserved. May not be scanned, copied or duplicated, or posted to a publicly accessible website, in whole or in part.

Problem 8–15A

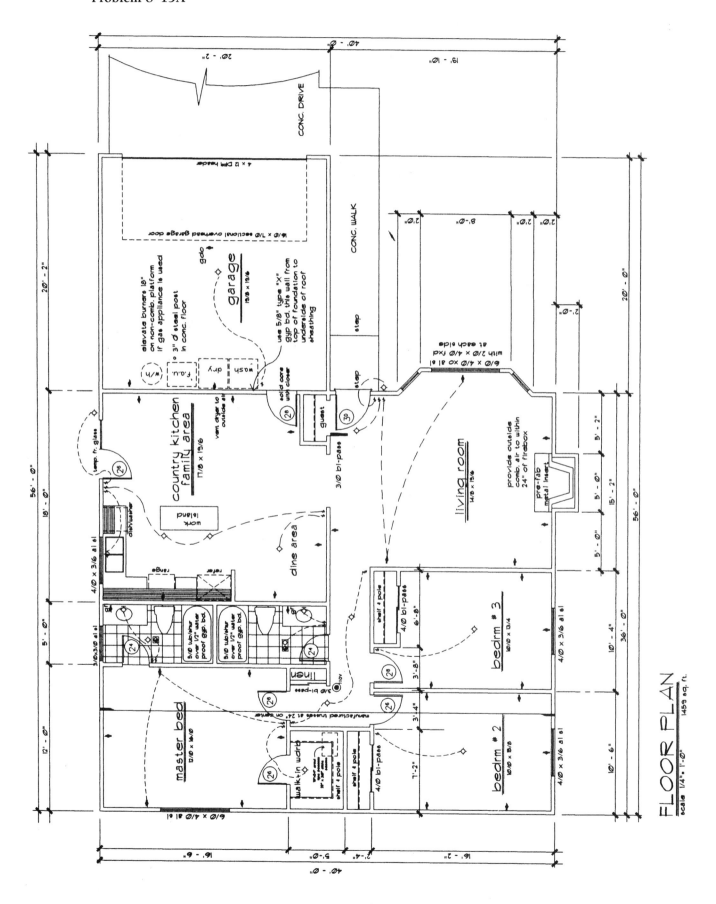

FLOOR PLAN

scale 1/4" = 1'-0"   1459 sq. ft.

© 2011 Cengage Learning. All Rights Reserved. May not be scanned, copied or duplicated, or posted to a publicly accessible website, in whole or in part.

Problem 8–15B

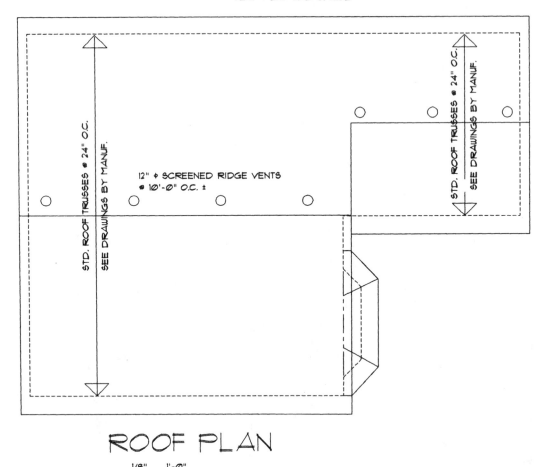

PROVIDE A SCREENED CLOSABLE
VENT @ EA. 3RD SPACE

12" Φ SCREENED RIDGE VENTS
@ 10'-0" O.C. ±

STD. ROOF TRUSSES @ 24" O.C.

SEE DRAWINGS BY MANUF.

STD. ROOF TRUSSES @ 24" O.C.

SEE DRAWINGS BY MANUF.

ROOF PLAN
1/8" 1'-0"

© 2011 Cengage Learning. All Rights Reserved. May not be scanned, copied or duplicated, or posted to a publicly accessible website, in whole or in part.

Problem 8–15C

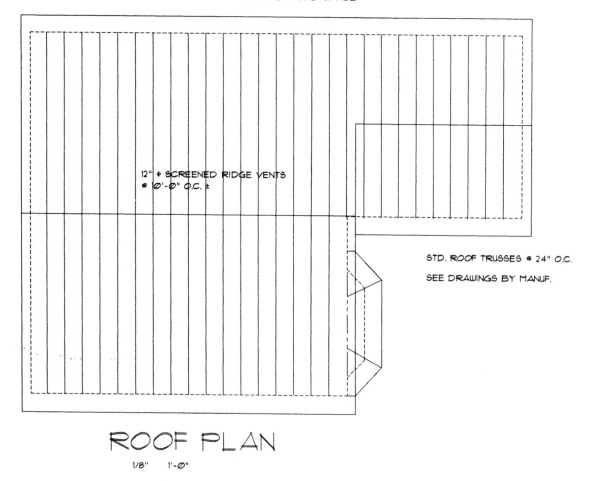

PROVIDE A SCREENED CLOSABLE
VENT @ EA. 3RD SPACE

12" ∅ SCREENED RIDGE VENTS
@ 10'-0" O.C. ±

STD. ROOF TRUSSES @ 24" O.C.

SEE DRAWINGS BY MANUF.

ROOF PLAN
1/8"   1'-0"

© 2011 Cengage Learning. All Rights Reserved. May not be scanned, copied or duplicated, or posted to a publicly accessible website, in whole or in part.

Problem 8–16A

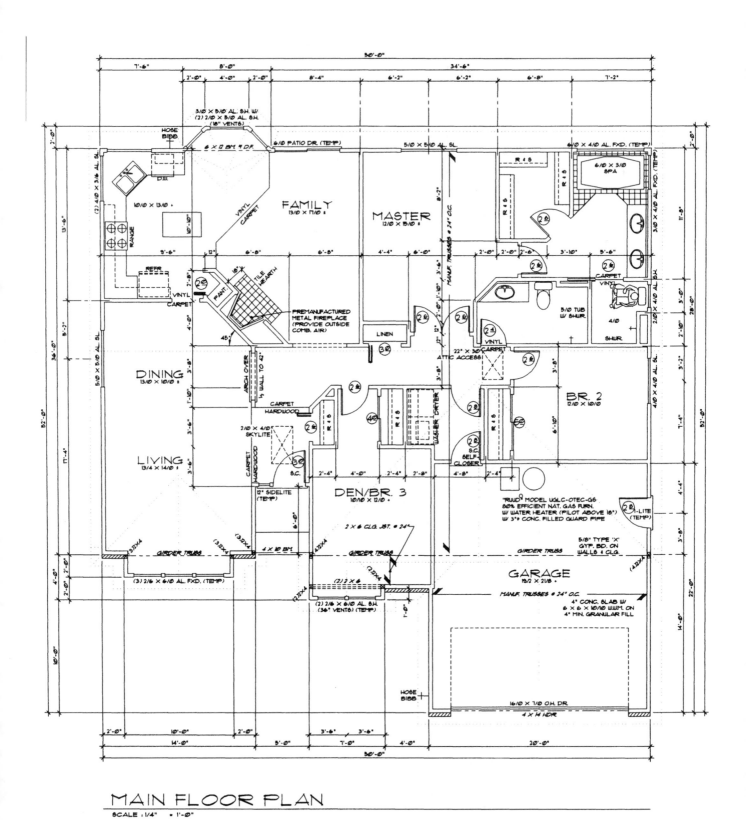

MAIN FLOOR PLAN

SCALE : 1/4" = 1'-0"

© 2011 Cengage Learning. All Rights Reserved. May not be scanned, copied or duplicated, or posted to a publicly accessible website, in whole or in part.

Problem 8–16B

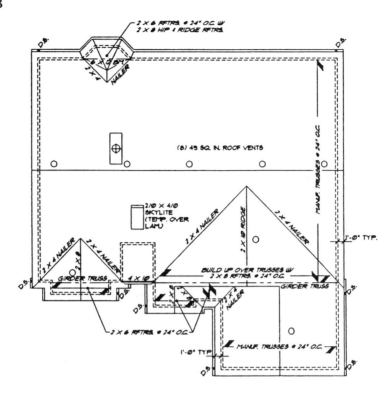

2 X 6 RFTRS. @ 24" O.C. W/
2 X 8 HIP & RIDGE RFTRS.

(8) 49 SQ. IN. ROOF VENTS

MANUF. TRUSSES @ 24" O.C.

2/0 X 4/0
SKYLITE
(TEMP. OVER
LAM)

2 X 4 NAILER

2 X 10 RIDGE

2 X 4 NAILER

2 X 4 NAILER

2 X 4 NAILER

1'-0" TYP.

BUILD UP OVER TRUSSES W/
2 X 8 RFTRS. @ 24" O.C.

GIRDER TRUSS

4 X 10

GIRDER TRUSS

2 X 4 NAILER

2 X 6 RFTRS. @ 24" O.C.

1'-0" TYP.

MANUF. TRUSSES @ 24" O.C.

ROOF PLAN
SCALE : 1/8" = 1'-0"

Problem 8–16C

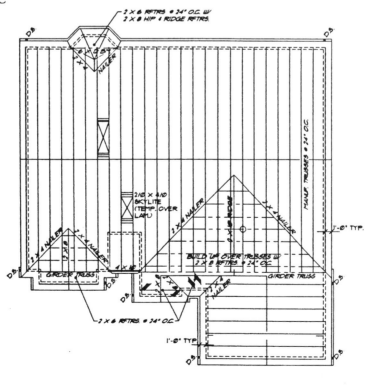

2 X 6 RFTRS. @ 24" O.C. W/
2 X 8 HIP & RIDGE RFTRS.

NAILER

MANUF. TRUSSES @ 24" O.C.

2/0 X 4/0
SKYLITE
(TEMP. OVER
LAM)

2 X 4 NAILER

2 X 10 RIDGE

2 X 4 NAILER

2 X 4 NAILER

2 X 4 NAILER

1'-0" TYP.

BUILD UP OVER TRUSSES W/
2 X 8 RFTRS. @ 24" O.C.

GIRDER TRUSS

4 X 10

GIRDER TRUSS

2 X 4 NAILER

2 X 6 RFTRS. @ 24" O.C.

1'-0" TYP.

ROOF PLAN
SCALE : 1/8" = 1'-0"

© 2011 Cengage Learning. All Rights Reserved. May not be scanned, copied or duplicated, or posted to a publicly accessible website, in whole or in part.

Problem 8–17A

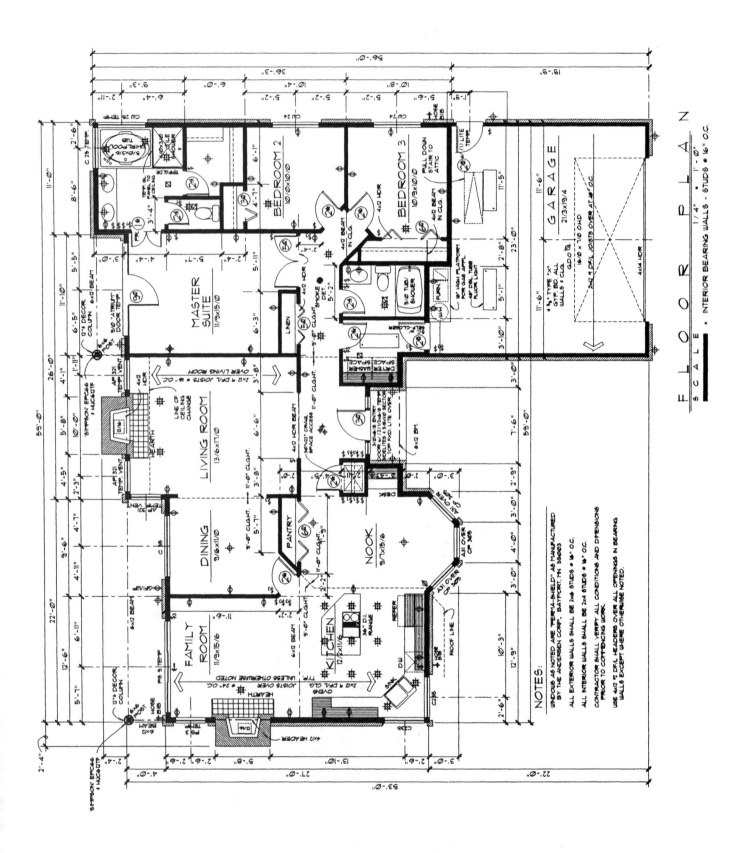

© 2011 Cengage Learning. All Rights Reserved. May not be scanned, copied or duplicated, or posted to a publicly accessible website, in whole or in part.

Problem 8–17B

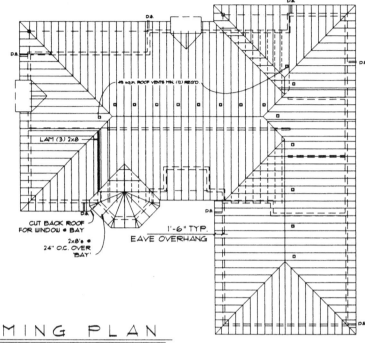

NOTES:

1. ALL RAFTERS TO BE 2 x 8 #2 DF/L @16" O.C. EXCEPT WHERE OTHERWISE NOTED.

2. ALL RIDGE BOARDS AND HIP RAFTERS SHALL BE 2 x 10 #2 DF/L.

3. ALL CEILING JOISTS SHALL BE 2 x 8 #2 DF/L @ SAME SPACINGS AS THE RAFTERS ABOVE.

4. REFER TO FLOOR PLAN FOR BEAM SIZES AND SPECIFICATIONS.

5. ALL FASCIA BOARDS TO BE 2 x 8 SELECT WESTERN RED CEDAR.

ROOF FRAMING PLAN
SCALE   1/4" ■ 1'-0"

© 2011 Cengage Learning. All Rights Reserved. May not be scanned, copied or duplicated, or posted to a publicly accessible website, in whole or in part.

Problem 8–18A

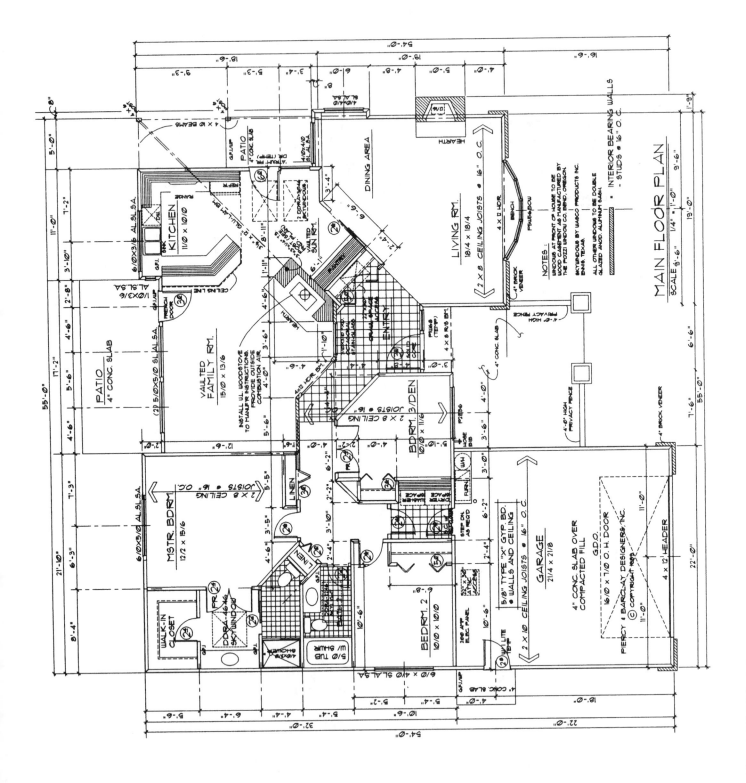

© 2011 Cengage Learning. All Rights Reserved. May not be scanned, copied or duplicated, or posted to a publicly accessible website, in whole or in part.

Problem 8–18B

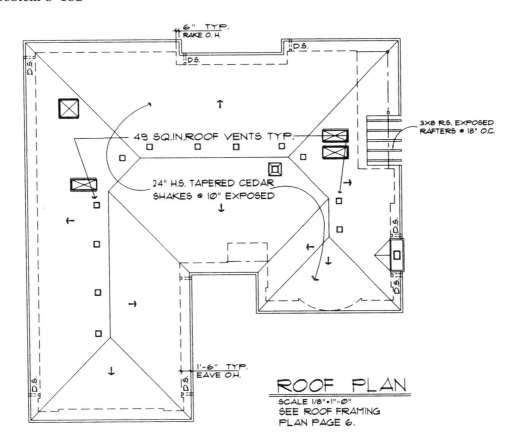

6" TYP.
RAKE O.H.

D.S.

D.S.

3X8 R.S. EXPOSED
RAFTERS @ 18" O.C.

49 SQ.IN. ROOF VENTS TYP.

24" H.S. TAPERED CEDAR
SHAKES @ 10" EXPOSED

D.S.

1'-6" TYP.
EAVE O.H.

D.S.

ROOF PLAN

SCALE 1/8"=1'-0"
SEE ROOF FRAMING
PLAN PAGE 6.

© 2011 Cengage Learning. All Rights Reserved. May not be scanned, copied or duplicated, or posted to a publicly accessible website, in whole or in part.

Problem 8–19A

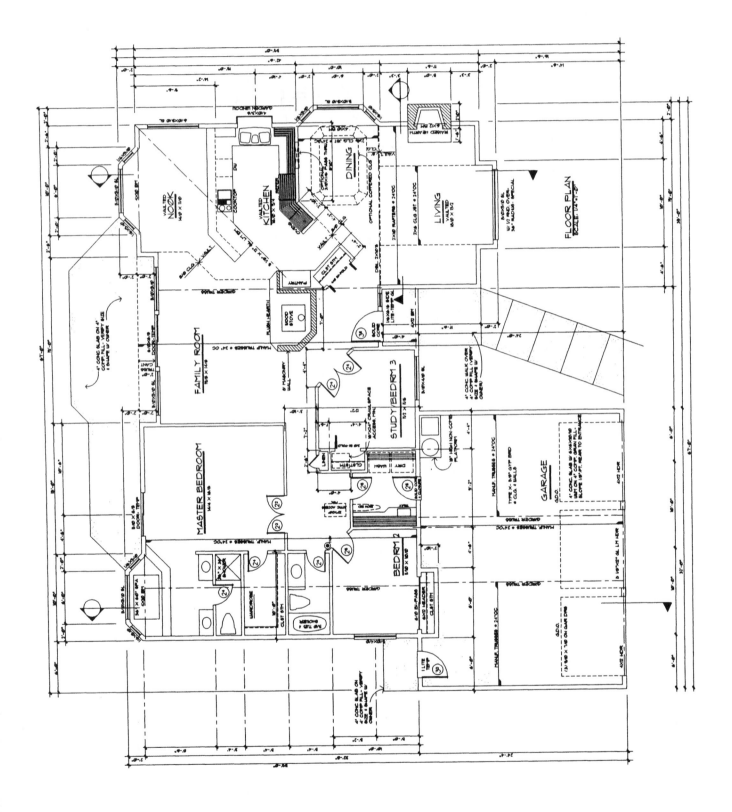

© 2011 Cengage Learning. All Rights Reserved. May not be scanned, copied or duplicated, or posted to a publicly accessible website, in whole or in part.

Problem 8–19B

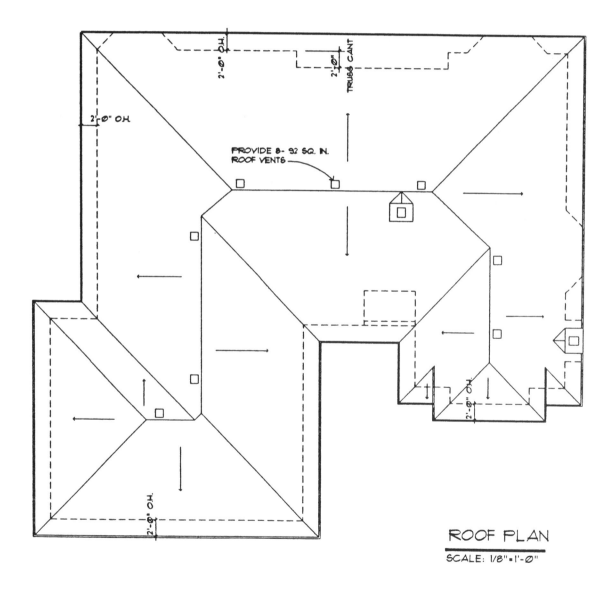

ROOF PLAN

SCALE: 1/8" = 1'-0"

© 2011 Cengage Learning. All Rights Reserved. May not be scanned, copied or duplicated, or posted to a publicly accessible website, in whole or in part.

Problem 8–20A

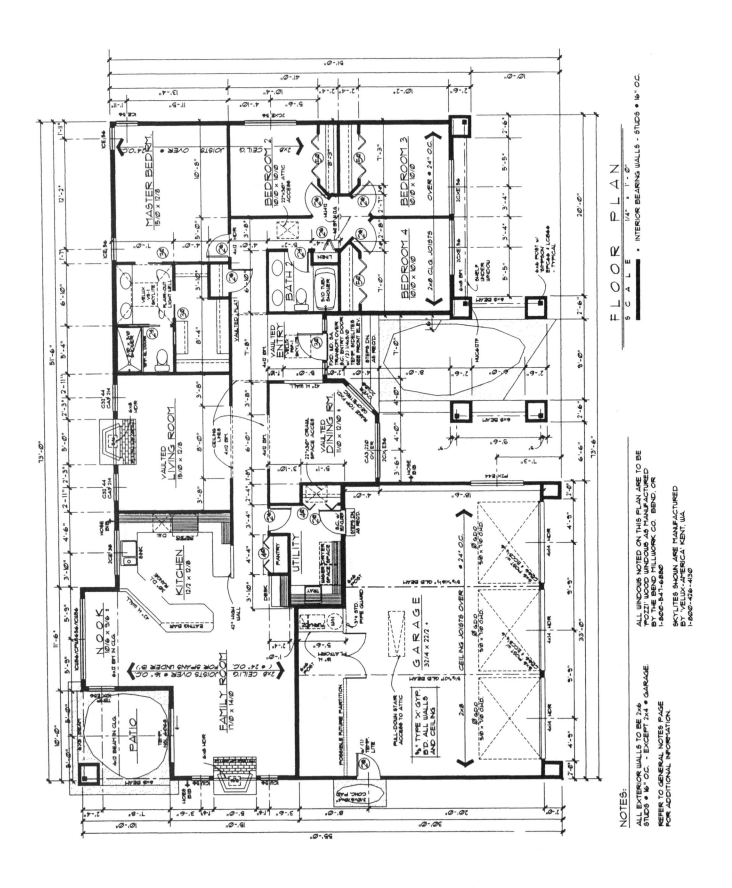

© 2011 Cengage Learning. All Rights Reserved. May not be scanned, copied or duplicated, or posted to a publicly accessible website, in whole or in part.

Problem 8–20B

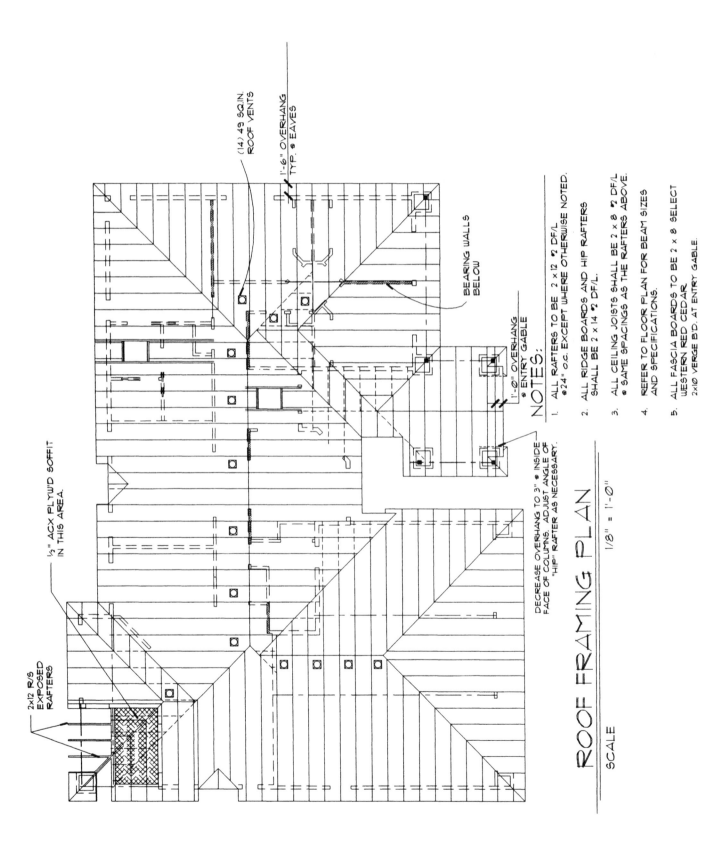

(14) 49 SQ.IN. ROOF VENTS

1'-6" OVERHANG TYP. @ EAVES

BEARING WALLS BELOW

1'-0" OVERHANG @ ENTRY GABLE

½" ACX PLYW'D SOFFIT IN THIS AREA.

2x12 R/S EXPOSED RAFTERS

DECREASE OVERHANG TO 3" @ INSIDE FACE OF COLUMNS. ADJUST ANGLE OF "HIP" RAFTER AS NECESSARY.

NOTES:

1. ALL RAFTERS TO BE 2 x 12 #2 DF/L @24" o.c. EXCEPT WHERE OTHERWISE NOTED.

2. ALL RIDGE BOARDS AND HIP RAFTERS SHALL BE 2 x 14 #2 DF/L.

3. ALL CEILING JOISTS SHALL BE 2 x 8 #2 DF/L @ SAME SPACINGS AS THE RAFTERS ABOVE.

4. REFER TO FLOOR PLAN FOR BEAM SIZES AND SPECIFICATIONS.

5. ALL FASCIA BOARDS TO BE 2 x 8 SELECT WESTERN RED CEDAR. 2x10 VERGE B'D. AT ENTRY GABLE.

ROOF FRAMING PLAN

SCALE 1/8" = 1'-0"

© 2011 Cengage Learning. All Rights Reserved. May not be scanned, copied or duplicated, or posted to a publicly accessible website, in whole or in part.

Problem 8–21A

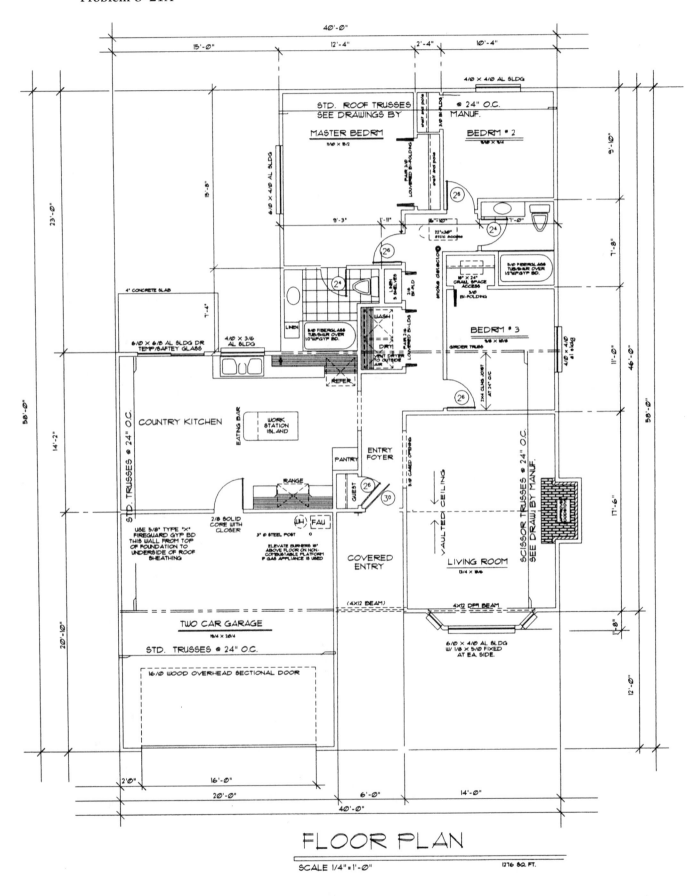

FLOOR PLAN

SCALE 1/4"=1'-0"

1276 SQ. FT.

© 2011 Cengage Learning. All Rights Reserved. May not be scanned, copied or duplicated, or posted to a publicly accessible website, in whole or in part.

Problem 8–21B

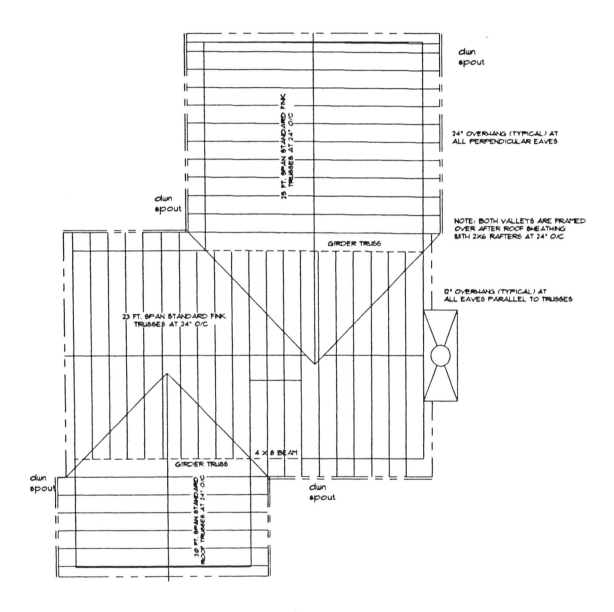

dwn spout

24" OVERHANG (TYPICAL) AT ALL PERPENDICULAR EAVES

25 FT. SPAN STANDARD FINK TRUSSES AT 24" O/C

dwn spout

NOTE: BOTH VALLEYS ARE FRAMED OVER AFTER ROOF SHEATHING WITH 2X6 RAFTERS AT 24" O/C

GIRDER TRUSS

12" OVERHANG (TYPICAL) AT ALL EAVES PARALLEL TO TRUSSES

23 FT. SPAN STANDARD FINK TRUSSES AT 24" O/C

4 X 8 BEAM

GIRDER TRUSS

dwn spout

dwn spout

20 FT. SPAN STANDARD ROOF TRUSSES AT 24" O/C

ROOF TRUSS PLAN

scale 1/8" = 1'-0"

© 2011 Cengage Learning. All Rights Reserved. May not be scanned, copied or duplicated, or posted to a publicly accessible website, in whole or in part.

Problem 8–22A

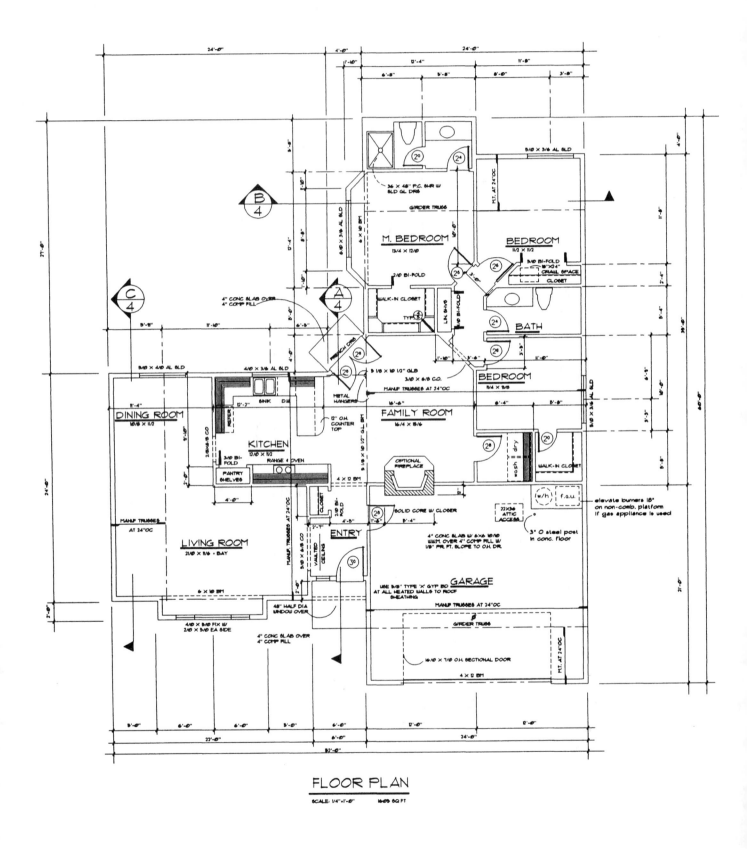

FLOOR PLAN

SCALE: 1/4"=1'-0"   1603 SQ FT

© 2011 Cengage Learning. All Rights Reserved. May not be scanned, copied or duplicated, or posted to a publicly accessible website, in whole or in part.

Problem 8–22B

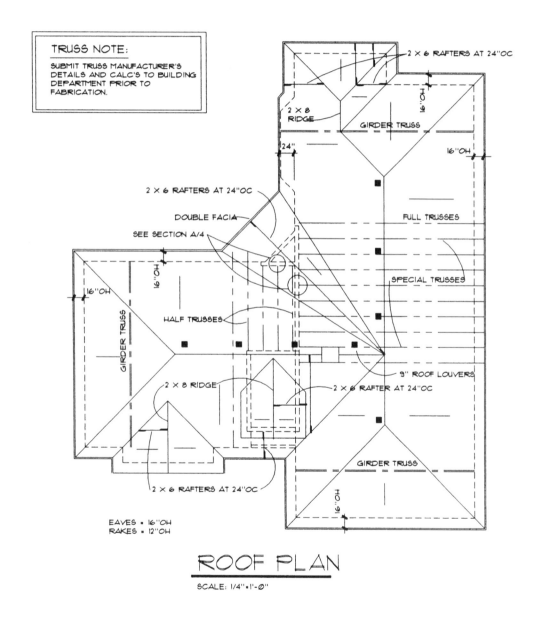

TRUSS NOTE:

SUBMIT TRUSS MANUFACTURER'S
DETAILS AND CALC'S TO BUILDING
DEPARTMENT PRIOR TO
FABRICATION.

2 × 6 RAFTERS AT 24"OC

2 × 8
RIDGE

GIRDER TRUSS

16"OH

24"

16"OH

2 × 6 RAFTERS AT 24"OC

DOUBLE FACIA

SEE SECTION A/4

FULL TRUSSES

16"OH

16"OH

SPECIAL TRUSSES

HALF TRUSSES

GIRDER TRUSS

9" ROOF LOUVERS

2 × 8 RIDGE

2 × 6 RAFTER AT 24"OC

2 × 6 RAFTERS AT 24"OC

GIRDER TRUSS

16"OH

EAVES = 16"OH
RAKES = 12"OH

ROOF PLAN

SCALE: 1/4"=1'-0"

© 2011 Cengage Learning. All Rights Reserved. May not be scanned, copied or duplicated, or posted to a publicly accessible website, in whole or in part.

Problem 8–23

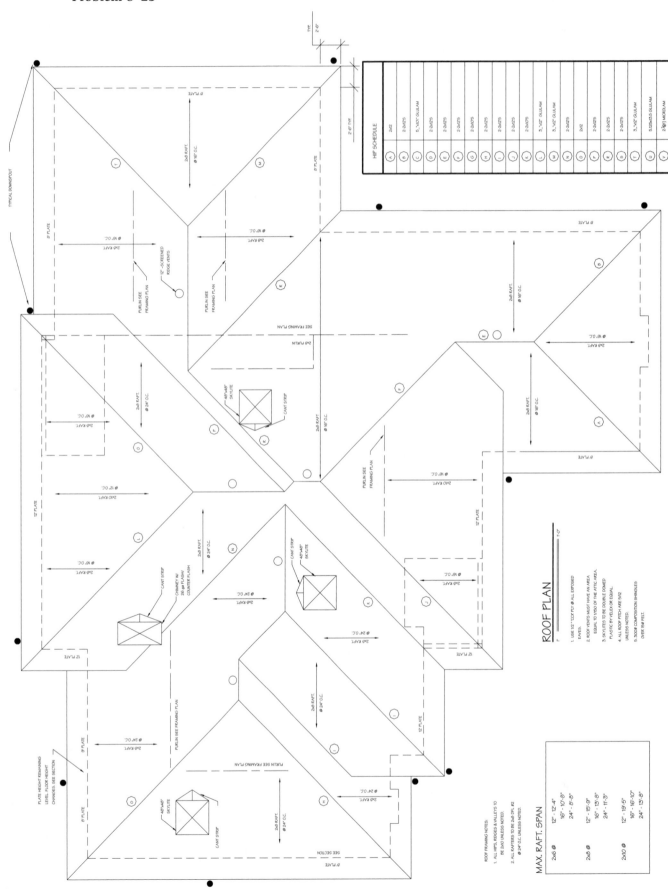

© 2011 Cengage Learning. All Rights Reserved. May not be scanned, copied or duplicated, or posted to a publicly accessible website, in whole or in part.

Problem 8–24

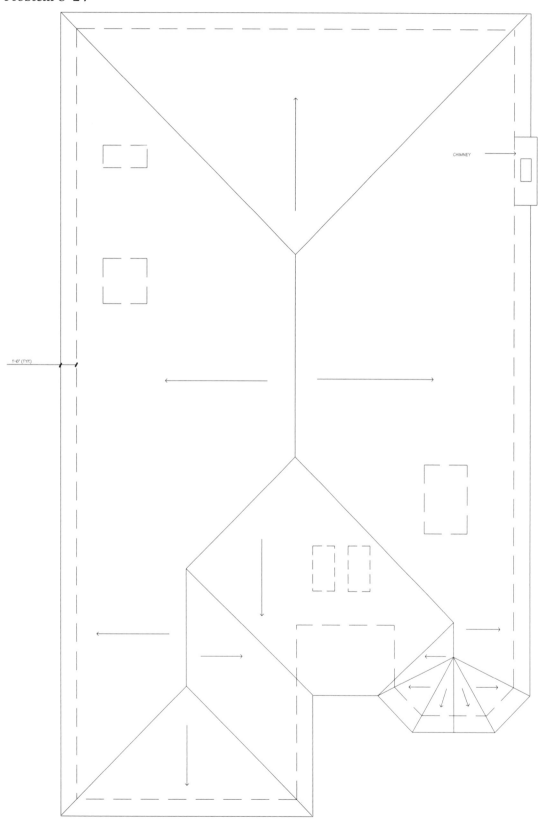

CHIMNEY

1'-6" (TYP.)

ROOF PLAN

SCALE 1/8" = 1'-0"

© 2011 Cengage Learning. All Rights Reserved. May not be scanned, copied or duplicated, or posted to a publicly accessible website, in whole or in part.

Problem 8–25

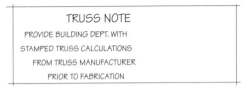

TRUSS NOTE
PROVIDE BUILDING DEPT. WITH
STAMPED TRUSS CALCULATIONS
FROM TRUSS MANUFACTURER
PRIOR TO FABRICATION

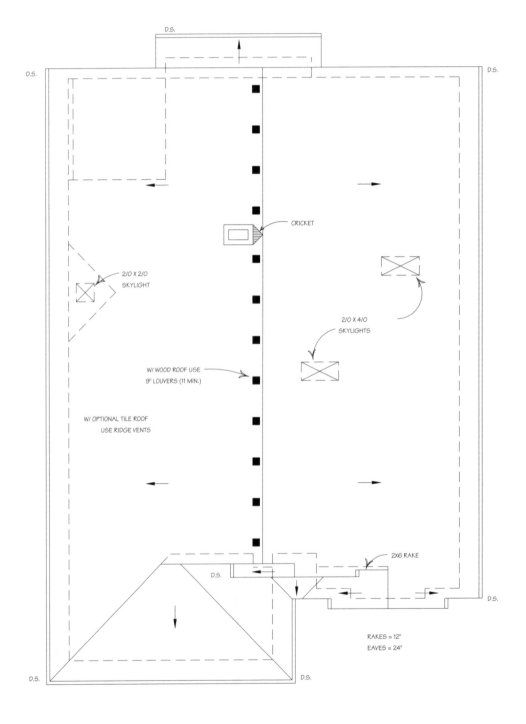

CRICKET

2/0 X 2/0
SKYLIGHT

2/0 X 4/0
SKYLIGHTS

W/ WOOD ROOF USE
9" LOUVERS (11 MIN.)

W/ OPTIONAL TILE ROOF
USE RIDGE VENTS

2X6 RAKE

D.S.

RAKES = 12"
EAVES = 24"

ROOF PLAN

SCALE 1/8" = 1'-0"

© 2011 Cengage Learning. All Rights Reserved. May not be scanned, copied or duplicated, or posted to a publicly accessible website, in whole or in part.

Problem 8–26

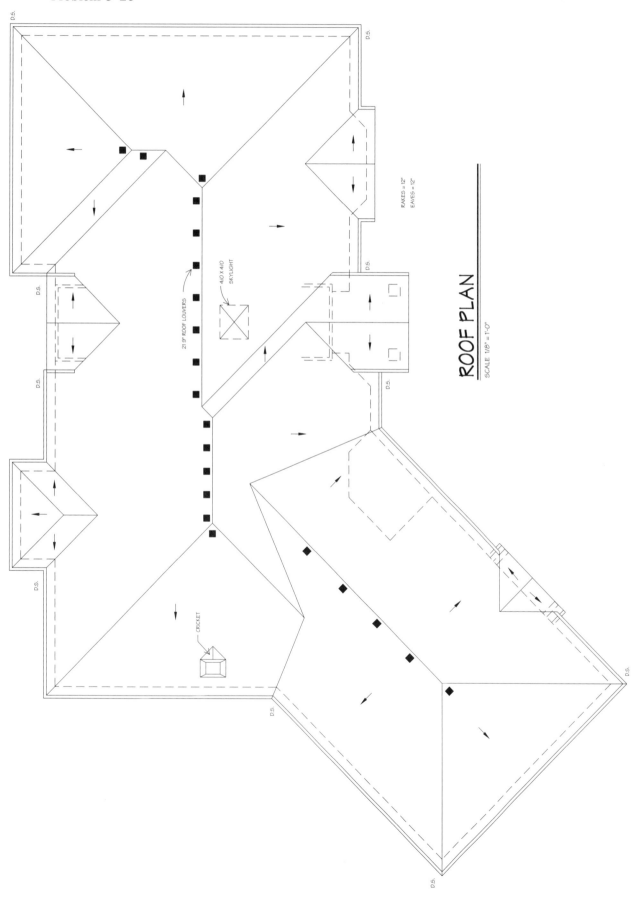

ROOF PLAN

SCALE 1/8" = 1'-0"

RAKES = 12"
EAVES = 12"

21'-9" ROOF LOUVERS

4/O X 4/O SKYLIGHT

CRICKET

D.S.

© 2011 Cengage Learning. All Rights Reserved. May not be scanned, copied or duplicated, or posted to a publicly accessible website, in whole or in part.

Problem 8–27

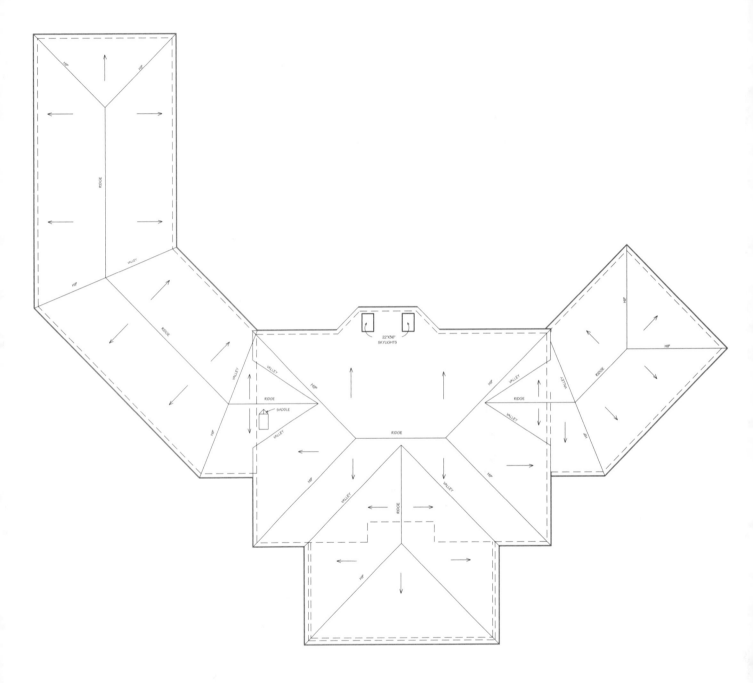

ROOF PLAN

SCALE: 1/16" = 1'-0"

© 2011 Cengage Learning. All Rights Reserved. May not be scanned, copied or duplicated, or posted to a publicly accessible website, in whole or in part.

Problem 8–28

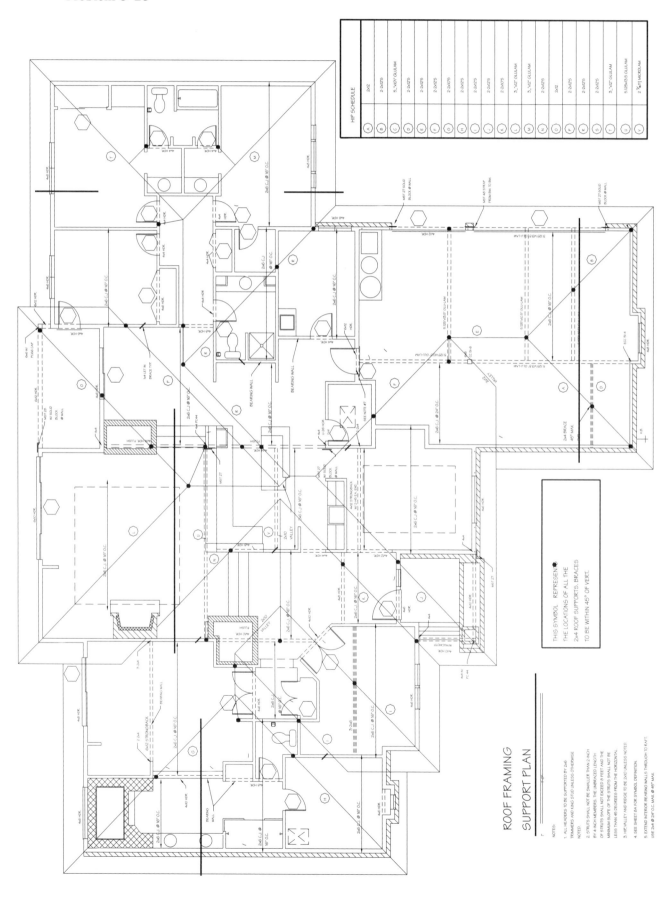

ROOF FRAMING
SUPPORT PLAN

© 2011 Cengage Learning. All Rights Reserved. May not be scanned, copied or duplicated, or posted to a publicly accessible website, in whole or in part.

Problem 8–29

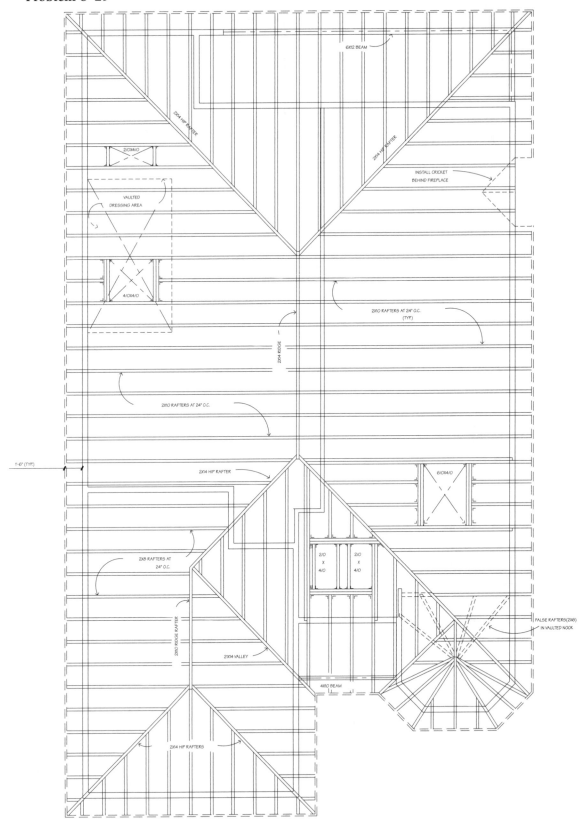

ROOF FRAMING PLAN

SCALE 1/4" = 1'-0"

© 2011 Cengage Learning. All Rights Reserved. May not be scanned, copied or duplicated, or posted to a publicly accessible website, in whole or in part.

Problem 8–30   See the floor plan in Problem 4–12 for the location of framing members.

Problem 8–31

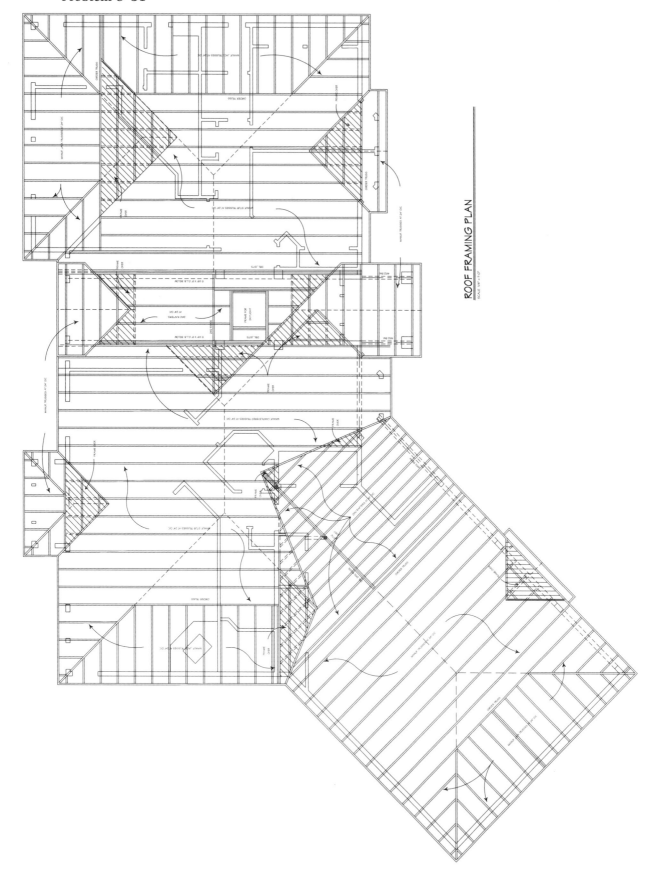

ROOF FRAMING PLAN
SCALE 1/4" = 1'-0"

© 2011 Cengage Learning. All Rights Reserved. May not be scanned, copied or duplicated, or posted to a publicly accessible website, in whole or in part.

Problem 8–32   See the floor plan in Problem 4–14 for the location of framing members.

Problem 8–33

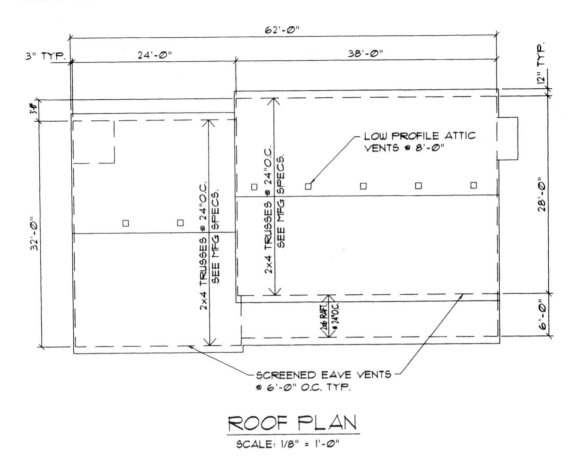

ROOF PLAN
SCALE: 1/8" = 1'-0"

Problem 8–34   Solutions will vary greatly based on the material used, the code used, and the allowable live and dead loads.

© 2011 Cengage Learning. All Rights Reserved. May not be scanned, copied or duplicated, or posted to a publicly accessible website, in whole or in part.

CHAPTER 9 ELEVATIONS

Problem 9–1

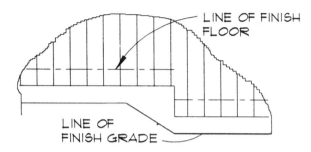

Problem 9–4

Problem 9–2

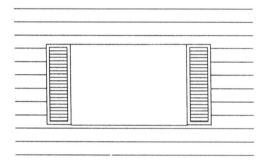

Problem 9–5

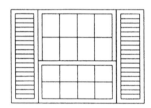

Problem 9–6

Problem 9–3

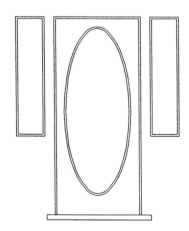

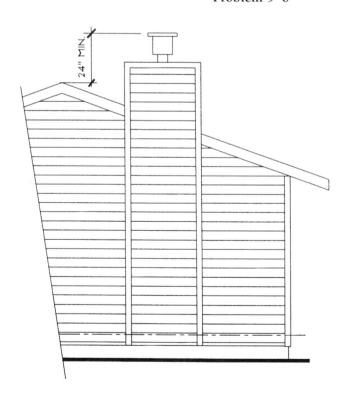

© 2011 Cengage Learning. All Rights Reserved. May not be scanned, copied or duplicated, or posted to a publicly accessible website, in whole or in part.

Problem 9–7

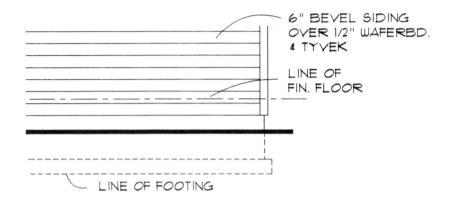

6" BEVEL SIDING
OVER 1/2" WAFERBD.
& TYVEK

LINE OF
FIN. FLOOR

LINE OF FOOTING

Problem 9–8

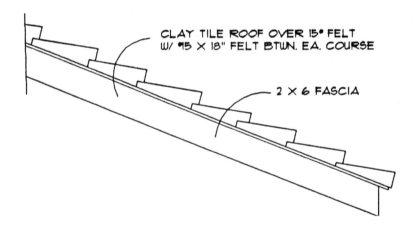

CLAY TILE ROOF OVER 15# FELT
W/ #15 X 18" FELT BTWN. EA. COURSE

2 X 6 FASCIA

Problem 9–9

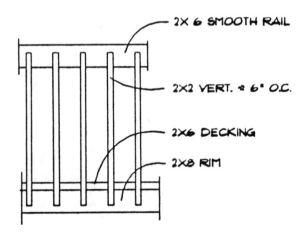

2X 6 SMOOTH RAIL

2X2 VERT. @ 6" O.C.

2X6 DECKING

2X8 RIM

© 2011 Cengage Learning. All Rights Reserved. May not be scanned, copied or duplicated, or posted to a publicly accessible website, in whole or in part.

Problem 9–10

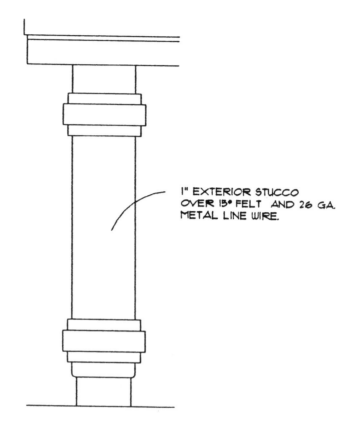

I" EXTERIOR STUCCO
OVER 15° FELT AND 26 GA.
METAL LINE WIRE.

Problem 9–11

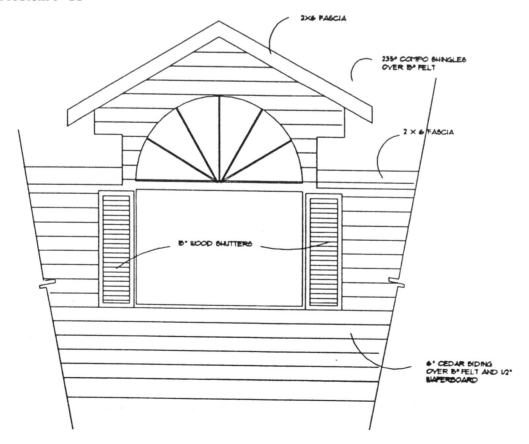

2X6 FASCIA

235° COMPO SHINGLES
OVER 15° FELT

2 X 6 FASCIA

15" WOOD SHUTTERS

6" CEDAR SIDING
OVER 15° FELT AND 1/2"
WAFERBOARD

© 2011 Cengage Learning. All Rights Reserved. May not be scanned, copied or duplicated, or posted to a publicly accessible website, in whole or in part.

Problem 9–12

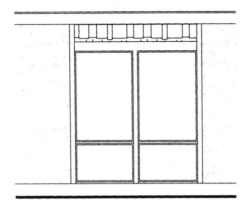

Problem 9–13

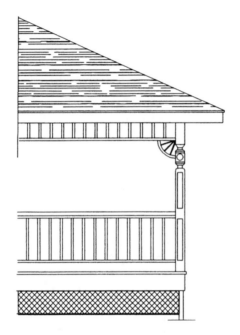

Problem 9–14

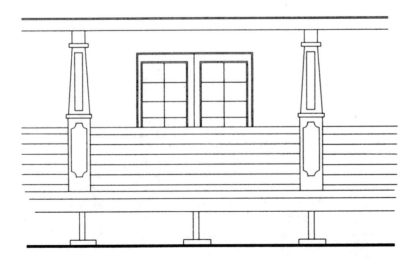

© 2011 Cengage Learning. All Rights Reserved. May not be scanned, copied or duplicated, or posted to a publicly accessible website, in whole or in part.

Problem 9–15

© 2011 Cengage Learning. All Rights Reserved. May not be scanned, copied or duplicated, or posted to a publicly accessible website, in whole or in part.

Problem 9–16

A.

FRONT ELEVATION

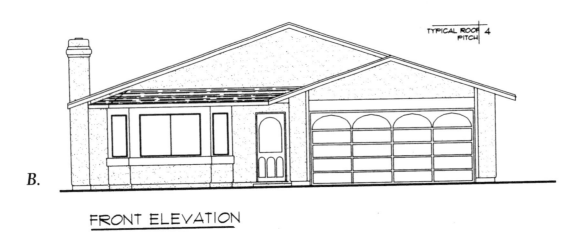

B.

FRONT ELEVATION

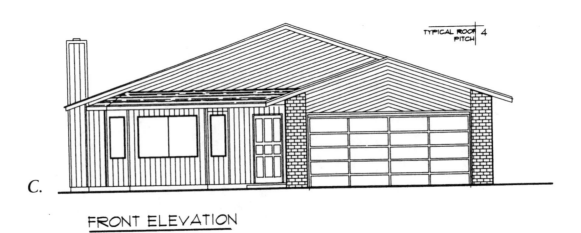

C.

FRONT ELEVATION

© 2011 Cengage Learning. All Rights Reserved. May not be scanned, copied or duplicated, or posted to a publicly accessible website, in whole or in part.

Problem 9–17

Problem 9–18A

Problem 9–18B

© 2011 Cengage Learning. All Rights Reserved. May not be scanned, copied or duplicated, or posted to a publicly accessible website, in whole or in part.

Problem 9–19

FRONT ELEVATION

Problem 9–20

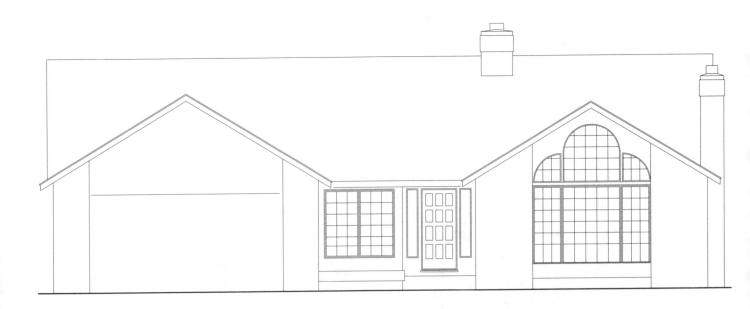

FRONT ELEVATION

© 2011 Cengage Learning. All Rights Reserved. May not be scanned, copied or duplicated, or posted to a publicly accessible website, in whole or in part.

Problem 9–21

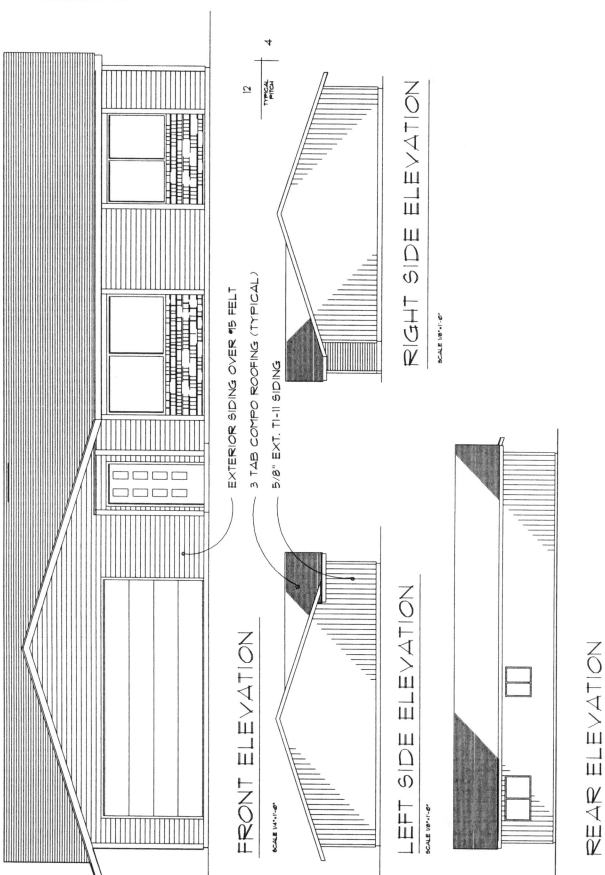

FRONT ELEVATION
SCALE 1/4"=1'-0"

EXTERIOR SIDING OVER #15 FELT

3 TAB COMPO ROOFING (TYPICAL)

5/8" EXT. T1-11 SIDING

12
—————
4
TYPICAL PITCH

RIGHT SIDE ELEVATION
SCALE 1/8"=1'-0"

LEFT SIDE ELEVATION
SCALE 1/8"=1'-0"

REAR ELEVATION
SCALE 1/8"=1'-0"

© 2011 Cengage Learning. All Rights Reserved. May not be scanned, copied or duplicated, or posted to a publicly accessible website, in whole or in part.

Problem 9–22

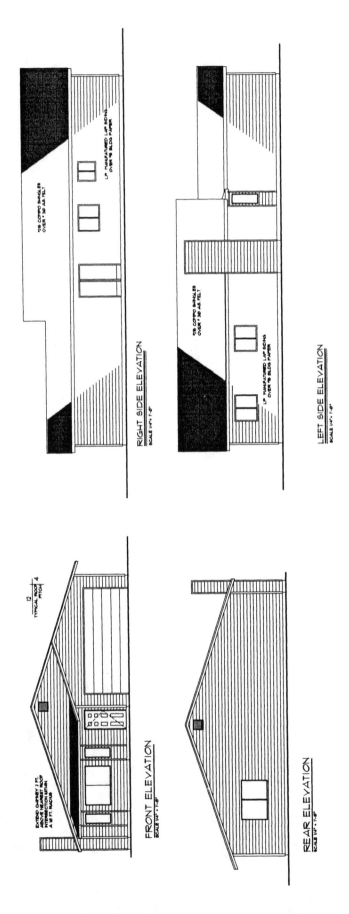

© 2011 Cengage Learning. All Rights Reserved. May not be scanned, copied or duplicated, or posted to a publicly accessible website, in whole or in part.

Problem 9–23

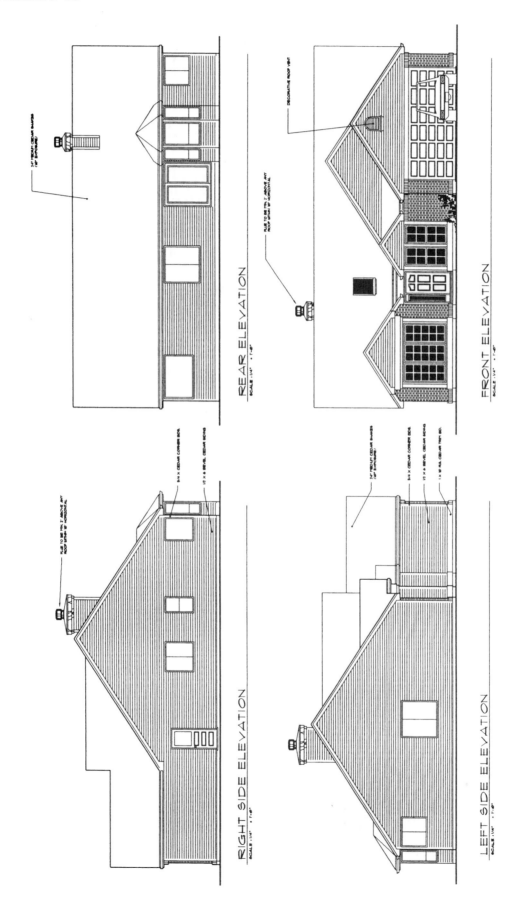

© 2011 Cengage Learning. All Rights Reserved. May not be scanned, copied or duplicated, or posted to a publicly accessible website, in whole or in part.

Problem 9–24

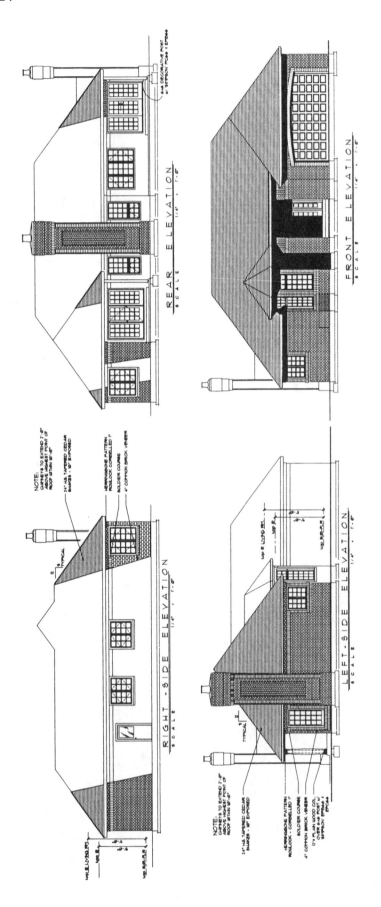

© 2011 Cengage Learning. All Rights Reserved. May not be scanned, copied or duplicated, or posted to a publicly accessible website, in whole or in part.

Problem 9–25

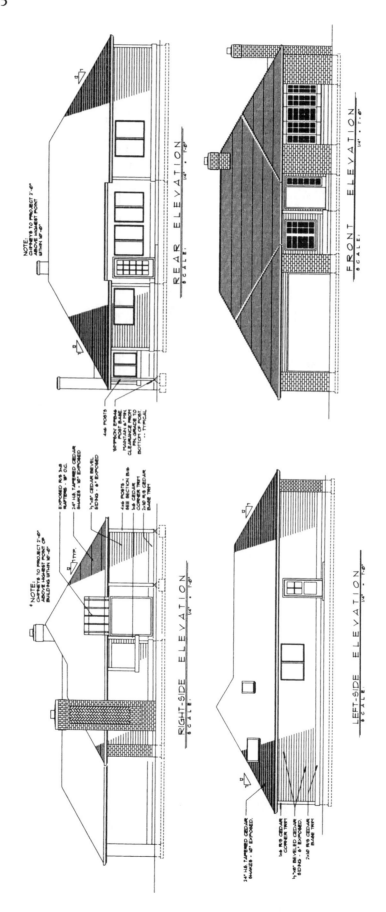

© 2011 Cengage Learning. All Rights Reserved. May not be scanned, copied or duplicated, or posted to a publicly accessible website, in whole or in part.

Problem 9–26

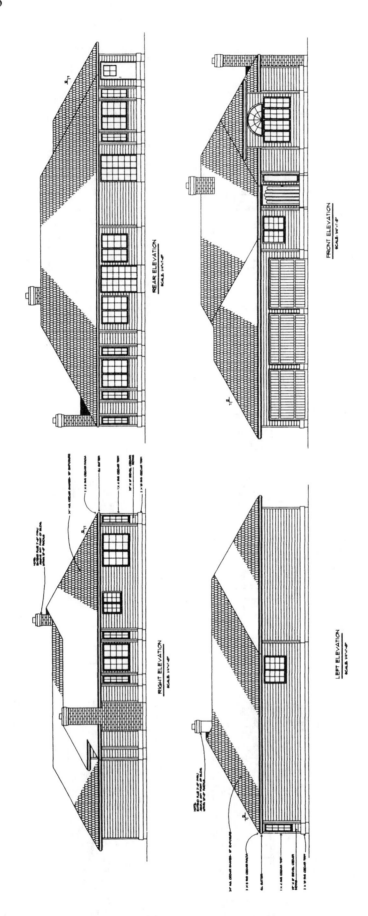

© 2011 Cengage Learning. All Rights Reserved. May not be scanned, copied or duplicated, or posted to a publicly accessible website, in whole or in part.

Problem 9–27

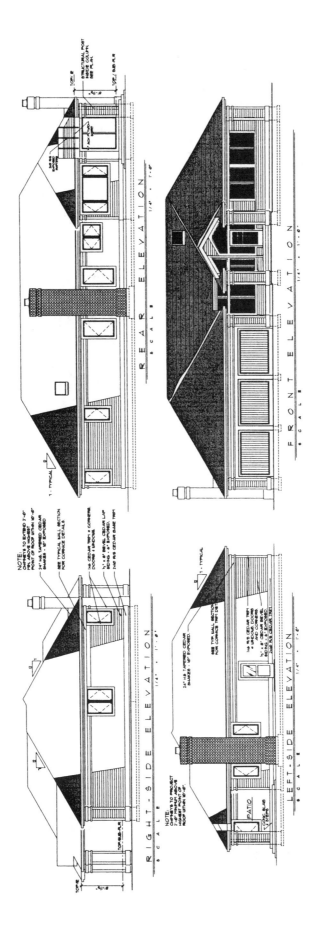

© 2011 Cengage Learning. All Rights Reserved. May not be scanned, copied or duplicated, or posted to a publicly accessible website, in whole or in part.

Problem 9–28

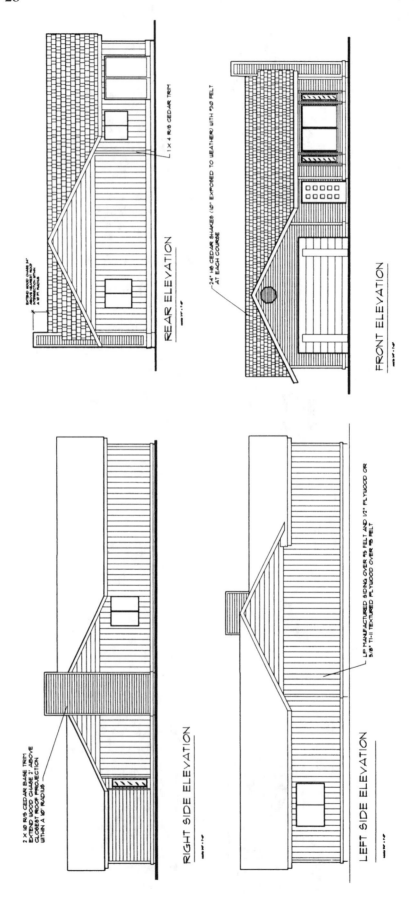

© 2011 Cengage Learning. All Rights Reserved. May not be scanned, copied or duplicated, or posted to a publicly accessible website, in whole or in part.

Problem 9–29

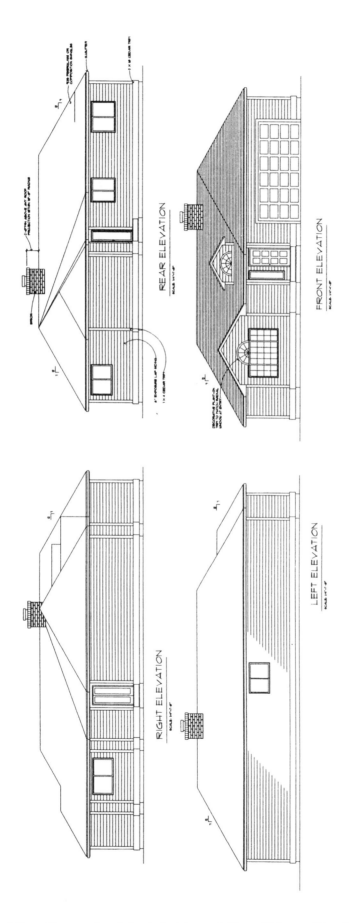

© 2011 Cengage Learning. All Rights Reserved. May not be scanned, copied or duplicated, or posted to a publicly accessible website, in whole or in part.

Problem 9–30

© 2011 Cengage Learning. All Rights Reserved. May not be scanned, copied or duplicated, or posted to a publicly accessible website, in whole or in part.

Problem 9–31

FRONT ELEVATION

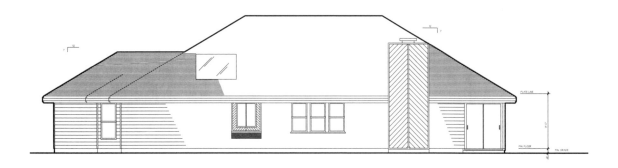

RIGHT ELEVATION

REAR ELEVATION

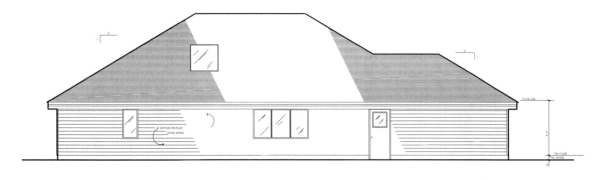

LEFT ELEVATION

© 2011 Cengage Learning. All Rights Reserved. May not be scanned, copied or duplicated, or posted to a publicly accessible website, in whole or in part.

Problem 9–32

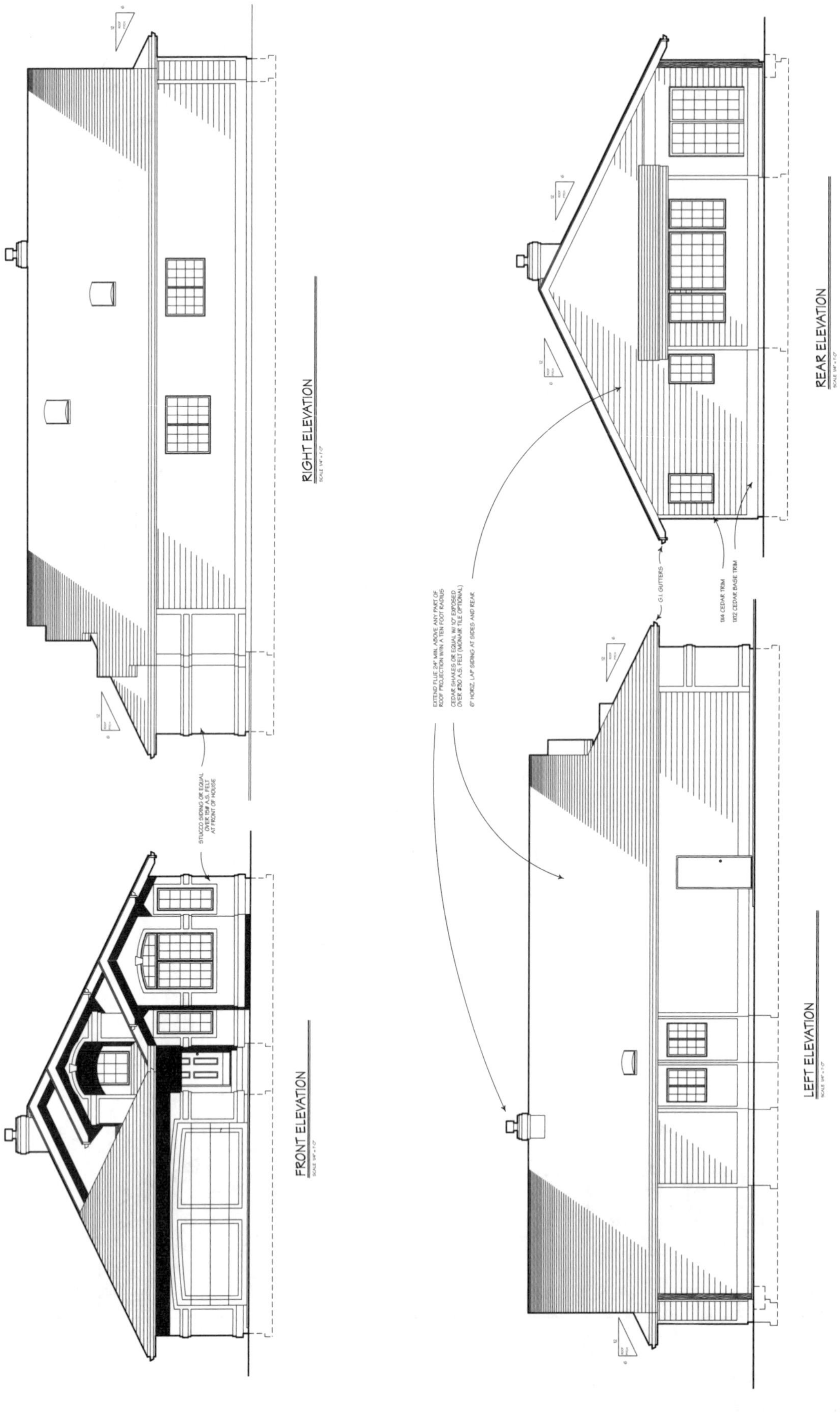

RIGHT ELEVATION

FRONT ELEVATION

REAR ELEVATION

LEFT ELEVATION

© 2011 Cengage Learning. All Rights Reserved. May not be scanned, copied or duplicated, or posted to a publicly accessible website, in whole or in part.

Problem 9–33

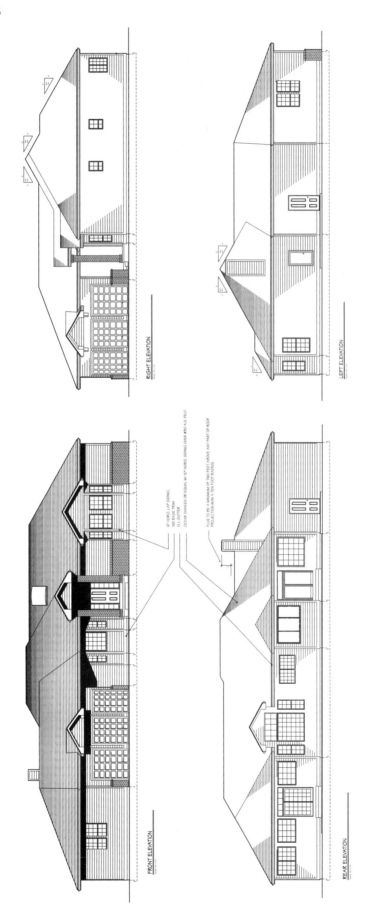

© 2011 Cengage Learning. All Rights Reserved. May not be scanned, copied or duplicated, or posted to a publicly accessible website, in whole or in part.

Problem 9–34

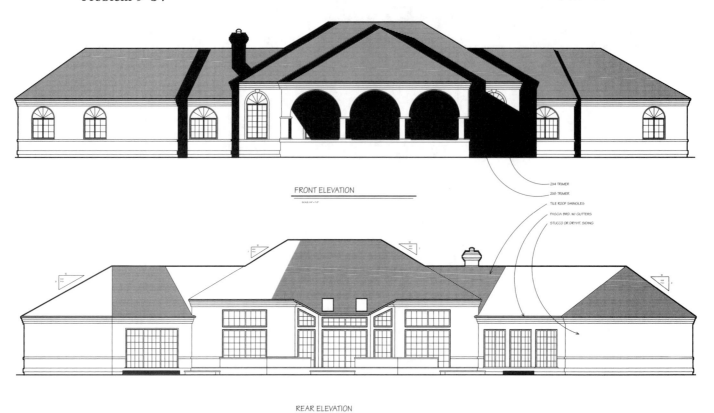

FRONT ELEVATION
SCALE 1/4" = 1'-0"

2X4 TRIMER
2X8 TRIMER
TILE ROOF SHINGLES
FASCIA BRD. W/ GUTTERS
STUCCO OR DRYVIT. SIDING

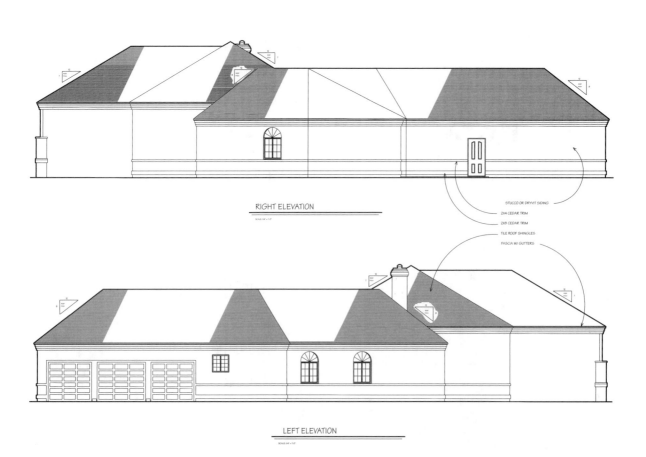

REAR ELEVATION
SCALE 1/4" = 1'-0"

RIGHT ELEVATION
SCALE 1/4" = 1'-0"

STUCCO OR DRYVIT SIDING
2X4 CEDAR TRIM
2X8 CEDAR TRIM
TILE ROOF SHINGLES
FASCIA W/ GUTTERS

LEFT ELEVATION
SCALE 1/4" = 1'-0"

© 2011 Cengage Learning. All Rights Reserved. May not be scanned, copied or duplicated, or posted to a publicly accessible website, in whole or in part.

Problem 9–35

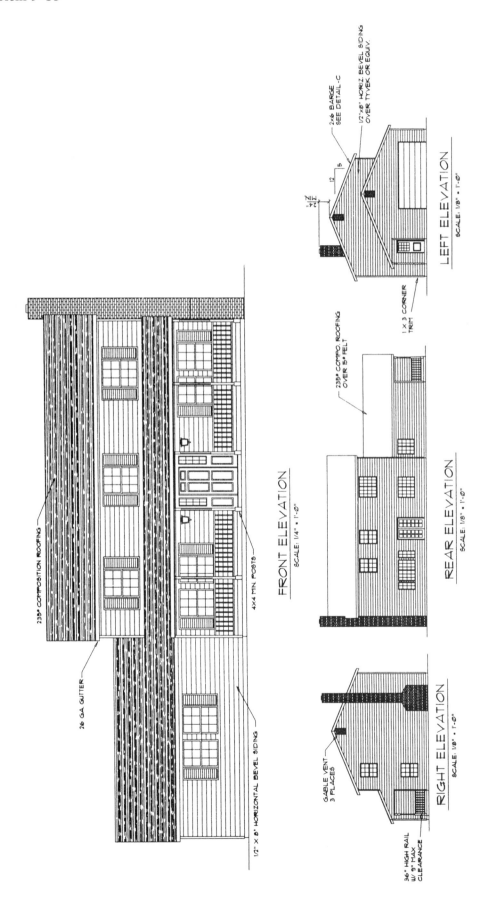

235# COMPOSITION ROOFING

26 GA. GUTTER

1/2" × 6" HORIZONTAL BEVEL SIDING

4×4 MIN POSTS

FRONT ELEVATION
SCALE: 1/4" = 1'-0"

2×6 BARGE
SEE DETAIL-C

1/2"×8" HORIZ. BEVEL SIDING
OVER TYVEK OR EQUIV.

12
5

3/12
24

LEFT ELEVATION
SCALE: 1/8" = 1'-0"

1 × 3 CORNER
TRIM

235# COMPO. ROOFING
OVER 15# FELT

REAR ELEVATION
SCALE: 1/8" = 1'-0"

GABLE VENT
3 PLACES

36" HIGH RAIL
W/ 5" MAX
CLEARANCE

RIGHT ELEVATION
SCALE: 1/8" = 1'-0"

© 2011 Cengage Learning. All Rights Reserved. May not be scanned, copied or duplicated, or posted to a publicly accessible website, in whole or in part.

CHAPTER 10 CABINET ELEVATIONS

Problem 10–1

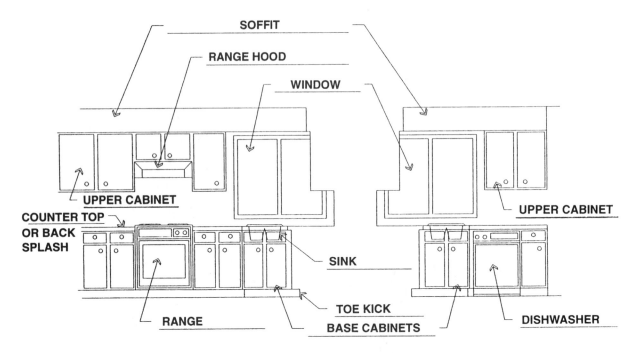

Courtesy of Alan Mascord Design Associates, Inc.

Problem 10–2

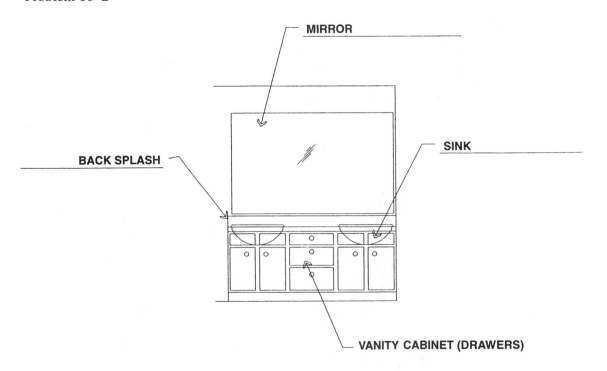

Courtesy of Alan Mascord Design Associates, Inc.

© 2011 Cengage Learning. All Rights Reserved. May not be scanned, copied or duplicated, or posted to a publicly accessible website, in whole or in part.

Problem 10–3

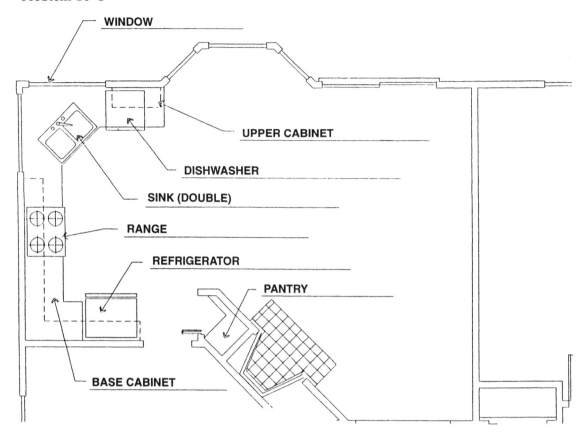

Courtesy of Alan Mascord Design Associates, Inc.

Problem 10–4

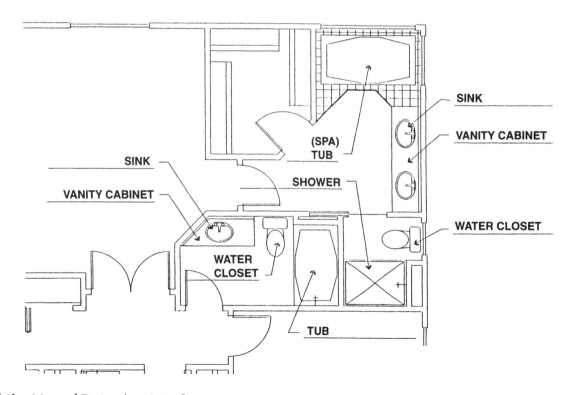

Courtesy of Alan Mascord Design Associates, Inc.

© 2011 Cengage Learning. All Rights Reserved. May not be scanned, copied or duplicated, or posted to a publicly accessible website, in whole or in part.

Problem 10–5

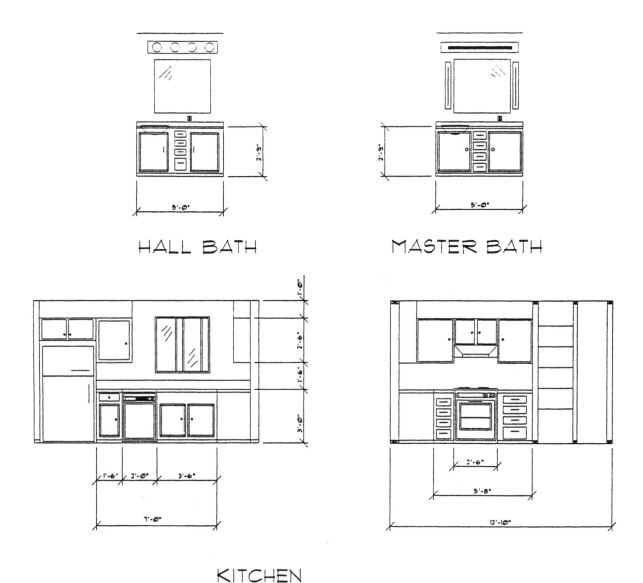

HALL BATH   MASTER BATH

KITCHEN

NOTE: DIMENSIONS GIVEN AS REFERENCE ONLY.
      YOUR ACTUAL DIMENSIONS ARE BASED ON
      YOUR FLOOR PLAN AND MAY BE DIFFERENT.

© 2011 Cengage Learning. All Rights Reserved. May not be scanned, copied or duplicated, or posted to a publicly accessible website, in whole or in part.

Problem 10–6

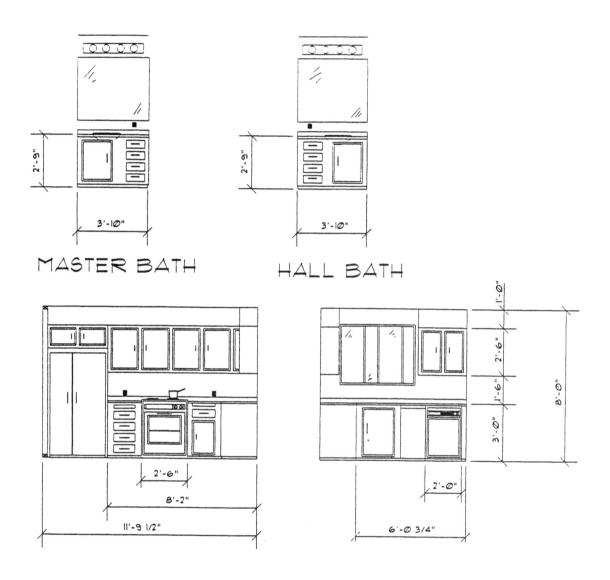

MASTER BATH   HALL BATH

KITCHEN

NOTE: DIMENSIONS GIVEN AS REFERENCE ONLY.
YOUR ACTUAL DIMENSIONS ARE BASED ON
YOUR FLOOR PLAN AND MAY BE DIFFERENT.

© 2011 Cengage Learning. All Rights Reserved. May not be scanned, copied or duplicated, or posted to a publicly accessible website, in whole or in part.

Problem 10–7

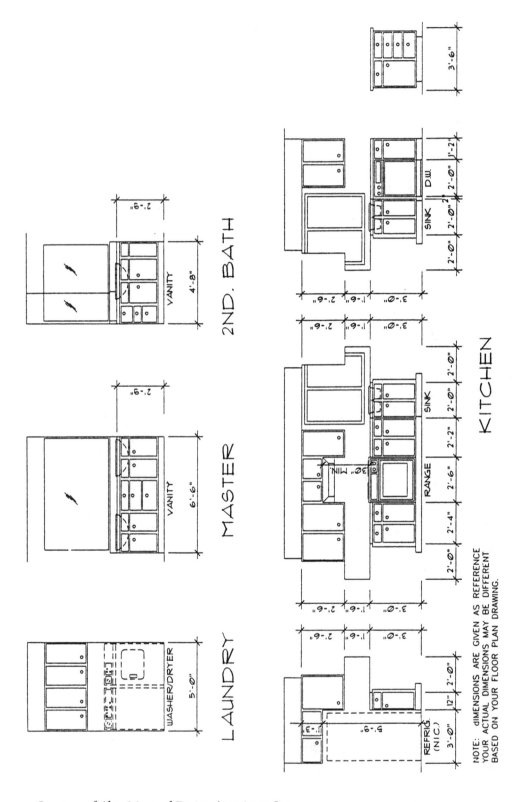

Courtesy of Alan Mascord Design Associates, Inc.

© 2011 Cengage Learning. All Rights Reserved. May not be scanned, copied or duplicated, or posted to a publicly accessible website, in whole or in part.

Problem 10–8

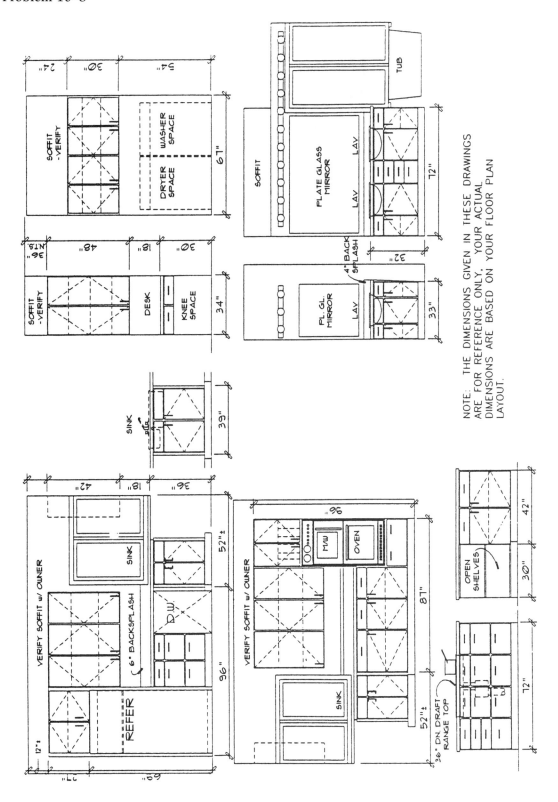

Courtesy of Piercy & Barclay Designers, Inc.

© 2011 Cengage Learning. All Rights Reserved. May not be scanned, copied or duplicated, or posted to a publicly accessible website, in whole or in part.

Problem 10–9

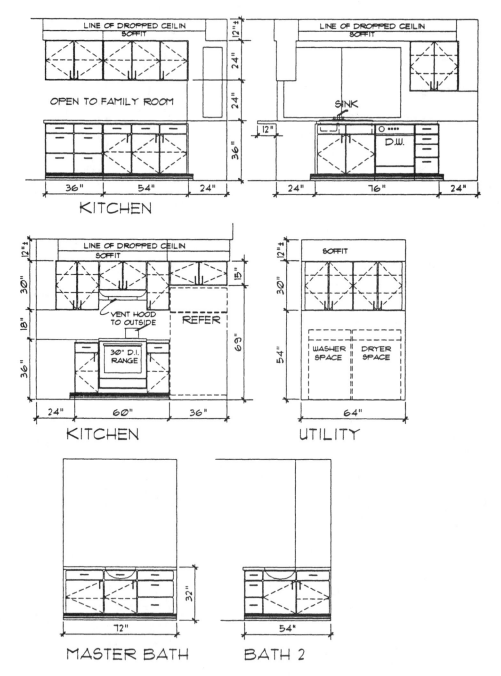

KITCHEN

KITCHEN   UTILITY

MASTER BATH   BATH 2

NOTE: DIMENSIONS ARE GIVEN FOR REFERENCE ONLY
YOUR ACTUAL DIMENSIONS MAY VARY BASED ON YOUR
FLOOR PLAN DRAWING.

Courtesy of Piercy & Barclay Designers, Inc.

© 2011 Cengage Learning. All Rights Reserved. May not be scanned, copied or duplicated, or posted to a publicly accessible website, in whole or in part.

Problem 10–10

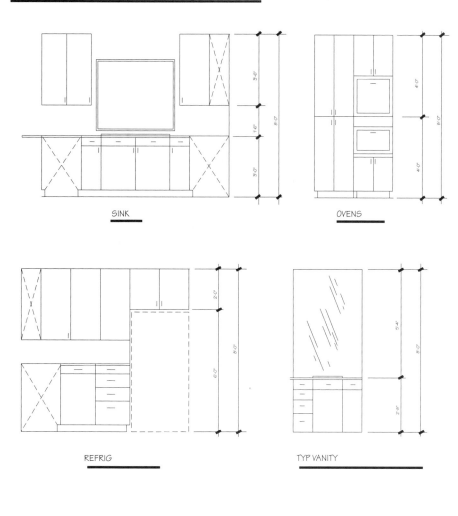

COOKTOP &DISHWASHER PENINSULA

SINK

OVENS

REFRIG

TYP VANITY

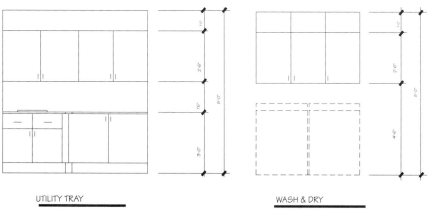

UTILITY TRAY

WASH & DRY

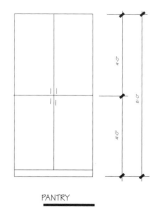

PANTRY

CABINET ELEVATIONS

SCALE: 3/8"=1'-0"

© 2011 Cengage Learning. All Rights Reserved. May not be scanned, copied or duplicated, or posted to a publicly accessible website, in whole or in part.

Problem 10–11

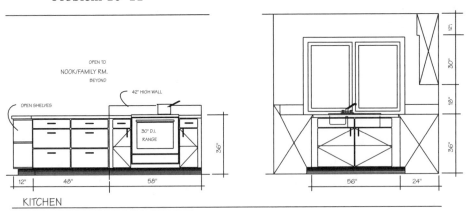

OPEN TO
NOOK/FAMILY RM.
BEYOND

42" HIGH WALL

OPEN SHELVES

30" D.I.
RANGE

36"

12"   48"   58"   56"   24"

KITCHEN

12"

30"

18"

36"

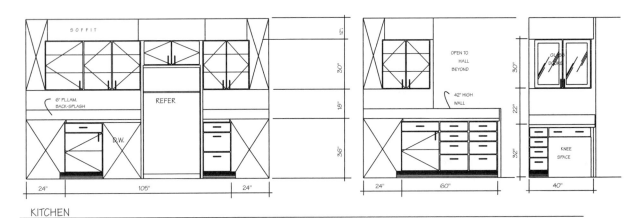

SOFFIT

6" PL.LAM.
BACK-SPLASH

REFER

D.W.

24"   105"   24"

12"

30"

18"

36"

OPEN TO
HALL
BEYOND

42" HIGH
WALL

GL.
DOORS

KNEE
SPACE

24"   60"   40"

30"

22"

32"

KITCHEN

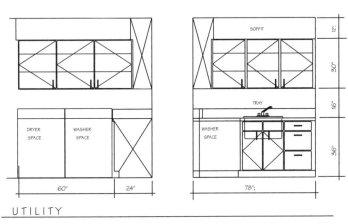

SOFFIT

TRAY

DRYER
SPACE

WASHER
SPACE

WASHER
SPACE

60"   24"   78"

12"

30"

16"

36"

UTILITY

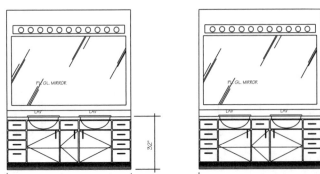

PL. GL. MIRROR

LAV   LAV

PL. GL. MIRROR

LAV   LAV

32"

78"   78"

MASTER   BATH # 2

CABINET ELEVATIONS

SCALE   3/8" = 1'-0"

© 2011 Cengage Learning. All Rights Reserved. May not be scanned, copied or duplicated, or posted to a publicly accessible website, in whole or in part.

Problem 10–12   Solutions vary widely based on floor plan design.

Problem 10–13

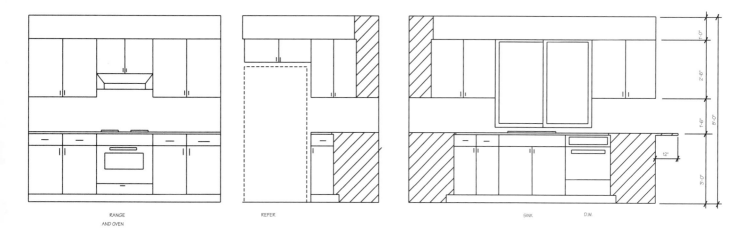

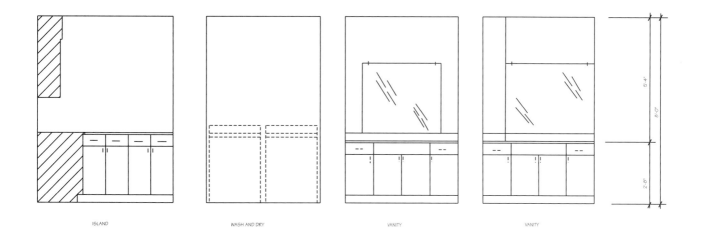

CABINET ELEVATIONS

SCALE: 1/4"=1'-0"

© 2011 Cengage Learning. All Rights Reserved. May not be scanned, copied or duplicated, or posted to a publicly accessible website, in whole or in part.

Problem 10–14   Solutions vary widely based on floor plan design.

Problem 10–15

SINK   D.W.   OVEN W/ M.W.   JENN-AIR W/ OVEN
                           W/ BREAD BD. BETWEEN

TRAY   WASH/DRY   TRAY   WASH/DRY   MARBLE CUTTING BLOCK   WET BAR

SINK   SPA TUB   SINK   SINK

CABINET ELEVATIONS

SCALE 1/4" = 1'-0"

© 2011 Cengage Learning. All Rights Reserved. May not be scanned, copied or duplicated, or posted to a publicly accessible website, in whole or in part.

Problem 10–16

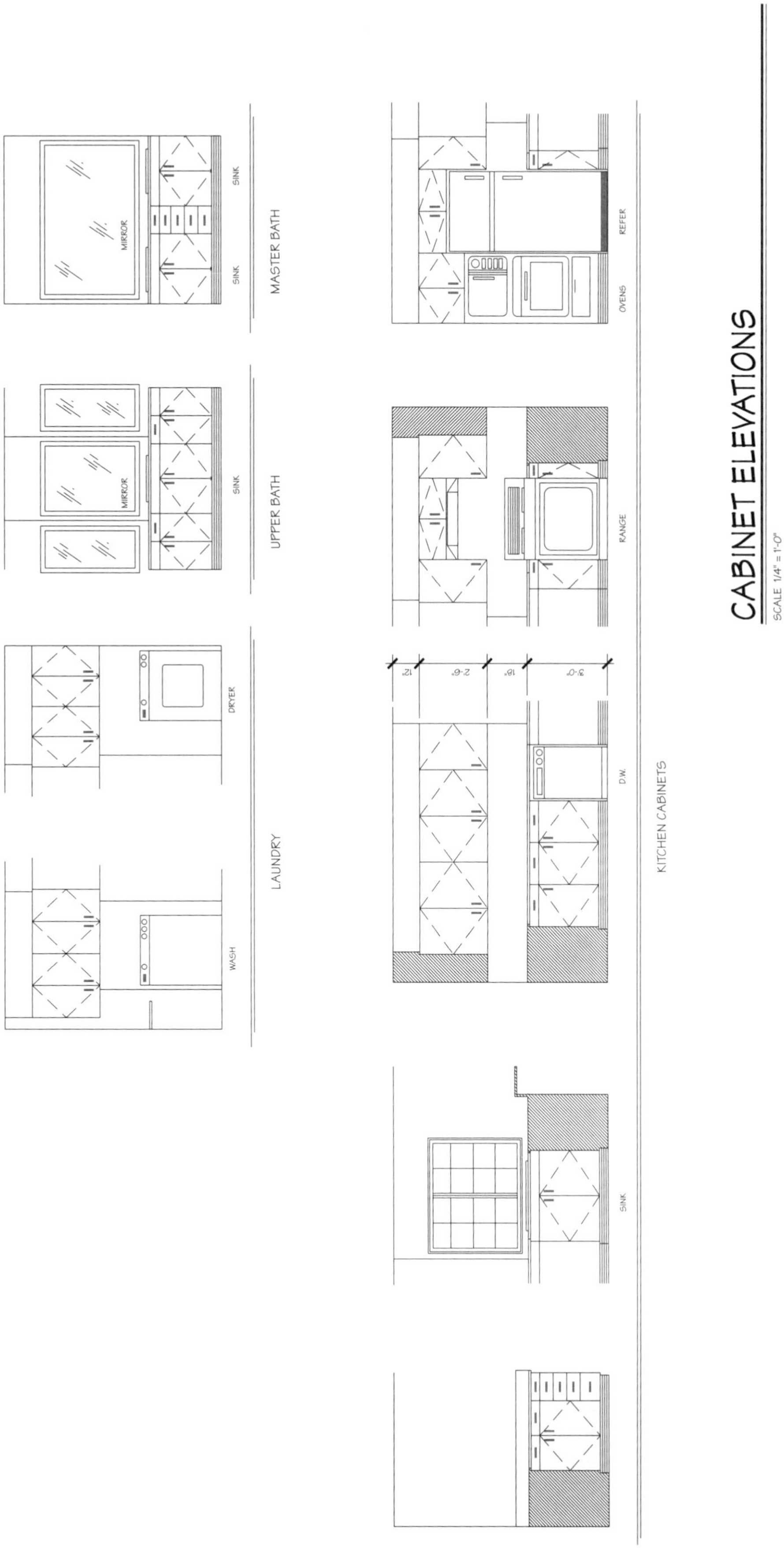

CABINET ELEVATIONS

SCALE 1/4" = 1'-0"

MASTER BATH

UPPER BATH

LAUNDRY

SINK

SINK

SINK

SINK

MIRROR

MIRROR

DRYER

WASH

REFER

OVENS

RANGE

D.W.

KITCHEN CABINETS

12"

2'-6"

18"

3'-0"

© 2011 Cengage Learning. All Rights Reserved. May not be scanned, copied or duplicated, or posted to a publicly accessible website, in whole or in part.

Problem 10–17

© 2011 Cengage Learning. All Rights Reserved. May not be scanned, copied or duplicated, or posted to a publicly accessible website, in whole or in part.

Problem 10–18

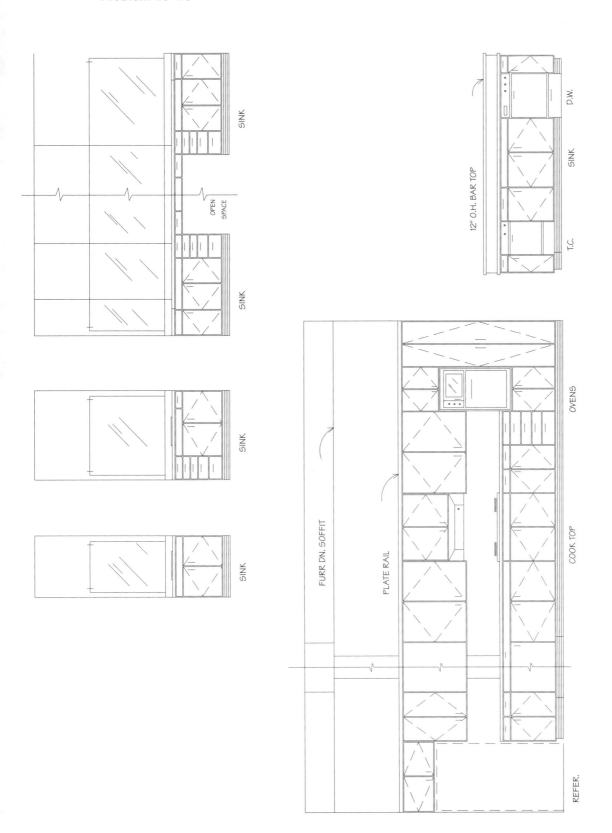

CABINET ELEVATIONS

SCALE: 1/4" = 1'-0"

Problem 10–19 Solutions vary widely based on floor plan design.

© 2011 Cengage Learning. All Rights Reserved. May not be scanned, copied or duplicated, or posted to a publicly accessible website, in whole or in part.

CHAPTER 11 FOUNDATIONS PLANS

Problem 11–1

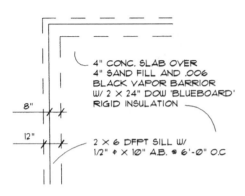

4" CONC. SLAB OVER
4" SAND FILL AND .006
BLACK VAPOR BARRIOR
W/ 2 × 24" DOW 'BLUEBOARD'
RIGID INSULATION

8"

12"

2 × 6 DFPT SILL W/
1/2" ◊ × 10" A.B. ◙ 6'-0" O.C

Problem 11–3

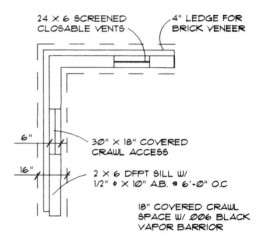

24 × 6 SCREENED
CLOSABLE VENTS

4" LEDGE FOR
BRICK VENEER

6"

16"

30" × 18" COVERED
CRAWL ACCESS

2 × 6 DFPT SILL W/
1/2" ◊ × 10" A.B. ◙ 6'-0" O.C

18" COVERED CRAWL
SPACE W/ 006 BLACK
VAPOR BARRIOR

Problem 11–2

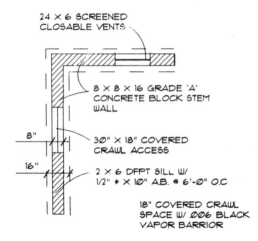

24 × 6 SCREENED
CLOSABLE VENTS

8 × 8 × 16 GRADE 'A'
CONCRETE BLOCK STEM
WALL

8"

16"

30" × 18" COVERED
CRAWL ACCESS

2 × 6 DFPT SILL W/
1/2" ◊ × 10" A.B. ◙ 6'-0" O.C

18" COVERED CRAWL
SPACE W/ 006 BLACK
VAPOR BARRIOR

Problem 11–4

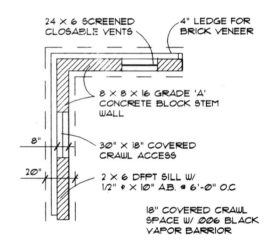

24 × 6 SCREENED
CLOSABLE VENTS

4" LEDGE FOR
BRICK VENEER

8 × 8 × 16 GRADE 'A'
CONCRETE BLOCK STEM
WALL

8"

20"

30" × 18" COVERED
CRAWL ACCESS

2 × 6 DFPT SILL W/
1/2" ◊ × 10" A.B. ◙ 6'-0" O.C

18" COVERED CRAWL
SPACE W/ 006 BLACK
VAPOR BARRIOR

© 2011 Cengage Learning. All Rights Reserved. May not be scanned, copied or duplicated, or posted to a publicly accessible website, in whole or in part.

Problem 11–5

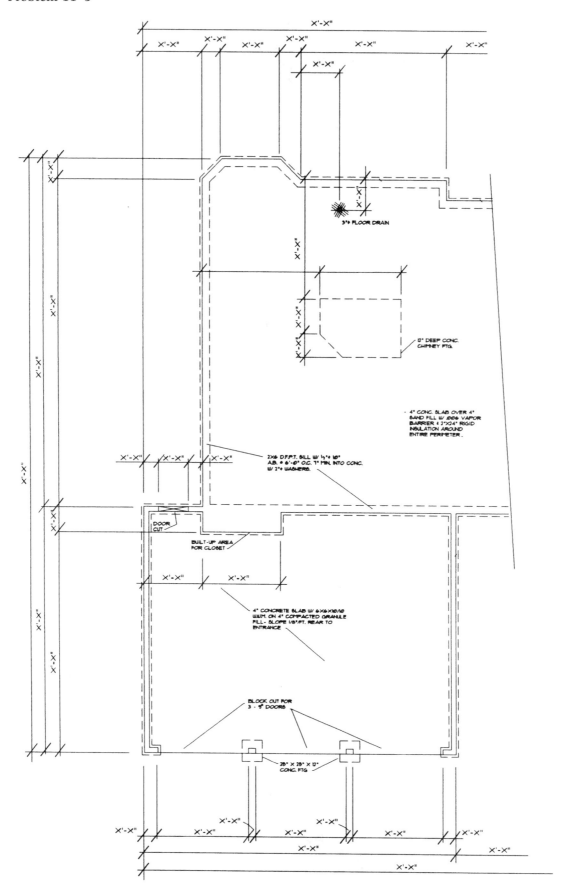

3"ø FLOOR DRAIN

12" DEEP CONC.
CHIMNEY FTG.

- 4" CONC. SLAB OVER 4"
SAND FILL W/ .006 VAPOR
BARRIER & 2"x24" RIGID
INSULATION AROUND
ENTIRE PERIMETER.

2X6 D.F.P.T. SILL W/ ½"ø 18"
A.B. @ 6'-0" O.C. 7" MIN. INTO CONC.
W/ 2"ø WASHERS.

DOOR
CUT

BUILT-UP AREA
FOR CLOSET

4" CONCRETE SLAB W/ 6x6x10/10
W.W.M. ON 4" COMPACTED GRANULE
FILL- SLOPE 1/8"/FT. REAR TO
ENTRANCE

BLOCK OUT FOR
3 - 9' DOORS

28" X 28" X 12"
CONC. FTG

© 2011 Cengage Learning. All Rights Reserved. May not be scanned, copied or duplicated, or posted to a publicly accessible website, in whole or in part.

Problem 11–6

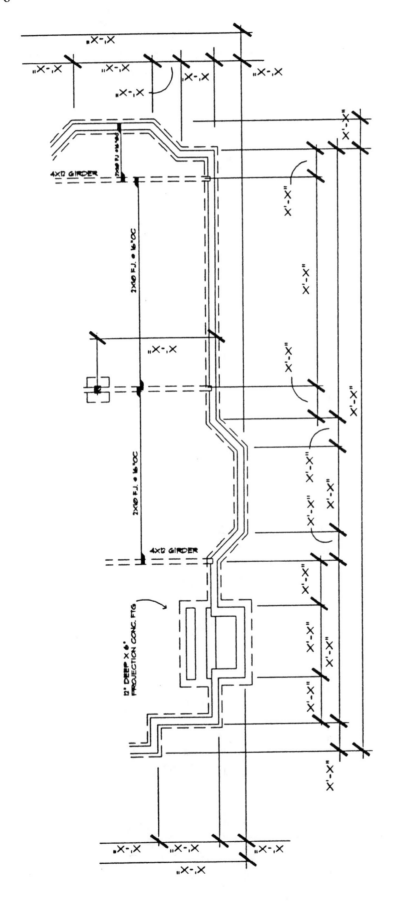

© 2011 Cengage Learning. All Rights Reserved. May not be scanned, copied or duplicated, or posted to a publicly accessible website, in whole or in part.

Problem 11–7

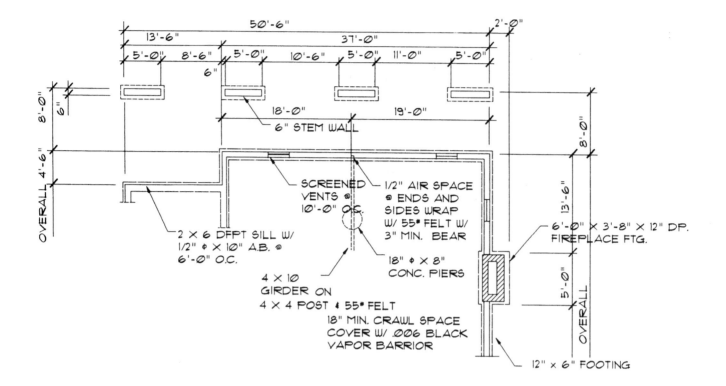

Problem 11–8

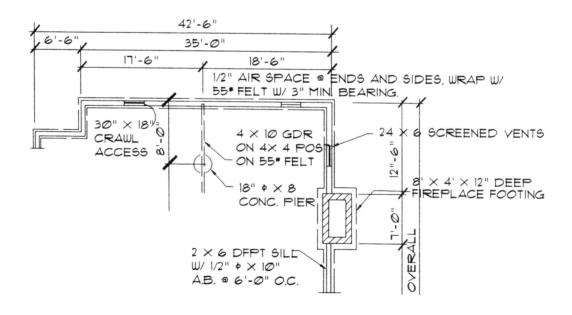

© 2011 Cengage Learning. All Rights Reserved. May not be scanned, copied or duplicated, or posted to a publicly accessible website, in whole or in part.

Problem 11–9

Drawing errors include:

a. Change 9'-0" to 8'-0" for post spacings.

b. Change 5'-0" to 4'-0" on right side girder spacing.

c. Add 34'-0" to right side overall dimension.

d. Change 30'-0" to 29'-6" on right side front.

e. Change 4'-41/2" to 4'-41/4" at garage front.

Problem 11–10

Starting in the upper left hand corner, errors include:

a. 6'-0" anchor bolt spacing, not 7'-0".

b. anchor bolts should extend 7" into concrete, not 5".

c. 4" compacted fill, not 2".

d. Note 1: assumed soil pressure to be 2000 PSF, not PSI.

e. Note 3: 2500 PSI, not PSF.

f. Note 3: 28 days, not 18.

g. Note 4: DFL #2, not DFE.

h. 3" minimum girder bearing, not 6".

i. crawl access should be 30" wide, not 24".

j. 18" deep crawl space, not 8".

Problem 11–11

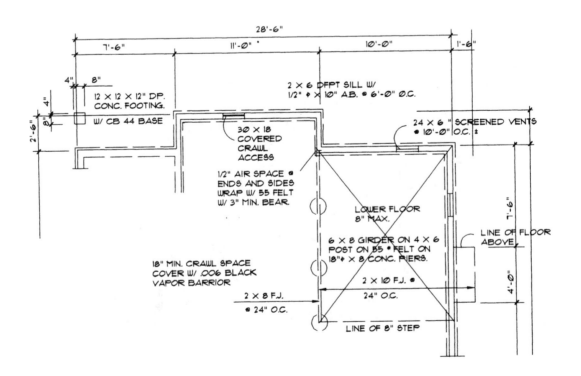

© 2011 Cengage Learning. All Rights Reserved. May not be scanned, copied or duplicated, or posted to a publicly accessible website, in whole or in part.

Problem 11–12

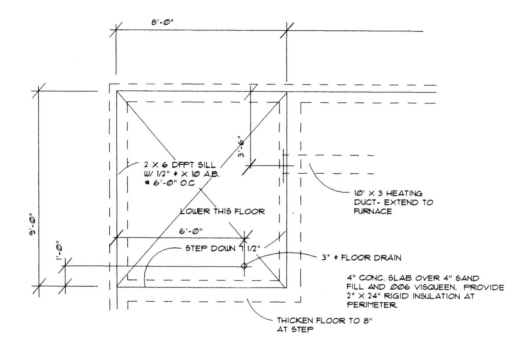

8'-0"

9'-0"

1'-0"

3'-6"

2 X 6 DFPT SILL
W/ 1/2" ⌀ X 10 A.B.
@ 6'-0" O.C

LOWER THIS FLOOR

10' X 3 HEATING
DUCT- EXTEND TO
FURNACE

6'-0"

STEP DOWN 1 1/2"

3" ⌀ FLOOR DRAIN

4" CONC. SLAB OVER 4" SAND
FILL AND .006 VISQUEEN. PROVIDE
2" X 24" RIGID INSULATION AT
PERIMETER.

THICKEN FLOOR TO 8"
AT STEP

Problem 11–13

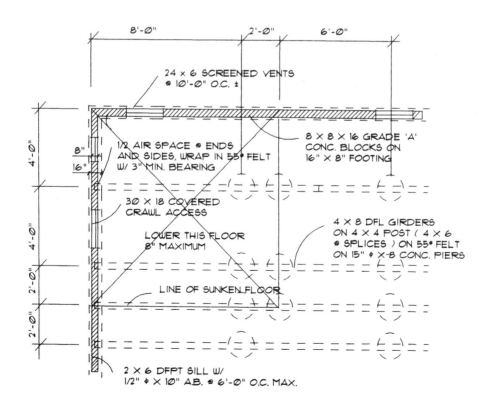

8'-0"   2'-0"   6'-0"

24 X 6 SCREENED VENTS
@ 10'-0" O.C. ±

4'-0"

8"

16"

1/2 AIR SPACE @ ENDS
AND SIDES, WRAP IN 55# FELT
W/ 3" MIN. BEARING

8 X 8 X 16 GRADE 'A'
CONC. BLOCKS ON
16" X 8" FOOTING

30 X 18 COVERED
CRAWL ACCESS

4'-0"

LOWER THIS FLOOR
8" MAXIMUM

4 X 8 DFL GIRDERS
ON 4 X 4 POST (4 X 6
@ SPLICES) ON 55# FELT
ON 15" ⌀ X-8 CONC. PIERS

2'-0"

LINE OF SUNKEN FLOOR

2'-0"

2 X 6 DFPT SILL W/
1/2" ⌀ X 10" A.B. @ 6'-0" O.C. MAX.

© 2011 Cengage Learning. All Rights Reserved. May not be scanned, copied or duplicated, or posted to a publicly accessible website, in whole or in part.

Problem 11–14

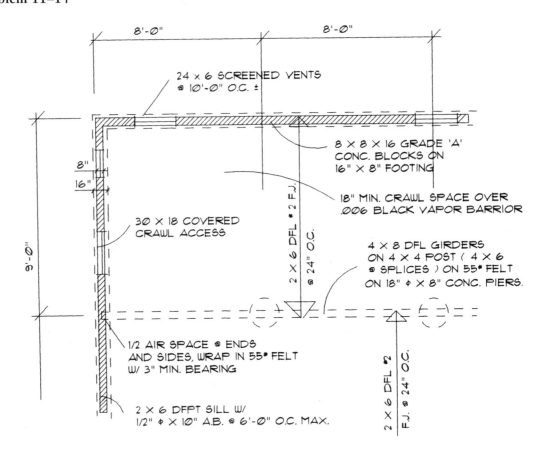

24 x 6 SCREENED VENTS
@ 10'-0" O.C. ±

8'-0"

8'-0"

8"

16"

9'-0"

30 x 18 COVERED
CRAWL ACCESS

8 X 8 X 16 GRADE 'A'
CONC. BLOCKS ON
16" X 8" FOOTING

18" MIN. CRAWL SPACE OVER
.006 BLACK VAPOR BARRIOR

4 X 8 DFL GIRDERS
ON 4 X 4 POST (4 X 6
@ SPLICES) ON 55# FELT
ON 18" ø X 8" CONC. PIERS.

2 X 6 DFL #2 F.J.
@ 24" O.C.

1/2 AIR SPACE @ ENDS
AND SIDES, WRAP IN 55# FELT
W/ 3" MIN. BEARING

2 X 6 DFPT SILL W/
1/2" ø X 10" A.B. @ 6'-0" O.C. MAX.

2 X 6 DFL #2
F.J. @ 24" O.C.

© 2011 Cengage Learning. All Rights Reserved. May not be scanned, copied or duplicated, or posted to a publicly accessible website, in whole or in part.

Problem 11–15

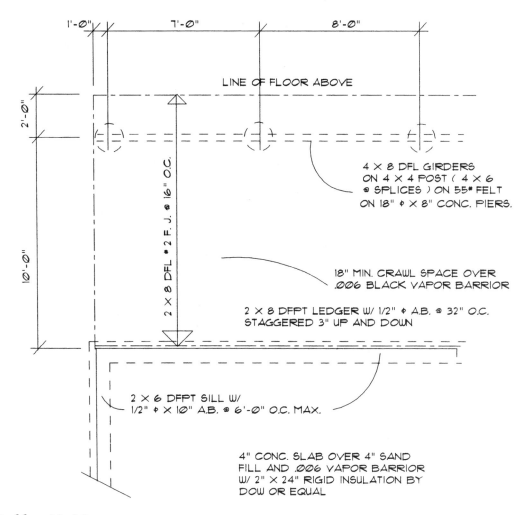

1'-0" 7'-0" 8'-0"

LINE OF FLOOR ABOVE

2'-0"

4 × 8 DFL GIRDERS
ON 4 × 4 POST (4 × 6
@ SPLICES) ON 55# FELT
ON 18" ⌀ × 8" CONC. PIERS.

2 × 8 DFL # 2 F. J. @ 16" O.C.

10'-0"

18" MIN. CRAWL SPACE OVER
.006 BLACK VAPOR BARRIOR

2 × 8 DFPT LEDGER W/ 1/2" ⌀ A.B. @ 32" O.C.
STAGGERED 3" UP AND DOWN

2 × 6 DFPT SILL W/
1/2" ⌀ × 10" A.B. @ 6'-0" O.C. MAX.

4" CONC. SLAB OVER 4" SAND
FILL AND .006 VAPOR BARRIOR
W/ 2" × 24" RIGID INSULATION BY
DOW OR EQUAL

Problem 11–16

Errors include:

Note 2: PSF not PSI

Note 3: 4" fill, not 2"

Note 4: 2500 PSL, not PSF

Note 4: 28 days, not 18 days

Note 6: 4" slabs, not 3"

Note 8: 18" not 15"

Note 9: 6 mil, not 4 mil

Note 10: 1 sq ft, not .5

Note 12: 1/2" air space, not 3/4"

Note 12: 3" minimum bearing, not 2"

Note 14: 4" drain, not 2"

© 2011 Cengage Learning. All Rights Reserved. May not be scanned, copied or duplicated, or posted to a publicly accessible website, in whole or in part.

Problem 11–17A

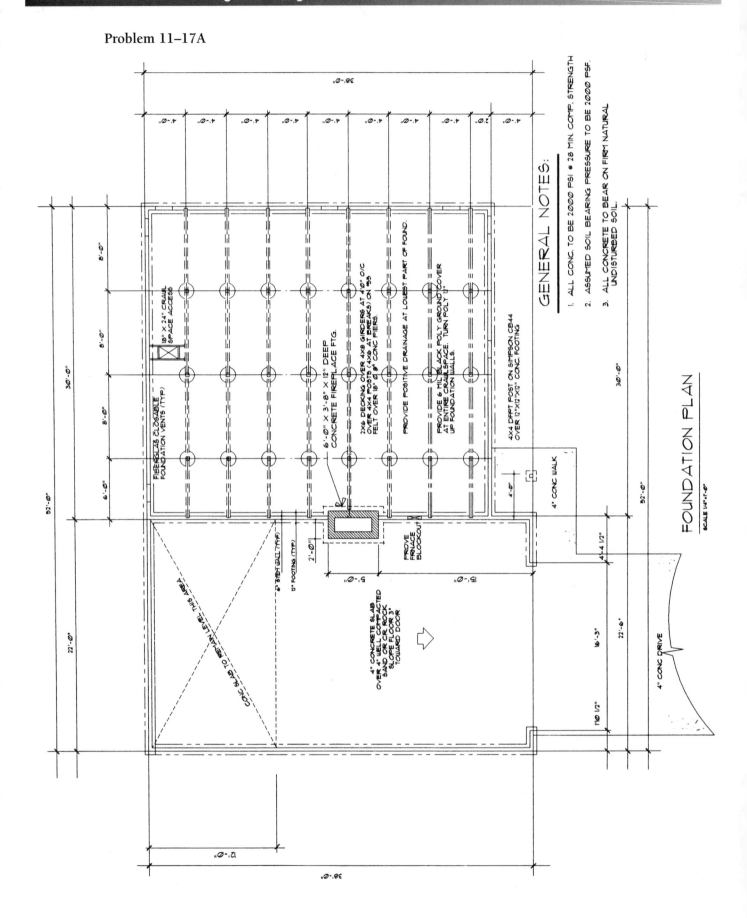

GENERAL NOTES:

1. ALL CONC. TO BE 2000 PSI @ 28 MIN. COMP. STRENGTH

2. ASSUMED SOIL BEARING PRESSURE TO BE 2000 PSF.

3. ALL CONCRETE TO BEAR ON FIRM NATURAL UNDISTURBED SOIL.

FOUNDATION PLAN

SCALE 1/4"-1'-0"

© 2011 Cengage Learning. All Rights Reserved. May not be scanned, copied or duplicated, or posted to a publicly accessible website, in whole or in part.

Problem 11–17B

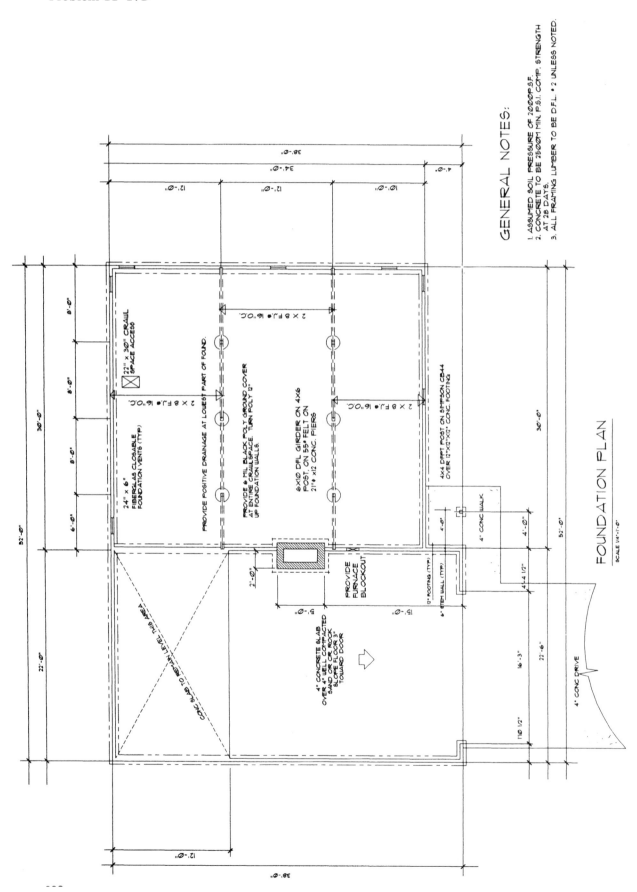

© 2011 Cengage Learning. All Rights Reserved. May not be scanned, copied or duplicated, or posted to a publicly accessible website, in whole or in part.

Problem 11–17C

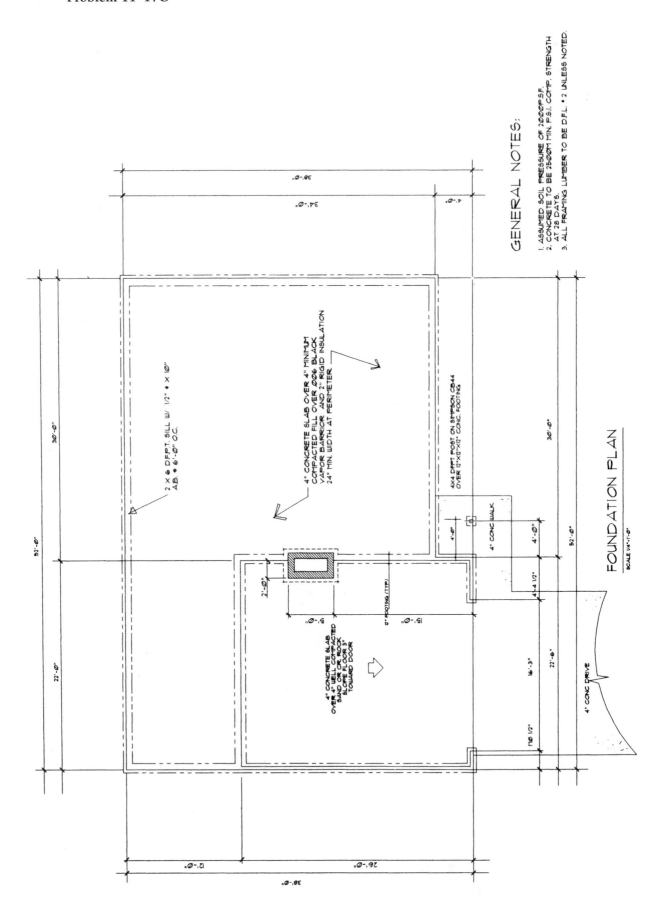

© 2011 Cengage Learning. All Rights Reserved. May not be scanned, copied or duplicated, or posted to a publicly accessible website, in whole or in part.

Problem 11–18A

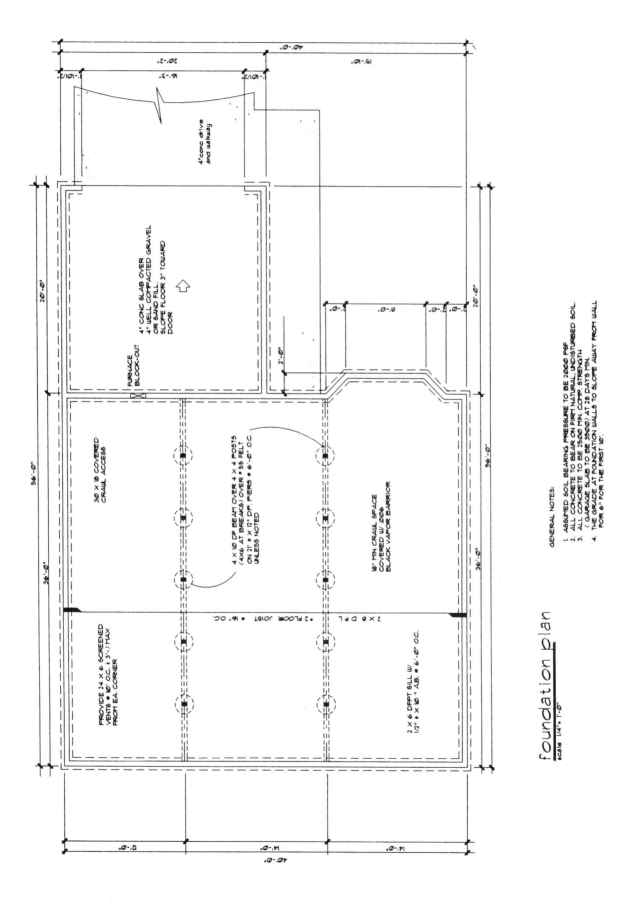

foundation plan
scale 1/4" = 1'-0"

GENERAL NOTES:

1. ASSUMED SOIL BEARING PRESSURE TO BE 2000 PSF
2. ALL CONCRETE TO BEAR ON FIRM NATURAL, UNDISTURBED SOIL.
3. ALL CONCRETE TO BE 2500 MIN. COMP. STRENGTH
   (GARAGE SLAB TO BE 3500) AT 28 DAYS MIN.
4. THE GRADE AT FOUNDATION WALLS TO SLOPE AWAY FROM WALL
   FOR 6" FOR THE FIRST 10'.

© 2011 Cengage Learning. All Rights Reserved. May not be scanned, copied or duplicated, or posted to a publicly accessible website, in whole or in part.

Problem 11–18B

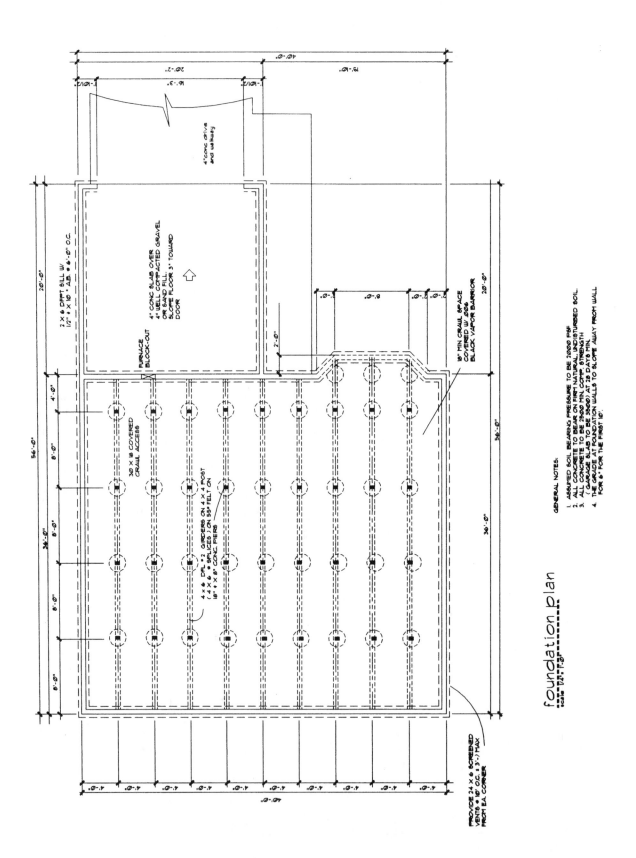

foundation plan

© 2011 Cengage Learning. All Rights Reserved. May not be scanned, copied or duplicated, or posted to a publicly accessible website, in whole or in part.

Problem 11–18C

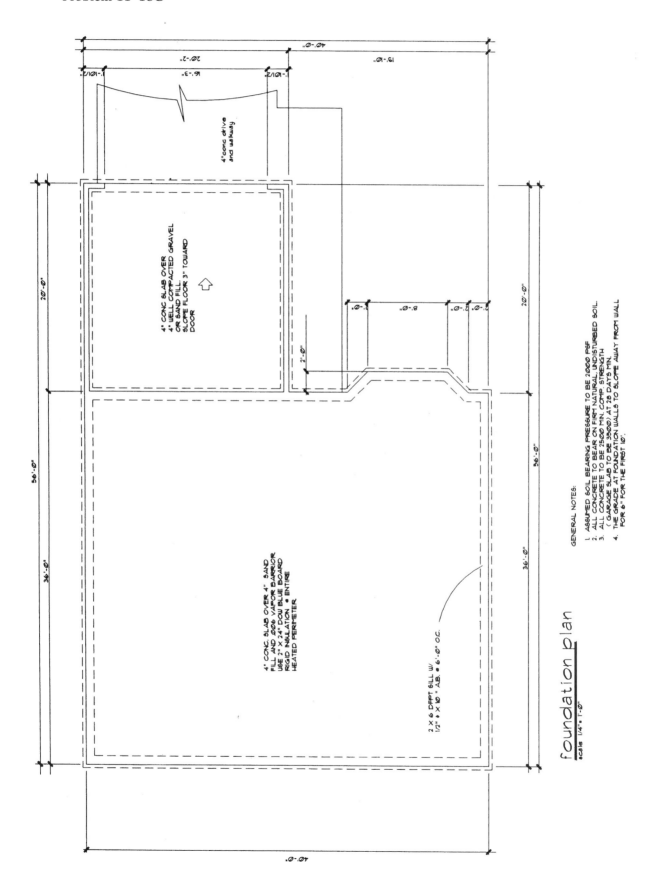

foundation plan
scale 1/4" = 1'-0"

4" CONC SLAB OVER
4" WELL COMPACTED GRAVEL
OR SAND FILL.
SLOPE FLOOR 3" TOWARD
DOOR

4" conc drive
and walkway

4" CONC SLAB OVER 4" SAND
FILL AND 006 VAPOR BARRIER
USE 2" X 24" DOW BLUE BOARD
RIGID INSULATION @ ENTIRE
HEATED PERIMETER

2 X 6 DFPT SILL W/
1/2" ø X 10" AB. @ 6'-0" OC.

GENERAL NOTES:

1. ASSUMED SOIL BEARING PRESSURE TO BE 2000 PSF
2. ALL CONCRETE TO BEAR ON FIRM NATURAL, UNDISTURBED SOIL.
3. ALL CONCRETE TO BE 2500 MIN. COMP. STRENGTH
   (GARAGE SLAB TO BE 3500) AT 28 DAYS MIN.
4. THE GRADE AT FOUNDATION WALLS TO SLOPE AWAY FROM WALL
   FOR 6" FOR THE FIRST 10'.

© 2011 Cengage Learning. All Rights Reserved. May not be scanned, copied or duplicated, or posted to a publicly accessible website, in whole or in part.

Problem 11–19A

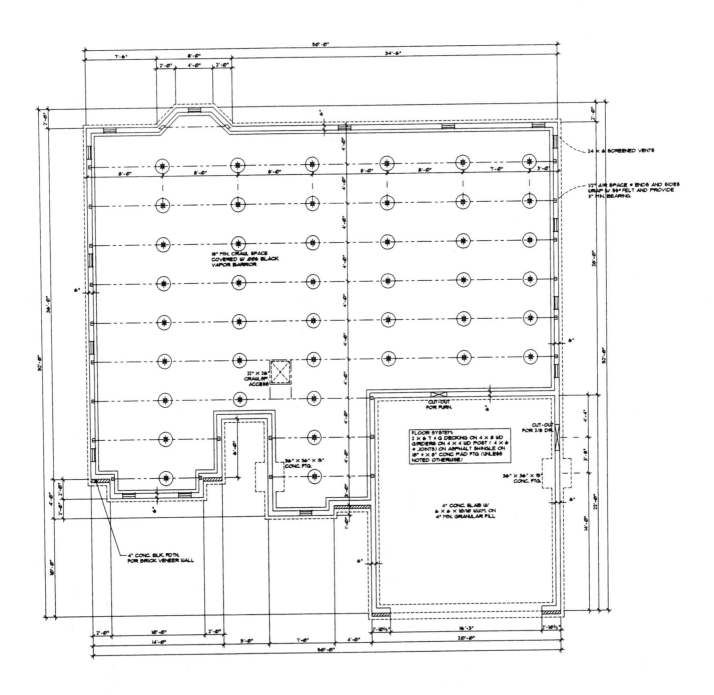

FOUNDATION PLAN
SCALE : 1/4" = 1'-0"

© 2011 Cengage Learning. All Rights Reserved. May not be scanned, copied or duplicated, or posted to a publicly accessible website, in whole or in part.

Problem 11-19B

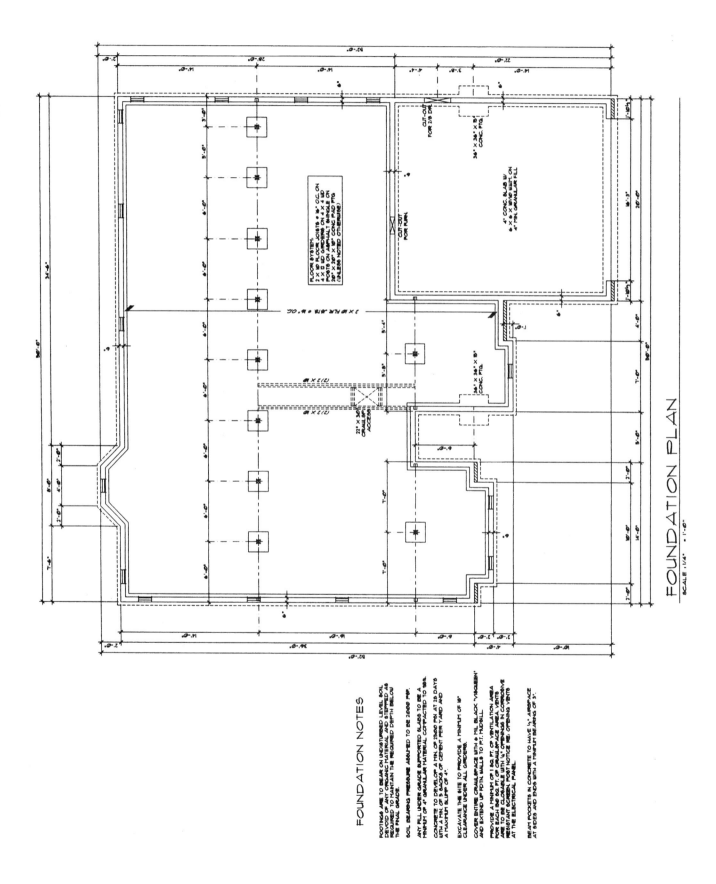

FOUNDATION PLAN

SCALE 1/4" = 1'-0"

FOUNDATION NOTES

© 2011 Cengage Learning. All Rights Reserved. May not be scanned, copied or duplicated, or posted to a publicly accessible website, in whole or in part.

Problem 11–20

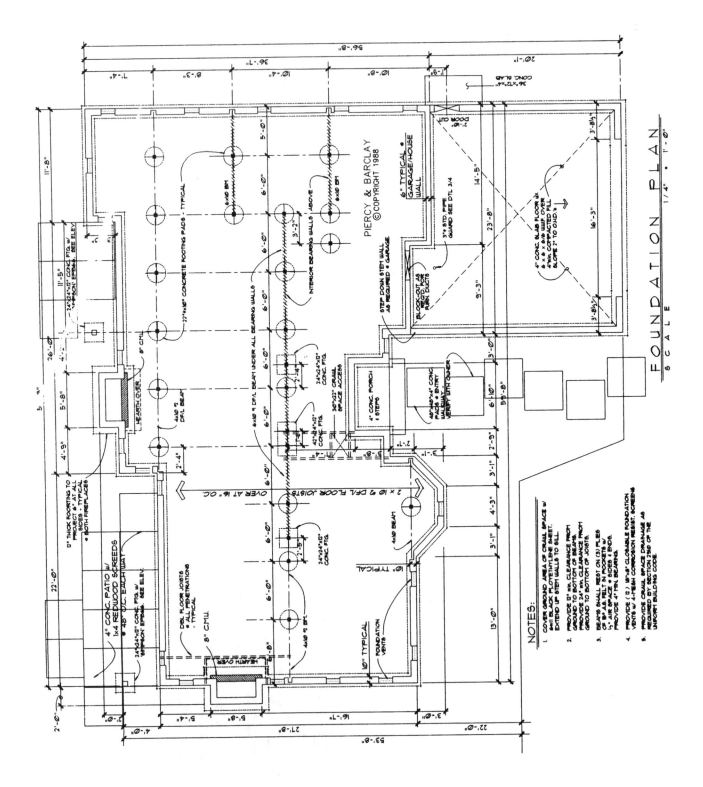

© 2011 Cengage Learning. All Rights Reserved. May not be scanned, copied or duplicated, or posted to a publicly accessible website, in whole or in part.

Problem 11–21

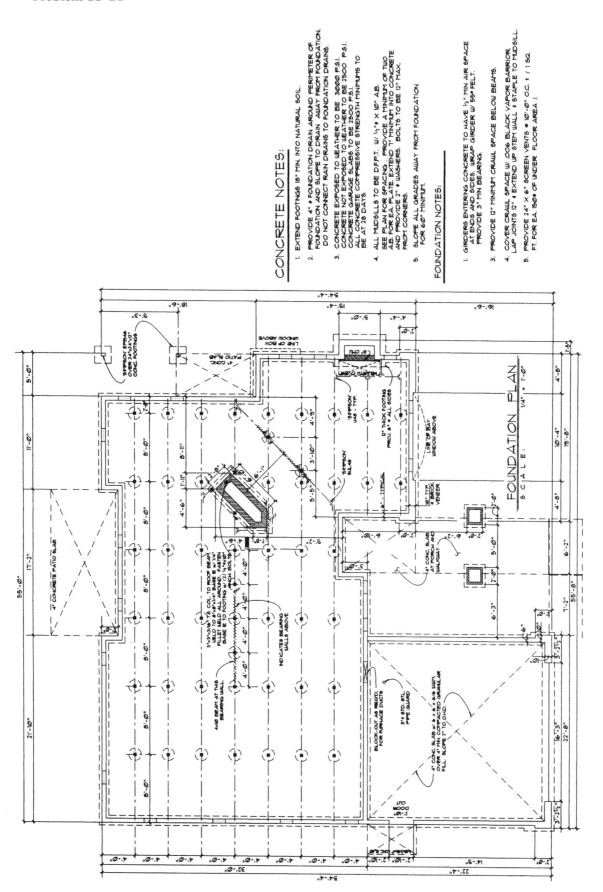

CONCRETE NOTES:

1. EXTEND FOOTINGS 18" MIN. INTO NATURAL SOIL.

2. PROVIDE 4" Ø FOUNDATION DRAIN AROUND PERIMETER OF FOUNDATION AND SLOPE TO DRAIN AWAY FROM FOUNDATION. DO NOT CONNECT RAIN DRAINS TO FOUNDATION DRAINS.

3. CONCRETE EXPOSED TO WEATHER TO BE 3000 P.S.I. CONCRETE NOT EXPOSED TO WEATHER TO BE 2500 P.S.I. CONCRETE GARAGE SLABS TO BE 2500 P.S.I. ALL CONCRETE COMPRESSIVE STRENGTH MINIMUMS TO BE AT 28 DAYS.

4. ALL MUDSILLS TO BE D.F.P.T. W/ ½"Ø X 10" A.B. SEE PLAN FOR SPACING. PROVIDE A MINIMUM OF TWO A.B. FOR EA. PLATE. EXTEND 7" MINIMUM INTO CONCRETE AND PROVIDE 2" Ø WASHERS. BOLTS TO BE 12" MAX. FROM CORNERS.

5. SLOPE ALL GRADES AWAY FROM FOUNDATION FOR 60" MINIMUM.

FOUNDATION NOTES:

1. GIRDERS ENTERING CONCRETE TO HAVE ½" MIN AIR SPACE AT ENDS AND SIDES. WRAP GIRDER W/ 55# FELT. PROVIDE 3" MIN BEARING.

2. PROVIDE 12" MINIMUM CRAWL SPACE BELOW BEAMS.

3. COVER CRAWL SPACE W/ .006 BLACK VAPOR BARRIOR. LAP JOINTS 12" & EXTEND UP STEM WALL 4 STAPLE TO MUDSILL.

4. PROVIDE 24" X 6" SCREEN VENTS @ 10'-0" O.C. ± (1 SQ. FT. FOR EA. 150# OF UNDER FLOOR AREA).

FOUNDATION PLAN

SCALE: ¼" = 1'-0"

© 2011 Cengage Learning. All Rights Reserved. May not be scanned, copied or duplicated, or posted to a publicly accessible website, in whole or in part.

Problem 11–22A

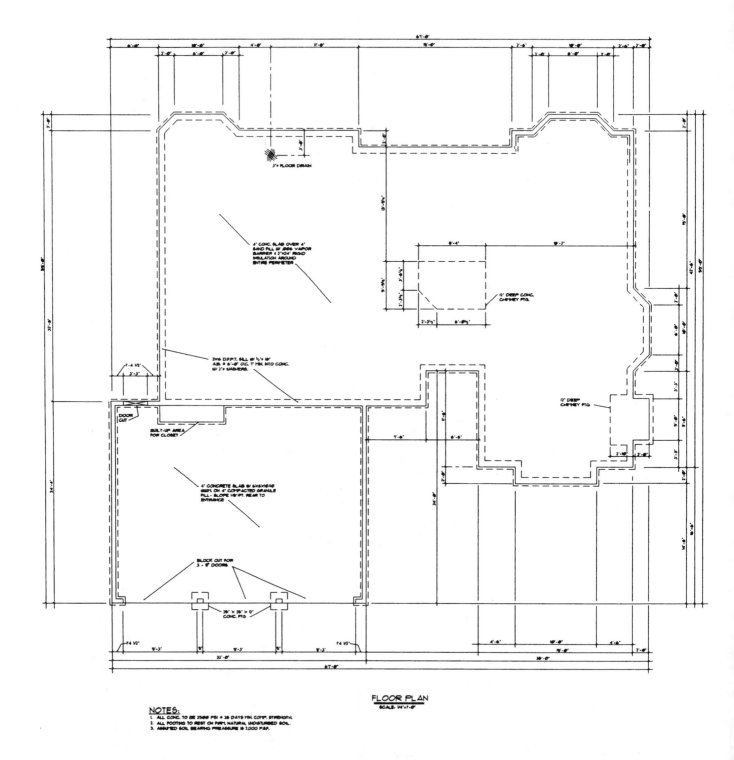

FLOOR PLAN
SCALE: 1/4" = 1'-0"

NOTES:
1. ALL CONC. TO BE 2500 PSI @ 28 DAYS MIN. COMP. STRENGTH.
2. ALL FOOTING TO REST ON FIRM NATURAL UNDISTURBED SOIL.
3. ASSUMED SOIL BEARING PRESSURE IS 2,000 P.S.F.

© 2011 Cengage Learning. All Rights Reserved. May not be scanned, copied or duplicated, or posted to a publicly accessible website, in whole or in part.

Problem 11–22B

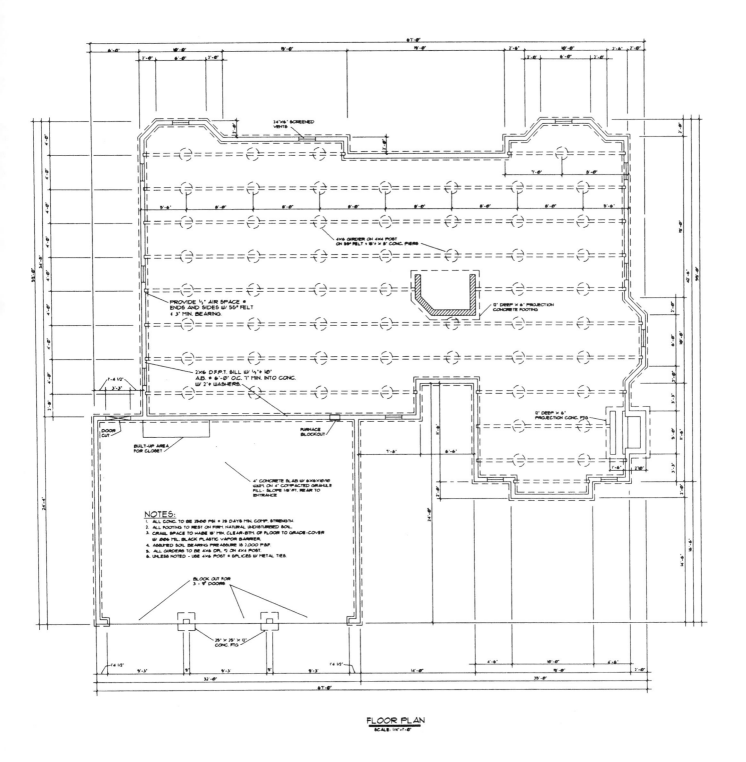

FLOOR PLAN
SCALE: 1/4"=1'-0"

© 2011 Cengage Learning. All Rights Reserved. May not be scanned, copied or duplicated, or posted to a publicly accessible website, in whole or in part.

Problem 11–22C

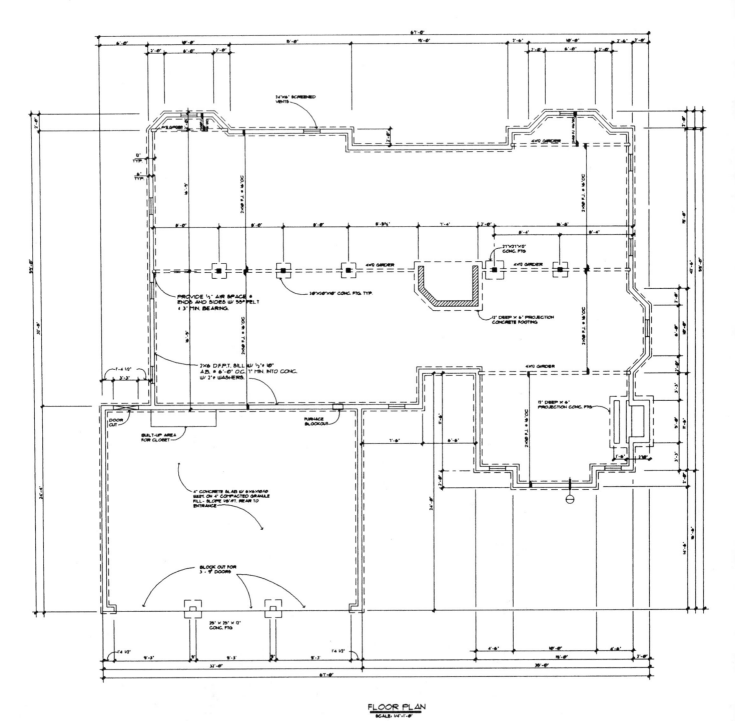

FLOOR PLAN
SCALE: 1/4"=1'-0"

NOTES:
1. ALL CONC. TO BE 2500 PSI @ 28 DAYS MIN. COMP. STRENGTH.
2. ALL FOOTING TO REST ON FIRM, NATURAL UNDISTURBED SOIL.
3. CRAWL SPACE TO HAVE 18" MIN. CLEAR-BTM. OF FLOOR TO GRADE-COVER W/.006 MIL BLACK PLASTIC VAPOR BARRIER.
4. ALL GIRDERS TO BE DFL #2 UNLESS NOTED.
5. ALL GIRDERS ON 4X4 POST-USE 4X6 POST @ SPLICES W/ METAL TIES.

© 2011 Cengage Learning. All Rights Reserved. May not be scanned, copied or duplicated, or posted to a publicly accessible website, in whole or in part.

Problem 11–23

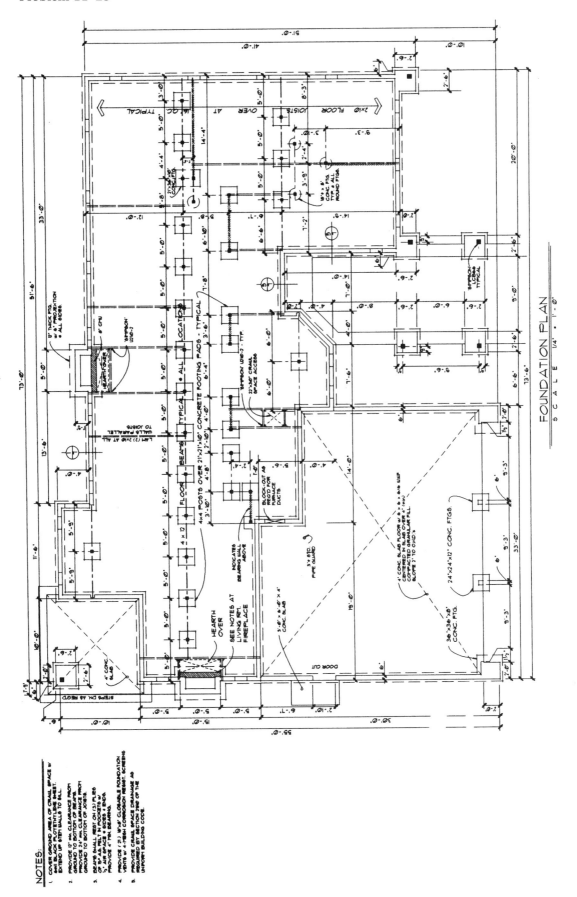

NOTES:

© 2011 Cengage Learning. All Rights Reserved. May not be scanned, copied or duplicated, or posted to a publicly accessible website, in whole or in part.

Problem 11–24

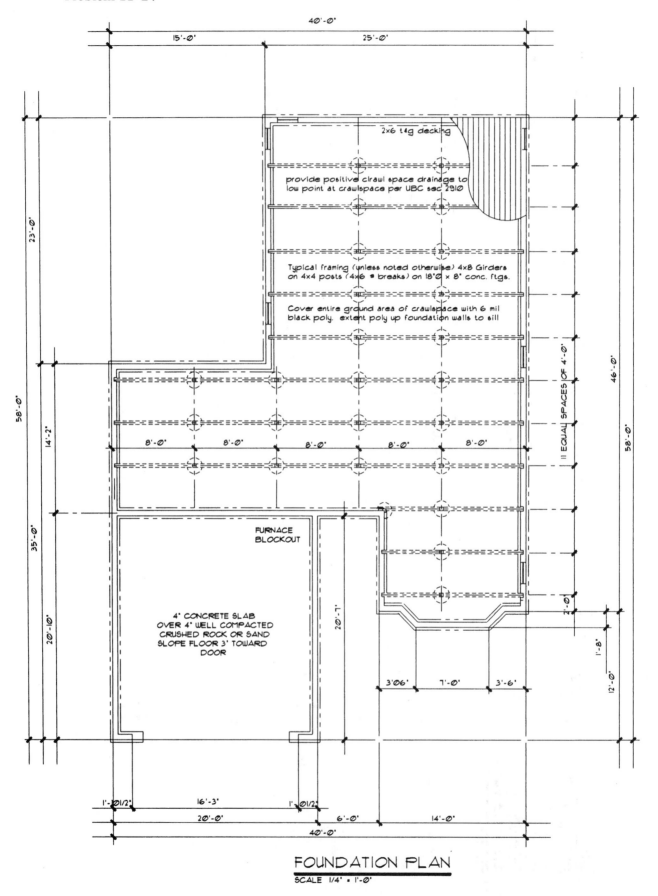

FOUNDATION PLAN

SCALE 1/4" ■ 1'-0"

© 2011 Cengage Learning. All Rights Reserved. May not be scanned, copied or duplicated, or posted to a publicly accessible website, in whole or in part.

Problem 11–25

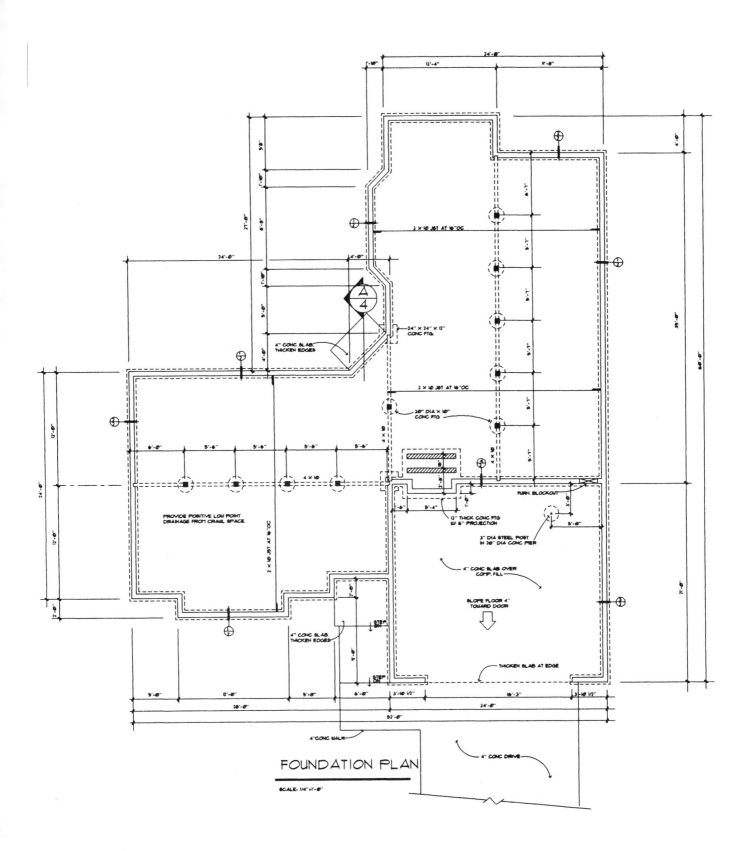

FOUNDATION PLAN

SCALE: 1/4"=1'-0"

© 2011 Cengage Learning. All Rights Reserved. May not be scanned, copied or duplicated, or posted to a publicly accessible website, in whole or in part.

Problem 11–26

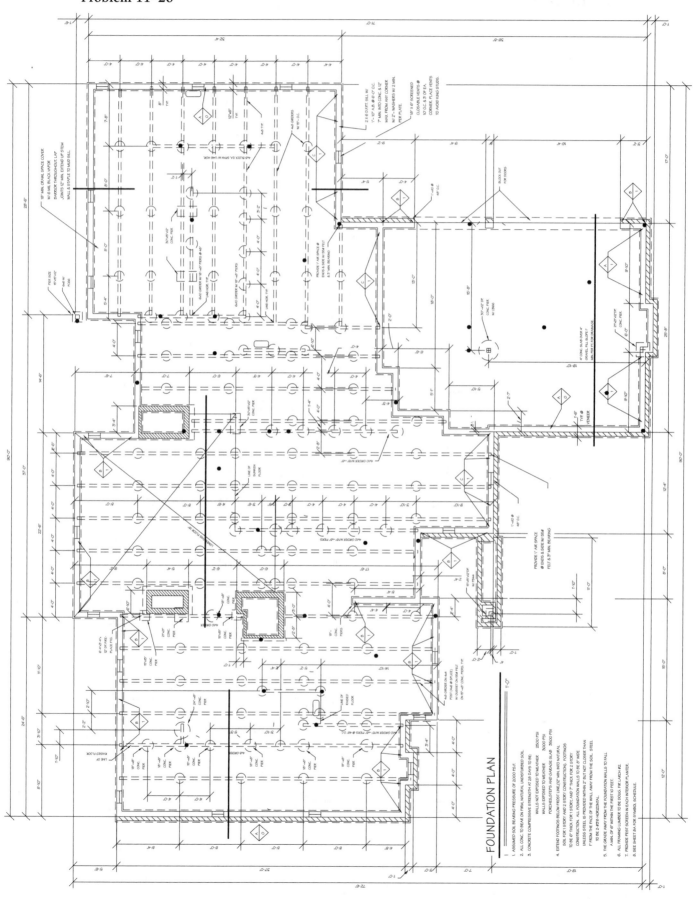

FOUNDATION PLAN

© 2011 Cengage Learning. All Rights Reserved. May not be scanned, copied or duplicated, or posted to a publicly accessible website, in whole or in part.

Problem 11–27

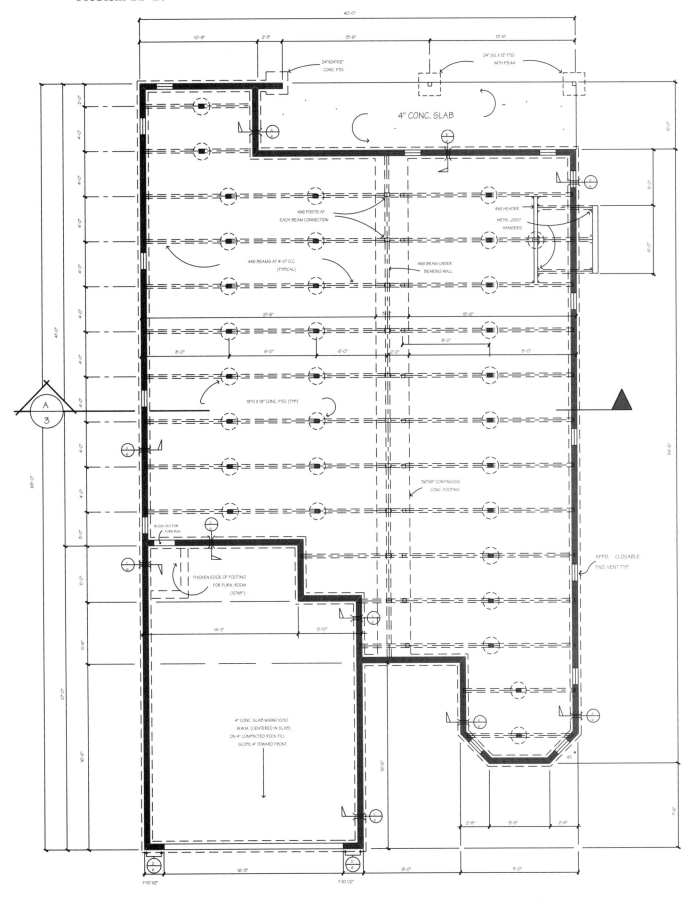

© 2011 Cengage Learning. All Rights Reserved. May not be scanned, copied or duplicated, or posted to a publicly accessible website, in whole or in part.

Problem 11–28

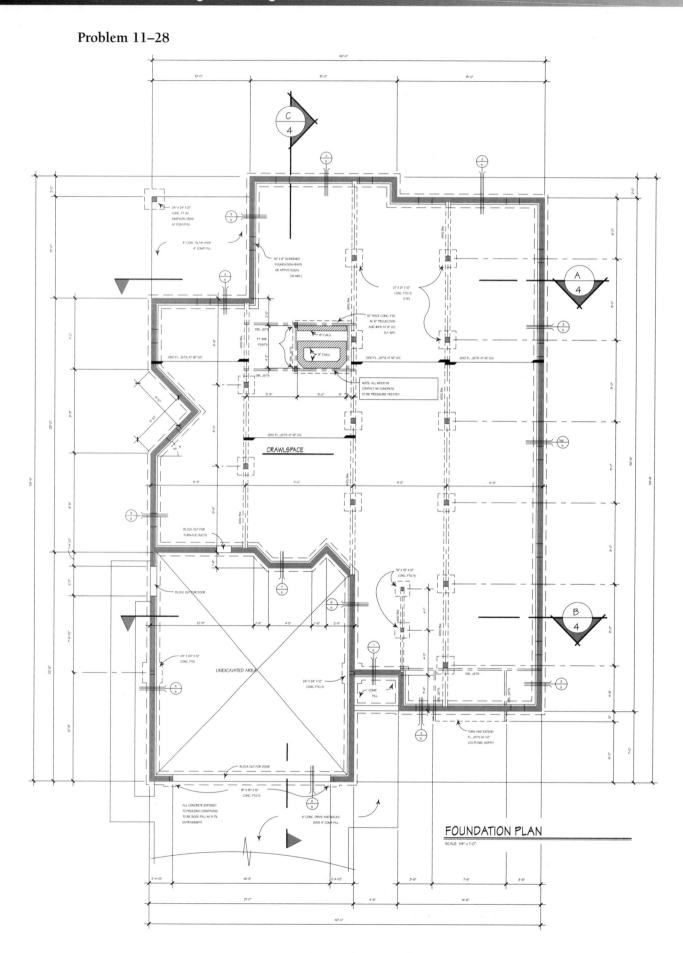

FOUNDATION PLAN
SCALE 1/4" = 1'-0"

© 2011 Cengage Learning. All Rights Reserved. May not be scanned, copied or duplicated, or posted to a publicly accessible website, in whole or in part.

Problem 11–29

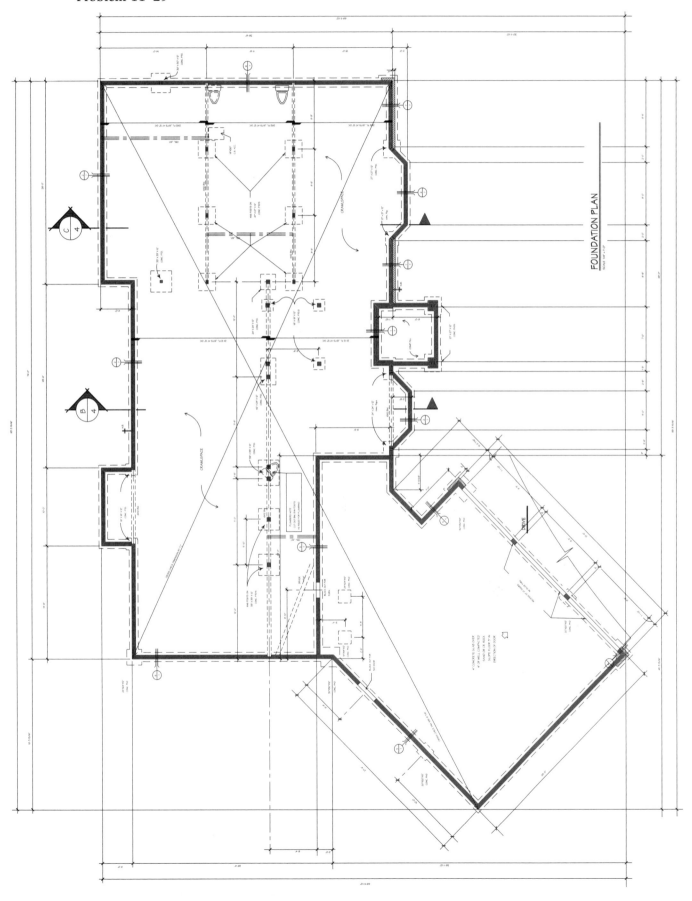

FOUNDATION PLAN

© 2011 Cengage Learning. All Rights Reserved. May not be scanned, copied or duplicated, or posted to a publicly accessible website, in whole or in part.

Problem 11–30

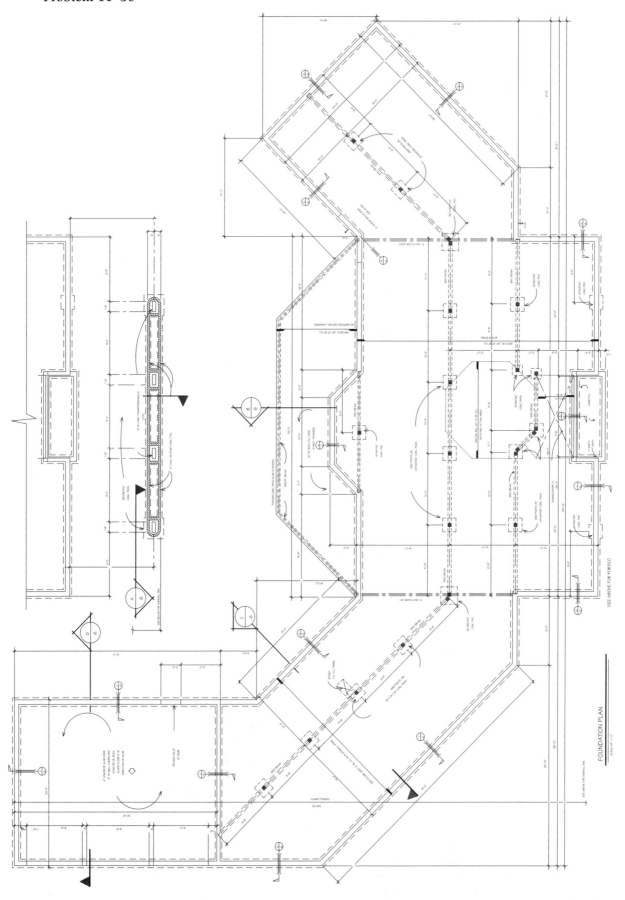

FOUNDATION PLAN

© 2011 Cengage Learning. All Rights Reserved. May not be scanned, copied or duplicated, or posted to a publicly accessible website, in whole or in part.

Problem 11–31

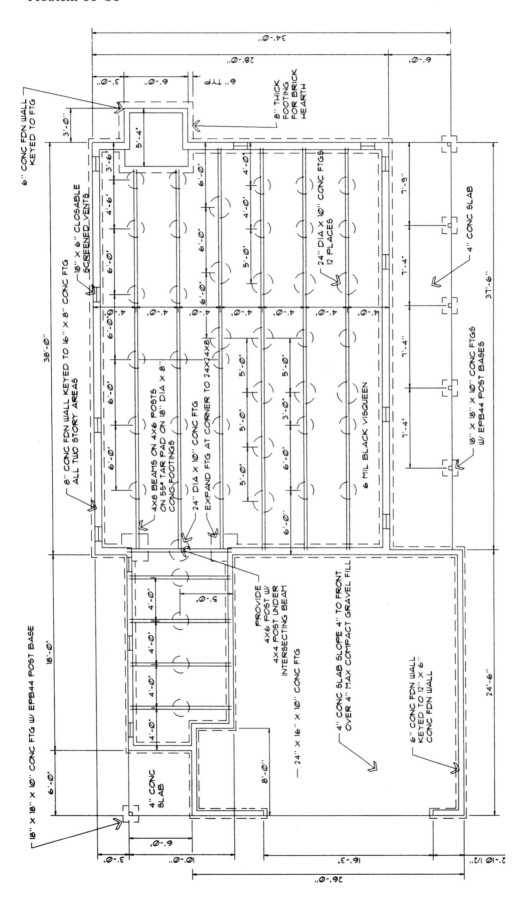

FOUNDATION PLAN

SCALE: 1/4" = 1'-0"

ALL FOOTINGS PLACED ON FIRM UNDISTURBED SOIL
BELOW UBC REQ'D FREEZE LINE
ALL CONC TO BE 2500 PSI AT 28 DAYS
PROVIDE A 22 x 30 MIN CRAWL SPACE ACCESS

© 2011 Cengage Learning. All Rights Reserved. May not be scanned, copied or duplicated, or posted to a publicly accessible website, in whole or in part.

CHAPTER 12 DETAILS

Problem 12–1

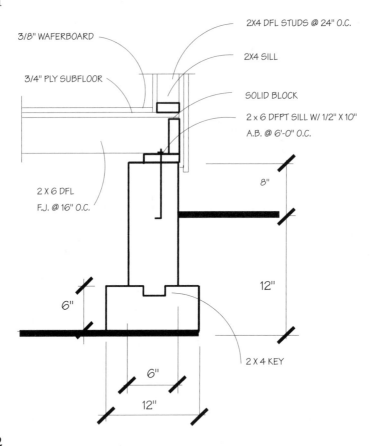

3/8" WAFERBOARD

3/4" PLY SUBFLOOR

2X4 DFL STUDS @ 24" O.C.

2X4 SILL

SOLID BLOCK

2 x 6 DFPT SILL W/ 1/2" X 10"
A.B. @ 6'-0" O.C.

2 X 6 DFL
F.J. @ 16" O.C.

8"

12"

6"

2 X 4 KEY

6"

12"

Problem 12–2

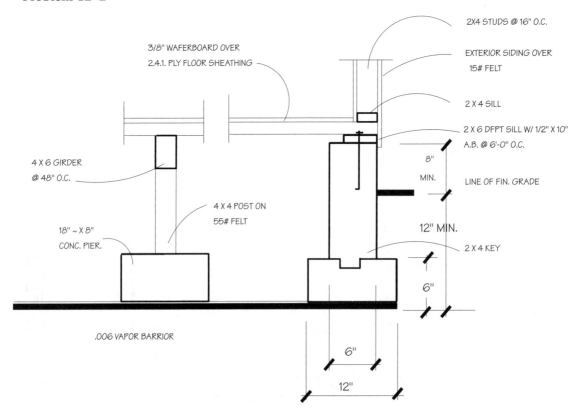

3/8" WAFERBOARD OVER
2.4.1. PLY FLOOR SHEATHING

2X4 STUDS @ 16" O.C.

EXTERIOR SIDING OVER
15# FELT

2 X 4 SILL

2 x 6 DFPT SILL W/ 1/2" X 10"
A.B. @ 6'-0" O.C.

4 X 6 GIRDER
@ 48" O.C.

4 X 4 POST ON
55# FELT

8"
MIN.

LINE OF FIN. GRADE

18" ~ X 8"
CONC. PIER.

12" MIN.

2 X 4 KEY

6"

.006 VAPOR BARRIOR

6"

12"

© 2011 Cengage Learning. All Rights Reserved. May not be scanned, copied or duplicated, or posted to a publicly accessible website, in whole or in part.

Problem 12–3

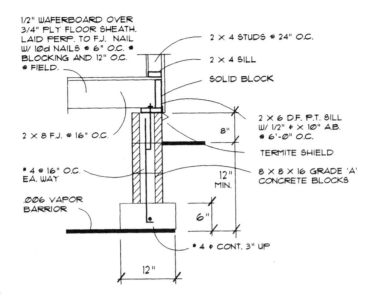

1/2" WAFERBOARD OVER 3/4" PLY FLOOR SHEATH. LAID PERP. TO F.J. NAIL W/ 10d NAILS ● 6" O.C. ● BLOCKING AND 12" O.C. ● FIELD.

2 × 4 STUDS ● 24" O.C.

2 × 4 SILL

SOLID BLOCK

2 × 6 D.F. P.T. SILL W/ 1/2" ◇ × 10" A.B. ● 6'-0" O.C.

2 × 8 F.J. ● 16" O.C.

8"

TERMITE SHIELD

● 4 ● 16" O.C. EA. WAY

12" MIN.

8 × 8 × 16 GRADE 'A' CONCRETE BLOCKS

.006 VAPOR BARRIOR

6"

● 4 ◇ CONT. 3" UP

12"

Problem 12–4

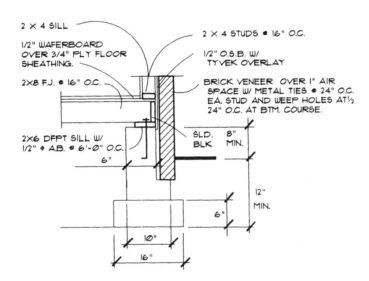

2 × 4 SILL

1/2" WAFERBOARD OVER 3/4" PLY FLOOR SHEATHING.

2×8 F.J. ● 16" O.C.

2×6 DFPT SILL W/ 1/2" ◇ A.B. ● 6'-0" O.C.

6"

2 × 4 STUDS ● 16" O.C.

1/2" O.S.B. W/ TYVEK OVERLAY

BRICK VENEER OVER 1" AIR SPACE W/ METAL TIES ● 24" O.C. EA. STUD AND WEEP HOLES AT½ 24" O.C. AT BTM. COURSE.

SLD. BLK

8" MIN.

12" MIN.

6"

10"

16"

Problem 12–5

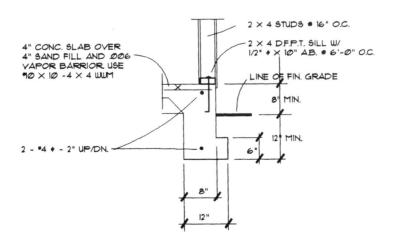

4" CONC. SLAB OVER 4" SAND FILL AND .006 VAPOR BARRIER USE 10 × 10 -4 × 4 WWM

2 × 4 STUDS ● 16" O.C.

2 × 4 D.F.P.T. SILL W/ 1/2" ◇ × 10" A.B. ● 6'-0" O.C.

LINE OF FIN. GRADE

8" MIN.

12" MIN.

2 - ●4 ◇ - 2" UP/DN.

6"

8"

12"

© 2011 Cengage Learning. All Rights Reserved. May not be scanned, copied or duplicated, or posted to a publicly accessible website, in whole or in part.

Problem 12–6

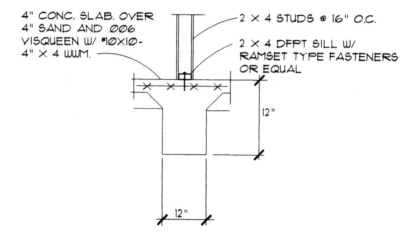

4" CONC. SLAB. OVER
4" SAND AND .006
VISQUEEN W/ #10X10-
4" X 4 WWM.

2 X 4 STUDS @ 16" O.C.

2 X 4 DFPT SILL W/
RAMSET TYPE FASTENERS
OR EQUAL

12"

12"

Problem 12–7

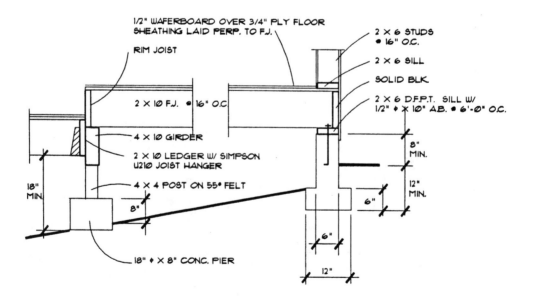

1/2" WAFERBOARD OVER 3/4" PLY FLOOR
SHEATHING LAID PERP. TO F.J.

RIM JOIST

2 X 10 F.J. @ 16" O.C.

4 X 10 GIRDER

2 X 10 LEDGER W/ SIMPSON
U210 JOIST HANGER

4 X 4 POST ON 55# FELT

18"
MIN.

8"

18" ø X 8" CONC. PIER

2 X 6 STUDS
@ 16" O.C.

2 X 6 SILL

SOLID BLK

2 X 6 D.F.P.T. SILL W/
1/2" ø X 10" A.B. @ 6'-0" O.C.

8"
MIN.

12"
MIN.

6"

6"

12"

© 2011 Cengage Learning. All Rights Reserved. May not be scanned, copied or duplicated, or posted to a publicly accessible website, in whole or in part.

Problem 12–8

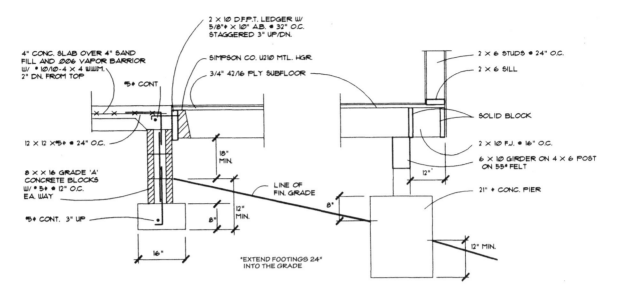

2 × 10 D.F.P.T. LEDGER W/
5/8"∅ × 10" A.B. ● 32" O.C.
STAGGERED 3" UP/DN.

4" CONC. SLAB OVER 4" SAND
FILL AND ∅∅6 VAPOR BARRIER
W/ ●10/10-4 × 4 WWM.
2" DN. FROM TOP

SIMPSON CO. U210 MTL. HGR

3/4" 42/16 PLY SUBFLOOR

2 × 6 STUDS ● 24" O.C.

2 × 6 SILL

●5∅ CONT

SOLID BLOCK

12 × 12 ×●5∅ ● 24" O.C.

2 × 10 F.J. ● 16" O.C.

6 × 10 GIRDER ON 4 × 6 POST
ON 55# FELT

8 × × 16 GRADE 'A'
CONCRETE BLOCKS
W/ ● 5∅ ● 12" O.C.
EA. WAY

18"
MIN.

LINE OF
FIN. GRADE

12"

21" ∅ CONC. PIER

●5∅ CONT. 3" UP

12"
MIN.

8"

8"

16"

"EXTEND FOOTINGS 24"
INTO THE GRADE

12" MIN.

Problem 12–9

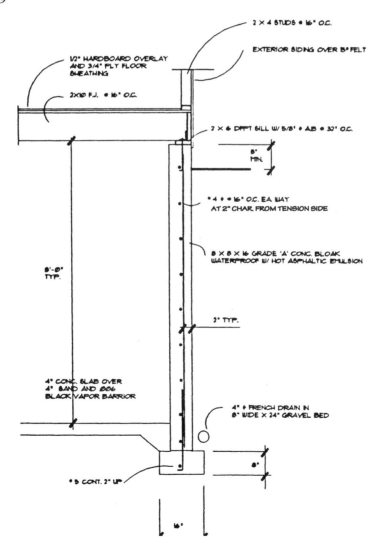

2 × 4 STUDS ● 16" O.C.

EXTERIOR SIDING OVER 15# FELT

1/2" HARDBOARD OVERLAY
AND 3/4" PLY FLOOR
SHEATHING

2×10 F.J. ● 16" O.C.

2 × 6 DFPT SILL W/ 5/8" ∅ AB ● 32" O.C.

8"
MIN.

●4 ∅ ● 16" O.C. EA. WAY
AT 2" CHAR FROM TENSION SIDE

8 × 8 × 16 GRADE 'A' CONC. BLOCK
WATERPROOF W/ HOT ASPHALTIC EMULSION

8'-0"
TYP.

2" TYP.

4" CONC. SLAB OVER
4" SAND AND ∅∅6
BLACK VAPOR BARRIOR

4" ∅ FRENCH DRAIN IN
8" WIDE × 24" GRAVEL BED

8"

● 5 CONT. 2" UP

16"

© 2011 Cengage Learning. All Rights Reserved. May not be scanned, copied or duplicated, or posted to a publicly accessible website, in whole or in part.

Problem 12–10

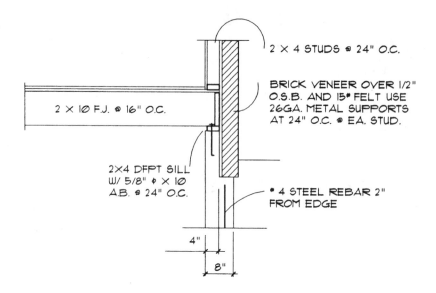

2 × 4 STUDS @ 24" O.C.

BRICK VENEER OVER 1/2" O.S.B. AND 15# FELT USE 26GA. METAL SUPPORTS AT 24" O.C. @ EA. STUD.

2 × 10 F.J. @ 16" O.C.

2×4 DFPT SILL W/ 5/8" Φ × 10 A.B. @ 24" O.C.

4 STEEL REBAR 2" FROM EDGE

4"

8"

Problem 12–11

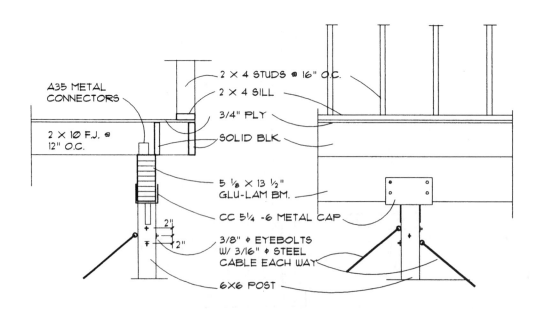

A35 METAL CONNECTORS

2 × 10 F.J. @ 12" O.C.

2 × 4 STUDS @ 16" O.C.

2 × 4 SILL

3/4" PLY

SOLID BLK.

5 1/8 × 13 1/2" GLU-LAM BM.

CC 5¼ -6 METAL CAP

2"

2"

3/8" Φ EYEBOLTS W/ 3/16" Φ STEEL CABLE EACH WAY

6×6 POST

© 2011 Cengage Learning. All Rights Reserved. May not be scanned, copied or duplicated, or posted to a publicly accessible website, in whole or in part.

Problem 12–12

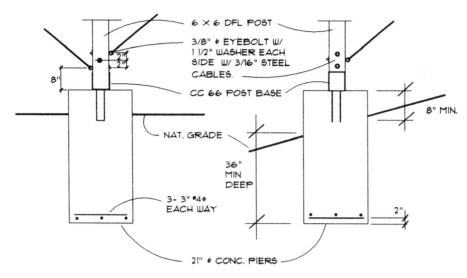

Problem 12–13

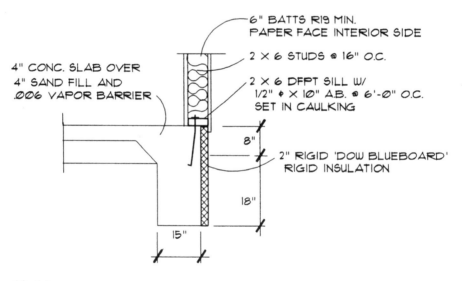

Problem 12–14

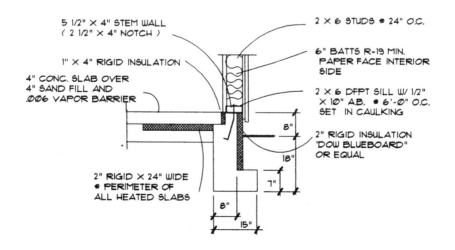

© 2011 Cengage Learning. All Rights Reserved. May not be scanned, copied or duplicated, or posted to a publicly accessible website, in whole or in part.

Problem 12–15

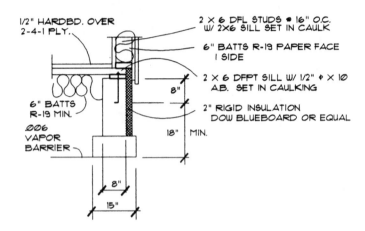

1/2" HARDBD. OVER
2-4-1 PLY.

2 × 6 DFL STUDS ● 16" O.C.
W/ 2X6 SILL SET IN CAULK

6" BATTS R-19 PAPER FACE
1 SIDE

2 × 6 DFPT SILL W/ 1/2" ⌀ × 10
A.B. SET IN CAULKING

8"

2" RIGID INSULATION
DOW BLUEBOARD OR EQUAL

6" BATTS
R-19 MIN.

.006
VAPOR
BARRIER

18" MIN.

8"

15"

Problem 12–16

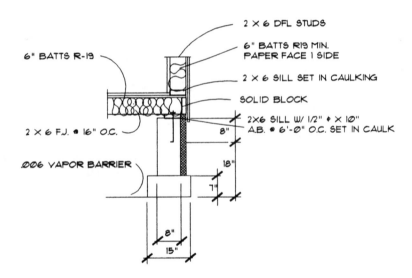

6" BATTS R-19

2 × 6 DFL STUDS

6" BATTS R19 MIN.
PAPER FACE 1 SIDE

2 × 6 SILL SET IN CAULKING

SOLID BLOCK

2X6 SILL W/ 1/2" ⌀ × 10"
A.B. ● 6'-0" O.C. SET IN CAULK

2 × 6 F.J. ● 16" O.C.

8"

.006 VAPOR BARRIER

18"

7"

8"

15"

Problem 12–17

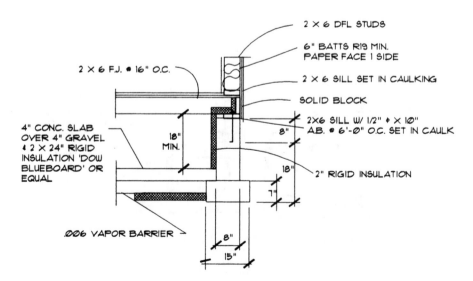

2 × 6 DFL STUDS

6" BATTS R19 MIN.
PAPER FACE 1 SIDE

2 × 6 F.J. ● 16" O.C.

2 × 6 SILL SET IN CAULKING

SOLID BLOCK

2X6 SILL W/ 1/2" ⌀ × 10"
A.B. ● 6'-0" O.C. SET IN CAULK

4" CONC. SLAB
OVER 4" GRAVEL
● 2 × 24" RIGID
INSULATION 'DOW
BLUEBOARD' OR
EQUAL

18"
MIN.

8"

18"

2" RIGID INSULATION

7"

.006 VAPOR BARRIER

8"

15"

© 2011 Cengage Learning. All Rights Reserved. May not be scanned, copied or duplicated, or posted to a publicly accessible website, in whole or in part.

Problem 12–18

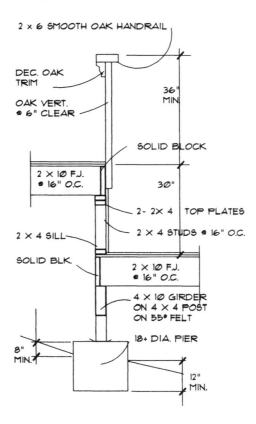

Problem 12–19

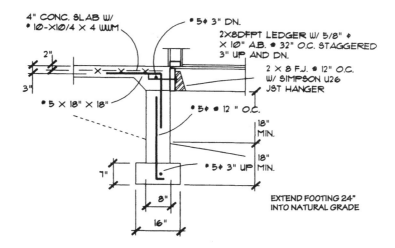

© 2011 Cengage Learning. All Rights Reserved. May not be scanned, copied or duplicated, or posted to a publicly accessible website, in whole or in part.

Problem 12–20

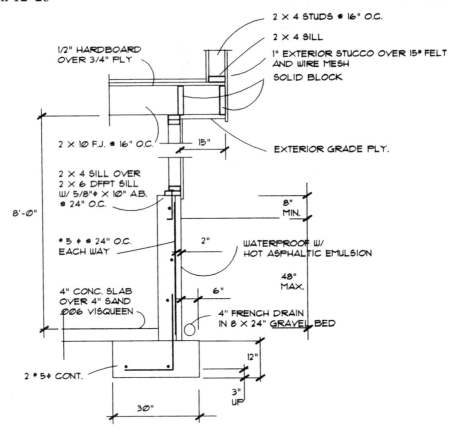

Problem 12–21

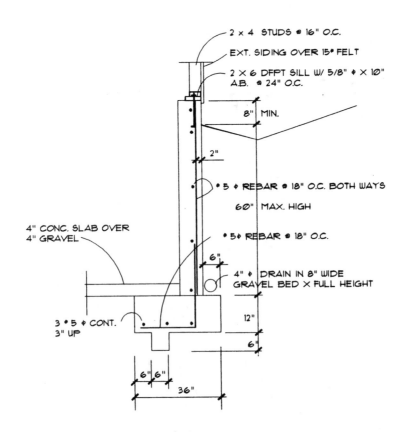

© 2011 Cengage Learning. All Rights Reserved. May not be scanned, copied or duplicated, or posted to a publicly accessible website, in whole or in part.

Problem 12–22

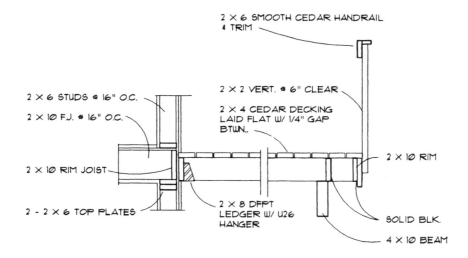

2 × 6 SMOOTH CEDAR HANDRAIL & TRIM

2 × 6 STUDS @ 16" O.C.

2 × 10 F.J. @ 16" O.C.

2 × 2 VERT. @ 6" CLEAR

2 × 4 CEDAR DECKING LAID FLAT W/ 1/4" GAP BTWN.

2 × 10 RIM

2 × 10 RIM JOIST

2 - 2 × 6 TOP PLATES

2 × 8 DFPT LEDGER W/ U26 HANGER

SOLID BLK.

4 × 10 BEAM

Problem 12–23

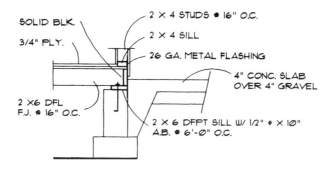

SOLID BLK.

3/4" PLY.

2 × 4 STUDS @ 16" O.C.

2 × 4 SILL

26 GA. METAL FLASHING

4" CONC. SLAB OVER 4" GRAVEL

2 ×6 DFL F.J. @ 16" O.C.

2 × 6 DFPT SILL W/ 1/2" ø × 10" A.B. @ 6'-0" O.C.

Problem 12–24

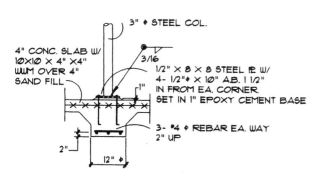

3" ø STEEL COL.

4" CONC. SLAB W/ 10X10 × 4" ×4" WWM OVER 4" SAND FILL

3/16

1/2" × 8 × 8 STEEL ₱ W/ 4- 1/2"ø × 10" A.B. 1 1/2" IN FROM EA. CORNER. SET IN 1" EPOXY CEMENT BASE

3- #4 ø REBAR EA. WAY 2" UP

2"

12" ø

Problem 12–25

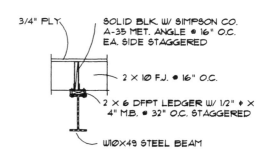

3/4" PLY.

SOLID BLK W/ SIMPSON CO. A-35 MET. ANGLE @ 16" O.C. EA. SIDE STAGGERED

2 × 10 F.J. @ 16" O.C.

2 × 6 DFPT LEDGER W/ 1/2" ø × 4" M.B. @ 32" O.C. STAGGERED

W10X49 STEEL BEAM

© 2011 Cengage Learning. All Rights Reserved. May not be scanned, copied or duplicated, or posted to a publicly accessible website, in whole or in part.

Problem 12–26

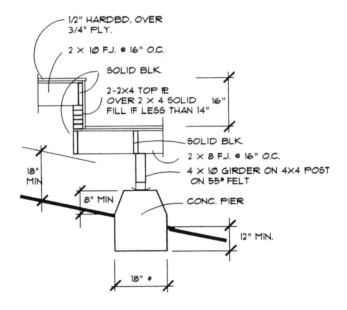

Problem 12–27

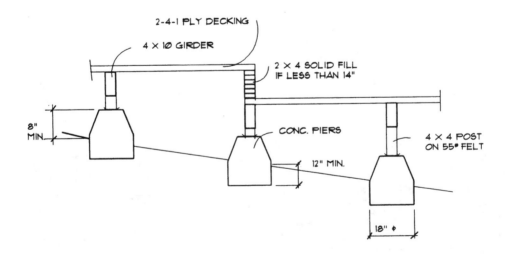

© 2011 Cengage Learning. All Rights Reserved. May not be scanned, copied or duplicated, or posted to a publicly accessible website, in whole or in part.

Problem 12–28

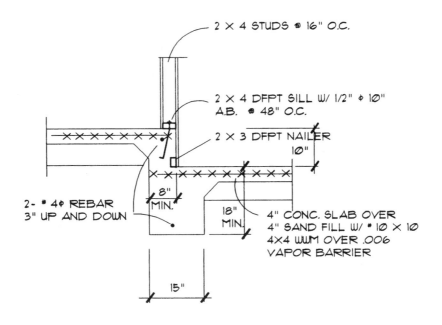

2 × 4 STUDS @ 16" O.C.

2 × 4 DFPT SILL W/ 1/2" φ 10"
A.B. @ 48" O.C.

2 × 3 DFPT NAILER

10"

2- # 4φ REBAR
3" UP AND DOWN

8"
MIN.

18"
MIN.

4" CONC. SLAB OVER
4" SAND FILL W/ # 10 × 10
4×4 WWM OVER .006
VAPOR BARRIER

15"

Problem 12–29

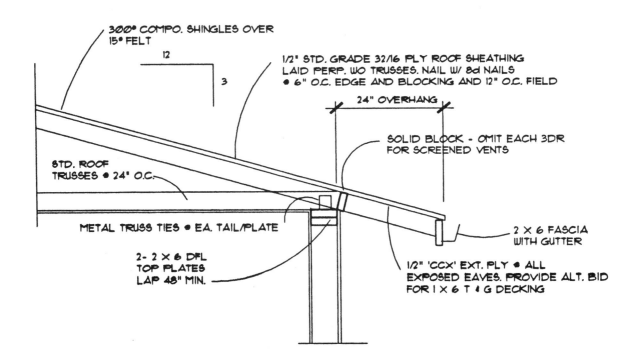

300# COMPO. SHINGLES OVER
15# FELT

12

3

1/2" STD. GRADE 32/16 PLY ROOF SHEATHING
LAID PERP. WO TRUSSES. NAIL W/ 8d NAILS
@ 6" O.C. EDGE AND BLOCKING AND 12" O.C. FIELD

24" OVERHANG

SOLID BLOCK - OMIT EACH 3DR
FOR SCREENED VENTS

STD. ROOF
TRUSSES @ 24" O.C.

METAL TRUSS TIES @ EA. TAIL/PLATE

2- 2 × 6 DFL
TOP PLATES
LAP 48" MIN.

2 × 6 FASCIA
WITH GUTTER

1/2" 'CCX' EXT. PLY @ ALL
EXPOSED EAVES. PROVIDE ALT. BID
FOR 1 × 6 T & G DECKING

© 2011 Cengage Learning. All Rights Reserved. May not be scanned, copied or duplicated, or posted to a publicly accessible website, in whole or in part.

Problem 12–30

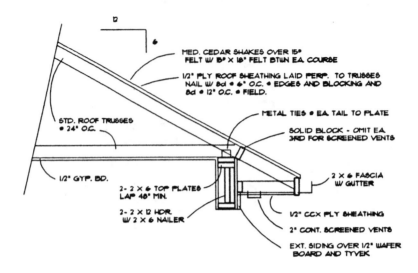

Problem 12–31

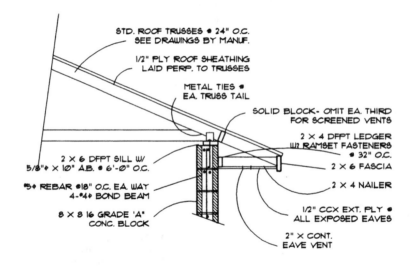

Problem 12–32

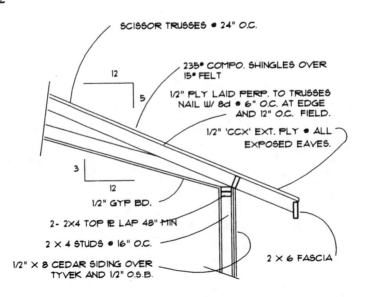

© 2011 Cengage Learning. All Rights Reserved. May not be scanned, copied or duplicated, or posted to a publicly accessible website, in whole or in part.

Problem 12–33

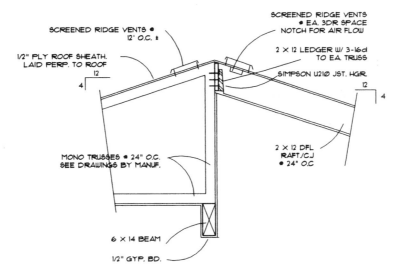

SCREENED RIDGE VENTS @
12' O.C. ±

SCREENED RIDGE VENTS
@ EA. 3DR SPACE
NOTCH FOR AIR FLOW

1/2" PLY ROOF SHEATH.
LAID PERP. TO ROOF

2 × 12 LEDGER W/ 3-16d
TO EA. TRUSS

SIMPSON U210 JST. HGR.

MONO TRUSSES @ 24" O.C.
SEE DRAWINGS BY MANUF.

2 × 12 DFL
RAFT./C.J
@ 24" O.C

6 × 14 BEAM

1/2" GYP. BD.

Problem 12–34

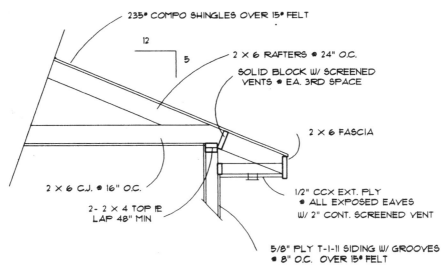

235# COMPO SHINGLES OVER 15# FELT

2 × 6 RAFTERS @ 24" O.C.

SOLID BLOCK W/ SCREENED
VENTS @ EA. 3RD SPACE

2 × 6 FASCIA

2 × 6 C.J. @ 16" O.C.

2- 2 × 4 TOP PL
LAP 48" MIN

1/2" CCX EXT. PLY
@ ALL EXPOSED EAVES
W/ 2" CONT. SCREENED VENT

5/8" PLY T-1-11 SIDING W/ GROOVES
@ 8" O.C. OVER 15# FELT

Problem 12–35

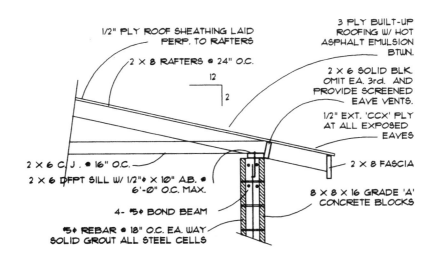

1/2" PLY ROOF SHEATHING LAID
PERP. TO RAFTERS

2 × 8 RAFTERS @ 24" O.C.

3 PLY BUILT-UP
ROOFING W/ HOT
ASPHALT EMULSION
BTWN.

2 × 6 SOLID BLK.
OMIT EA. 3rd. AND
PROVIDE SCREENED
EAVE VENTS.

1/2" EXT. 'CCX' PLY
AT ALL EXPOSED
EAVES

2 × 6 C.J. @ 16" O.C.

2 × 6 DFPT SILL W/ 1/2"∅ × 10" A.B.
6'-0" O.C. MAX.

4- #5∅ BOND BEAM

#5∅ REBAR @ 18" O.C. EA. WAY
SOLID GROUT ALL STEEL CELLS

2 × 8 FASCIA

8 × 8 × 16 GRADE 'A'
CONCRETE BLOCKS

© 2011 Cengage Learning. All Rights Reserved. May not be scanned, copied or duplicated, or posted to a publicly accessible website, in whole or in part.

Problem 12–36

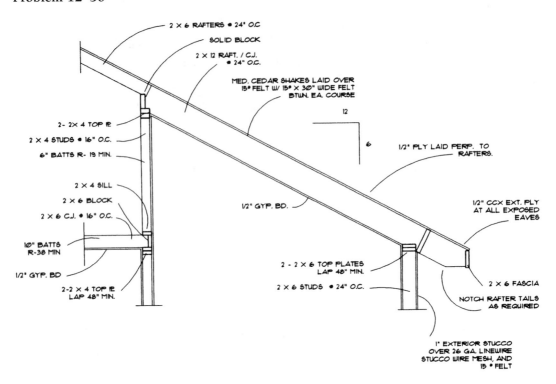

2 × 6 RAFTERS @ 24" O.C

SOLID BLOCK

2 × 12 RAFT. / C.J. @ 24" O.C.

MED. CEDAR SHAKES LAID OVER 15# FELT W/ 15# × 30" WIDE FELT BTWN. EA. COURSE

2- 2× 4 TOP P.

2 × 4 STUDS @ 16" O.C.

6" BATTS R- 19 MIN.

2 × 4 SILL

2 × 6 BLOCK

2 × 6 C.J. @ 16" O.C.

10" BATTS R-38 MIN

1/2" GYP. BD

2-2 × 4 TOP P. LAP 48" MIN.

1/2" GYP. BD.

12

6

1/2" PLY LAID PERP. TO RAFTERS.

1/2" CCX EXT. PLY AT ALL EXPOSED EAVES

2 - 2 × 6 TOP PLATES LAP 48" MIN.

2 × 6 STUDS @ 24" O.C.

2 × 6 FASCIA

NOTCH RAFTER TAILS AS REQUIRED

1" EXTERIOR STUCCO OVER 26 GA. LINEWIRE STUCCO WIRE MESH, AND 15 # FELT

Problem 12–37

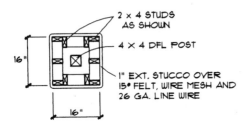

2 × 4 STUDS AS SHOWN

4 × 4 DFL POST

1" EXT. STUCCO OVER 15# FELT, WIRE MESH AND 26 GA. LINE WIRE

16"

16"

Problem 12–38

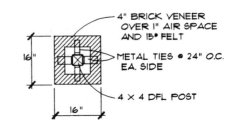

4" BRICK VENEER OVER 1" AIR SPACE AND 15# FELT

METAL TIES @ 24" O.C. EA. SIDE

4 × 4 DFL POST

16"

16"

Problem 12–39

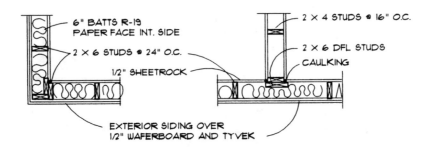

6" BATTS R-19 PAPER FACE INT. SIDE

2 × 4 STUDS @ 16" O.C.

2 × 6 STUDS @ 24" O.C.

2 × 6 DFL STUDS

1/2" SHEETROCK

CAULKING

EXTERIOR SIDING OVER 1/2" WAFERBOARD AND TYVEK

© 2011 Cengage Learning. All Rights Reserved. May not be scanned, copied or duplicated, or posted to a publicly accessible website, in whole or in part.

Problem 12–40

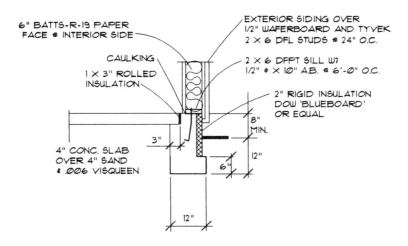

6" BATTS-R-19 PAPER
FACE @ INTERIOR SIDE

CAULKING

1 X 3" ROLLED
INSULATION

4" CONC. SLAB
OVER 4" SAND
& .006 VISQUEEN

EXTERIOR SIDING OVER
1/2" WAFERBOARD AND TYVEK
2 X 6 DFL STUDS @ 24" O.C.

2 X 6 DFPT SILL W7
1/2" Φ X 10" A.B. @ 6'-0" O.C.

2" RIGID INSULATION
DOW 'BLUEBOARD'
OR EQUAL

8" MIN.

3"

12"

6"

12"

Problem 12–41

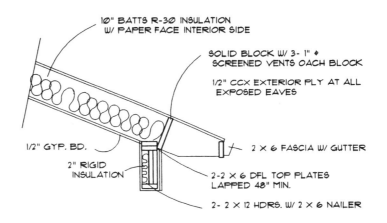

10" BATTS R-30 INSULATION
W/ PAPER FACE INTERIOR SIDE

SOLID BLOCK W/ 3- 1" Φ
SCREENED VENTS @ACH BLOCK

1/2" CCX EXTERIOR PLY AT ALL
EXPOSED EAVES

1/2" GYP. BD.

2" RIGID
INSULATION

2 X 6 FASCIA W/ GUTTER

2-2 X 6 DFL TOP PLATES
LAPPED 48" MIN.

2- 2 X 12 HDRS. W/ 2 X 6 NAILER

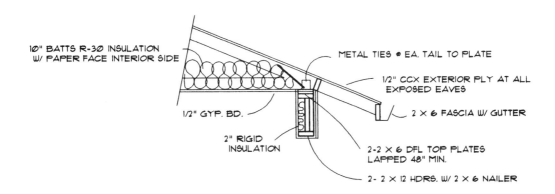

10" BATTS R-30 INSULATION
W/ PAPER FACE INTERIOR SIDE

1/2" GYP. BD.

2" RIGID
INSULATION

METAL TIES @ EA. TAIL TO PLATE

1/2" CCX EXTERIOR PLY AT ALL
EXPOSED EAVES

2 X 6 FASCIA W/ GUTTER

2-2 X 6 DFL TOP PLATES
LAPPED 48" MIN.

2- 2 X 12 HDRS. W/ 2 X 6 NAILER

© 2011 Cengage Learning. All Rights Reserved. May not be scanned, copied or duplicated, or posted to a publicly accessible website, in whole or in part.

Problem 12–42

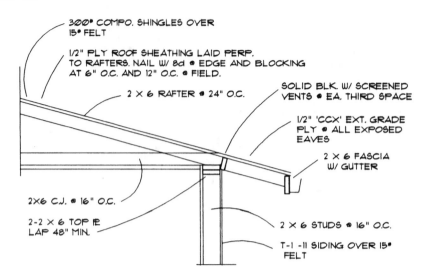

300# COMPO. SHINGLES OVER 15# FELT

1/2" PLY ROOF SHEATHING LAID PERP. TO RAFTERS. NAIL W/ 8d ● EDGE AND BLOCKING AT 6" O.C. AND 12" O.C. ● FIELD.

2 × 6 RAFTER ● 24" O.C.

SOLID BLK. W/ SCREENED VENTS ● EA. THIRD SPACE

1/2" 'CCX' EXT. GRADE PLY ● ALL EXPOSED EAVES

2 × 6 FASCIA W/ GUTTER

2×6 C.J. ● 16" O.C.

2-2 × 6 TOP P. LAP 48" MIN.

2 × 6 STUDS ● 16" O.C.

T-1 -11 SIDING OVER 15# FELT

Problem 12–43

Problem 12–44

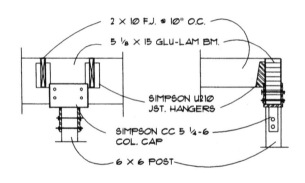

2 × 10 F.J. ● 10" O.C.

5 1/8 × 15 GLU-LAM BM.

SIMPSON U210 JST. HANGERS

SIMPSON CC 5 1/4-6 COL. CAP

6 × 6 POST

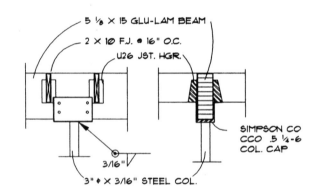

5 1/8 × 15 GLU-LAM BEAM

2 × 10 F.J. ● 16" O.C.

U26 JST. HGR.

SIMPSON CO CCO .5 1/4-6 COL. CAP

3/16"

3" ● X 3/16" STEEL COL.

Problem 12–45

Problem 12–46

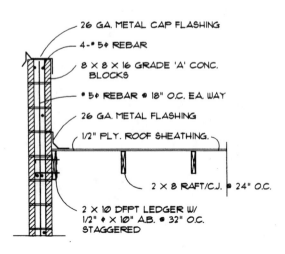

26 GA. METAL CAP FLASHING

4-● 5● REBAR

8 × 8 × 16 GRADE 'A' CONC. BLOCKS

● 5● REBAR ● 18" O.C. EA. WAY

26 GA. METAL FLASHING

1/2" PLY. ROOF SHEATHING.

2 × 8 RAFT/C.J. ● 24" O.C.

2 × 10 DFPT LEDGER W/ 1/2" ● X 10" A.B. ● 32" O.C. STAGGERED

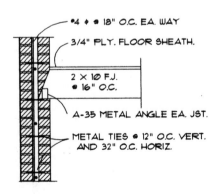

●4 ● ● 18" O.C. EA. WAY

3/4" PLY. FLOOR SHEATH.

2 × 10 F.J. ● 16" O.C.

A-35 METAL ANGLE EA. JST.

METAL TIES ● 12" O.C. VERT. AND 32" O.C. HORIZ.

© 2011 Cengage Learning. All Rights Reserved. May not be scanned, copied or duplicated, or posted to a publicly accessible website, in whole or in part.

Problem 12–47

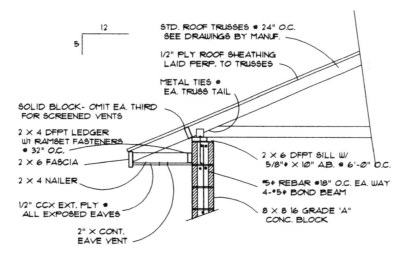

12
5

STD. ROOF TRUSSES @ 24" O.C.
SEE DRAWINGS BY MANUF.

1/2" PLY ROOF SHEATHING
LAID PERP. TO TRUSSES

METAL TIES @
EA. TRUSS TAIL

SOLID BLOCK- OMIT EA. THIRD
FOR SCREENED VENTS

2 X 4 DFPT LEDGER
W/ RAMSET FASTENERS
@ 32" O.C.

2 X 6 FASCIA

2 X 4 NAILER

1/2" CCX EXT. PLY @
ALL EXPOSED EAVES

2" X CONT.
EAVE VENT

2 X 6 DFPT SILL W/
5/8"Ø X 10" A.B. @ 6'-0" O.C.

#5Ø REBAR @18" O.C. EA. WAY
4-#5Ø BOND BEAM

8 X 8 16 GRADE 'A'
CONC. BLOCK

Problem 12–48

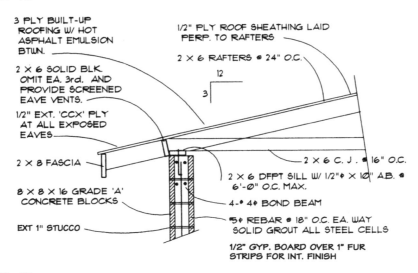

3 PLY BUILT-UP
ROOFING W/ HOT
ASPHALT EMULSION
BTWN.

2 X 6 SOLID BLK.
OMIT EA. 3rd. AND
PROVIDE SCREENED
EAVE VENTS.

1/2" EXT. 'CCX' PLY
AT ALL EXPOSED
EAVES.

2 X 8 FASCIA

8 X 8 X 16 GRADE 'A'
CONCRETE BLOCKS

EXT 1" STUCCO

1/2" PLY ROOF SHEATHING LAID
PERP. TO RAFTERS

2 X 6 RAFTERS @ 24" O.C.

12
3

2 X 6 C. J. @ 16" O.C.

2 X 6 DFPT SILL W/ 1/2"Ø X 10" A.B. @
6'-0" O.C. MAX.

4-#4Ø BOND BEAM

#5Ø REBAR @ 18" O.C. EA. WAY
SOLID GROUT ALL STEEL CELLS

1/2" GYP. BOARD OVER 1" FUR
STRIPS FOR INT. FINISH

Problem 12–49

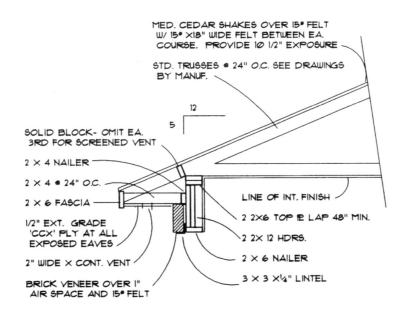

MED. CEDAR SHAKES OVER 15# FELT
W/ 15# X18" WIDE FELT BETWEEN EA.
COURSE. PROVIDE 10 1/2" EXPOSURE

STD. TRUSSES @ 24" O.C. SEE DRAWINGS
BY MANUF.

12
5

SOLID BLOCK- OMIT EA.
3RD FOR SCREENED VENT

2 X 4 NAILER

2 X 4 @ 24" O.C.

2 X 6 FASCIA

1/2" EXT. GRADE
'CCX' PLY AT ALL
EXPOSED EAVES

2" WIDE X CONT. VENT

BRICK VENEER OVER 1"
AIR SPACE AND 15# FELT

LINE OF INT. FINISH

2 2X6 TOP Ø LAP 48" MIN.

2 2X 12 HDRS.

2 X 6 NAILER

3 X 3 X¼" LINTEL

© 2011 Cengage Learning. All Rights Reserved. May not be scanned, copied or duplicated, or posted to a publicly accessible website, in whole or in part.

Problem 12–50

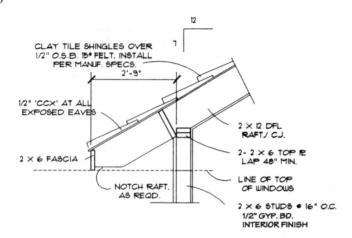

CLAY TILE SHINGLES OVER
1/2" O.S.B. 15# FELT. INSTALL
PER MANUF. SPECS.

2'-9"

1/2" 'CCX' AT ALL
EXPOSED EAVES

2 X 6 FASCIA

12

2 X 12 DFL
RAFT./ C.J.

2- 2 X 6 TOP PL
LAP 48" MIN.

LINE OF TOP
OF WINDOWS

NOTCH RAFT.
AS REQD.

2 X 6 STUDS ● 16" O.C.
1/2" GYP. BD.
INTERIOR FINISH

© 2011 Cengage Learning. All Rights Reserved. May not be scanned, copied or duplicated, or posted to a publicly accessible website, in whole or in part.

CHAPTER 13 SECTIONS

Problem 13–1A

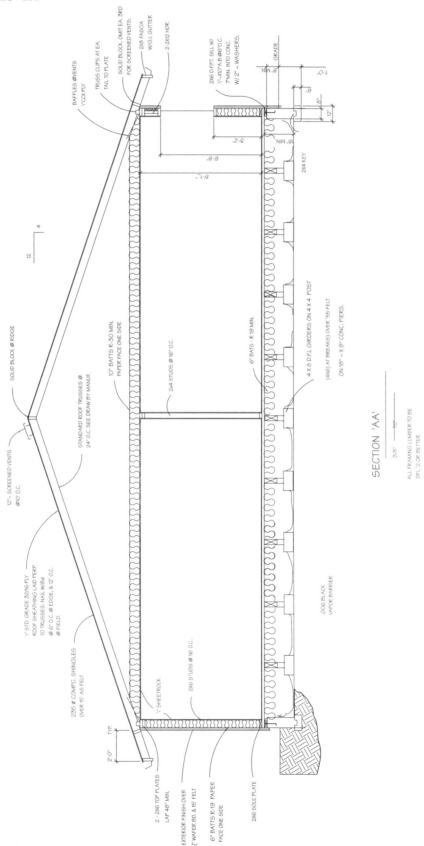

SOLID BLOCK @ RIDGE

BAFFLES @ VENTS
½" CCX PLY

TRUSS CLIPS AT EA.
TAIL TO PLATE

SOLID BLOCK. OMIT EA. 3RD
FOR SCREENED VENTS.

2×8 FASCIA
W/ G.I. GUTTER

2 - 2×12 HDR

2×6 D.F.P.T. SILL W/
1" - X10" A.B. @ 6' O.C.
7" MIN. INTO CONC.
W/ 2" - WASHERS.

4" MIN.

GRADE

1'-0"

6"

8"

12"

18" MIN.

3'-2"

6'-8"

8'-1"

2×4 KEY

4 X 8 D.F.L GIRDERS ON 4 X 4 POST

(4×6) AT BREAKS) OVER '55 FELT
ON 18" – X 8" CONC. PIERS.

6" BATTS - R 19 MIN.

.006 BLACK
VAPOR BARRIER

12" SCREENED VENTS
@ 10' O.C.

STANDARD ROOF TRUSSES @
24" O.C. SEE DRAW BY MANUF.

10" BATTS R-30 MIN.
PAPER FACE ONE SIDE

2×4 STUDS @ 16" O.C.

235 # COMPO. SHINGLES
OVER 15# AS FELT

½" STD. GRADE 32/16 PLY
ROOF SHEATHING LAID PERP.
TO TRUSSES. NAIL W/ 8d
@ 6" O.C. @ EDGE, & 12" O.C.
@ FIELD.

½" SHEETROCK

2×6 STUDS @ 16' O.C.

2 - 2×6 TOP PLATES
LAP 48" MIN.

EXTERIOR FINISH OVER
⅜" WAFER BD. & 15# FELT

6" BATTS R-19 PAPER
FACE ONE SIDE

2×6 SOLE PLATE

2'-0"

TYP.

4
12

SECTION 'AA'
3/8" = 1'0"

ALL FRAMING LUMBER TO BE
DFL '2 OR BETTER

© 2011 Cengage Learning. All Rights Reserved. May not be scanned, copied or duplicated, or posted to a publicly accessible website, in whole or in part.

Problem 13–1B

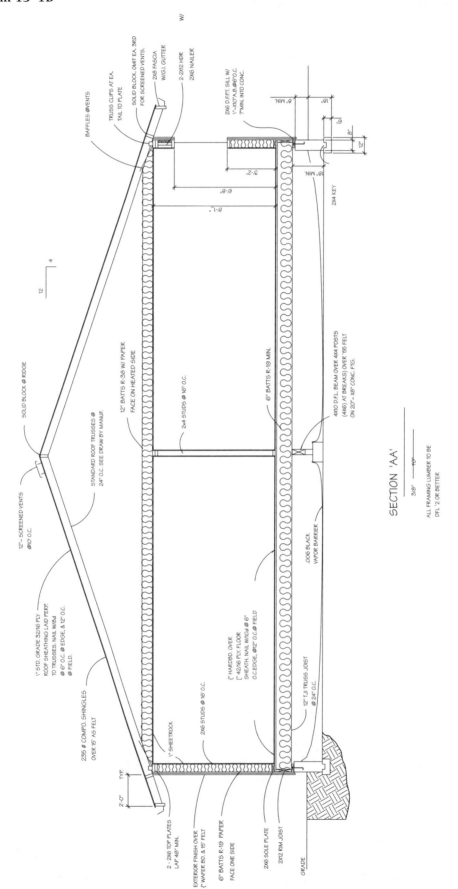

SECTION 'AA'

3/8" = 1'-0"

ALL FRAMING LUMBER TO BE
DFL '2' OR BETTER

© 2011 Cengage Learning. All Rights Reserved. May not be scanned, copied or duplicated, or posted to a publicly accessible website, in whole or in part.

Problem 13–1C

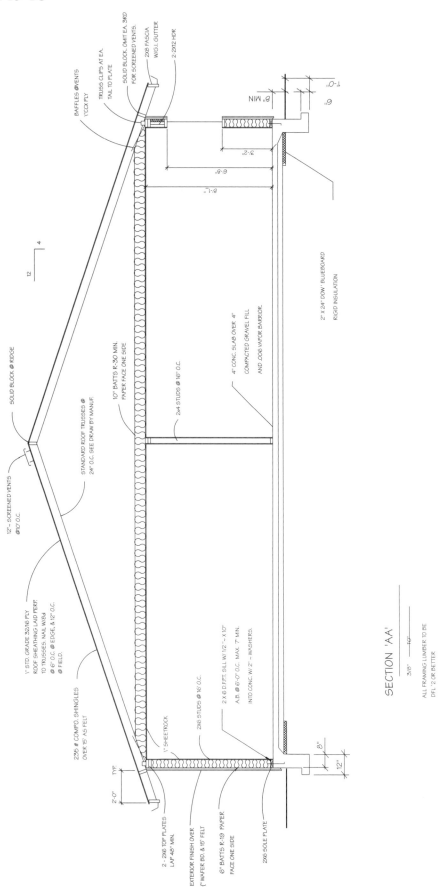

BAFFLES @ VENTS

TRUSS CLIPS AT EA. TAIL TO PLATE

SOLID BLOCK OMIT EA. 3RD FOR SCREENED VENTS.

2X8 FASCIA W/ G.I. GUTTER

2-2X12 HDR

1'-0"

8" MIN

6"

3'-2"

6'-8"

8'-1"

SOLID BLOCK @ RIDGE

4

12

1" STD. GRADE 32/16 PLY ROOF SHEATHING LAID PERP. TO TRUSSES. NAIL W/8d @ 6" O.C. @ EDGE, & 12" O.C. @ FIELD.

1" CCX PLY

10" BATTS R-30 MIN. PAPER FACE ONE SIDE

2X4 STUDS @ 16" O.C.

4" CONC. SLAB OVER 4" COMPACTED GRAVEL FILL AND .006 VAPOR BARRIOR.

2" X 24" DOW' BLUEBOARD RIGID INSULATION

STANDARD ROOF TRUSSES @ 24" O.C. SEE DRAW BY MANUF.

12" SCREENED VENTS @ 10' O.C.

235 # COMPO. SHINGLES OVER 15 # FELT

1" SHEETROCK

2X6 STUDS @ 16" O.C.

2 X 6 D.F.P.T. SILL W/ 1/2" – X 10" A.B. @ 6'-0" O.C. MAX. 7" MIN. INTO CONC. W/ 2" – WASHERS.

2X6 SOLE PLATE

8"

12"

2'-0"

TYP.

2 - 2X6 TOP PLATES LAP 48" MIN.

EXTERIOR FINISH OVER 1" WAFER BD. & 15" FELT

6" BATTS R-19 PAPER FACE ONE SIDE

SECTION 'AA'

3/8" = 1'-0"

ALL FRAMING LUMBER TO BE DFL 2 OR BETTER

© 2011 Cengage Learning. All Rights Reserved. May not be scanned, copied or duplicated, or posted to a publicly accessible website, in whole or in part.

Problem 13–2A

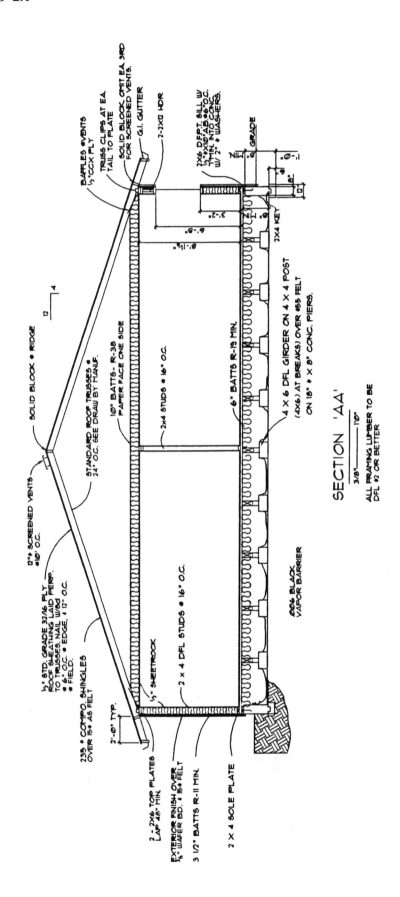

SECTION 'AA'

3/8" —— 1'0"

ALL FRAMING LUMBER TO BE
DFL #2 OR BETTER

© 2011 Cengage Learning. All Rights Reserved. May not be scanned, copied or duplicated, or posted to a publicly accessible website, in whole or in part.

Problem 13–2B

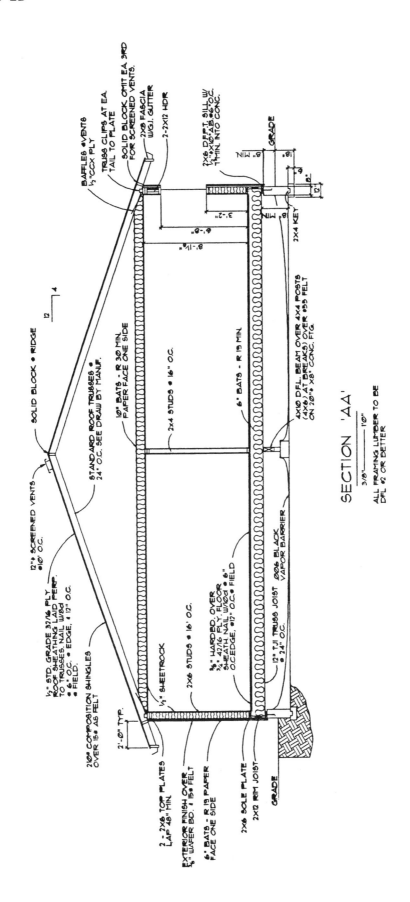

SECTION 'AA'

3/8" = 1'0"

ALL FRAMING LUMBER TO BE
DFL #2 OR BETTER

BAFFLES @ VENTS
½" CCX PLY
TRUSS CLIPS AT EA.
TAIL TO PLATE
2X8 FASCIA
W/G.I. GUTTER
2-2X12 HDR
SOLID BLOCK OMIT EA. 3RD
FOR SCREENED VENTS.
2X6 DF.PT. SILL W/
1½"X10"AB @6" O.C.
7"MIN INTO CONC.
GRADE

SOLID BLOCK @ RIDGE
STANDARD ROOF TRUSSES @
24" O.C. SEE DRAW BY MANF.
10" BATS - R 30 MIN
PAPER FACE ONE SIDE
2X4 STUDS @ 16" O.C.
6" BATS - R 19 MIN
4X10 DFL. BEAM OVER 4X4 POSTS
(4X6) AT BREAKS) OVER #55 FELT
ON 12"Ø X8' CONC. FTG.

12"Ø SCREENED VENTS
@10' O.C.
½" STD. GRADE 32/16 PLY
ROOF SHEATHING LAID PERP.
TO TRUSSES. NAIL W/8d
@ 6" O.C. @ EDGE, @ 12" O.C.
@ FIELD.
¼" SHEETROCK
2X6 STUDS @ 16" O.C.
⅝" HARDBD. OVER
¾" 42/16 PLY. FLOOR
SHEATH. NAIL W/10d @ 6"
O.C.EDGE, @12" O.C. @ FIELD
12" TJI TRUSS JOIST @
24" O.C.
006 BLACK
VAPOR BARRIER

210# COMPOSITION SHINGLES
OVER 15# AS FELT
2'-Ø" TYP.
2 - 2X6 TOP PLATES
LAP 48" MIN.
EXTERIOR FINISH OVER
⅝" WAFER BD. / 15# FELT
6" BATS - R 19 MIN
FACE ONE SIDE
2X6 SOLE PLATE
2X12 RIM JOIST
GRADE

2X4 KEY

© 2011 Cengage Learning. All Rights Reserved. May not be scanned, copied or duplicated, or posted to a publicly accessible website, in whole or in part.

Problem 13–2C

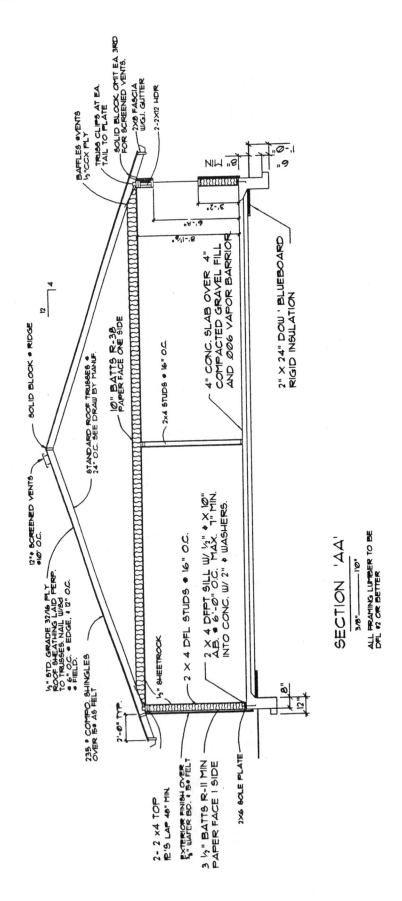

SECTION 'AA'

3/8" = 1'0"

ALL FRAMING LUMBER TO BE
DFL #2 OR BETTER.

© 2011 Cengage Learning. All Rights Reserved. May not be scanned, copied or duplicated, or posted to a publicly accessible website, in whole or in part.

Problem 13–3A

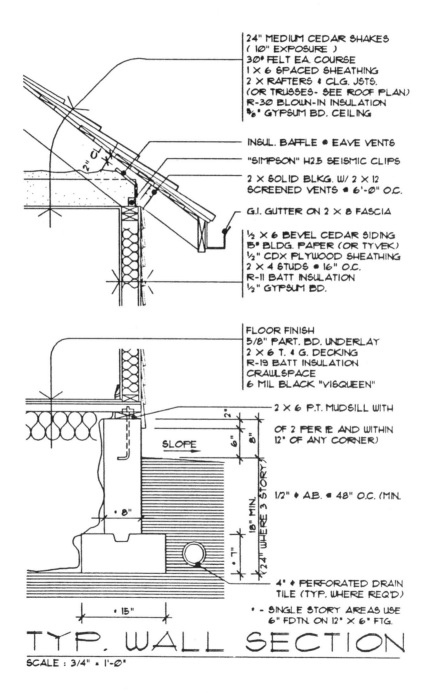

24" MEDIUM CEDAR SHAKES
(10" EXPOSURE)
30# FELT EA. COURSE
1 X 6 SPACED SHEATHING
2 X RAFTERS & CLG. JSTS.
(OR TRUSSES- SEE ROOF PLAN)
R-30 BLOWN-IN INSULATION
⅝" GYPSUM BD. CEILING

INSUL. BAFFLE @ EAVE VENTS

"SIMPSON" H2.5 SEISMIC CLIPS

2 X SOLID BLKG. W/ 2 X 12
SCREENED VENTS @ 6'-0" O.C.

G.I. GUTTER ON 2 X 8 FASCIA

½ X 6 BEVEL CEDAR SIDING
15# BLDG. PAPER (OR TYVEK)
½" CDX PLYWOOD SHEATHING
2 X 4 STUDS @ 16" O.C.
R-11 BATT INSULATION
½" GYPSUM BD.

FLOOR FINISH
5/8" PART. BD. UNDERLAY
2 X 6 T. & G. DECKING
R-19 BATT INSULATION
CRAWLSPACE
6 MIL BLACK "VISQUEEN"

2 X 6 P.T. MUDSILL WITH

OF 2 PER 12 AND WITHIN
12" OF ANY CORNER)

½" ⌀ A.B. @ 48" O.C. (MIN.

SLOPE

4" ⌀ PERFORATED DRAIN
TILE (TYP. WHERE REQ'D)

* - SINGLE STORY AREAS USE
6" FDTN. ON 12" X 6" FTG.

TYP. WALL SECTION

SCALE : 3/4" = 1'-0"

© 2011 Cengage Learning. All Rights Reserved. May not be scanned, copied or duplicated, or posted to a publicly accessible website, in whole or in part.

Problem 13–3A (Continued)

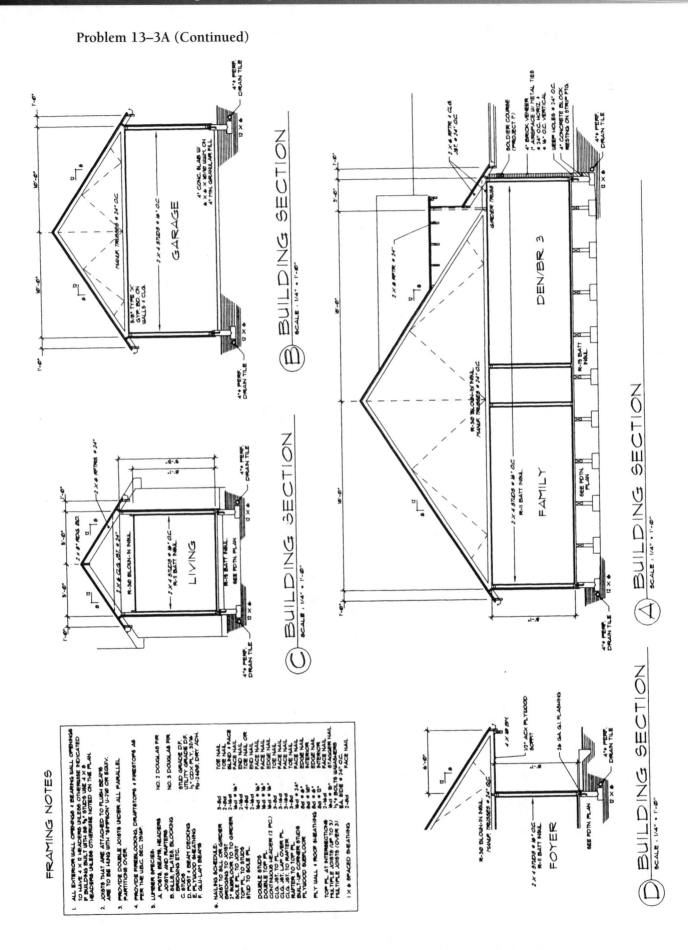

© 2011 Cengage Learning. All Rights Reserved. May not be scanned, copied or duplicated, or posted to a publicly accessible website, in whole or in part.

Problem 13–3B

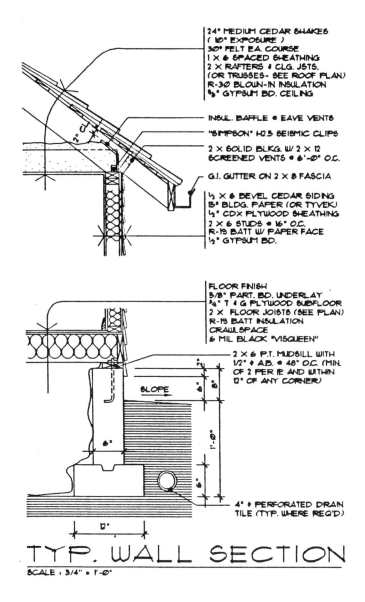

24" MEDIUM CEDAR SHAKES
(10" EXPOSURE)
30# FELT EA. COURSE
1 X 6 SPACED SHEATHING
2 X RAFTERS & CLG. JSTS.
(OR TRUSSES- SEE ROOF PLAN)
R-30 BLOWN-IN INSULATION
5/8" GYPSUM BD. CEILING

INSUL. BAFFLE @ EAVE VENTS

"SIMPSON" H2.5 SEISMIC CLIPS

2 X SOLID BLKG. W/ 2 X 12
SCREENED VENTS @ 6'-0" O.C.

G.I. GUTTER ON 2 X 8 FASCIA

1/2 X 6 BEVEL CEDAR SIDING
15# BLDG. PAPER (OR TYVEK)
1/2" CDX PLYWOOD SHEATHING
2 X 6 STUDS @ 16" O.C.
R-19 BATT W/ PAPER FACE
1/2" GYPSUM BD.

FLOOR FINISH
5/8" PART. BD. UNDERLAY
3/4" T & G PLYWOOD SUBFLOOR
2 X FLOOR JOISTS (SEE PLAN)
R-19 BATT INSULATION
CRAWLSPACE
6 MIL BLACK "VISQUEEN"

2 X 6 P.T. MUDSILL WITH
1/2" ∅ A.B. @ 48" O.C. (MIN.
OF 2 PER P AND WITHIN
12" OF ANY CORNER)

SLOPE

4" ∅ PERFORATED DRAIN
TILE (TYP. WHERE REQ'D)

TYP. WALL SECTION
SCALE : 3/4" = 1'-0"

© 2011 Cengage Learning. All Rights Reserved. May not be scanned, copied or duplicated, or posted to a publicly accessible website, in whole or in part.

Problem 13–3B (Continued)

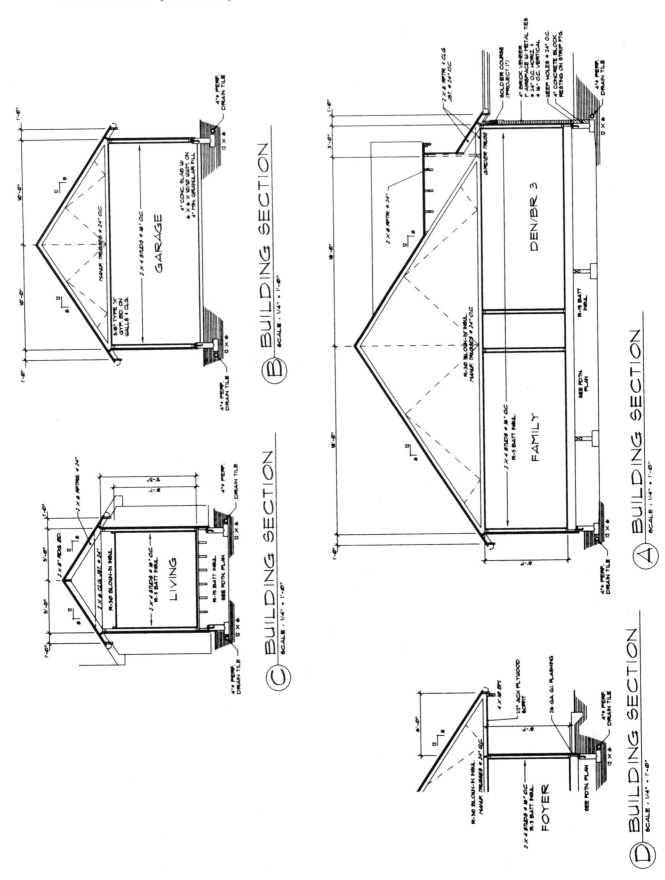

© 2011 Cengage Learning. All Rights Reserved. May not be scanned, copied or duplicated, or posted to a publicly accessible website, in whole or in part.

Problem 13–3C

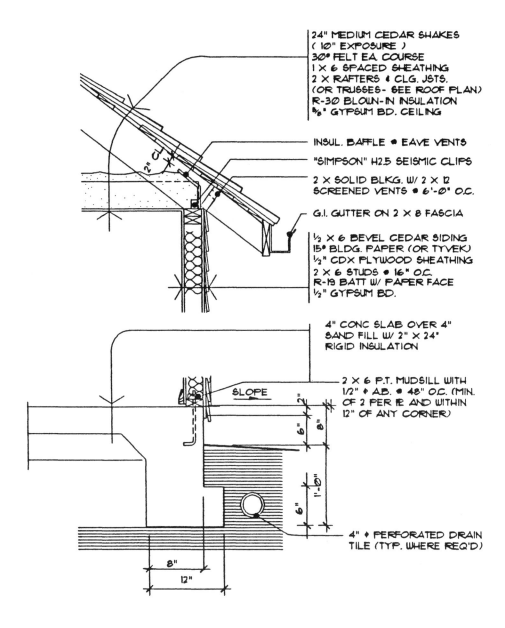

24" MEDIUM CEDAR SHAKES
(10" EXPOSURE)
30# FELT EA COURSE
1 X 6 SPACED SHEATHING
2 X RAFTERS & CLG. JSTS.
(OR TRUSSES- SEE ROOF PLAN)
R-30 BLOWN-IN INSULATION
⅝" GYPSUM BD. CEILING

INSUL. BAFFLE @ EAVE VENTS

"SIMPSON" H2.5 SEISMIC CLIPS

2 X SOLID BLKG. W/ 2 X 12
SCREENED VENTS @ 6'-0" O.C.

G.I. GUTTER ON 2 X 8 FASCIA

½ X 6 BEVEL CEDAR SIDING
15# BLDG. PAPER (OR TYVEK)
½" CDX PLYWOOD SHEATHING
2 X 6 STUDS @ 16" O.C.
R-19 BATT W/ PAPER FACE
½" GYPSUM BD.

4" CONC SLAB OVER 4"
SAND FILL W/ 2" X 24"
RIGID INSULATION

2 X 6 P.T. MUDSILL WITH
½" ⌀ A.B. @ 48" O.C. (MIN.
OF 2 PER PC AND WITHIN
12" OF ANY CORNER)

SLOPE

4" ⌀ PERFORATED DRAIN
TILE (TYP. WHERE REQ'D)

TYP. WALL SECTION

SCALE : 3/4" = 1'-0"

© 2011 Cengage Learning. All Rights Reserved. May not be scanned, copied or duplicated, or posted to a publicly accessible website, in whole or in part.

Problem 13–3C (Continued)

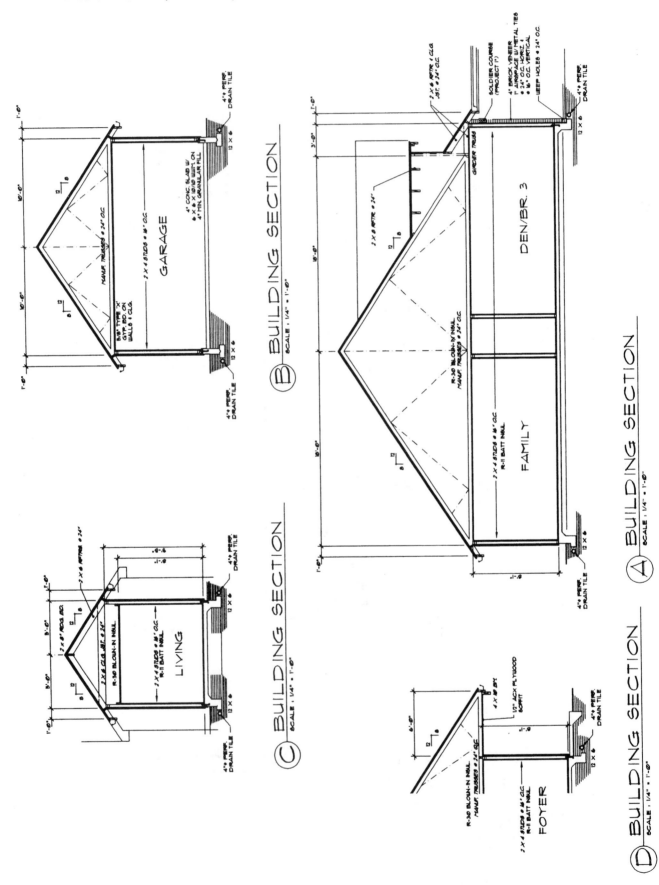

© 2011 Cengage Learning. All Rights Reserved. May not be scanned, copied or duplicated, or posted to a publicly accessible website, in whole or in part.

Problem 13–4 A–E

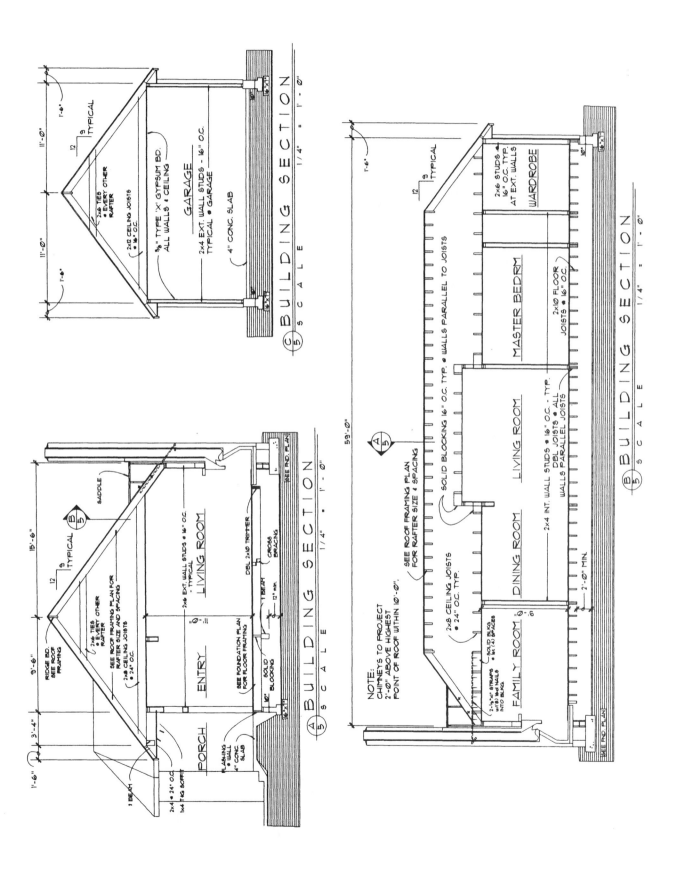

© 2011 Cengage Learning. All Rights Reserved. May not be scanned, copied or duplicated, or posted to a publicly accessible website, in whole or in part.

Problem 13–4 A–E (Continued)

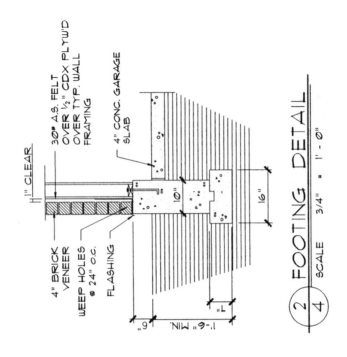

30# A.S. FELT OVER ½" CDX PLYW'D OVER TYP. WALL FRAMING

4" CONC. GARAGE SLAB

1" CLEAR

4" BRICK VENEER

WEEP HOLES @ 24" O.C.

FLASHING

10"

16"

"L"

6"

1'-6" MIN.

② FOOTING DETAIL
④ SCALE   3/4" = 1' - 0"

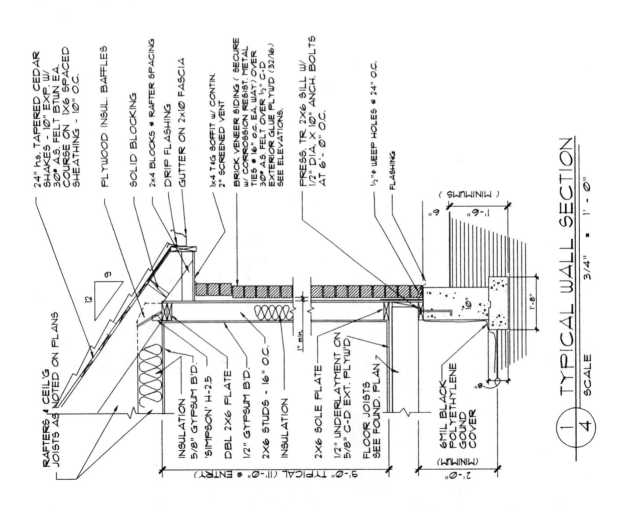

24" hs. TAPERED CEDAR SHAKES - 10" EXP. W/ 30# A.S. FELT BTWN EA. COURSE ON 1X6 SPACED SHEATHING - 10" O.C.

PLYWOOD INSUL. BAFFLES

SOLID BLOCKING

2x4 BLOCKS @ RAFTER SPACING

DRIP FLASHING

GUTTER ON 2x10 FASCIA

1x4 T&G SOFFIT W/ CONTIN. 2" SCREENED VENT

BRICK VENEER SIDING (SECURE W/ CORROSION RESIST. METAL TIES @ 16" O.C. EA. WAY) OVER 30# A.S. FELT OVER ½" C-D EXTERIOR GLUE PLYW'D (32/16) SEE ELEVATIONS.

PRESS. TR. 2x6 SILL W/ ½" DIA. X 10" ANCH. BOLTS AT 6'- 0" O.C.

½" WEEP HOLES @ 24" O.C.

FLASHING

RAFTERS & CEIL'G JOISTS AS NOTED ON PLANS

INSULATION

5/8" GYPSUM B'D.

'SIMPSON' H-2.5

DBL 2x6 PLATE

½" GYPSUM B'D.

2x6 STUDS - 16" O.C.

INSULATION

2x6 SOLE PLATE

½" UNDERLAYMENT ON 5/8" C-D EXT. PLYW'D

FLOOR JOISTS SEE FOUND. PLAN

6MIL BLACK POLYETHYLENE GOUND COVER

12
6

1" min.

9'-6" TYPICAL (11'-0" @ ENTRY)

6"

1'-6"

(MINIMUM)

1'-8"

10"

2'-0"

(MINIMUM)

① TYPICAL WALL SECTION
④ SCALE   3/4" = 1' - 0"

© 2011 Cengage Learning. All Rights Reserved. May not be scanned, copied or duplicated, or posted to a publicly accessible website, in whole or in part.

Problem 13–5 A–E

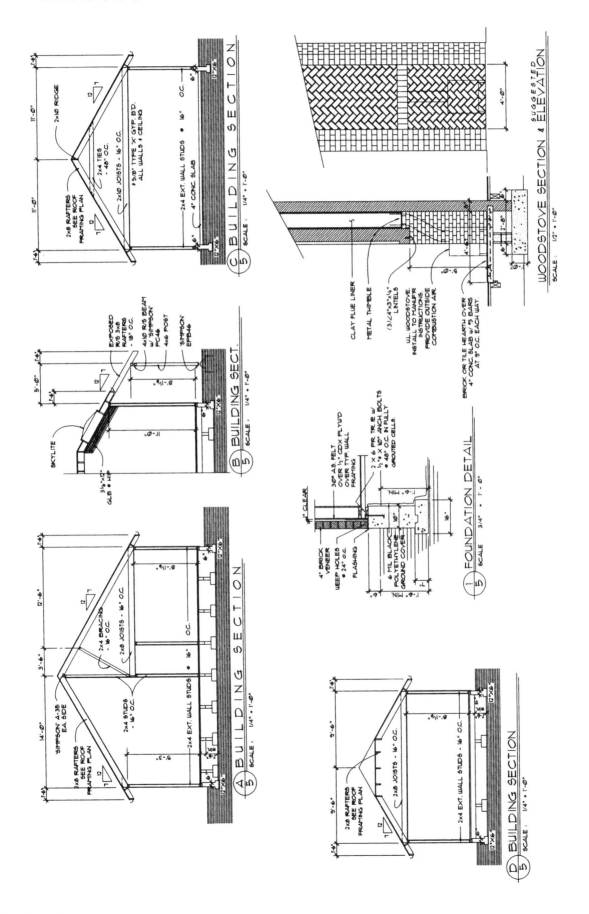

© 2011 Cengage Learning. All Rights Reserved. May not be scanned, copied or duplicated, or posted to a publicly accessible website, in whole or in part.

Problem 13–6A

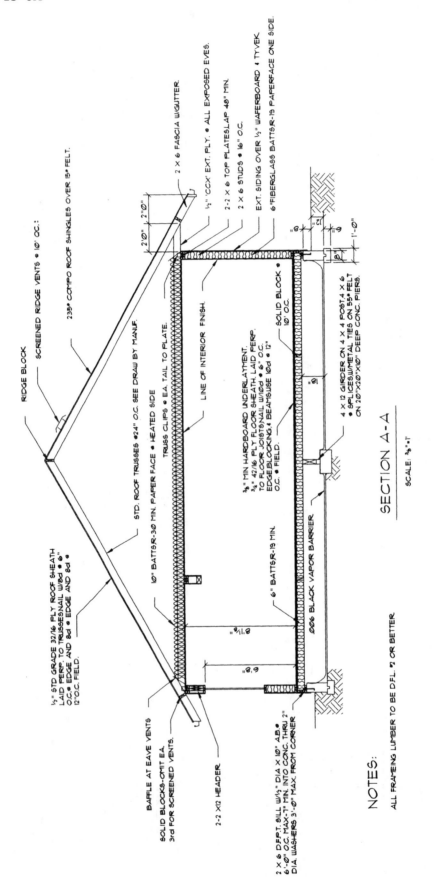

RIDGE BLOCK

SCREENED RIDGE VENTS @ 10' O.C. :

235# COMPO ROOF SHINGLES OVER 15# FELT.

2 × 6 FASCIA W/GUTTER.

½ "CCX" EXT. PLY. ● ALL EXPOSED EVES.

2-2 × 6 TOP PLATES, LAP 48" MIN.

2 × 6 STUDS @ 16" O.C.

EXT. SIDING OVER ½" WAFERBOARD & TYVEK

6"FIBERGLASS BATTS R-19 PAPERFACE ONE SIDE.

STD. ROOF TRUSSES @24" O.C. SEE DRAW BY MANUF.

10" BATTS R-30 MIN. PAPER FACE ● HEATED SIDE

TRUSS CLIPS ● EA. TAIL TO PLATE.

LINE OF INTERIOR FINISH.

⅜" MIN HARDBOARD UNDERLAYMENT.
¾" 42/16 PLY FLOOR SHEATH. LAID PERP.
TO FLOOR JOISTS NAIL W/10d ● 6" O.C.
EDGE BLOCKING, 4 BEAMS USE 10d @ 12"
O.C. ● FIELD.

SOLID BLOCK ●
10' O.C.

4 × 12 GIRDER ON 4 × 4 POST, 4 × 6
● SPLICES W/METAL TIES ON 55# FELT
ON 20"X20"X10" DEEP CONC. PIERS.

006 BLACK VAPOR BARRIER

6" BATTS R-19 MIN.

2-2 X12 HEADER

2 × 6 DF.P.T. SILL W/½" DIA × 10" A.B. ●
6'-0" O.C. MAX-7" MIN. INTO CONC. THRU 2"
DIA. WASHERS 3'-0" MAX FROM CORNER

BAFFLE AT EAVE VENTS
SOLID BLOCKS-OMIT EA.
3rd FOR SCREENED VENTS.

½" STD GRADE 32/16 PLY ROOF SHEATH
LAID PERP. TO TRUSSES NAIL W/8d ● 6"
O.C.● EDGE AND 8d ● EDGE AND 8d ●
12"O.C. FIELD.

8'-11"

6'-8"

1'-0"

SECTION A-A

SCALE: ⅜"=1'

NOTES:

ALL FRAMING LUMBER TO BE DF.L. #2 OR BETTER

© 2011 Cengage Learning. All Rights Reserved. May not be scanned, copied or duplicated, or posted to a publicly accessible website, in whole or in part.

Problem 13–6B

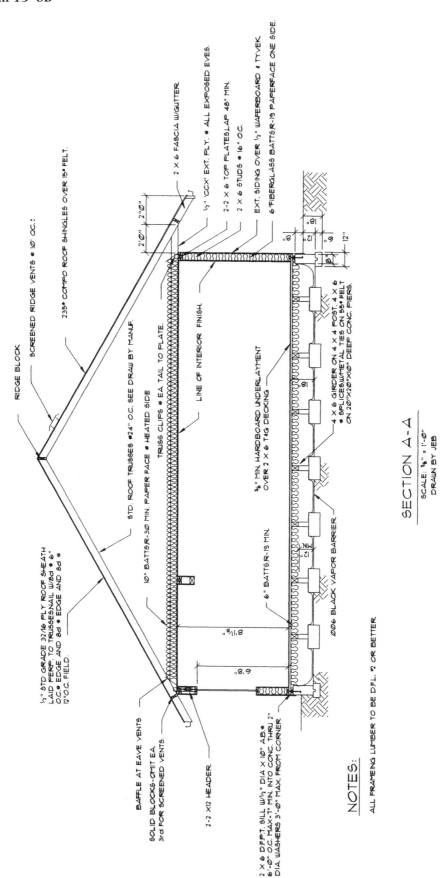

SECTION A-A

SCALE: ⅜" = 1'-0"
DRAWN BY JEB

RIDGE BLOCK

SCREENED RIDGE VENTS @ 10' O.C.:

235# COMPO ROOF SHINGLES OVER 15# FELT.

2 × 6 FASCIA W/GUTTER

½" 'CCX' EXT. PLY. @ ALL EXPOSED EVES.

2-2 × 6 TOP PLATES LAP 48" MIN.

2 × 6 STUDS @ 16" O.C.

EXT. SIDING OVER ½" WAFERBOARD & TYVEK

6"FIBERGLASS BATT S R-19 PAPERFACE ONE SIDE.

STD. ROOF TRUSSES @24" O.C. SEE DRAW BY MANUF.

TRUSS CLIPS @ EA. TAIL TO PLATE.

LINE OF INTERIOR FINISH.

10" BATTS R-30 MIN. PAPER FACE @ HEATED SIDE

⅜" MIN. HARDBOARD UNDERLAYMENT OVER 2 × 6 T&G DECKING

4 × 6 GIRDER ON 4 × 4 POST. 4 × 6 @ SPLICES W/METAL TIES ON 55# FELT ON 20"×20"×10" DEEP CONC. PIERS.

6" BATTS R-19 MIN.

.006 BLACK VAPOR BARRIER

½" STD GRADE 32/16 PLY ROOF SHEATH LAID PERP. TO TRUSSES NAIL W/8d @ 6" O.C. @ EDGE AND 8d @ EDGE AND 8d @ 12"O.C. FIELD.

BAFFLE AT EAVE VENTS

SOLID BLOCKS-OMIT EA. 3rd FOR SCREENED VENTS.

2-2 ×12 HEADER

2 × 6 DF.P.T. SILL W/½" DIA × 10" A.B. @ 6'-0" O.C. MAX-"T" MIN. INTO CONC. THRU 2" DIA. WASHERS 3'-0" MAX FROM CORNER

NOTES:

ALL FRAMING LUMBER TO BE D.F.L. 2 OR BETTER

2'0" 2"0"

8" 12" 6"

12" 8"

8"

8,9"

8,11"

© 2011 Cengage Learning. All Rights Reserved. May not be scanned, copied or duplicated, or posted to a publicly accessible website, in whole or in part.

Problem 13–6C

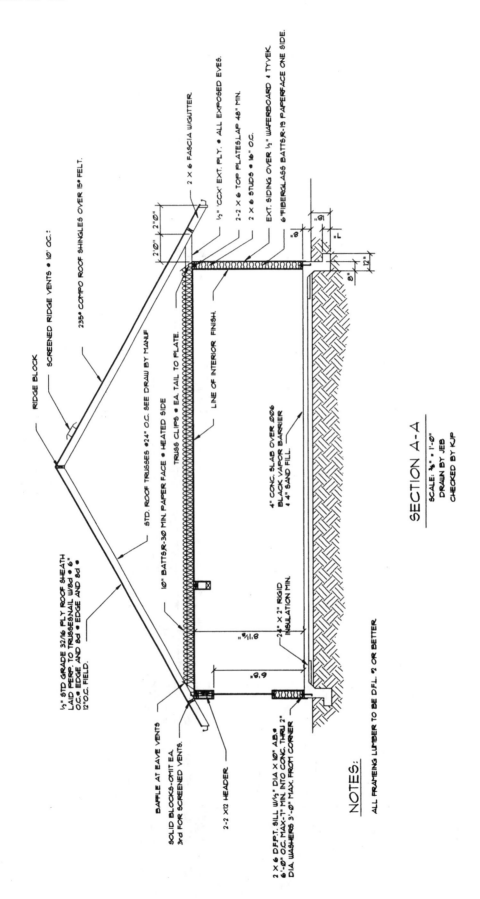

SECTION A-A

SCALE: ⅜" = 1'-0"
DRAWN BY JEB
CHECKED BY KJP

NOTES:

ALL FRAMING LUMBER TO BE D.FL. 2 OR BETTER

© 2011 Cengage Learning. All Rights Reserved. May not be scanned, copied or duplicated, or posted to a publicly accessible website, in whole or in part.

Problem 13–7 A–K

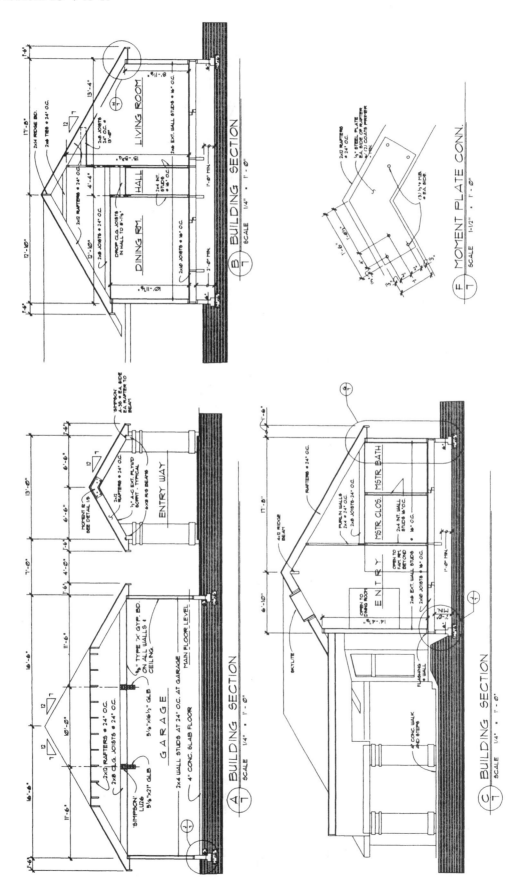

© 2011 Cengage Learning. All Rights Reserved. May not be scanned, copied or duplicated, or posted to a publicly accessible website, in whole or in part.

Problem 13–7 A–K (Continued)

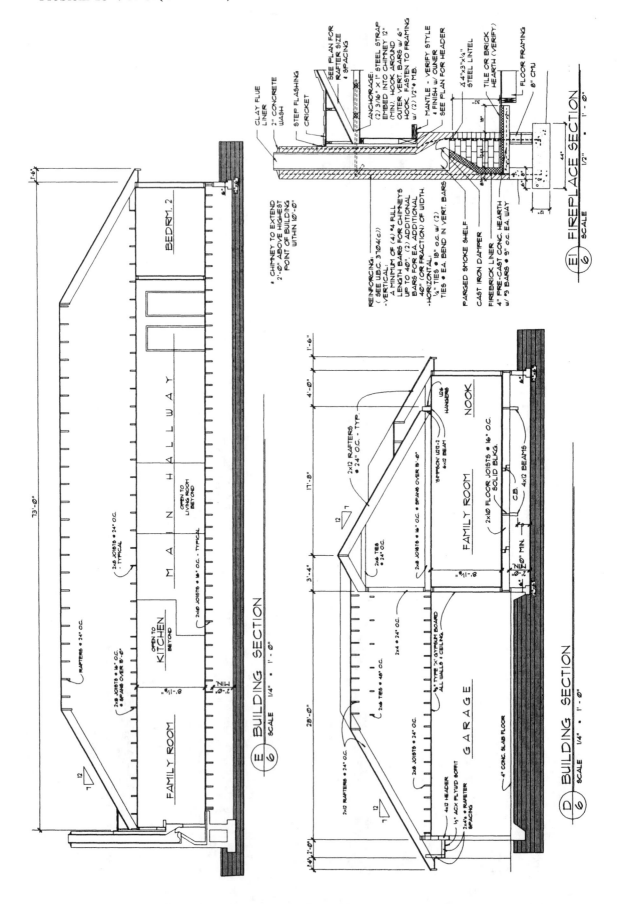

© 2011 Cengage Learning. All Rights Reserved. May not be scanned, copied or duplicated, or posted to a publicly accessible website, in whole or in part.

Problem 13–7 A–K (Continued)

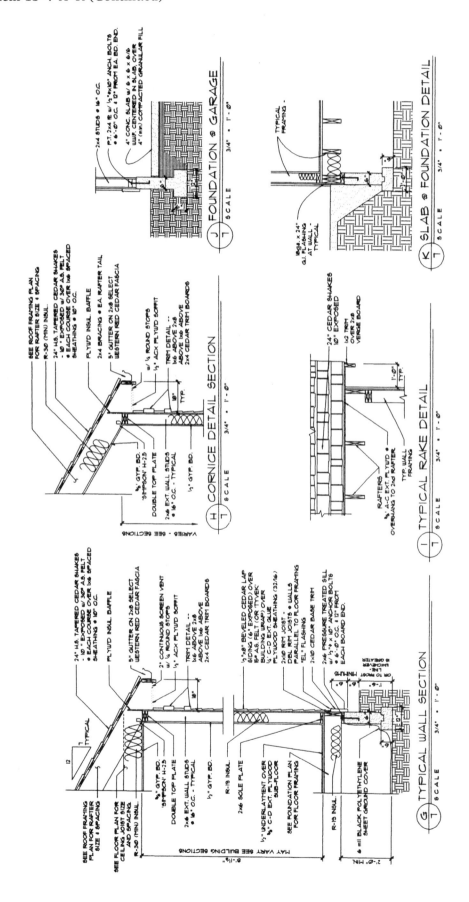

© 2011 Cengage Learning. All Rights Reserved. May not be scanned, copied or duplicated, or posted to a publicly accessible website, in whole or in part.

Problem 13–8

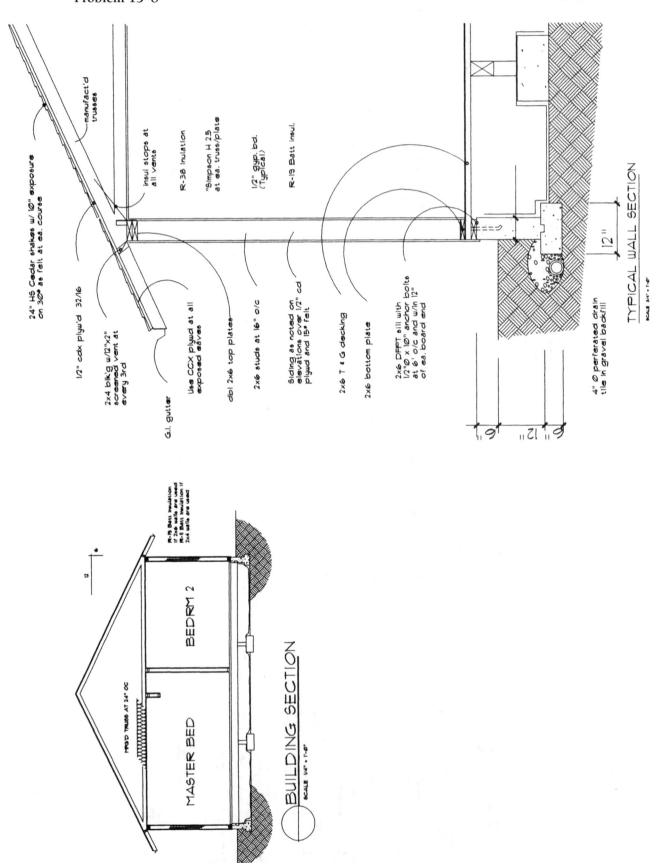

24" HS Cedar shakes w/ 10" exposure on 30# ae felt at ea. course

manufact'd trusses

insul stops at all vents

R-38 Insulation

"Simpson H 2.5 at ea. truss/plate

1/2" gyp. bd. (Typical)

R-19 Batt insul.

1/2" cdx plywd 32/16

2x4 blk'g w/ 1/2"x2" screened vent at every 3rd

G.I. gutter

Use CCX plywd at all exposed eaves

dbl 2x6 top plates

2x6 studs at 16" o/c

Siding as noted on elevations over 1/2" cd plywd and 15# felt

2x6 T & G decking

2x6 bottom plate

2x6 DFPT sill with 1/2"∅ x 10" anchor bolts at 6' o/c and w/in 12" of ea. board end

4" ∅ perforated drain tile in gravel backfill

TYPICAL WALL SECTION
SCALE 3/4" = 1'-0"

12"

6"
12"
6"

R-19 Batt insulation if 2x6 walls are used
R-11 Batt insulation if 2x4 walls are used

HD'D TRUSS AT 24" OC

MASTER BED

BEDRM 2

BUILDING SECTION
SCALE 1/4" = 1'-0"

© 2011 Cengage Learning. All Rights Reserved. May not be scanned, copied or duplicated, or posted to a publicly accessible website, in whole or in part.

Problem 13–9

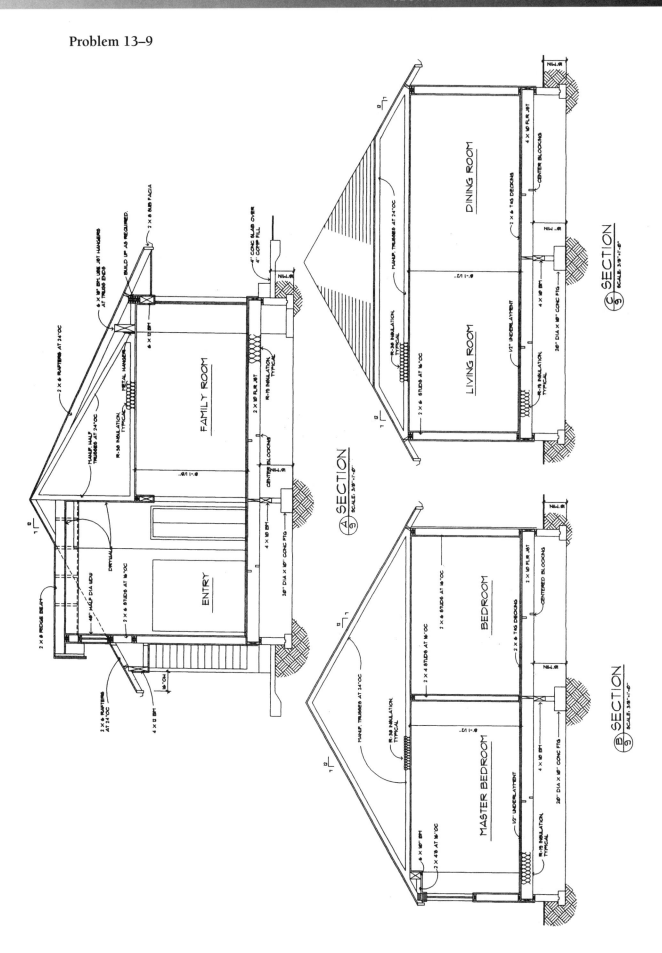

© 2011 Cengage Learning. All Rights Reserved. May not be scanned, copied or duplicated, or posted to a publicly accessible website, in whole or in part.

Problem 13–10

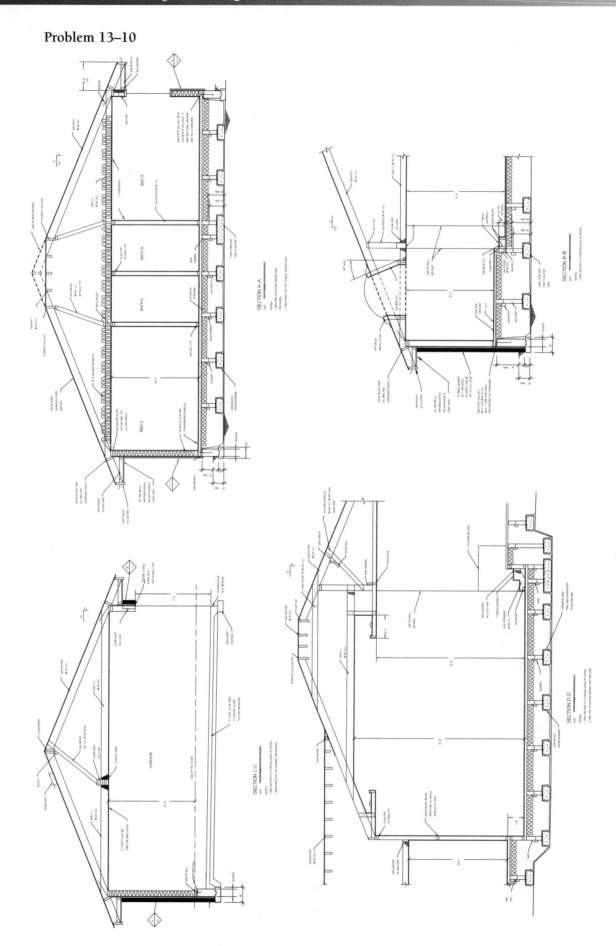

© 2011 Cengage Learning. All Rights Reserved. May not be scanned, copied or duplicated, or posted to a publicly accessible website, in whole or in part.

Problem 13–11

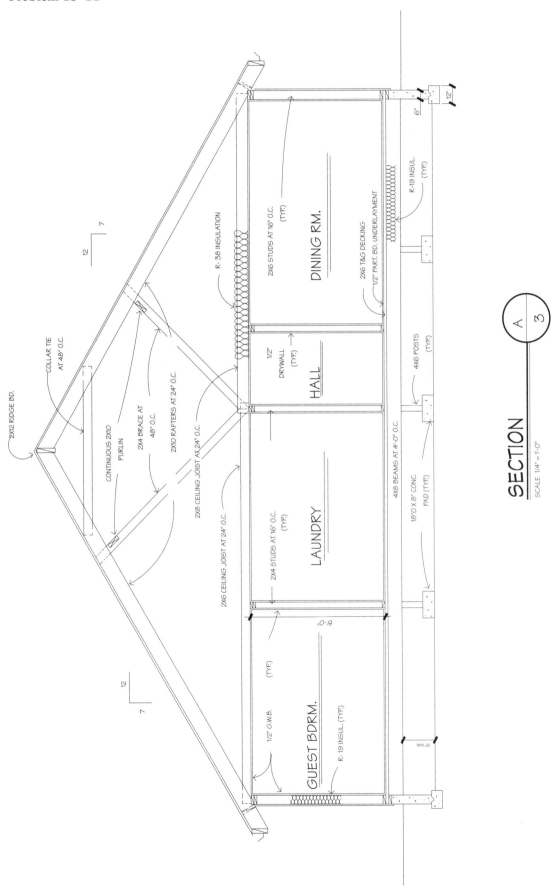

© 2011 Cengage Learning. All Rights Reserved. May not be scanned, copied or duplicated, or posted to a publicly accessible website, in whole or in part.

Problem 13–12

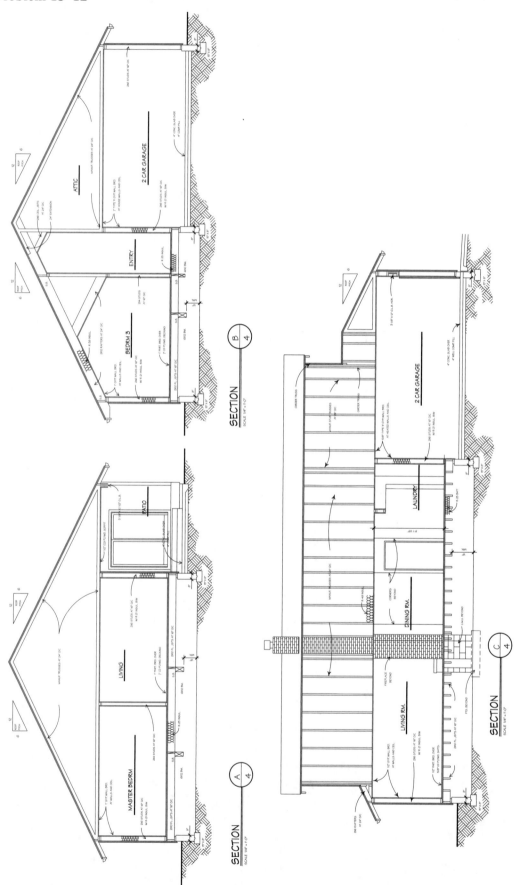

© 2011 Cengage Learning. All Rights Reserved. May not be scanned, copied or duplicated, or posted to a publicly accessible website, in whole or in part.

Problem 13–13

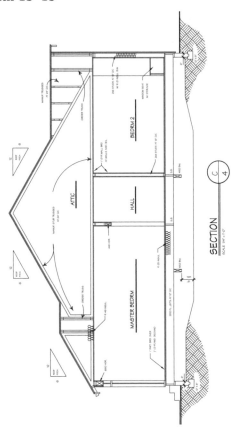

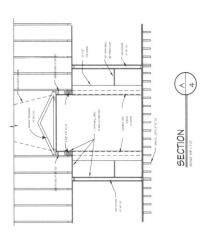

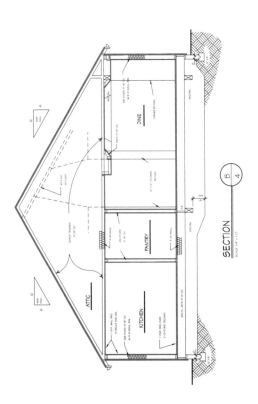

© 2011 Cengage Learning. All Rights Reserved. May not be scanned, copied or duplicated, or posted to a publicly accessible website, in whole or in part.

Problem 13–14

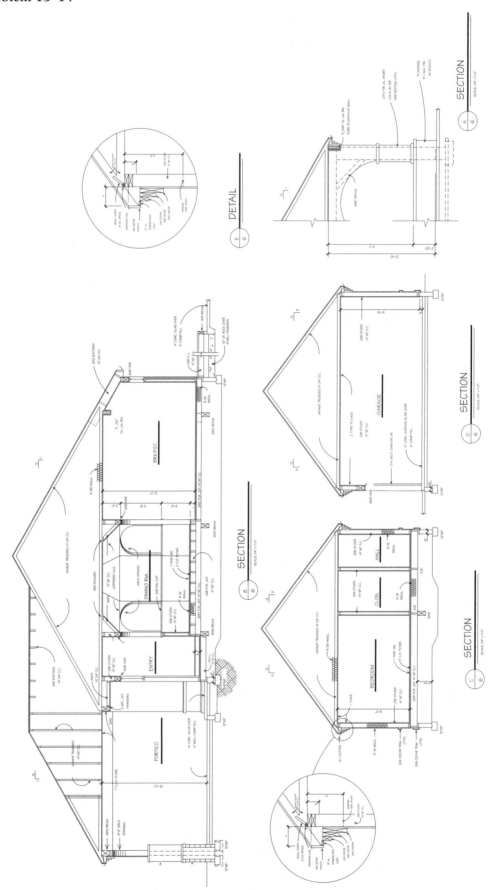

© 2011 Cengage Learning. All Rights Reserved. May not be scanned, copied or duplicated, or posted to a publicly accessible website, in whole or in part.

Problem 13–15

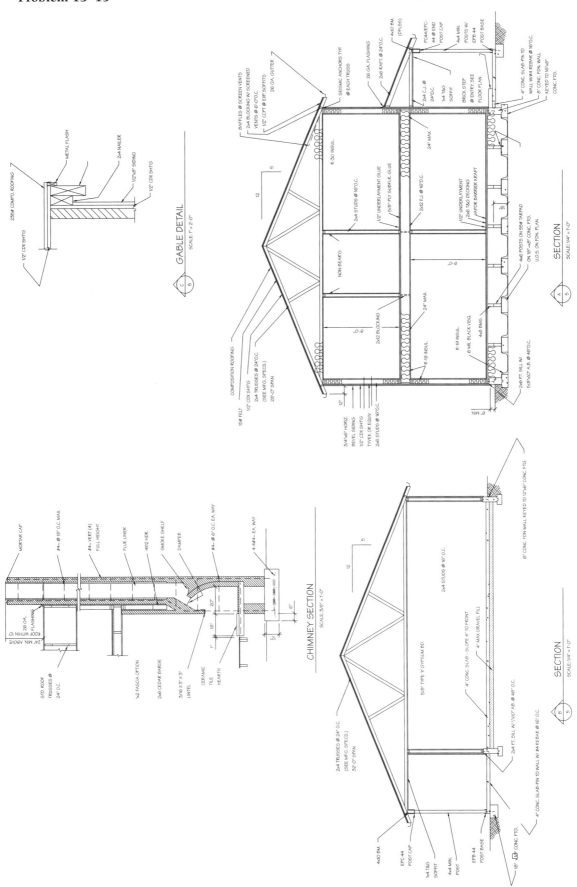

© 2011 Cengage Learning. All Rights Reserved. May not be scanned, copied or duplicated, or posted to a publicly accessible website, in whole or in part.

CHAPTER 14 STAIR SECTIONS

Problem 14–1

1. Head room
2. 6'-8" min
3. Individual run 10"
4. Handrail 34" min. 38" max. above nosing
5. Individual rise max. 7 3/4"
6. Floor joist
7. Interior finish
8. Header
9. Stringer
10. 5/8" type "X" gypsum board

Problem 14–2

1. Handrail min. 34"-38" max
2. Nosing
3. Tread
4. Metal hanger or ledger
5. Support for floor and stair
6. Floor joist
7. Interior finish
8. Header
9. Stringer
10. 1/2" gypsum board

© 2011 Cengage Learning. All Rights Reserved. May not be scanned, copied or duplicated, or posted to a publicly accessible website, in whole or in part.

Problem 14–3

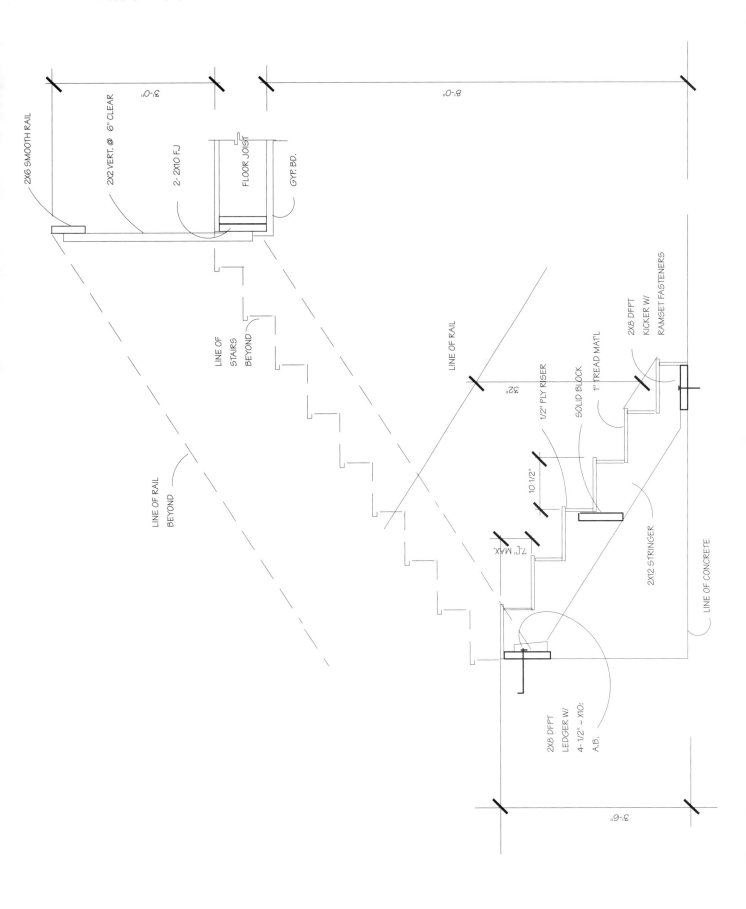

2X6 SMOOTH RAIL

2X2 VERT. @ 6" CLEAR

2- 2X10 F.J

FLOOR JOIST

GYP. BD.

3'-0"

8'-0"

LINE OF STAIRS BEYOND

LINE OF RAIL BEYOND

LINE OF RAIL

32"

1/2" PLY RISER

SOLID BLOCK

1" TREAD MAT'L

2X8 DFPT KICKER W/ RAMSET FASTENERS

10 1/2"

7 ¾" MAX.

2X12 STRINGER

LINE OF CONCRETE

2X8 DFPT LEDGER W/ 4- 1/2" ~ X10: A.B.

3'-6"

© 2011 Cengage Learning. All Rights Reserved. May not be scanned, copied or duplicated, or posted to a publicly accessible website, in whole or in part.

Problem 14–4

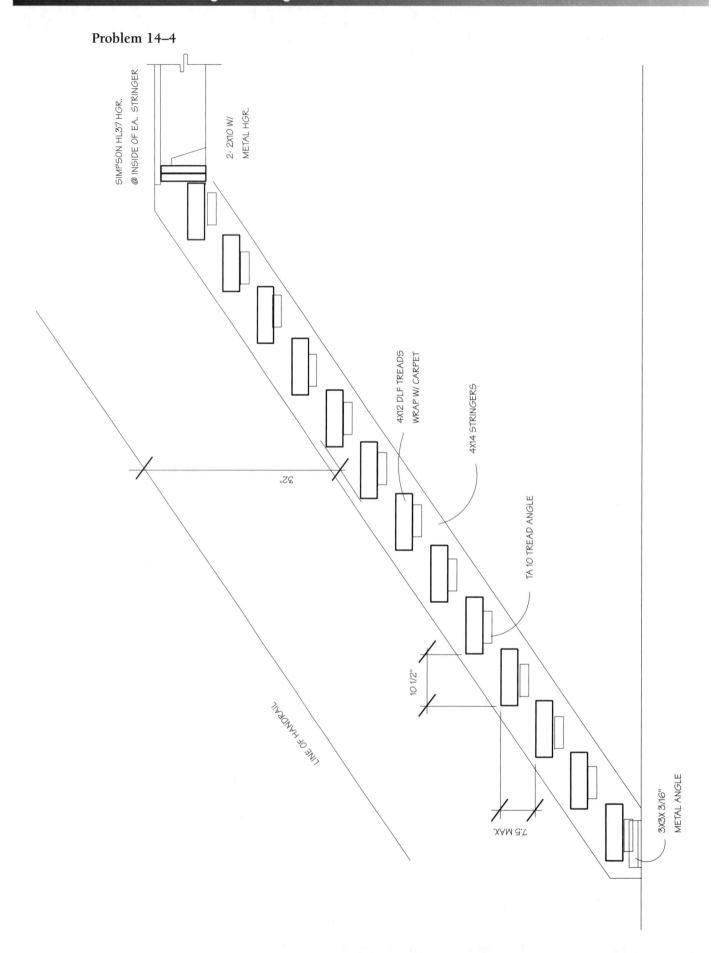

SIMPSON HL37 HGR.
@ INSIDE OF EA. STRINGER

2- 2X10 W/
METAL HGR.

4X12 DLF TREADS
WRAP W/ CARPET

4X14 STRINGERS

TA 10 TREAD ANGLE

32"

LINE OF HANDRAIL

10 1/2"

7.5 MAX.

3X3X 3/16"
METAL ANGLE

© 2011 Cengage Learning. All Rights Reserved. May not be scanned, copied or duplicated, or posted to a publicly accessible website, in whole or in part.

Problem 14–5

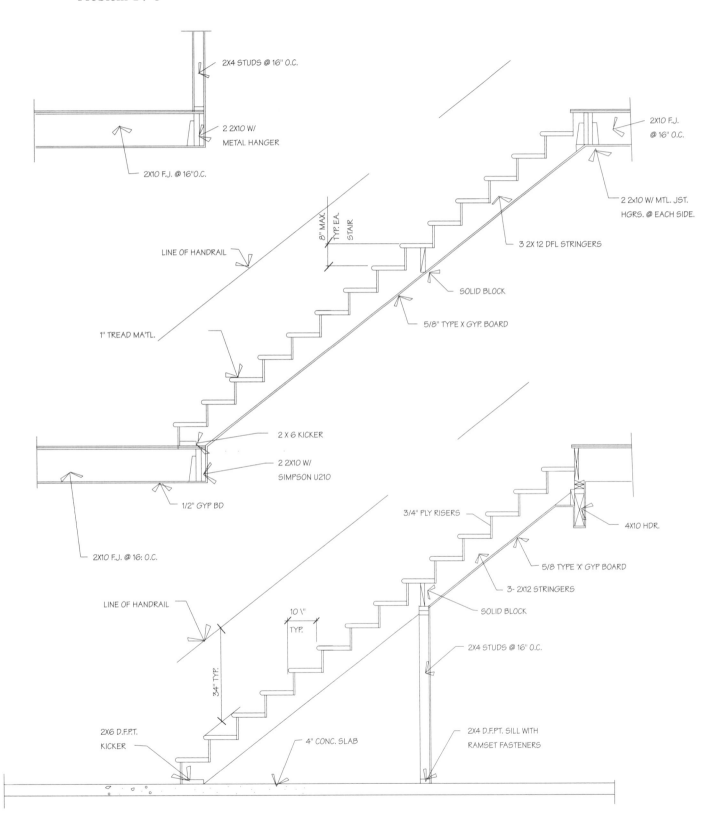

2X4 STUDS @ 16" O.C.

2 2X10 W/ METAL HANGER

2X10 F.J. @ 16"O.C.

2X10 F.J. @ 16" O.C.

2 2X10 W/ MTL. JST. HGRS. @ EACH SIDE.

8" MAX. TYP. EA. STAIR

LINE OF HANDRAIL

3 2X 12 DFL STRINGERS

SOLID BLOCK

1" TREAD MA'TL.

5/8" TYPE X GYP. BOARD

2 X 6 KICKER

2 2X10 W/ SIMPSON U210

1/2" GYP BD

3/4" PLY RISERS

4X10 HDR.

5/8 TYPE 'X' GYP BOARD

3- 2X12 STRINGERS

SOLID BLOCK

2X10 F.J. @ 16: O.C.

LINE OF HANDRAIL

10 \"
TYP.

2X4 STUDS @ 16" O.C.

34" TYP.

2X6 D.F.P.T. KICKER

4" CONC. SLAB

2X4 D.F.PT. SILL WITH RAMSET FASTENERS

STAIR SECTION

© 2011 Cengage Learning. All Rights Reserved. May not be scanned, copied or duplicated, or posted to a publicly accessible website, in whole or in part.

Problem 14–6

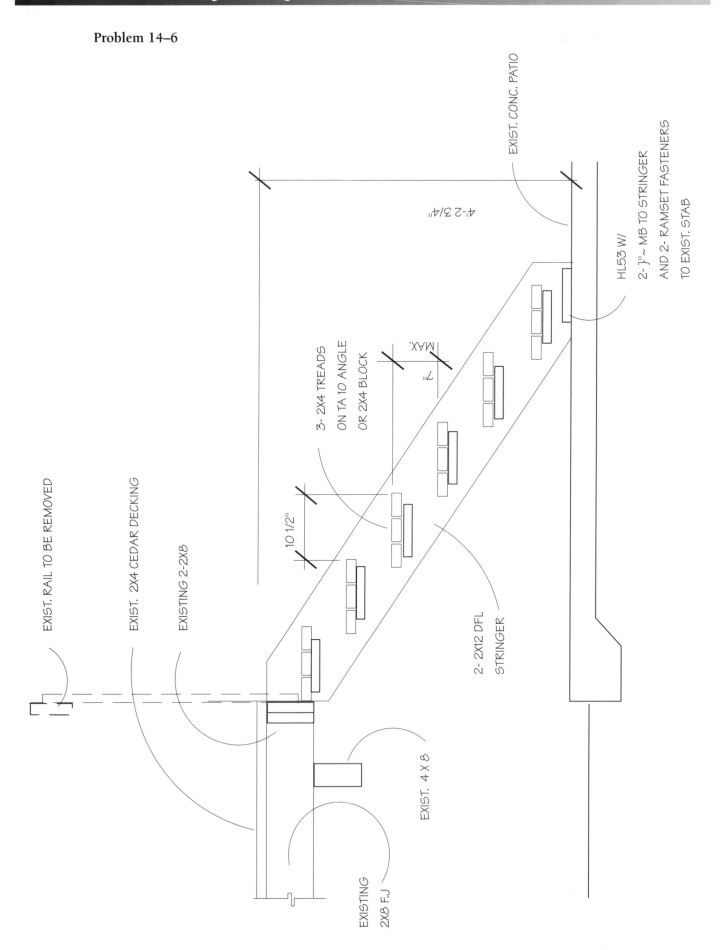

© 2011 Cengage Learning. All Rights Reserved. May not be scanned, copied or duplicated, or posted to a publicly accessible website, in whole or in part.

Problem 14–7

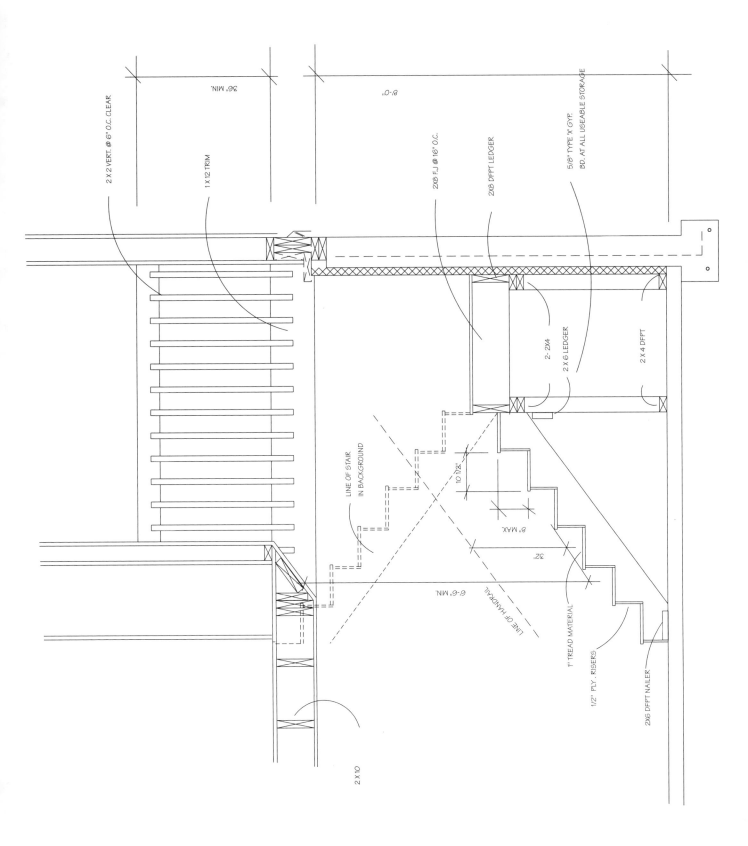

2 X 2 VERT. @ 6" O.C. CLEAR

1 X 12 TRIM

36" MIN.

8'-0"

2X8 F.J. @ 16" O.C.

2X8 DFPT LEDGER

5/8" TYPE 'X' GYP.
BD. AT ALL USEABLE STORAGE

2- 2X4

2 X 6 LEDGER

2 X 4 DFPT

LINE OF STAIR
IN BACKGROUND

10 1/8"

8" MAX.

32"

6'-6" MIN.

LINE OF HANDRAIL

1" TREAD MATERIAL

1/2" PLY. RISERS

2X6 DFPT NAILER

2 X 10

© 2011 Cengage Learning. All Rights Reserved. May not be scanned, copied or duplicated, or posted to a publicly accessible website, in whole or in part.

Problem 14–8

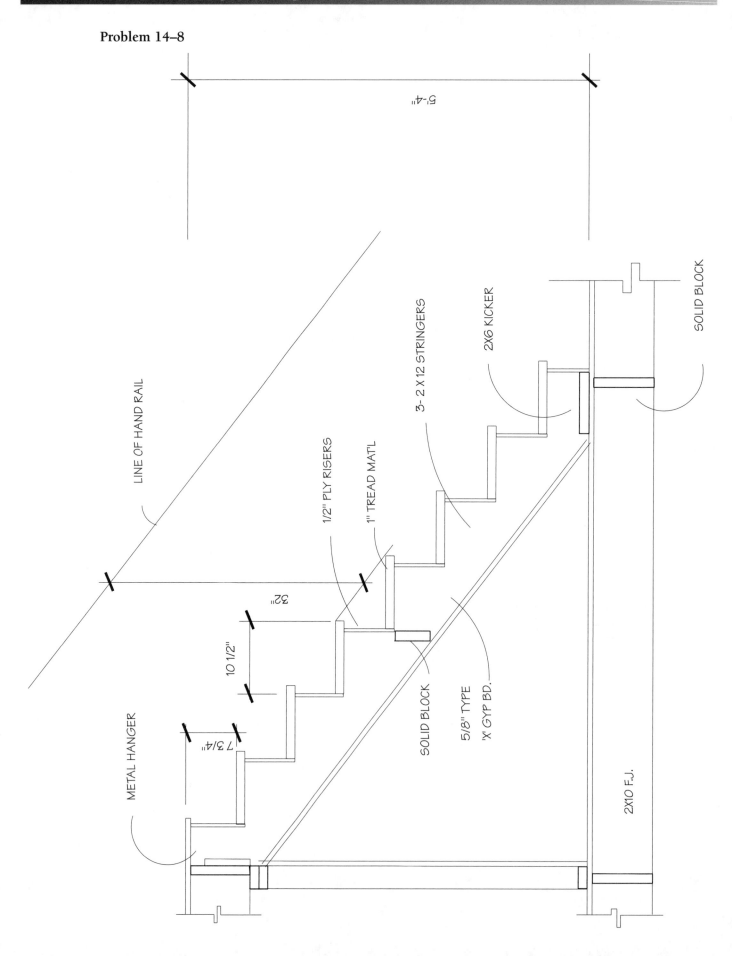

5'-4"

LINE OF HAND RAIL

1/2" PLY RISERS

1" TREAD MAT'L

3- 2 X 12 STRINGERS

2X6 KICKER

SOLID BLOCK

32"

10 1/2"

7 3/4"

METAL HANGER

SOLID BLOCK

5/8" TYPE 'X' GYP BD.

2X10 F.J.

© 2011 Cengage Learning. All Rights Reserved. May not be scanned, copied or duplicated, or posted to a publicly accessible website, in whole or in part.

Problem 14–9

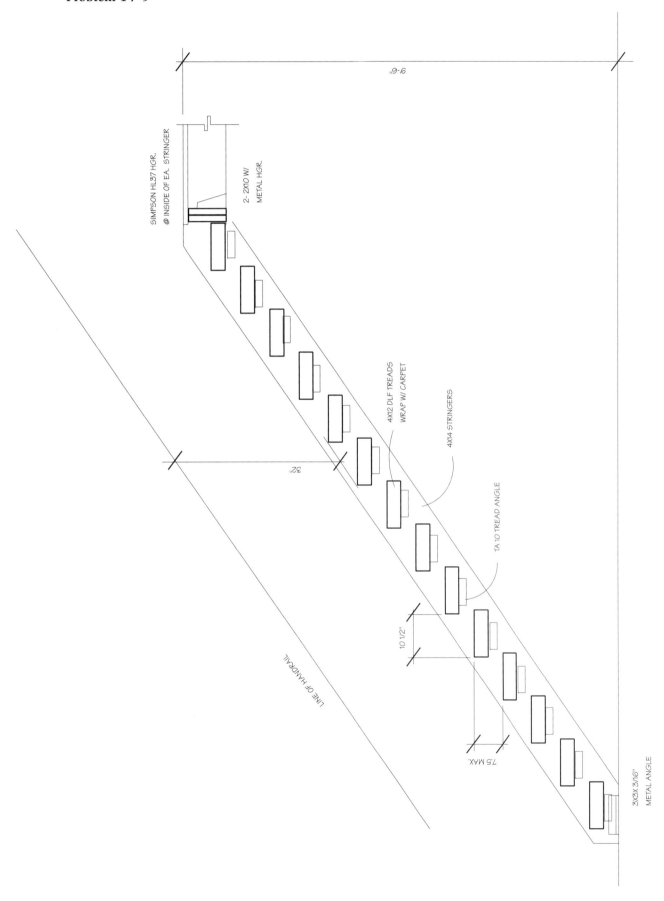

© 2011 Cengage Learning. All Rights Reserved. May not be scanned, copied or duplicated, or posted to a publicly accessible website, in whole or in part.

Problem 14–10

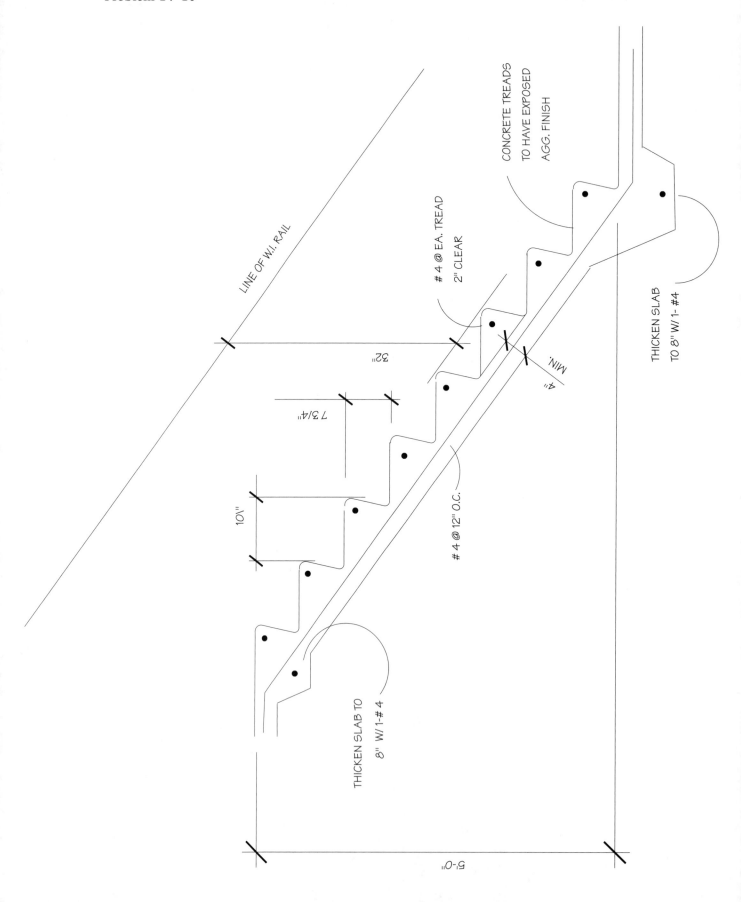

LINE OF W.I. RAIL

CONCRETE TREADS
TO HAVE EXPOSED
AGG. FINISH

#4 @ EA. TREAD
2" CLEAR

32"

THICKEN SLAB
TO 8" W/ 1- #4

4"
MIN.

7 3/4"

10"

#4 @ 12" O.C.

THICKEN SLAB TO
8" W/ 1- #4

5'-0"

© 2011 Cengage Learning. All Rights Reserved. May not be scanned, copied or duplicated, or posted to a publicly accessible website, in whole or in part.

CHAPTER 15 FIREPLACE SECTIONS

Problem 15–1

1. Steel strap
2. Header
3. Smoke chamber
4. Lintel
5. Damper
6. Fire brick
7. Hearth
8. Reinforcing steel
9. Concrete block
10. Fireplace width + 12"

11. 12" deep
12. 4"
13. 4"
14. 20" minimum
15. 18" minimum
16. 4"
17. Smoke shelf
18. #4 vertical reinforcing minimum
19. Flue liner
20. Bond beam @ each floor

Problem 15–2

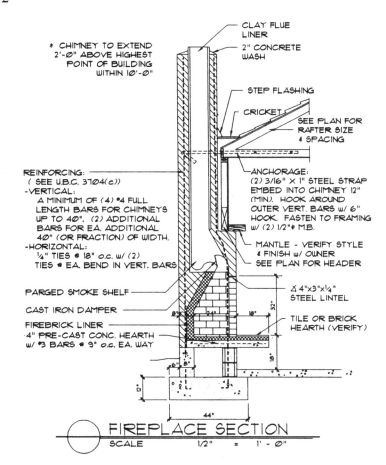

CLAY FLUE LINER

2" CONCRETE WASH

STEP FLASHING

CRICKET

SEE PLAN FOR RAFTER SIZE & SPACING

* CHIMNEY TO EXTEND 2'-Ø" ABOVE HIGHEST POINT OF BUILDING WITHIN 1Ø'-Ø"

REINFORCING:
(SEE U.B.C. 3704(c))
-VERTICAL:
A MINIMUM OF (4) #4 FULL LENGTH BARS FOR CHIMNEYS UP TO 40". (2) ADDITIONAL BARS FOR EA. ADDITIONAL 40" (OR FRACTION) OF WIDTH.
-HORIZONTAL:
¼" TIES @ 18" o.c. w/ (2) TIES @ EA. BEND IN VERT. BARS

ANCHORAGE:
(2) 3/16" X 1" STEEL STRAP EMBED INTO CHIMNEY 12" (MIN). HOOK AROUND OUTER VERT. BARS w/ 6" HOOK. FASTEN TO FRAMING w/ (2) 1/2"Ø M.B.

MANTLE - VERIFY STYLE & FINISH w/ OWNER SEE PLAN FOR HEADER

PARGED SMOKE SHELF

CAST IRON DAMPER

FIREBRICK LINER

4" PRE-CAST CONC. HEARTH w/ #3 BARS @ 9" o.c. EA. WAY

∠ 4"x3"x¼" STEEL LINTEL

TILE OR BRICK HEARTH (VERIFY)

FIREPLACE SECTION
SCALE   1/2" = 1'-Ø"

© 2011 Cengage Learning. All Rights Reserved. May not be scanned, copied or duplicated, or posted to a publicly accessible website, in whole or in part.

Problem 15–3

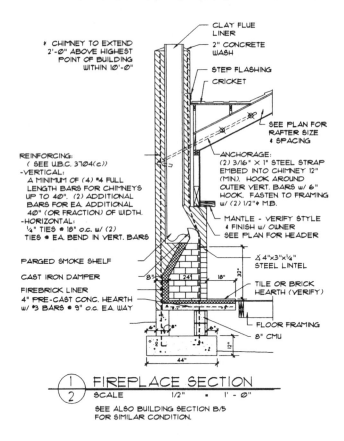

CLAY FLUE LINER
2" CONCRETE WASH
STEP FLASHING
CRICKET

✱ CHIMNEY TO EXTEND 2'-0" ABOVE HIGHEST POINT OF BUILDING WITHIN 10'-0"

SEE PLAN FOR RAFTER SIZE ♦ SPACING

REINFORCING:
(SEE U.B.C. 3704(c))
-VERTICAL:
A MINIMUM OF (4) #4 FULL LENGTH BARS FOR CHIMNEYS UP TO 40". (2) ADDITIONAL BARS FOR EA. ADDITIONAL 40" (OR FRACTION) OF WIDTH.
-HORIZONTAL:
¼" TIES ● 18" o.c. w/ (2) TIES ● EA. BEND IN VERT. BARS

ANCHORAGE:
(2) 3/16" X 1" STEEL STRAP EMBED INTO CHIMNEY 12" (MIN). HOOK AROUND OUTER VERT. BARS w/ 6" HOOK. FASTEN TO FRAMING w/ (2) 1/2"♦ M.B.

MANTLE - VERIFY STYLE ♦ FINISH w/ OWNER SEE PLAN FOR HEADER

PARGED SMOKE SHELF
CAST IRON DAMPER
FIREBRICK LINER
4" PRE-CAST CONC. HEARTH w/ #3 BARS ● 9" o.c. EA. WAY

∠ 4"x3"x¼" STEEL LINTEL
TILE OR BRICK HEARTH (VERIFY)
FLOOR FRAMING
8" CMU

8" 24I 18" 32" 44" 12"

① ② FIREPLACE SECTION
SCALE 1/2" ● 1' - 0"
SEE ALSO BUILDING SECTION B/5 FOR SIMILAR CONDITION.

Problem 15–4

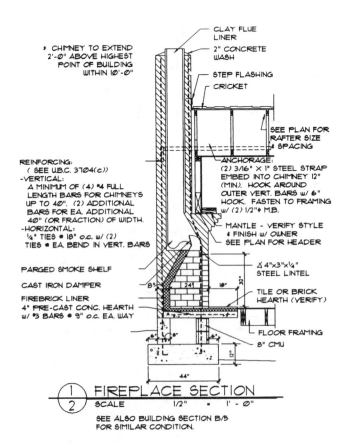

CLAY FLUE LINER
2" CONCRETE WASH
STEP FLASHING
CRICKET

✱ CHIMNEY TO EXTEND 2'-0" ABOVE HIGHEST POINT OF BUILDING WITHIN 10'-0"

SEE PLAN FOR RAFTER SIZE ♦ SPACING

REINFORCING:
(SEE U.B.C. 3704(c))
-VERTICAL:
A MINIMUM OF (4) #4 FULL LENGTH BARS FOR CHIMNEYS UP TO 40". (2) ADDITIONAL BARS FOR EA. ADDITIONAL 40" (OR FRACTION) OF WIDTH.
-HORIZONTAL:
¼" TIES ● 18" o.c. w/ (2) TIES ● EA. BEND IN VERT. BARS

ANCHORAGE:
(2) 3/16" X 1" STEEL STRAP EMBED INTO CHIMNEY 12" (MIN). HOOK AROUND OUTER VERT. BARS w/ 6" HOOK. FASTEN TO FRAMING w/ (2) 1/2"♦ M.B.

MANTLE - VERIFY STYLE ♦ FINISH w/ OWNER SEE PLAN FOR HEADER

PARGED SMOKE SHELF
CAST IRON DAMPER
FIREBRICK LINER
4" PRE-CAST CONC. HEARTH w/ #3 BARS ● 9" o.c. EA. WAY

∠ 4"x3"x¼" STEEL LINTEL
TILE OR BRICK HEARTH (VERIFY)
FLOOR FRAMING
8" CMU

8" 24I 18" 32" 44" 12"

① ② FIREPLACE SECTION
SCALE 1/2" ● 1' - 0"
SEE ALSO BUILDING SECTION B/5 FOR SIMILAR CONDITION.

© 2011 Cengage Learning. All Rights Reserved. May not be scanned, copied or duplicated, or posted to a publicly accessible website, in whole or in part.

Problem 15–5

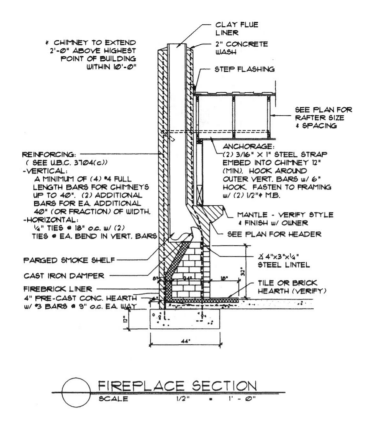

* CHIMNEY TO EXTEND 2'-0" ABOVE HIGHEST POINT OF BUILDING WITHIN 10'-0"

CLAY FLUE LINER

2" CONCRETE WASH

STEP FLASHING

SEE PLAN FOR RAFTER SIZE & SPACING

ANCHORAGE:
(2) 3/16" X 1" STEEL STRAP EMBED INTO CHIMNEY 12" (MIN). HOOK AROUND OUTER VERT. BARS w/ 6" HOOK. FASTEN TO FRAMING w/ (2) 1/2"⌀ M.B.

REINFORCING:
(SEE U.B.C. 3704(c))
-VERTICAL:
A MINIMUM OF (4) #4 FULL LENGTH BARS FOR CHIMNEYS UP TO 40". (2) ADDITIONAL BARS FOR EA. ADDITIONAL 40" (OR FRACTION) OF WIDTH.
-HORIZONTAL:
¼" TIES @ 18" O.C. w/ (2) TIES @ EA. BEND IN VERT. BARS

MANTLE - VERIFY STYLE & FINISH w/ OWNER

SEE PLAN FOR HEADER

¼ 4"x3"x¼" STEEL LINTEL

PARGED SMOKE SHELF

CAST IRON DAMPER

FIREBRICK LINER

4" PRE-CAST CONC. HEARTH w/ #3 BARS @ 9" O.C. EA. WAY

TILE OR BRICK HEARTH (VERIFY)

44"

FIREPLACE SECTION
SCALE   1/2" = 1'-0"

Problem 15–6

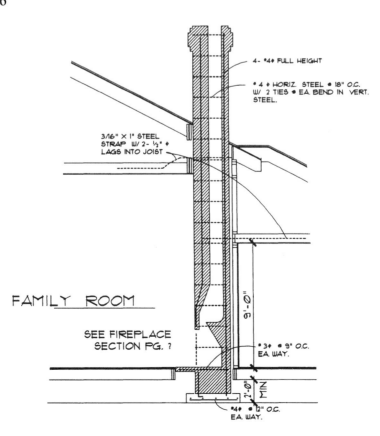

4- #4⌀ FULL HEIGHT

#4 ⌀ HORIZ. STEEL @ 18" O.C. W/ 2 TIES @ EA. BEND IN VERT. STEEL.

3/16" X 1" STEEL STRAP W/ 2- ½ ⌀ LAGS INTO JOIST

FAMILY ROOM

SEE FIREPLACE SECTION PG. ?

9'-0"

#3⌀ @ 9" O.C. EA. WAY.

2'-0" MIN

#4⌀ @ 12" O.C. EA. WAY.

© 2011 Cengage Learning. All Rights Reserved. May not be scanned, copied or duplicated, or posted to a publicly accessible website, in whole or in part.

Problem 15–7

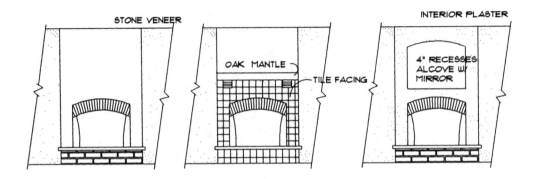

Problem 15–8

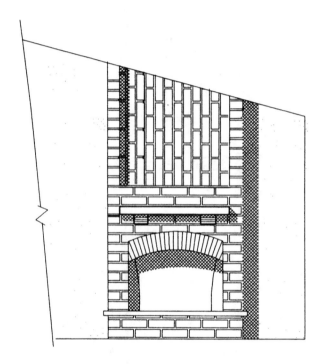

© 2011 Cengage Learning. All Rights Reserved. May not be scanned, copied or duplicated, or posted to a publicly accessible website, in whole or in part.

Problem 15–9

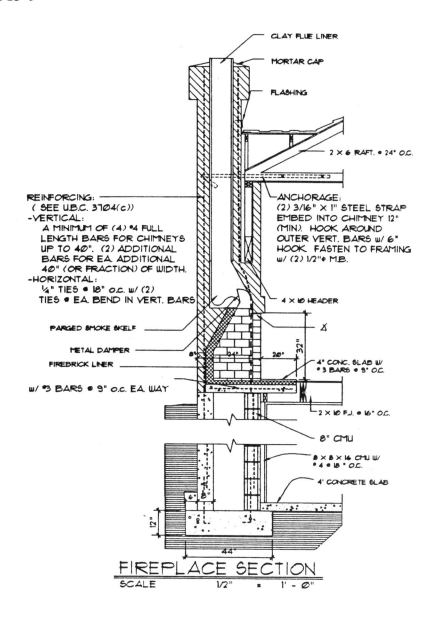

CLAY FLUE LINER

MORTAR CAP

FLASHING

2 × 6 RAFT. ● 24" O.C.

REINFORCING:
(SEE U.B.C. 3704(c))
-VERTICAL:
    A MINIMUM OF (4) ●4 FULL
    LENGTH BARS FOR CHIMNEYS
    UP TO 40". (2) ADDITIONAL
    BARS FOR EA. ADDITIONAL
    40" (OR FRACTION) OF WIDTH.
-HORIZONTAL:
    ¼" TIES ● 18" O.C. w/ (2)
    TIES ● EA. BEND IN VERT. BARS

ANCHORAGE:
(2) 3/16" × 1" STEEL STRAP
EMBED INTO CHIMNEY 12"
(MIN). HOOK AROUND
OUTER VERT. BARS w/ 6"
HOOK. FASTEN TO FRAMING
w/ (2) 1/2"● M.B.

4 × 10 HEADER

PARGED SMOKE SHELF

METAL DAMPER

FIREBRICK LINER

w/ ●3 BARS ● 9" O.C. EA. WAY

32"

8"   24"   20"

4" CONC. SLAB W/
●3 BARS ● 9" O.C.

2 × 10 F.J. ● 16" O.C.

8" CMU

8 × 8 × 16 CMU W/
●4 ● 18" O.C.

4' CONCRETE SLAB

12"   6" 8"   8"   9"

44"

FIREPLACE SECTION
SCALE   1/2"   =   1' - 0"

Problem 15–10

1. No fireplace section required.
2. No fireplace section required.
3. No fireplace section required.
4. The fireplace should resemble Problem Solution 15–4 or 15–5 depending on the floor framing used.
5. The fireplace should resemble Problem Solution 15–2.
6. The fireplace should resemble Problem Solution 15–3.
7. The fireplace should resemble Problem Solution 15–4.
8. The fireplace should resemble Problem Solution 15–2.
9. The fireplace should resemble Problem Solution 15–4.
10. The fireplace should resemble Problem Solution 15–9.

© 2011 Cengage Learning. All Rights Reserved. May not be scanned, copied or duplicated, or posted to a publicly accessible website, in whole or in part.

CHAPTERE 16 DESIGN CRITERIA AND STRUCTURAL LOADING

Problem 16–1	250#
Problem 16–2	350#
Problem 16–3	7.500#
Problem 16–4	12" = 640#, 16" = 832#, 24" = 1280#
Problem 16–5	1120#
Problem 16–6	10,080#
Problem 16–7	4640#
Problem 16–8	3600#
Problem 16–9	No weight is supported with a truss roof
Problem 16–10	No load, no footing required
Problem 16–11	600# per lineal foot, 14,000 # total roof weight
Problem 16–12	600# per lineal foot, 14,000 # total roof weight
Problem 16–13	None
Problem 16–14	Wall = 80#, floor = 650#, 730 × 13' = 9490#
Problem 16–15	5' × 730# = 3650#
Problem 16–16	Roof = 15.5 × 10# = 155#
	Upper wall = 8' × 10# = 80#
	Floor = 6' × 10# = 60#
	Lower wall = 8' × 10# = 80#
	Total dead load = 375#
Problem 16–17	8' × 25# = 200#/ 2 = 100#
Problem 16–18	16' × 40# = 640#/lineal foot
Problem 16–19	(8.5 + 1.5) × 40# = 400#/lineal foot
Problem 16–20	(7.5 + 8.5) × 40# = 640#/lineal foot
Problem 16–21	640# (roof) + (8' × 10#) wall + (16' × 50#) floor + 8' × 10# wall = 1600#/lineal foot
Problem 16–22	1600# × 4' = 6400# per pier
Problem 16–23	(8.5 + 1.5) × 40# = 400#/lineal foot
Problem 16–24	400# (roof) + (8' × 10#) wall + (8.5' × 50#) floor + 8' × 10# wall = 985#/lineal foot
Problem 16–25	(8.5 + 1.5) × 10# + (8 × 10# × 2) + 8.5 × 10# = 345#/lineal foot
Problem 16–26	2 × 8 DFL #2 at 16 = 12'–0"
	Hem-fir at 16" = 12'–10"
	Spruce-Pine Fir at 16" = 12'–3"
	Southern Pine at 16" = 13'–1"

© 2011 Cengage Learning. All Rights Reserved. May not be scanned, copied or duplicated, or posted to a publicly accessible website, in whole or in part.

Problem 16–27	2 × 6 DFL #2 at 16 = 17'–4"
	Hem-fir at 16" = 17'–8"
	Spruce-Pine Fir at 16" = 16'–11"
	Southern Pine at 16" = 17'–8"
Problem 16–28	Rafters at 24" O.C.
	2 × 10 DFL #2
	2 × 10 Hem-fir
	2 × 10 Spruce-Pine Fir
	2 × 10 Southern Pine
Problem 16–29	4 × 12 beam with 12" × 12" concrete pier
Problem 16–30	2 × 12
Problem 16–31	4 × 12 beam with 18" × 12" diameter pier
Problem 16–32	4 × 12
Problem 16–33	Yes
Problem 16–34	Yes
Problem 16–35	3 1/8" × 10 1/2"
Problem 16–36	24" diameter
Problem 16–37	6 × 14
Problem 16–38	4 × 12
Problem 16–39	5 1/8" × 13 1/2"
Problem 16–40	6 × 14

© 2011 Cengage Learning. All Rights Reserved. May not be scanned, copied or duplicated, or posted to a publicly accessible website, in whole or in part.

CHAPTER 17 CONSTRUCTION SPECIFICATIONS, PERMITS, AND CONTRACTS

Problem 17–1   Answers will vary depending on the home that is used and the materials used on the home.

© 2011 Cengage Learning. All Rights Reserved. May not be scanned, copied or duplicated, or posted to a publicly accessible website, in whole or in part.

Problem 17–2

BUILDING PERMIT APPLICATION

Amount Due _____

Project Location (Address) **3456 Barrington Drive, Your City, State Zip Code**

Nearest Cross Street **Washington Street**

Subdivision Name **Barrington Heights**

Township **25** Range **1E** Section **36** Lot **8** Block **1**

Lot Size **15000** (Sq. Ft.) Building Area **2000** (Sq. Ft.) Basement Area **—** (Sq. Ft.) Tax Lot **2400** Garage Area **576** (Sq. Ft.)

Stories **1** Bedrooms **3** Water Source **Public** Sewage Disposal **Public**

Estimated Cost of Labor and Material **$88,500**

Plans and Specifications made by **[Student name]** accompany this application.

Owner's Name **[Instructor name]** Builder's Name **[Student name]**

Address **[fictitious]** Address **[Student address]**

City _____ State _____ City _____ State _____

Phone _____ Zip _____ Phone _____ Zip _____

I certify that I am registered under the provisions of ORS Chapter 701 and my registration is in full force and effect. I also agree to build according to the above description, accompanying plans and specifications, the State of Oregon Building Code, and to the conditions set forth below.

[Student signature] **[SS# or fictitious]**

APPLICANT HOMEBUILDER'S REGISTRATION NO. DATE

I agree to build according to the above description, accompanying plans and specifications, the State of Oregon Building Code, and to the conditions set forth below.

[Today's date]

APPLICANT DATE

TO BE FILLED IN BY APPLICANT

© 2011 Cengage Learning. All Rights Reserved. May not be scanned, copied or duplicated, or posted to a publicly accessible website, in whole or in part.

Problem 17–3

FORM No. 144—BUILDING CONTRACT (Fixed Price—No Service Charge).

TN

THIS AGREEMENT, Made the ....today.......... *day of* ....this month.............., *19* ...yr..., *by and between* ....[Student name].............., *hereinafter called the Contractor, and* ....[Instructor name].............., *hereinafter called the Owner, WITNESSETH:*

The parties hereto, each in consideration of the promises of the other, agree as follows:

ARTICLE I: The contractor shall and will perform all the work for the

Construction of approximate 2000–square foot house to be located at 3456 Barrington Drive, your City, State, Zip Code. Also known as Lot 8, Block 1, Barrington Heights, your County and State.

as shown on the drawings and described in the specifications therefor prepared by ....[Student name]..........

....;

said drawings, specifications and this contract hereinafter, for brevity, are called "contract documents"; they are identified by the signatures of the parties hereto and hereby are made a part hereof. All said work is to be done under the direction of ....[Student name]..........

who, for brevity hereinafter is designated as "supervisor." (Publisher's note: If the owner himself is to supervise said work, simply insert the word "owner" in the blank space immediately preceding.) The supervisor's decision as to the true construction and meaning of the drawings and specifications shall be final and binding upon both parties. All of said drawings and specifications including those hereinafter mentioned have been and will be prepared by the owner at his expense and are to remain his property; said drawings and specifications are loaned to the contractor for the purposes of this contract and at the completion of the work are to be returned to the owner; none of said contract documents shall be used by, submitted or shown to third parties without owner's written consent.

ARTICLE II: The contractor shall commence work within ....10.......... *days from the date hereof and substantially complete the same on or before* ..4 mos. from date above.., *19* ...... *. At all times the supervisor shall have access to said work for the purpose of inspecting the same and the progress thereof. Should completion be delayed by reason of the fault of the owner or of any other contractor employed by him or by fire, casualty, strikes, delays in obtaining materials or other reasons beyond the contractor's control, then the completion date shall be extended for a period equivalent to the time lost for such reasons. Should the parties be unable to agree as to the period of such extension, the question shall be referred to arbitration as hereunder provided. However, the contractor shall take special precautions to protect his work during freezing weather and shall be fully responsible for the effect of such weather upon said work.*

ARTICLE III: Subject to the provisions for adjustment set forth in ARTICLE V hereof, the owner shall pay to the contractor for the performance of this contract, in current funds, the sum of $ ....88,500.........., *payable at the following times:*

1. One–third upon completion of foundation.

2. One–third upon completion of drywall.

3. One–third 30 days after posting completion notice.

NOTE—This form not suitable for use as a retail installment contract where a finance charge is being made.

© 2011 Cengage Learning. All Rights Reserved. May not be scanned, copied or duplicated, or posted to a publicly accessible website, in whole or in part.

Problem 17–3 (Continued)

Sales tax, if any, shall be paid by the owner in addition to the fixed price mentioned above. Should any progress payments be provided for above, the same shall not include or be based upon any salary, allowance or compensation to the contractor, if an individual, or any officer of the contractor, if a corporation, nor shall it include any of the contractor's overhead or general expenses of any kind; before any such progress payment is made, the contractor shall deliver to the supervisor receipts, vouchers or other evidence satisfactory to the supervisor showing contractor's payment for materials, labor and other items for which the contractor seeks payment, including payments to subcontractors, if any. After three days' written notice to the contractor, bills for labor or materials not paid by the contractor when due, may be paid by the owner and deducted from any payment due or to become due to the contractor. After similar notice, liens, if any are filed, including attorney's fees and costs claimed therein, may be paid, settled or compromised by the owner and amounts paid therefor shall likewise be deducted. However, the contractor shall have the right to contest any such bills, claims or liens.

Final payment shall be made within _____ days after the completion of said work as certified in writing by the supervisor; however, before the latter shall so certify, the contractor shall submit evidence satisfactory to the supervisor that all payrolls, material bills and other indebtedness connected with the work have been fully paid, including those incurred by each and all of contractor's subcontractors. Provided always, that no payment made to the contractor pursuant to the terms hereof shall be construed as an acceptance of any work or materials not in accordance with the contract documents.

ARTICLE IV: In his performance of said work, contractor shall obtain at his own expense all necessary permits and comply with all applicable laws, ordinances, building codes and regulations of any public authority and be responsible for any infraction or violation thereof and any expense or damages resulting from any such infraction or violation. If the parties are unable to agree upon the dollar amount of contractor's responsibility under this paragraph, the matter shall be referred to arbitration as hereinafter provided. Any work claimed by the supervisor to be defective shall be uncovered by the contractor so that a complete inspection may be made; the contractor further agrees promptly (1) to remove from the job site all materials, whether or not incorporated in the work, condemned by any public authority, (2) to take down and remove all portions of the work likewise condemned or deemed by the supervisor as failing in any way to conform to any of said contract documents and (3) to replace all faulty work and materials.

ARTICLE V: No eliminations or alterations shall be made in the work except upon written order of the supervisor. Should any such eliminations or alterations require new plans or specifications, the owner shall supply the same at his expense. Should any of said eliminations or alterations require an adjustment of the agreed price (upward or downward) such adjustment shall be evidenced by the written agreement of the parties. Should they not be able so to agree, the work shall go on nevertheless under the order mentioned above and the determination of the proper adjustment shall be referred to arbitration as hereinafter provided.

ARTICLE VI: The owner reserves the right to let other contracts in connection with the improvement of which the work herein undertaken by the contractor is a part. In such event, due written notice of such other contracts shall be given promptly to the contractor and the latter shall afford said other contractors a reasonable opportunity for the storage of their materials and the execution of their contracts and shall properly coordinate his work within theirs. In this connection, should the contractor suffer loss by reason of any delay brought about by said other contractors, the owner agrees to reimburse the contractor for such loss; on the other hand, the contractor agrees that if he shall delay the work of said other contractors so as to cause loss for which the owner shall become liable, then he shall reimburse the owner for any such loss. If the parties are unable to agree as to the amounts so to be reimbursed, all questions relative thereto shall be submitted to arbitration as hereinafter provided.

ARTICLE VII: The contractor may subcontract any part of said work but not the whole thereof. Within seven days after entering into any such subcontract, the contractor shall notify the supervisor in writing of the names of said subcontractors and the work to be undertaken by each of them. In this connection, the contractor shall be fully responsible to the owner for the acts and omissions of any of said subcontractors or of persons either directly or indirectly employed by them. Nothing contained herein shall create any contractual relation between any such subcontractor and the owner.

ARTICLE VIII: At no time shall the contractor or any of his subcontractors employ on the work any unfit person or anyone not skilled in the work assigned to him. Any employee adjudged by the supervisor to be incompetent or unfit immediately shall be discharged and shall not again be employed upon the work. Should the contractor at any time be adjudged a bankrupt or should a receiver be appointed for his affairs or should he neglect to supply sufficient properly skilled workmen or supply materials of the proper quality or fail in any respect to prosecute the work with promptness and diligence (except because of matters for which an extension of the completion date is above provided for) or comply with said contract documents or any thereof, then in any of such events, after seven days' written notice to the contractor, the owner may, if the contractor is still in default, terminate the contractor's right to continue said work and may take exclusive possession of the premises and of all materials, tools and appliances thereon and finish the work by whatever method he may deem expedient. In such case the contractor shall not be entitled to receive any further payment until the work is finished. If the unpaid balance of the contract price shall exceed the expense of finishing the work, including compensation to the owner for additional managerial and administrative expenses, such excess shall be paid to the contractor; however, if such expense shall exceed such unpaid balance, the contractor shall pay the difference to the owner. If the parties are unable to agree upon the amounts so to be paid, the question shall be submitted to arbitration as hereinafter provided.

ARTICLE IX: All materials incorporated in any structure in connection with said work by the contractor shall, as soon as incorporated, become the property of the owner. At all times the owner, at his expense, shall effect and maintain fire insurance, with extended coverage, upon the entire structure on which the work under this contract is to be done, in an amount equal to the full insurable value thereof; said insurance shall cover materials on the work site intended by the contractor to be incorporated into said structure but not yet incorporated as well as contractor's temporary buildings incident to the said work. The insured in such policy or policies shall include the owner, the contractor and such other persons as either of them may designate. Loss, if any, shall be made payable to said insured as their respective interests may appear. Certificates showing the existence of such insurance shall be delivered to the contractor if he so requests. The owner shall have power, in his sole discretion to adjust and settle any loss with the insurer which he may deem reasonable. If loss should occur and the parties hereto are unable to agree as to the division of the proceeds thereof, the question as to the amount as to which each insured shall be entitled shall be referred to arbitration as hereinafter provided.

ARTICLE X: At all times the contractor shall take all necessary precautions for the safety of persons on the work by whomsoever employed; he shall comply with all workers' compensation and similar legislation and further shall maintain at his expense public liability insurance against claims for damages because of bodily injury, including death and property damage, which may arise during his operations and those of all subcontractors under him. The insured in all such liability policies shall be the parties hereto and any others which they, or either of them, shall designate. The said insurance shall be written for not less than $ 250,000 for injuries, including death, to any one person in any one accident; not less than $ 500,000 for bodily injury, including death, to more than one person in any one accident, and $ 50,000 property damage. The contractor shall deliver to the owner within ten days after the date hereof, one or more certificates from a responsible insurance company or companies satisfactory to the owner, showing the existence of such insurance. No such insurance shall be cancelled without ten days' prior written notice to the owner.

ARTICLE XI: All disputes, claims or questions subject to arbitration under this contract shall be submitted to three arbitrators, one to be designated by the owner, one by the contractor and the two thus selected to choose the third arbitrator; each party hereto shall have the right to appear before said arbitrators either in person, by attorney or other representative and to present witnesses or evidence, if desired; the decision of the majority of said arbitrators shall be final, binding and conclusive upon all parties hereto; the parties further agree that the decision of the arbitrators shall be a condition precedent to any right of legal action which either party hereto may have against the other. The work herein contracted for shall not be delayed during any arbitration proceedings except by mutual written agreement of the parties. The expense of such arbitration shall be shared equally by the parties hereto.

© 2011 Cengage Learning. All Rights Reserved. May not be scanned, copied or duplicated, or posted to a publicly accessible website, in whole or in part.

Problem 17–3 (Continued)

ARTICLE XII: The contractor shall keep the premises (especially that part thereof under the floors thereof) free from accumulation of waste materials or rubbish and at the completion of the work shall remove all of his tools, scaffoldings and supplies and leave the premises broom-clean, or its equivalent.

ARTICLE XIII: If the owner should require a completion bond from the contractor, the premium therefor shall be added to the contract price and paid by the owner on delivery of said bond to him.

ARTICLE XIV: If the contractor employs a foreman or superintendent on said work, all directions and instructions given to the latter shall be as binding as if given to the contractor.

ARTICLE XV: The contractor agrees at all times to keep said work and the real estate on which the same is to be constructed free and clear of all construction and materialmen's liens, including liens on behalf of any subcontractor or person claiming under any such subcontractor and to defend and save the owner harmless therefrom.

ARTICLE XVI: In all respects the contractor shall be deemed to be an independent contractor.

ARTICLE XVII: In the event of any suit or action arising out of this contract, the losing party therein agrees to pay to the prevailing party therein the latter's costs and reasonable attorney's fees to be fixed by the trial court and in the event of an appeal, the prevailing party's costs and reasonable attorney's fees in the appellate court to be fixed by the appellate court.

ARTICLE XVIII: Any notice given by one party hereto to the other shall be sufficient if in writing, contained in a sealed envelope with postage thereon fully prepaid and deposited in the U. S. Registered Mails; any such notice conclusively shall be deemed received by the addressee thereof on the day of such deposit. If such notice is intended for the owner, the envelope containing the same shall be addressed to the owner at the following address: [Instructor's name, fictitious address and phone number may be used]
....,
and if intended for the contractor, if addressed to [Student name, address, and phone number]
....

ARTICLE XIX: In construing this contract and where the context so requires, the singular shall be deemed to include the plural, the masculine shall include the feminine and the neuter and all grammatical changes shall be made and implied so that this contract shall apply equally to individuals and to corporations; further, the word "work" shall mean and include the entire job undertaken to be performed by the contractor as described in the contract documents, and each thereof, together with all services, labor and materials necessary to be used and furnished to complete the same, except for the preparation of the said plans and specifications and further except the compensation of the said supervisor.

ARTICLE XX: The parties hereto further agree

that this contract is valid for a period of 60 days. If, for reasons out of the contractor's control, construction has not begun by the end of this 60–day period, contractor has the right to rebid and revise the contract.

IN WITNESS WHEREOF, the parties have hereunto set their hands in duplicate.

[Student signature]   [Fictitious signature]
....
CONTRACTOR   OWNER

....

© 2011 Cengage Learning. All Rights Reserved. May not be scanned, copied or duplicated, or posted to a publicly accessible website, in whole or in part.

CHAPTER 18 PRESENTATION DRAWINGS

Problem 18–1

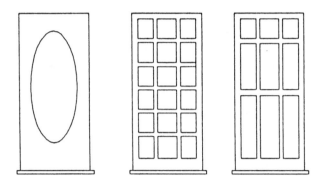

ANSWERS WILL VARY GREATLY

Problem 18–2

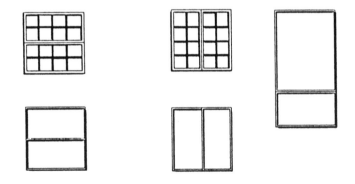

ANSWERS WILL VARY GREATLY

Problem 18–3

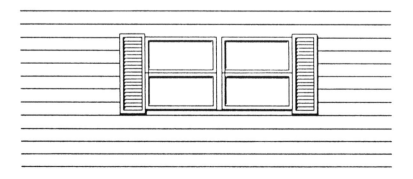

© 2011 Cengage Learning. All Rights Reserved. May not be scanned, copied or duplicated, or posted to a publicly accessible website, in whole or in part.

Problem 18–4

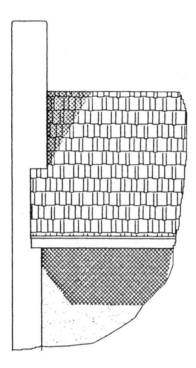

Problem 18–5

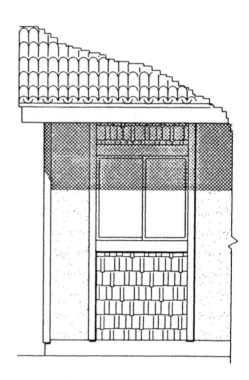

Problem 18–6

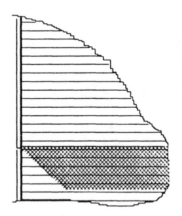
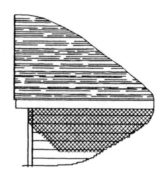

© 2011 Cengage Learning. All Rights Reserved. May not be scanned, copied or duplicated, or posted to a publicly accessible website, in whole or in part.

Problem 18–7

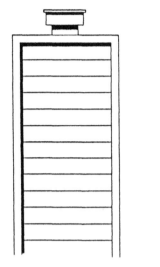

Problem 18–8

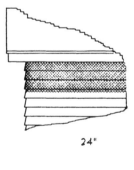

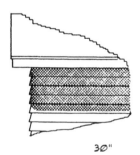

24"

30"

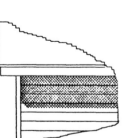

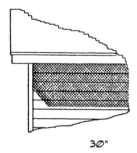

24"

30"

© 2011 Cengage Learning. All Rights Reserved. May not be scanned, copied or duplicated, or posted to a publicly accessible website, in whole or in part.

Problem 18–9

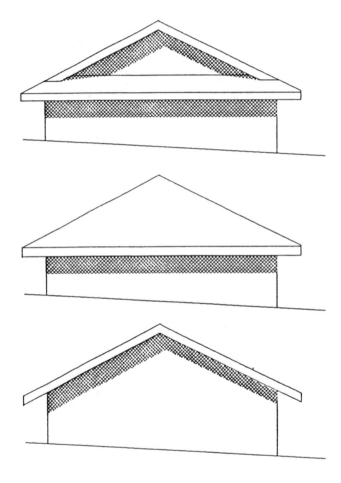

© 2011 Cengage Learning. All Rights Reserved. May not be scanned, copied or duplicated, or posted to a publicly accessible website, in whole or in part.

Problem 18–10

© 2011 Cengage Learning. All Rights Reserved. May not be scanned, copied or duplicated, or posted to a publicly accessible website, in whole or in part.

Problem 18–11

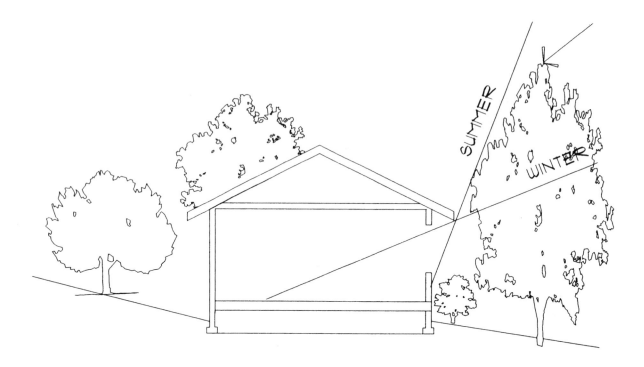

Problem 18–12

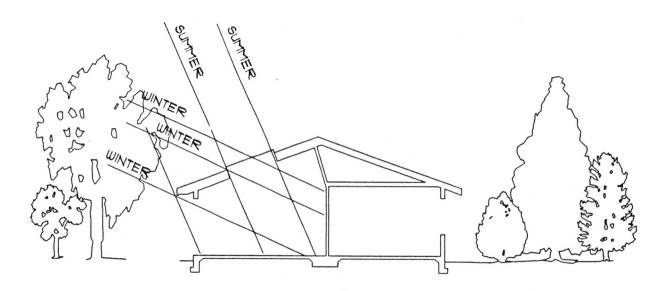

© 2011 Cengage Learning. All Rights Reserved. May not be scanned, copied or duplicated, or posted to a publicly accessible website, in whole or in part.

Problem 18–13   Student drawings will vary greatly. Projects should resemble Figure 41–26 from the textbook and should include the shape of the property, the outline of the structure, the shape of the roof, access streets, driveways, walkways, curb cuts, and planting.

Problem 18–14   The rendered floor plan for each project presented in Chapter 14 will vary greatly. Each plan should include the basic floor plan showing walls, doors, windows, cabinets, plumbing fixtures, and room names and sizes. Finishes such as tile, concrete, or wood plank floors should be shown for interior surfaces as well as exterior decks and patios. A north arrow, shrubs, and a car should also be included.

Problem 18–15   Student drawings will vary greatly. Projects should resemble Figure 41–23 from the textbook.

Problem 18–16   Student drawings will vary greatly. Projects should resemble Figure 41-30 from the textbook and should include the base elevation with all siding and roofing materials represented. Shade and shadows, as well as planting and a car, should be represented.

Problem 18–17   Students' samples will vary greatly. projects should be parallel, square to borders, and free of wrinkles.

© 2011 Cengage Learning. All Rights Reserved. May not be scanned, copied or duplicated, or posted to a publicly accessible website, in whole or in part.

Problem 18–18

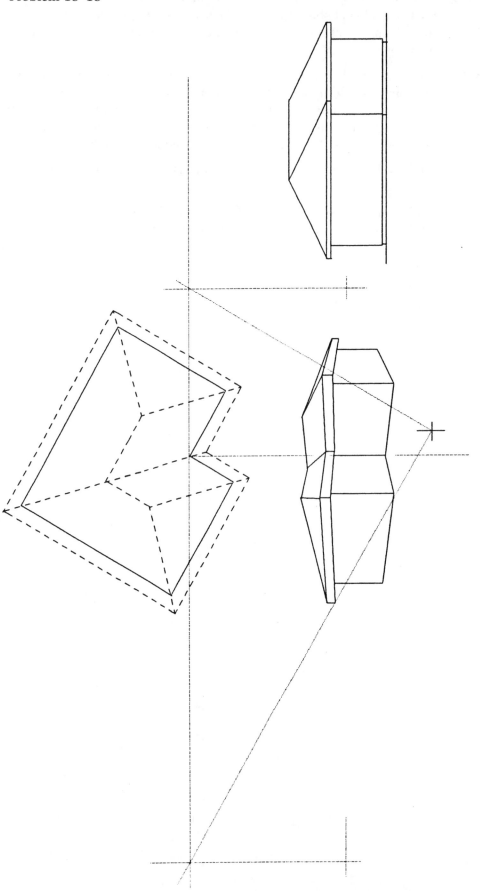

ANSWERS WILL VARY GREATLY

© 2011 Cengage Learning. All Rights Reserved. May not be scanned, copied or duplicated, or posted to a publicly accessible website, in whole or in part.

Problem 18–19

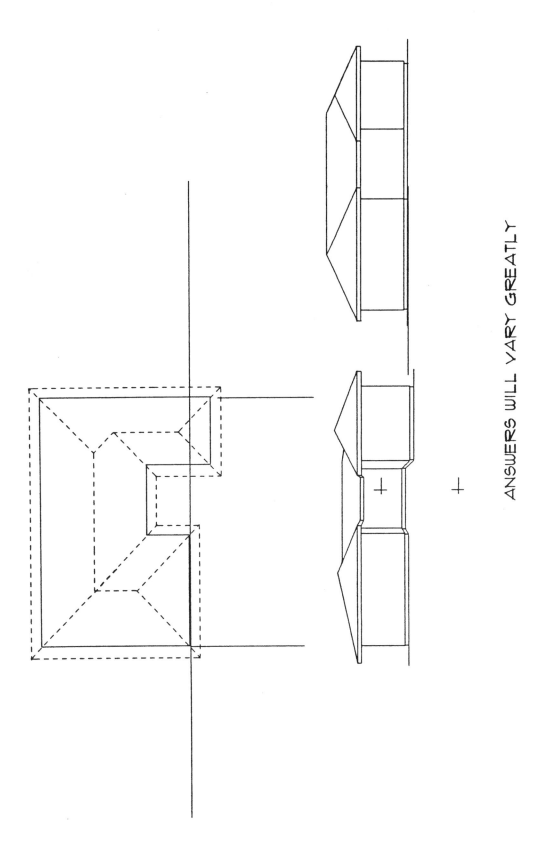

ANSWERS WILL VARY GREATLY

© 2011 Cengage Learning. All Rights Reserved. May not be scanned, copied or duplicated, or posted to a publicly accessible website, in whole or in part.

Problem 18–20

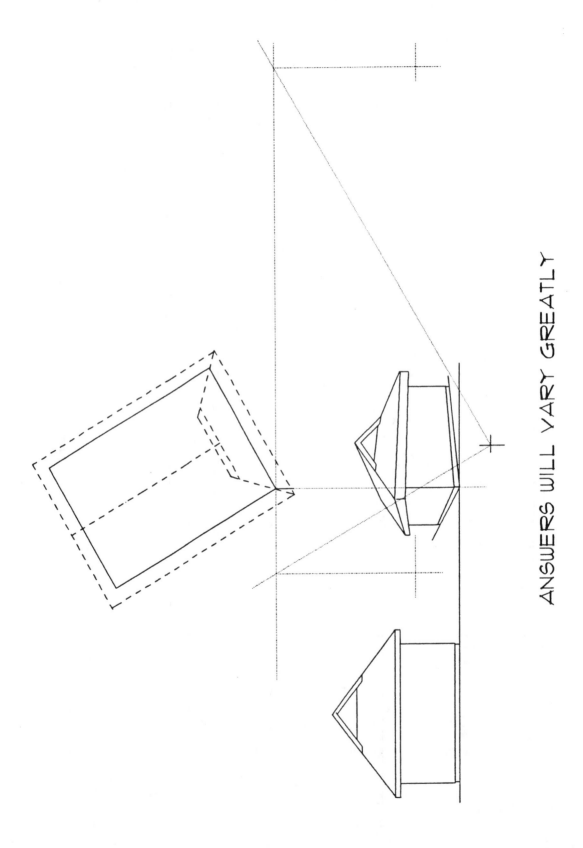

ANSWERS WILL VARY GREATLY

© 2011 Cengage Learning. All Rights Reserved. May not be scanned, copied or duplicated, or posted to a publicly accessible website, in whole or in part.

Problem 18–21

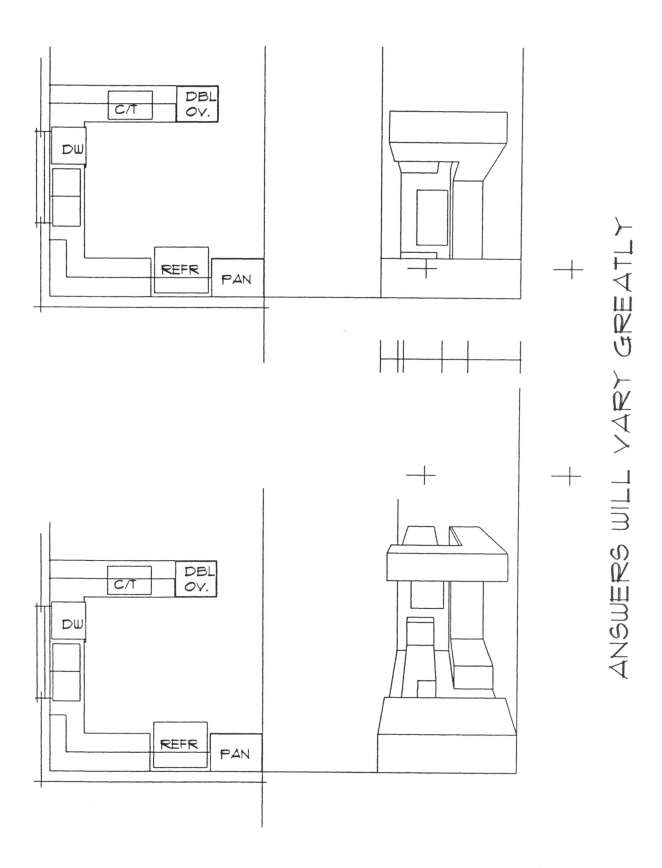

ANSWERS WILL VARY GREATLY

© 2011 Cengage Learning. All Rights Reserved. May not be scanned, copied or duplicated, or posted to a publicly accessible website, in whole or in part.

© 2011 Cengage Learning. All Rights Reserved. May not be scanned, copied or duplicated, or posted to a publicly accessible website, in whole or in part.

SECTION 2

Advanced Residential Projects

For all Advanced Residential Projects, student solutions will vary. A complete set of plans may include the following drawing elements:

1. Floor plans
2. Elevations
3. Foundation plans
4. Roof plans
5. Typical Section, Sections, Details, Fireplace and Stair Sections, if applicable
6. Cabinet elevations

Optional plans (if not presented on the previous plans):

1. Electrical plan
2. Plumbing plan
3. HVAC plan

© 2011 Cengage Learning. All Rights Reserved. May not be scanned, copied or duplicated, or posted to a publicly accessible website, in whole or in part.

Problem 1   Two-story

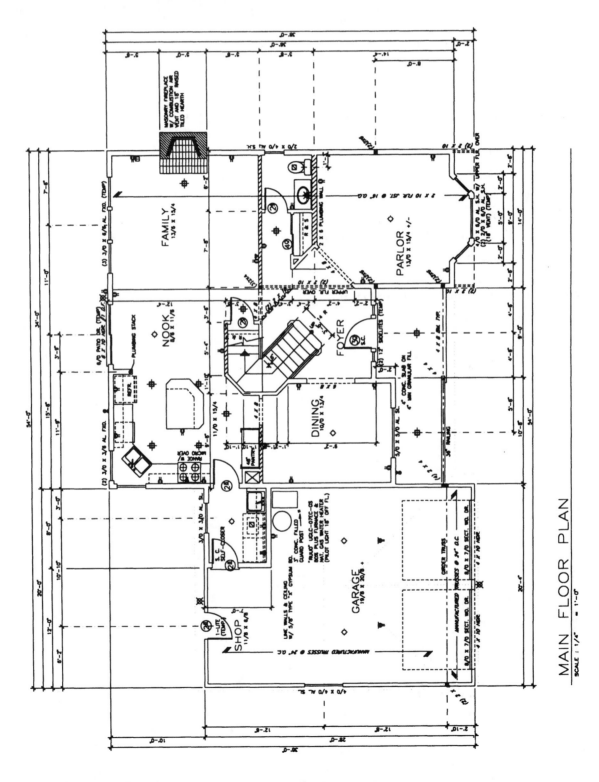

MAIN FLOOR PLAN
SCALE : 1/4" = 1'-0"

© 2011 Cengage Learning. All Rights Reserved. May not be scanned, copied or duplicated, or posted to a publicly accessible website, in whole or in part.

Problem 1   Two-story (Continued)

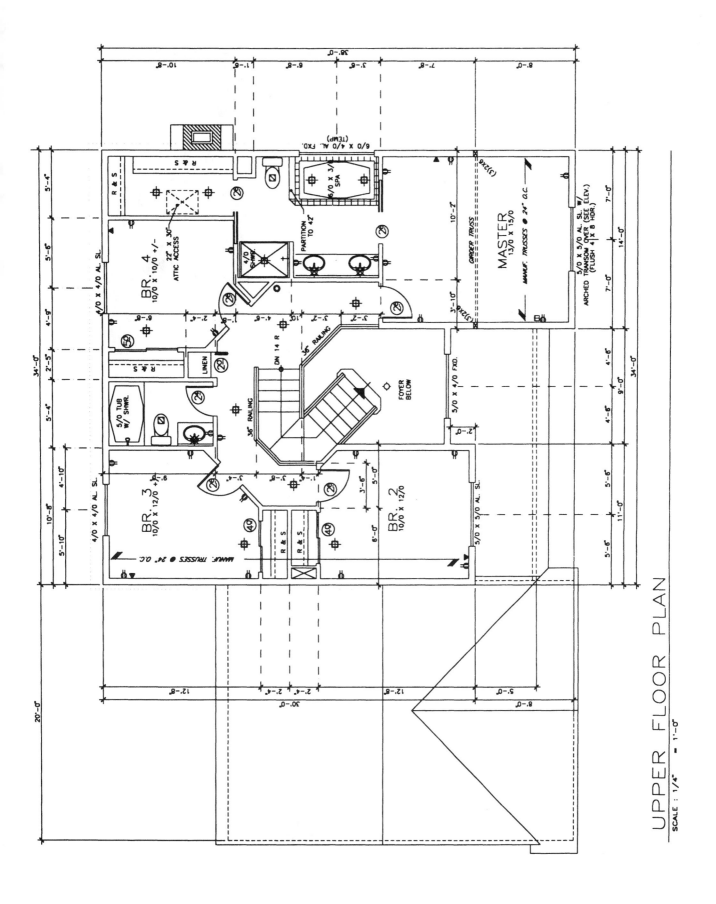

UPPER FLOOR PLAN

SCALE : 1/4" = 1'-0"

© 2011 Cengage Learning. All Rights Reserved. May not be scanned, copied or duplicated, or posted to a publicly accessible website, in whole or in part.

Problem 1   Two-story (Continued)

FRONT ELEVATION
SCALE : 1/4" = 1'-0"

LEFT SIDE ELEVATION
SCALE : 1/4" = 1'-0"

GENERAL NOTES

© 2011 Cengage Learning. All Rights Reserved. May not be scanned, copied or duplicated, or posted to a publicly accessible website, in whole or in part.

Problem 1   Two-story (Continued)

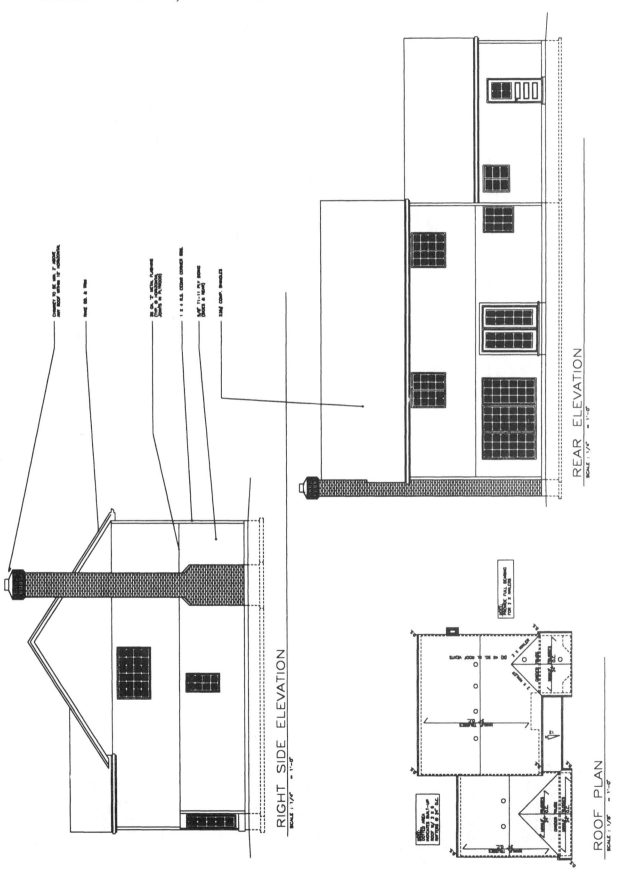

© 2011 Cengage Learning. All Rights Reserved. May not be scanned, copied or duplicated, or posted to a publicly accessible website, in whole or in part.

Problem 1   Two-story (Continued)

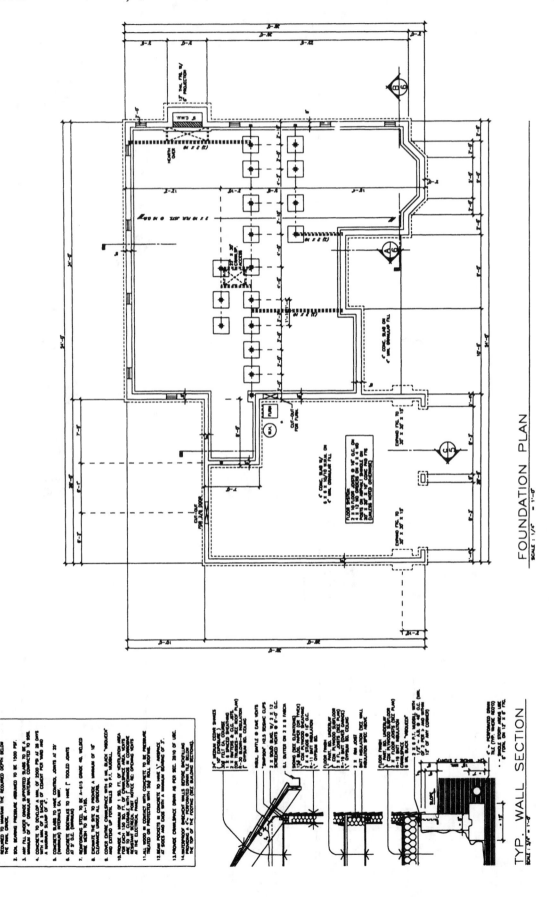

FOUNDATION PLAN

SCALE : 1/4" = 1'-0"

FOUNDATION NOTES

TYP. WALL SECTION

SCALE : 1/4" = 1'-0"

© 2011 Cengage Learning. All Rights Reserved. May not be scanned, copied or duplicated, or posted to a publicly accessible website, in whole or in part.

Problem 1   Two-story (Continued)

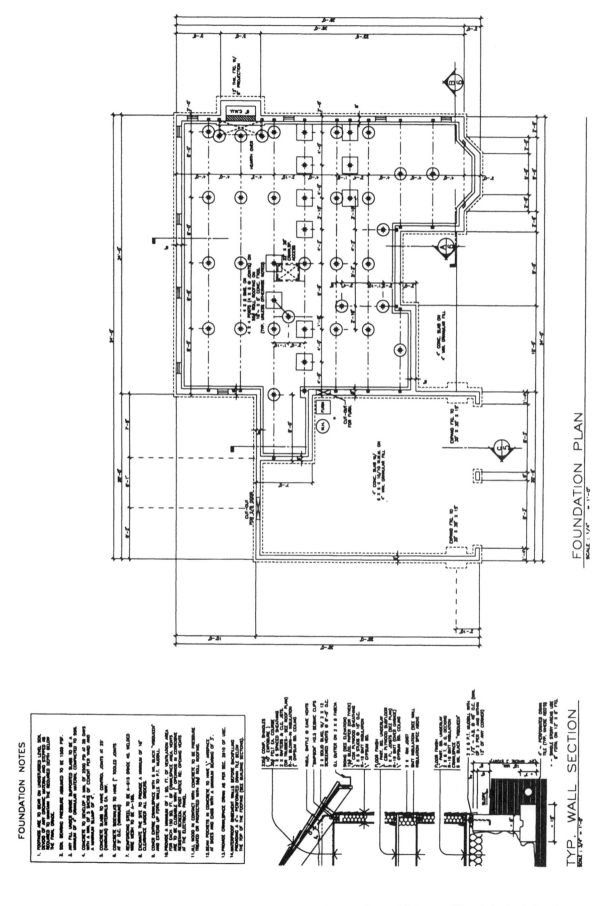

FOUNDATION PLAN

TYP. WALL SECTION

FOUNDATION NOTES

© 2011 Cengage Learning. All Rights Reserved. May not be scanned, copied or duplicated, or posted to a publicly accessible website, in whole or in part.

Problem 1   Two-story (Continued)

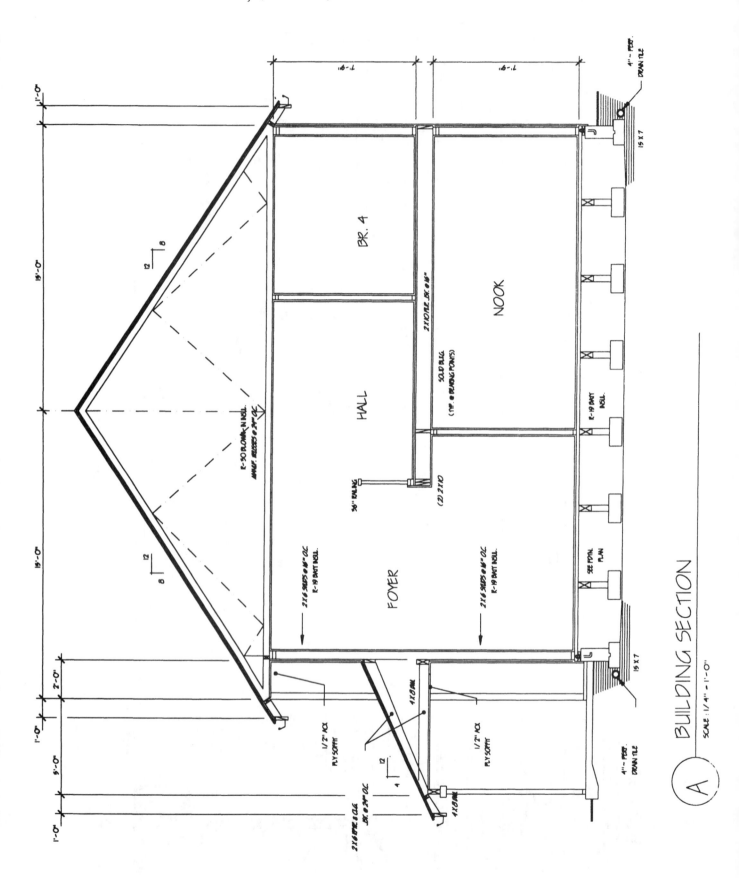

BUILDING SECTION

SCALE : 1/4" = 1'-0"

A

© 2011 Cengage Learning. All Rights Reserved. May not be scanned, copied or duplicated, or posted to a publicly accessible website, in whole or in part.

Problem 1   Two-story (Continued)

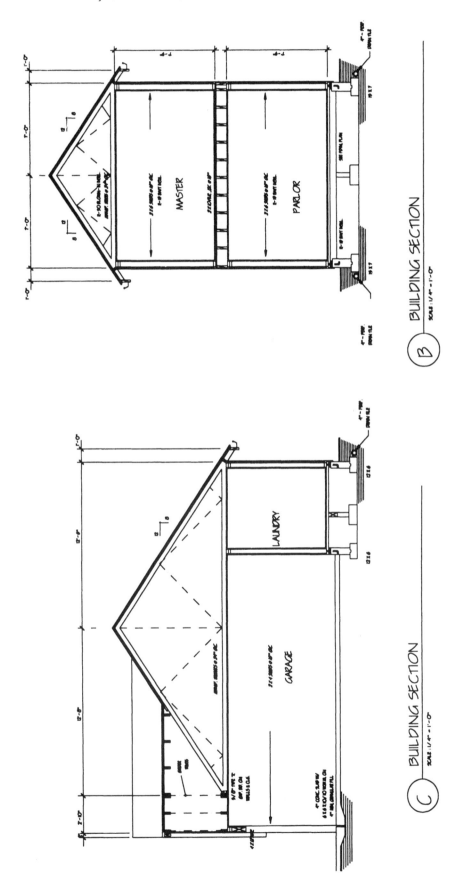

© 2011 Cengage Learning. All Rights Reserved. May not be scanned, copied or duplicated, or posted to a publicly accessible website, in whole or in part.

Problem 1   Two-story (Continued)

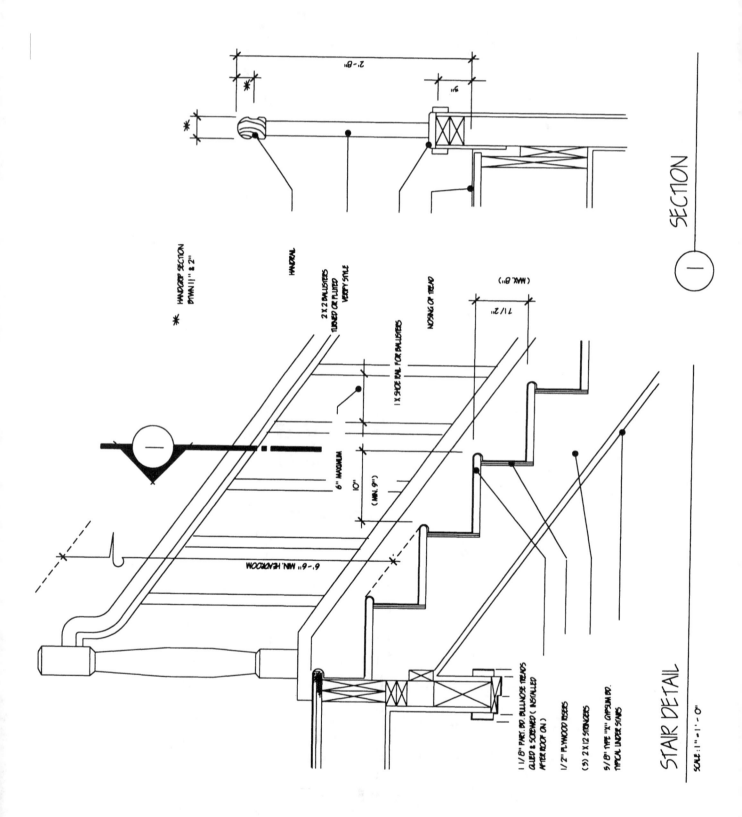

SECTION

STAIR DETAIL

SCALE: 1" = 1'-0"

© 2011 Cengage Learning. All Rights Reserved. May not be scanned, copied or duplicated, or posted to a publicly accessible website, in whole or in part.

Problem 1   Two-story (Continued)

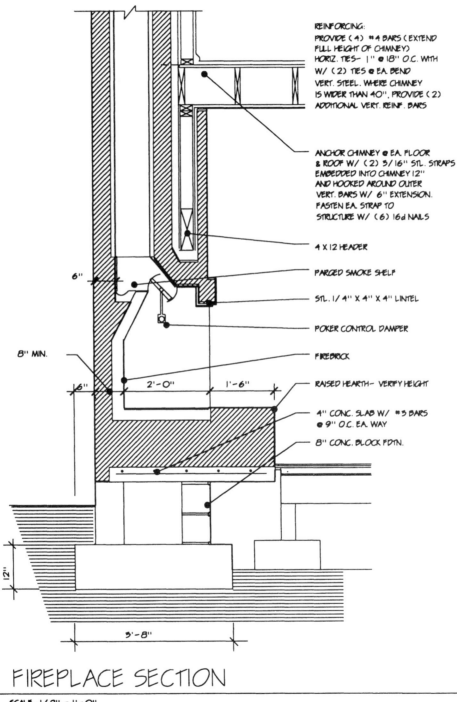

REINFORCING:
PROVIDE (4) #4 BARS (EXTEND FULL HEIGHT OF CHIMNEY)
HORIZ. TIES- 1" @ 18" O.C. WITH W/ (2) TIES @ EA. BEND
VERT. STEEL. WHERE CHIMNEY IS WIDER THAN 40", PROVIDE (2) ADDITIONAL VERT. REINF. BARS

ANCHOR CHIMNEY @ EA. FLOOR & ROOF W/ (2) 3/16" STL. STRAPS EMBEDDED INTO CHIMNEY 12" AND HOOKED AROUND OUTER VERT. BARS W/ 6" EXTENSION. FASTEN EA. STRAP TO STRUCTURE W/ (6) 16d NAILS

4 X 12 HEADER

PARGED SMOKE SHELF

STL. 1/4" X 4" X 4" LINTEL

POKER CONTROL DAMPER

FIREBRICK

RAISED HEARTH— VERIFY HEIGHT

4" CONC. SLAB W/ #3 BARS @ 9" O.C. EA. WAY

8" CONC. BLOCK FDTN.

6"

8" MIN.

6"

2'-0"   1'-6"

12"

3'-8"

FIREPLACE SECTION

SCALE : 1/2" = 1'-0"

© 2011 Cengage Learning. All Rights Reserved. May not be scanned, copied or duplicated, or posted to a publicly accessible website, in whole or in part.

Problem 1   Two-story (Continued)

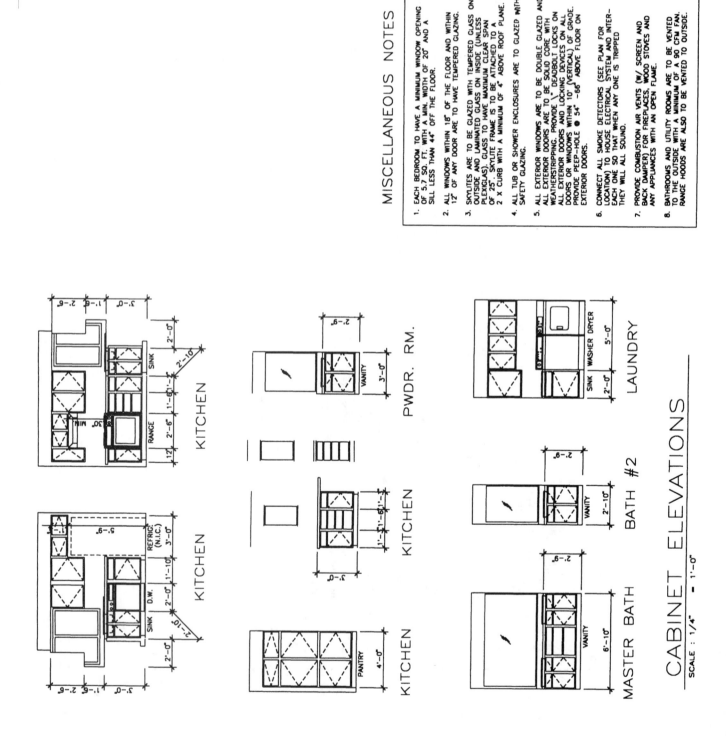

MISCELLANEOUS NOTES

1. EACH BEDROOM TO HAVE A MINIMUM WINDOW OPENING OF 5.7 SQ. FT. WITH A MIN. WIDTH OF 20" AND A SILL LESS THAN 44" OFF THE FLOOR.

2. ALL WINDOWS WITHIN 18" OF THE FLOOR AND WITHIN 12" OF ANY DOOR ARE TO HAVE TEMPERED GLAZING.

3. SKYLITES ARE TO BE GLAZED WITH TEMPERED GLASS ON OUTSIDE AND LAMINATED GLASS ON INSIDE (UNLESS PLEXIGLAS). GLASS TO HAVE MAXIMUM CLEAR SPAN OF 25". SKYLITE FRAME IS TO BE ATTACHED TO A 2 × CURB WITH A MINIMUM OF 4" ABOVE ROOF PLANE.

4. ALL TUB OR SHOWER ENCLOSURES ARE TO GLAZED WITH SAFETY GLAZING.

5. ALL EXTERIOR WINDOWS ARE TO BE DOUBLE GLAZED AND ALL EXTERIOR DOORS ARE TO BE SOLID CORE WITH WEATHERSTRIPPING. PROVIDE 1" DEADBOLT LOCKS ON ALL EXTERIOR DOORS AND LOCKING DEVICES ON ALL DOORS OR WINDOWS WITHIN 10' (VERTICAL) OF GRADE. PROVIDE PEEP-HOLE @ 54" -66" ABOVE FLOOR ON EXTERIOR DOORS.

6. CONNECT ALL SMOKE DETECTORS (SEE PLAN FOR LOCATION) TO HOUSE ELECTRICAL SYSTEM AND INTER-CONNECT EACH ONE SO THAT WHEN ANY ONE IS TRIPPED THEY WILL ALL SOUND.

7. PROVIDE COMBUSTION AIR VENTS (W/ SCREEN AND BACK DAMPER) FOR FIREPLACES, WOOD STOVES AND ANY APPLIANCES WITH AN OPEN FLAME.

8. BATHROOMS AND UTILITY ROOMS ARE TO BE VENTED TO THE OUTSIDE WITH A MINIMUM OF A 90 CFM FAN. RANGE HOODS ARE ALSO TO BE VENTED TO OUTSIDE.

KITCHEN

KITCHEN

PWDR. RM.

KITCHEN

KITCHEN

LAUNDRY

BATH #2

MASTER BATH

CABINET ELEVATIONS

SCALE : 1/4" = 1'-0"

© 2011 Cengage Learning. All Rights Reserved. May not be scanned, copied or duplicated, or posted to a publicly accessible website, in whole or in part.

Problem 2   One-story with Full Basement

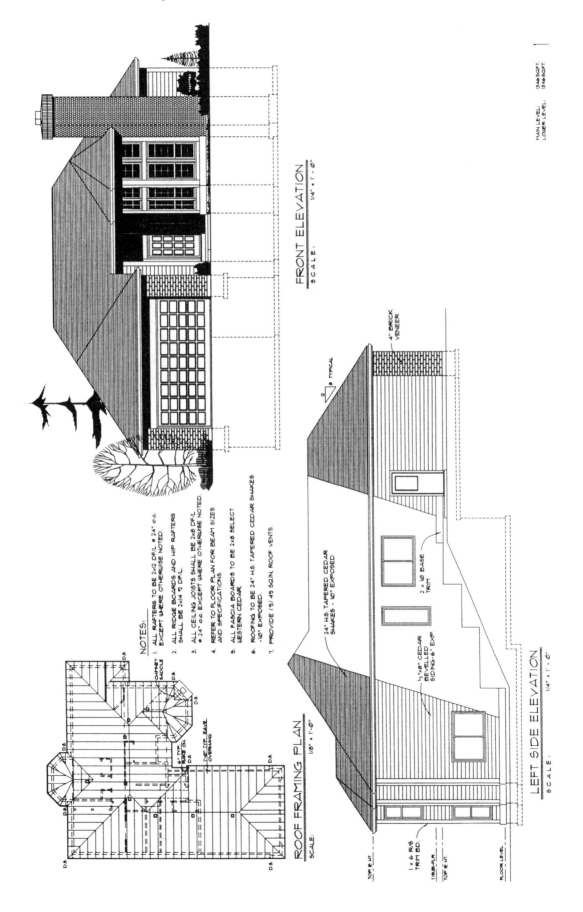

MAIN LEVEL: 1346 SQFT.
LOWER LEVEL: 1346 SQFT.

FRONT ELEVATION
SCALE: 1/4" = 1'-0"

4" BRICK
VENEER

12 TYPICAL

24" H.S. TAPERED CEDAR
SHAKES - 10" EXPOSED

2 x 10 BASE
TRIM

1/2 x 8" CEDAR
BEVELLED
SIDING - 6" EXP.

LEFT SIDE ELEVATION
SCALE: 1/4" = 1'-0"

1 x 6 R/S
TRIM BD.

TOP #1 HT.

TOP WALL PLATE
TOP #1 HT.

FLOOR LEVEL

NOTES:

1. ALL RAFTERS TO BE 2x12 DF/L @ 24" O.C.
    EXCEPT WHERE OTHERWISE NOTED.

2. ALL RIDGE BOARDS AND HIP RAFTERS
    SHALL BE 2x14 #2 DF/L.

3. ALL CEILING JOISTS SHALL BE 2x8 DF/L
    @ 24" O.C. EXCEPT WHERE OTHERWISE NOTED.

4. REFER TO FLOOR PLAN FOR BEAM SIZES
    AND SPECIFICATIONS.

5. ALL FASCIA BOARDS TO BE 2x8 SELECT
    WESTERN CEDAR.

6. ROOFING TO BE 24" H.S. TAPERED CEDAR SHAKES
    - 10" EXPOSED.

7. PROVIDE (3) 49 SQ.IN. ROOF VENTS.

ROOF FRAMING PLAN
SCALE: 1/8" = 1'-0"

CHIMNEY
SADDLE

6" TYP
RAKE O.H.

1-6" TYP. EAVE
OVERHANG

© 2011 Cengage Learning. All Rights Reserved. May not be scanned, copied or duplicated, or posted to a publicly accessible website, in whole or in part.

Problem 2   One-story with Full Basement (Continued)

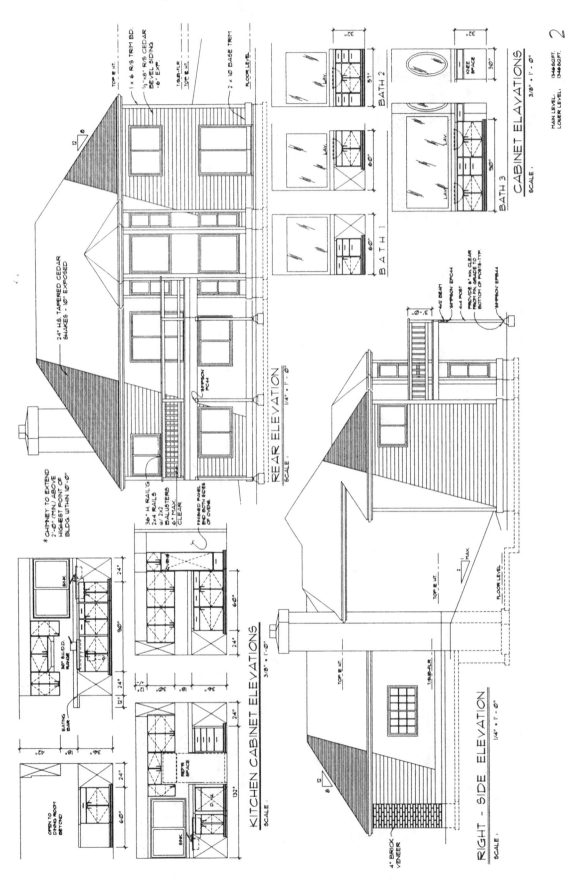

© 2011 Cengage Learning. All Rights Reserved. May not be scanned, copied or duplicated, or posted to a publicly accessible website, in whole or in part.

Problem 2   One-story with Full Basement (Continued)

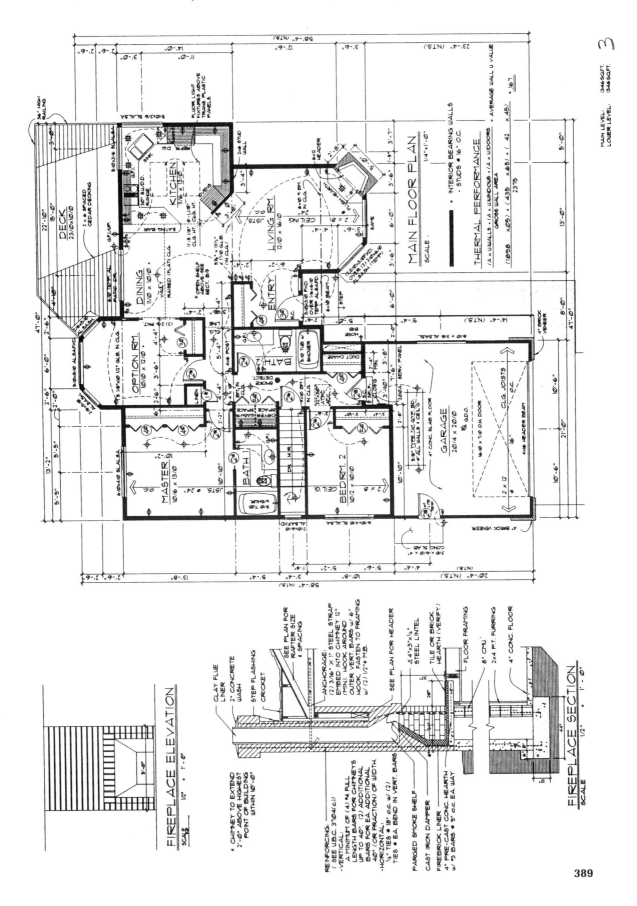

389

© 2011 Cengage Learning. All Rights Reserved. May not be scanned, copied or duplicated, or posted to a publicly accessible website, in whole or in part.

Problem 2   One-story with Full Basement (Continued)

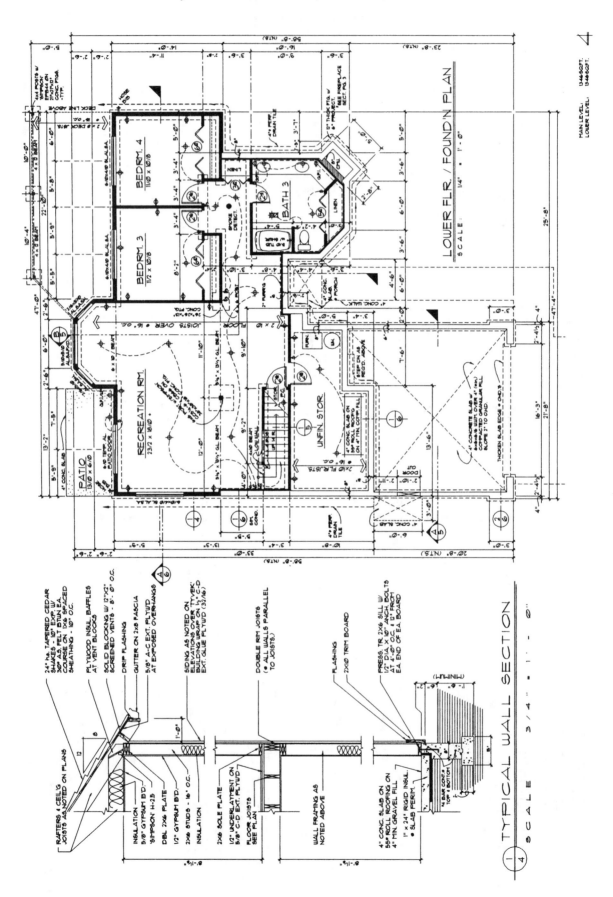

© 2011 Cengage Learning. All Rights Reserved. May not be scanned, copied or duplicated, or posted to a publicly accessible website, in whole or in part.

Problem 2   One-story with Full Basement (Continued)

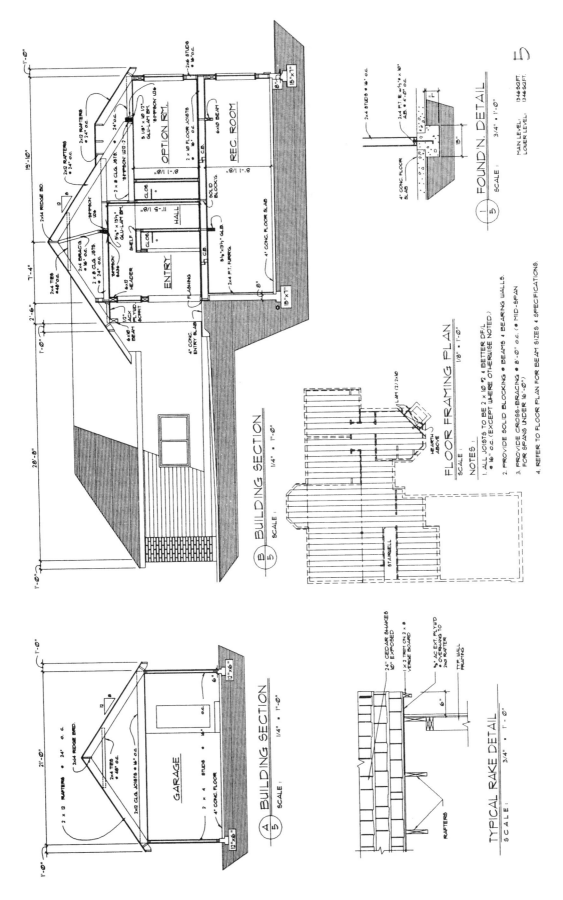

© 2011 Cengage Learning. All Rights Reserved. May not be scanned, copied or duplicated, or posted to a publicly accessible website, in whole or in part.

Problem 2 One-story with Full Basement (Continued)

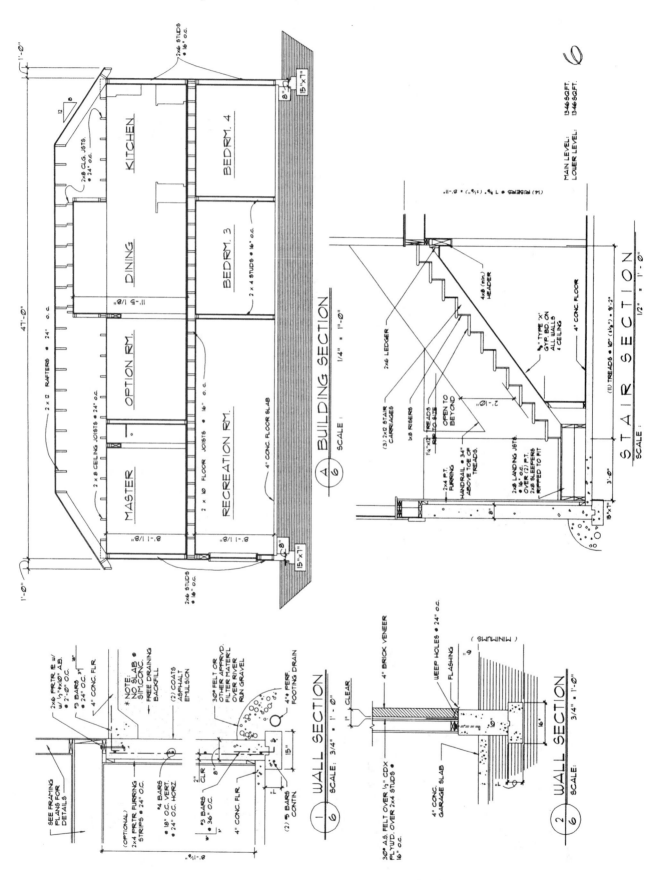

© 2011 Cengage Learning. All Rights Reserved. May not be scanned, copied or duplicated, or posted to a publicly accessible website, in whole or in part.

Problem 3   Split level

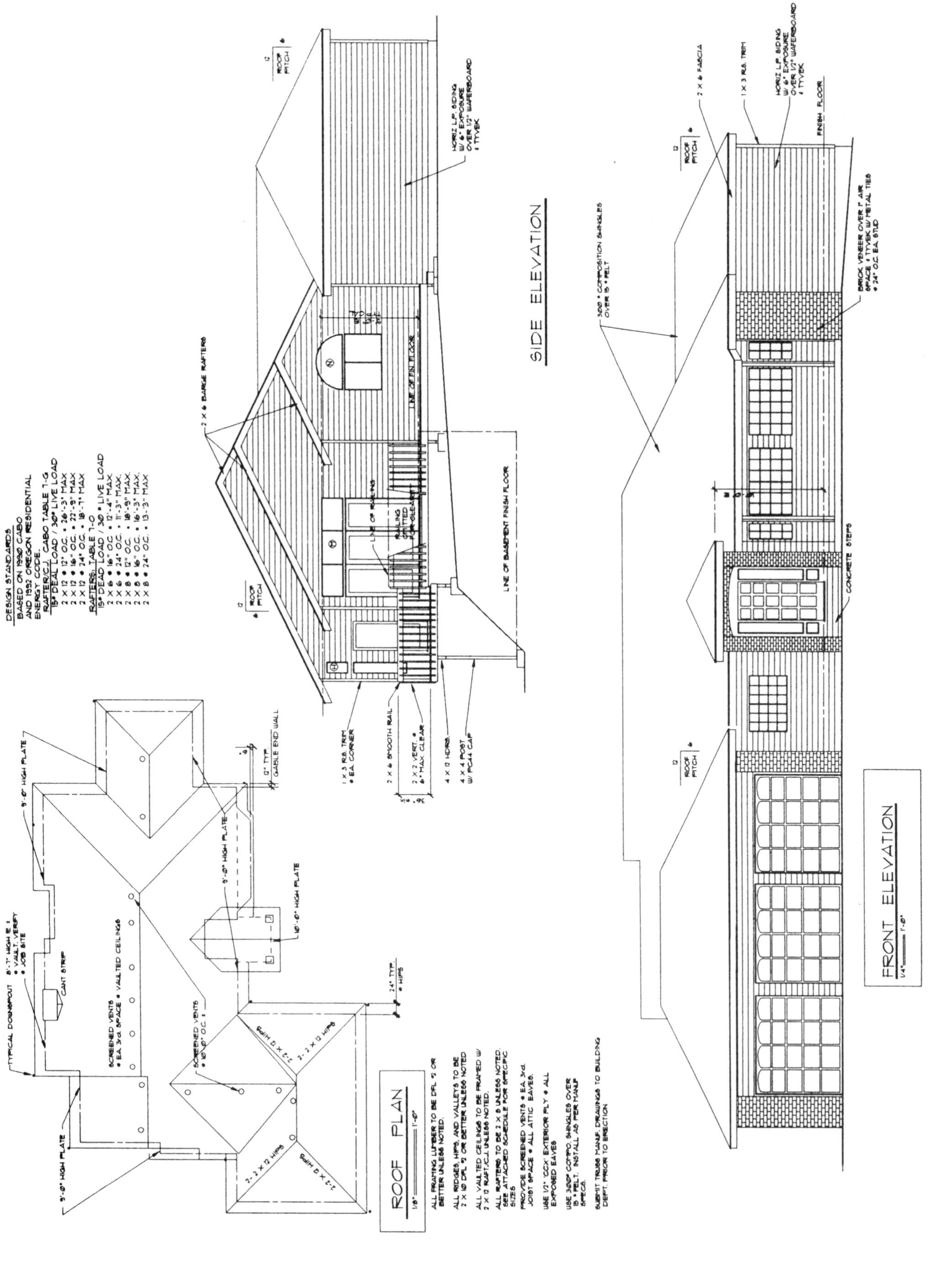

SIDE ELEVATION

FRONT ELEVATION
1/4"

ROOF PLAN
1/8"

DESIGN STANDARDS
BASED ON 1990 CABO
AND 1992 OREGON RESIDENTIAL
ENERGY CODE.

© 2011 Cengage Learning. All Rights Reserved. May not be scanned, copied or duplicated, or posted to a publicly accessible website, in whole or in part.

Problem 3   Split level (Continued)

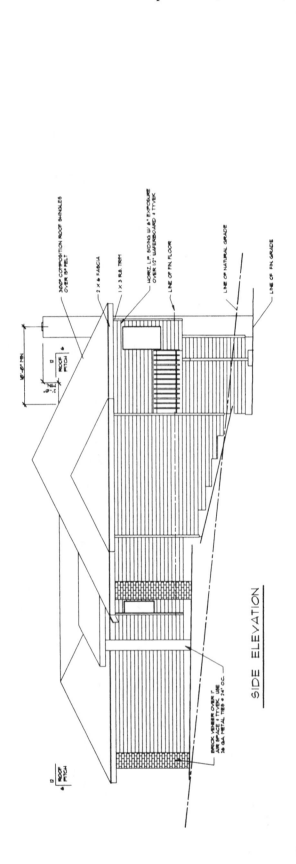

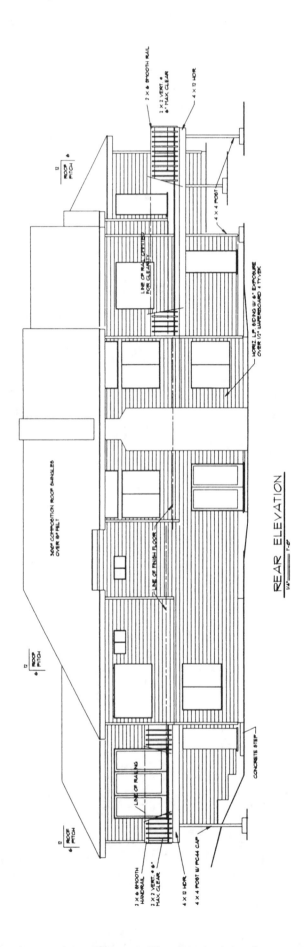

© 2011 Cengage Learning. All Rights Reserved. May not be scanned, copied or duplicated, or posted to a publicly accessible website, in whole or in part.

Problem 3   Split level (Continued)

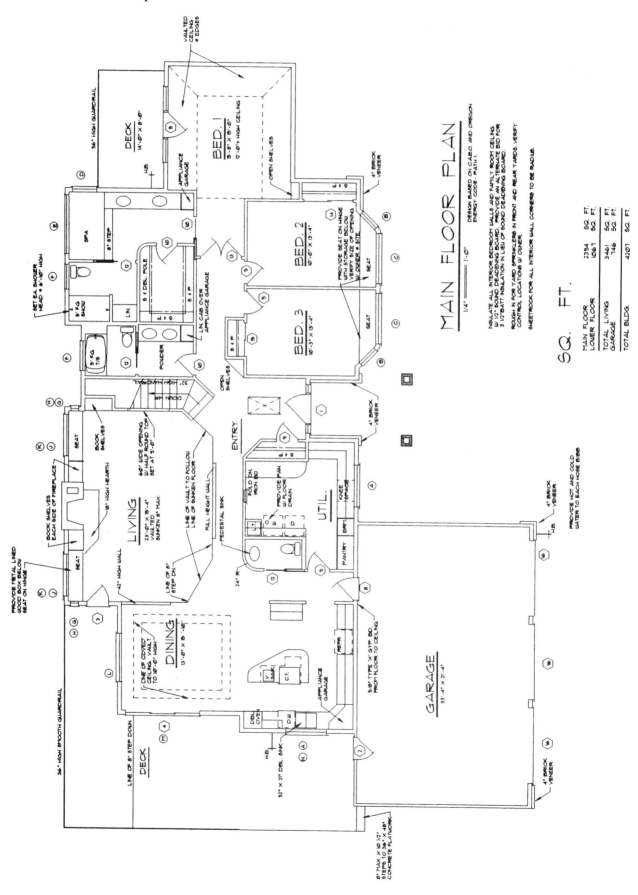

© 2011 Cengage Learning. All Rights Reserved. May not be scanned, copied or duplicated, or posted to a publicly accessible website, in whole or in part.

Problem 3   Split level (Continued)

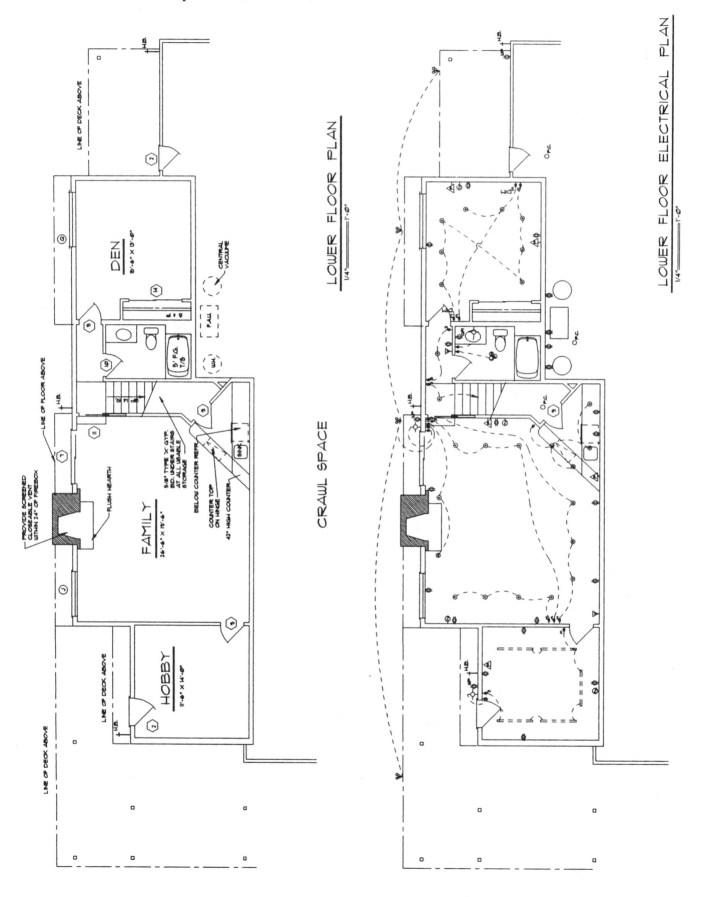

LOWER FLOOR PLAN

LOWER FLOOR ELECTRICAL PLAN

© 2011 Cengage Learning. All Rights Reserved. May not be scanned, copied or duplicated, or posted to a publicly accessible website, in whole or in part.

Problem 3   Split level (Continued)

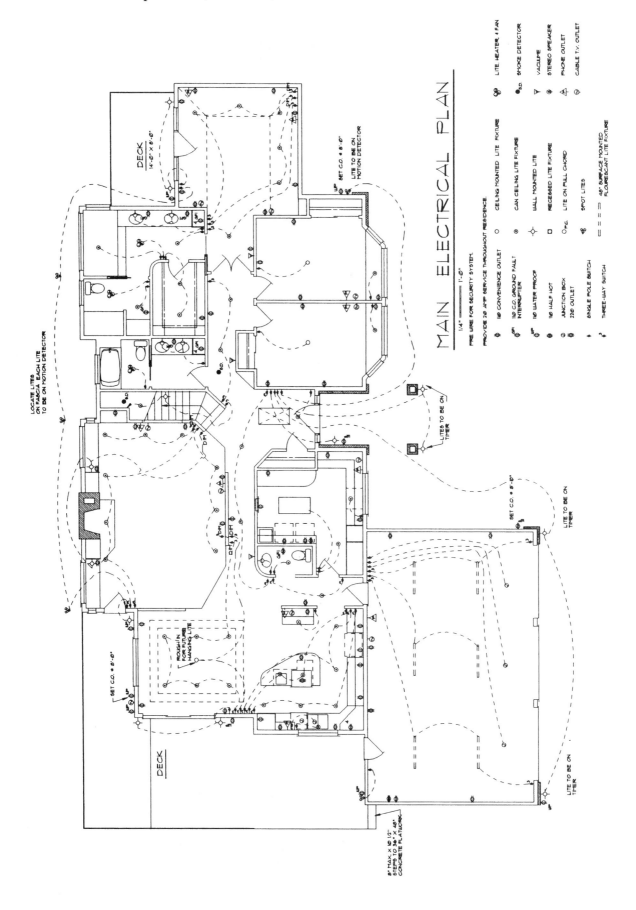

© 2011 Cengage Learning. All Rights Reserved. May not be scanned, copied or duplicated, or posted to a publicly accessible website, in whole or in part.

Problem 3   Split level (Continued)

FASTENER SCHEDULE

DESCRIPTION OF BUILDING MATERIAL	NUMBER & TYPE OF FASTENERS (1,2,3)	SPACING OF FASTENERS

ALTERNATE ATTACHMENTS
TABLE NO R 4623A (1)

NOMINAL THICKNESS	DESCRIPTION (12) OF FASTENERS & LENGTH	SPACING OF FASTENERS	
		EDGES	INTERMEDIATE SUPPORTS

FLOOR UNDERLAYMENT, PLYWOOD, HARDBOARD, PARTICLEBOARD

FRAMING NOTES:

NOTES SHALL APPLY TO ALL LEVELS.

1. ALL FRAMING LUMBER TO BE DFL #2 STUDS & BTR.
2. FRAME ALL EXTERIOR WALLS W/ 2 x 6 STUDS @ 16" O.C. FRAME ALL INTERIOR NON-BEARING WALLS W/ 2 x 6 STUDS @ 24" O.C.
3. USE 2 x 6 NAILER AT THE BOTTOM OF ALL 2-2x10 OR 4 x HEADERS @ EXTERIOR WALLS. BACK HEADER W/ 2" RIGID INSULATION.
4. ALL SHEAR PANELS TO BE 1/2" PLY NAILED W/ 8d'S @ 4" O.C. AT EDGE AND BLOCKING AND 6 @ 8' O.C. @ FIELD.
5. PLYWOOD ROOF SHEATHING TO BE 1/2" STD. GRADE 32/16 PLY. LAID PERP. TO RAFTERS. NAIL W/ 8d @ 6' O.C. EDGES AND 12" O.C. AT FIELD
6. PROVIDE 3/4" STD. GRADE T. & G PLY. FLOOR SHEATHING LAID PERP. TO FLOOR JOIST. NAIL W/ 10d @ 6 46" O.C. EDGES AND BLOCKING AND 12" O.C. @ FIELD. COVER W/ 3/8" HARDBOARD.
7. BLOCK ALL WALLS OVER 10'-0" HIGH AT MID HEIGHT.
8. LET-IN BRACES TO BE 1 x 4 DIAG BRACES @ 45° FOR ALL INTERIOR LOAD-BEARING WALLS.

DOOR SCHEDULE

SYM	SIZE	TYPE	QUAN
1	3'-6" X 8'-0"	S.C. RAISED PANEL	1
2	2'-8" X 6'-8"	METAL INSUL.	3
3	2'-8" X 6'-8"	1-LITE FRENCH	1
4	5'-0" X 6'-8"	SLIDING - TEMPERED	1
5	3'-0" X 6'-8"	1-LITE FRENCH	1
7	6'-0" X 6'-8"	SLIDING - TEMPERED	1
8	2'-8" X 6'-8"	METAL INSUL. / SELF CLOSING	1
9	2'-6" X 6'-8"	INTERIOR	4
10	2'-8" X 6'-8"	INTERIOR	4
11	2'-6" X 6'-8"	POCKET	4
13	PR 2'-6" X 6'-8"	PR 1-LITE FRENCH	1
14	6'-0" X 6'-8"	BI-PASS	2
15	4'-0" X 6'-8"	BI-PASS	1
16	9'-0" X 8'-0"	OVERHEAD GARAGE	3

DOOR NOTES:
1. FRONT DOOR TO BE RATED AT 0.54 OR LESS.
2. EXTERIOR DOORS IN HEATED WALLS TO BE U 0.20 OR LESS.
3. DOORS THAT EXCEED 50% GLASS ARE TO BE U 0.40 OR LESS.
4. ALL INTERIOR DOORS TO BE RAISED 6 PANEL DOORS.

WINDOW SCHEDULE

SYM	SIZE	TYPE	QUAN
A	5'-0" X 3'-6"	SLDG. W/ GRIDS	1
B	2'-6" X 4'-0"	CASEMENT W/ GRIDS	2
C	6'-0" X 4'-0"	SLIDING W/ GRIDS	2
D	3'-0" X 5'-0"	CASEMENT - TEMPERED	2
E	7'-0" X 5'-0"	FIXED - TEMPERED	1
F	3'-0" X 5'-0"	FIXED	2
G	1'-0" X 5'-0"	FIXED	2
H	1'-6" X 2'-0"	TRANSOM	2
J	5'-0" X 5'-0"	SLDG.	3
K	3'-0" X 2'-0"	TRANSOM	2
L	6'-0" X 5'-0"	FIXED	1
M	9'-0" X 2'-0"	TRANSOM	1
N	5'-0" X 2'-6"	1/2" ROUND	1
Q	6'-0" X 5'-0"	SLDG.	1

WINDOW NOTES:
1. ALL WINDOW TO BE U-.40 MIN. PROVIDE ALT. BIDD FOR U-.33 IF FLAT CEILINGS ARE INSULATED TO R-49.
2. ALL WINDOW TO BE MILGARD OR EQUAL VINYL FRAME WINDOWS
3. ALL BEDROOM WINDOW TO BE SET AT 6'-1/2" OFF FIN FLOOR.
4. ALL WINDOW HEADERS TO BE SET AT 6'-1/2" UNLESS NOTED.
5. UNLESS NOTED ALL HEADERS OVER EXTERIOR DOORS AND WINDOW TO BE 4" WIDE WITH 2" RIGID INSULATION BACKER. SEE TYPICAL SECTION.

SKYLITES:
1. ALL SKYLITES TO BE VELUX OR EQUAL DOUBLE DOMED PLASTIC OPENABLE SKYLITES. U-.50 MIN.

DESIGN STANDARDS
BASED ON 1990 CABO AND 1993 OREGON RESIDENTIAL ENERGY CODE.

RAFTERS/CD CABO TABLE 7-G
15# DEAD LOAD / 30# LIVE LOAD
2 x 12 @ 12" O.C. 26'-3" MAX
2 x 10 @ 16" O.C. 22'-3" MAX
2 x 12 @ 24" O.C. 18'-7" MAX

RAFTERS, TABLE 7-O
15# DEAD LOAD / 30# LIVE LOAD
2 x 6 @ 12" O.C. 13'-4" MAX
2 x 6 @ 24" O.C. 11'-3" MAX
2 x 8 @ 12" O.C. 18'-5" MAX
2 x 8 @ 24" O.C. 13'-3" MAX

FLOOR JOIST, TABLE 6-A
LIVE LOAD 40# / DEAD LOAD 10#
2 x 10 @ 12" O.C. 18'-5" MAX
2 x 10 @ 16" O.C. 16'-5" MAX
2 x 12 @ 24" O.C. 14'-7" MAX

DECK FLOOR JOIST /BEAMS
LIVE LOAD 60#, HEAD LOAD 10
2 x 6 @ 8" O.C. 13'-0" SPAN
2 x 8 @ 12" O.C. 13'-0" MAX
2 x 8 @ 16" O.C. 11'-0" MAX

© 2011 Cengage Learning. All Rights Reserved. May not be scanned, copied or duplicated, or posted to a publicly accessible website, in whole or in part.

Problem 3   Split level (Continued)

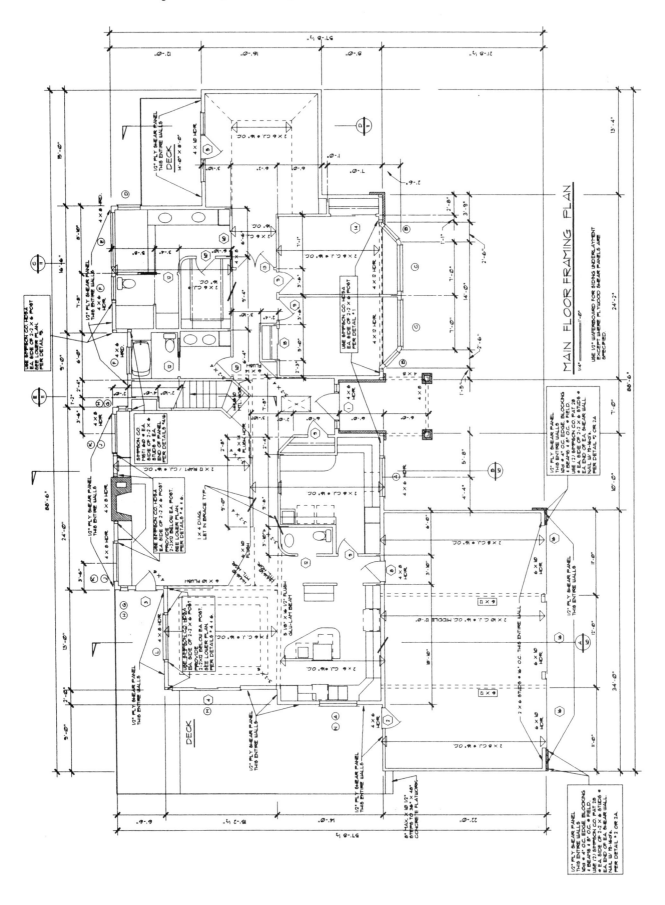

© 2011 Cengage Learning. All Rights Reserved. May not be scanned, copied or duplicated, or posted to a publicly accessible website, in whole or in part.

Problem 3   Split level (Continued)

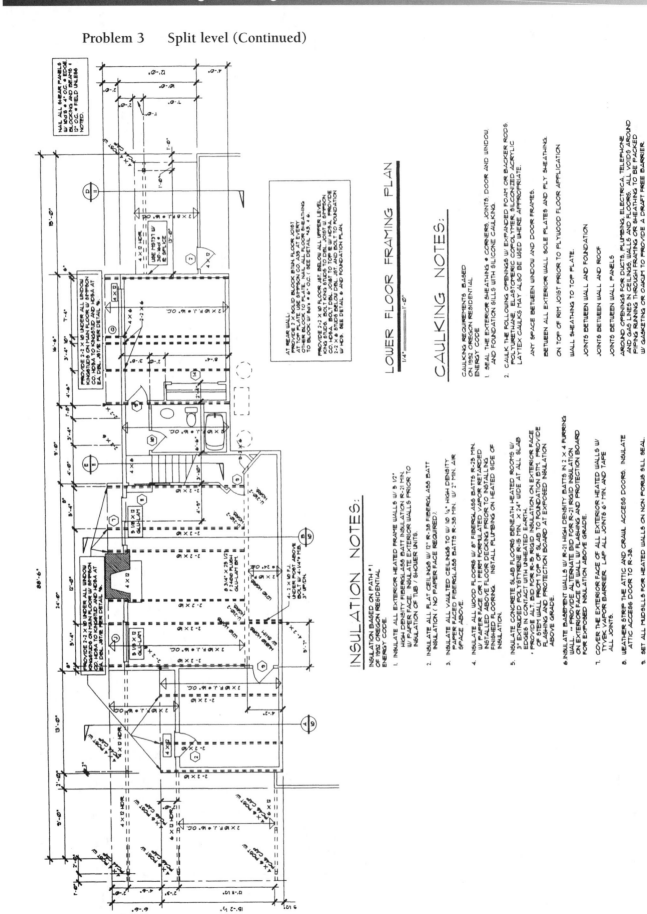

LOWER FLOOR FRAMING PLAN
1/4"

CAULKING NOTES:

CAULKING REQUIREMENTS BASED ON 1992 OREGON RESIDENTIAL ENERGY CODE

1. SEAL THE EXTERIOR SHEATHING • CORNERS, JOINTS, DOOR AND WINDOW AND FOUNDATION SILLS WITH SILICONE CAULKING.

2. CAULK THE FOLLOWING OPENINGS W/ EXPANDED FOAM OR BACKER RODS POLYURETHANE, ELASTOMERIC COPOLYMER, SILICONIZED ACRYLIC LATEX CAULKS MAY ALSO BE USED WHERE APPROPRIATE.

   ANY SPACE BETWEEN WINDOW AND DOOR FRAMES.

   BETWEEN ALL EXTERIOR WALL SOLE PLATES AND PLY SHEATHING

   ON TOP OF RIM JOIST PRIOR TO PLYWOOD FLOOR APPLICATION

   WALL SHEATHING TO TOP PLATE.

   JOINTS BETWEEN WALL AND FOUNDATION

   JOINTS BETWEEN WALL AND ROOF

   JOINTS BETWEEN WALL PANELS

   AROUND OPENINGS FOR DUCTS, PLUMBING, ELECTRICAL, TELEPHONE AND GAS LINES IN CEILINGS, WALLS AND FLOORS. ALL VOIDS AROUND PIPING RUNNING THROUGH FRAMING OR SHEATHING TO BE PACKED W/ GASKETING OR OAKUM TO PROVIDE A DRAFT FREE BARRIER

INSULATION NOTES:

INSULATION BASED ON PATH # 1 OF 1992 OREGON RESIDENTIAL ENERGY CODE.

1. INSULATE ALL EXTERIOR HEATED FRAME WALLS W/ 5 1/2" HIGH DENSITY FIBERGLASS BATT INSULATION R-21 MIN. W/ PAPER FACE. INSULATE EXTERIOR WALLS PRIOR TO INSULATION OF TUB / SHOWER UNITS.

2. INSULATE ALL FLAT CEILINGS W/ 12" R-38 FIBERGLASS BATT INSULATION (NO PAPER FACE REQUIRED).

3. INSULATE ALL VAULTED CEILINGS TO W/ 10 1/2" HIGH DENSITY PAPER FACED FIBERGLASS BATTS R-38 MIN. W/ 2" MIN. AIR SPACE ABOVE.

4. INSULATE ALL WOOD FLOORS W/ 8" FIBERGLASS BATTS R-25 MIN. W/ PAPER FACE OR I PERM FORMULATED VAPOR RETARDED INSTALLED ABOVE FLOOR DECKING PRIOR TO INSTALLING FINISHED FLOORING. INSTALL PLUMBING ON HEATED SIDE OF INSULATION.

5. INSULATE CONCRETE SLAB FLOORS BENEATH HEATED ROOMS W/ 3" EXTRUDED POLYSTYRENE R-15 MIN. X 24" WIDE AT ALL SLAB EDGES IN CONTACT WITH UNHEATED EARTH. PROVIDE ALT. BID FOR R-8 RIGID INSULATION ON EXTERIOR FACE OF STEM WALL FROM TOP OF SLAB FOUNDATION BTM. PROVIDE FLASHING AND PROTECTION BOARD AT EXPOSED INSULATION ABOVE GRADE.

6. INSULATE BASEMENT WALLS W/ R-21 HIGH DENSITY BATTS IN 2 X 4 FURRING WALL. .. PROVIDE ALTERNATE BID FOR R-21 RIGID INSULATION ON EXTERIOR FACE OF WALL W/ FLASHING AND PROTECTION BOARD FOR EXPOSED INSULATION ABOVE GRADE.

7. COVER THE EXTERIOR FACE OF ALL EXTERIOR HEATED WALLS W/ TYVEK VAPOR BARRIER. LAP ALL JOINTS 6" MIN. AND TAPE ALL JOINTS.

8. WEATHER STRIP THE ATTIC AND CRAWL ACCESS DOORS. INSULATE ATTIC ACCESS DOOR TO R-38.

9. SET ALL MUDSILLS FOR HEATED WALLS ON NON POROUS SILL SEAL.

10. INSULATE ALL HEATING DUCTS IN UNHEATED AREAS TO R-8. INSULATION TO HAVE A FLAME SPREAD RATING OF 50 MAX. W/ AND A SMOKE DEVELOPMENT RATING OF 100 MAX. ALL DUCT SEATS TO BE SEALED.

© 2011 Cengage Learning. All Rights Reserved. May not be scanned, copied or duplicated, or posted to a publicly accessible website, in whole or in part.

Problem 3   Split level (Continued)

FOOTING INSULATION DETAILS

© 2011 Cengage Learning. All Rights Reserved. May not be scanned, copied or duplicated, or posted to a publicly accessible website, in whole or in part.

Problem 3   Split level (Continued)

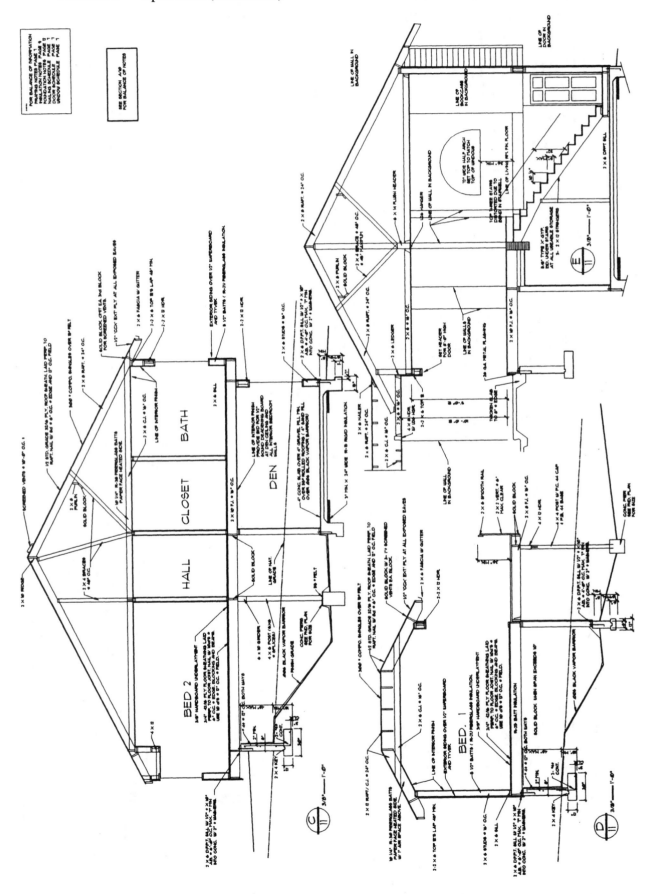

© 2011 Cengage Learning. All Rights Reserved. May not be scanned, copied or duplicated, or posted to a publicly accessible website, in whole or in part.

Problem 3   Split level (Continued)

FOUNDATION PLAN

© 2011 Cengage Learning. All Rights Reserved. May not be scanned, copied or duplicated, or posted to a publicly accessible website, in whole or in part.

Problem 4   Two-story

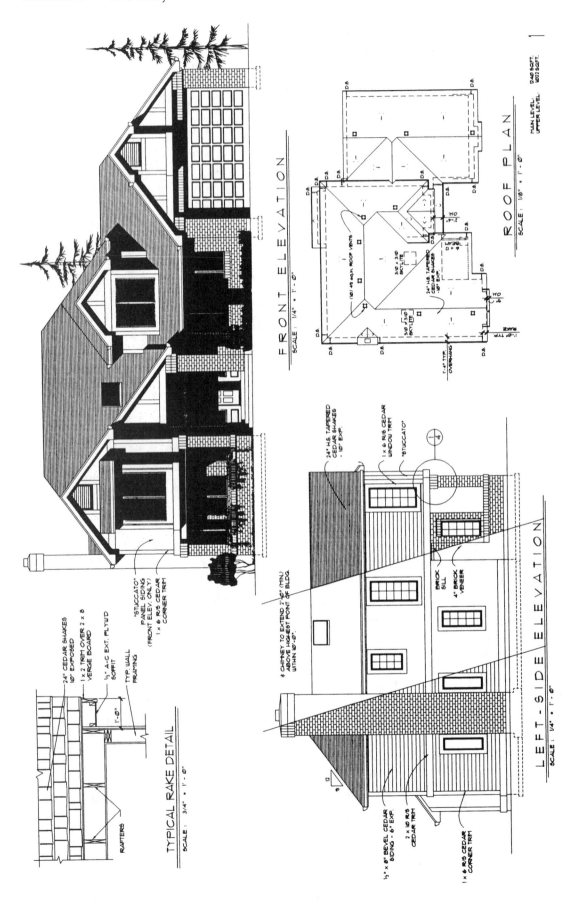

© 2011 Cengage Learning. All Rights Reserved. May not be scanned, copied or duplicated, or posted to a publicly accessible website, in whole or in part.

Problem 4   Two-story (Continued)

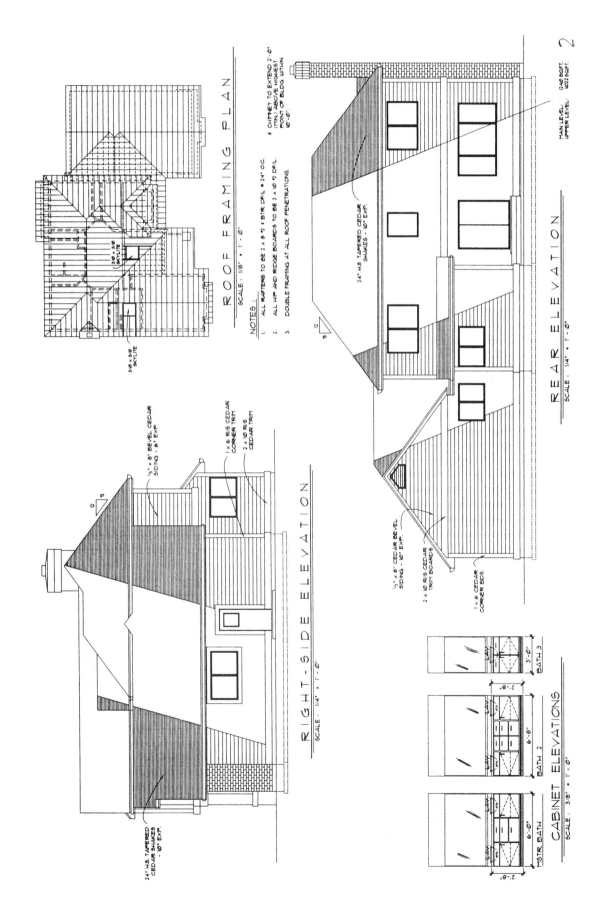

© 2011 Cengage Learning. All Rights Reserved. May not be Scanned, copied or duplicated, or posted to a publicly accessible website, in whole or in part.

Problem 4   Two-story (Continued)

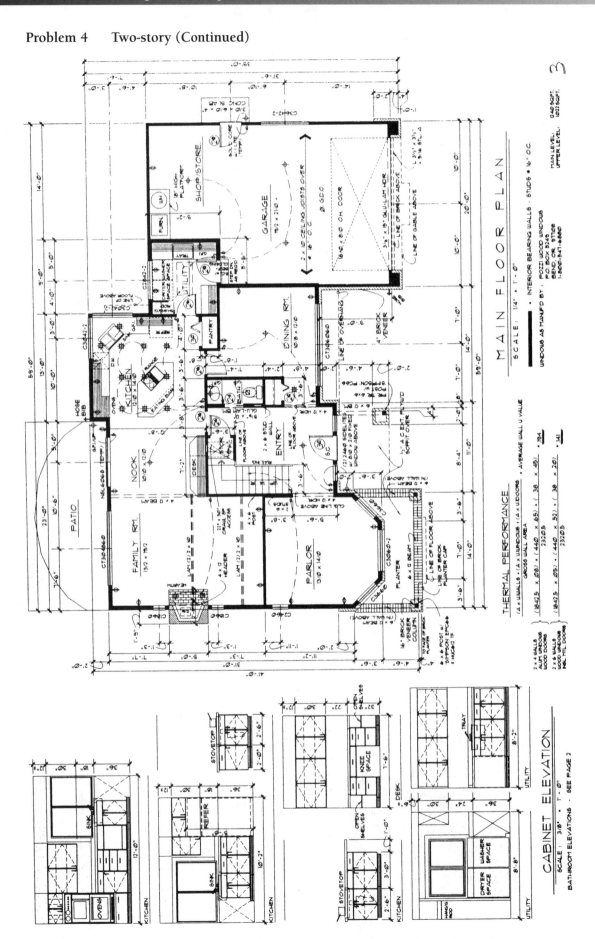

© 2011 Cengage Learning. All Rights Reserved. May not be scanned, copied or duplicated, or posted to a publicly accessible website, in whole or in part.

Problem 4   Two-story (Continued)

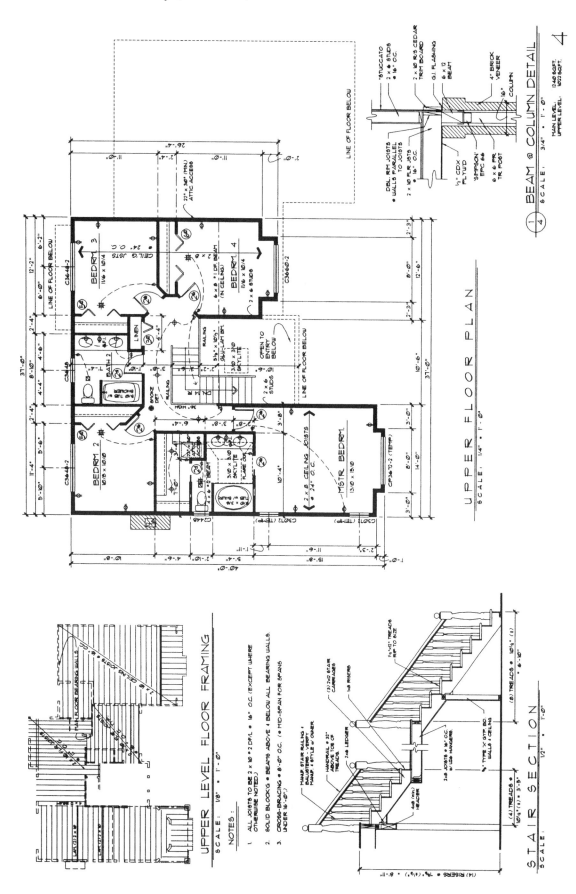

© 2011 Cengage Learning. All Rights Reserved. May not be scanned, copied or duplicated, or posted to a publicly accessible website, in whole or in part.

Problem 4   Two-story (Continued)

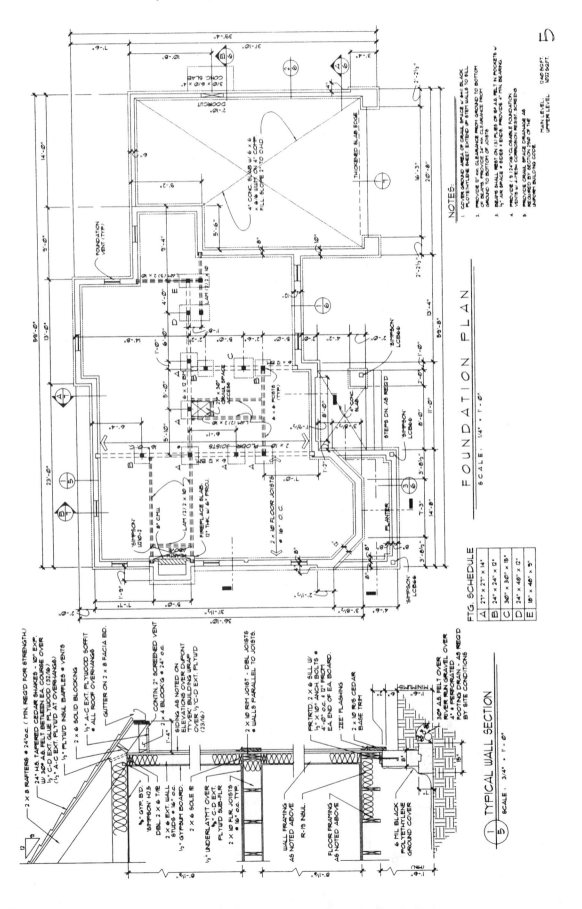

© 2011 Cengage Learning. All Rights Reserved. May not be scanned, copied or duplicated, or posted to a publicly accessible website, in whole or in part.

Problem 4   Two-story (Continued)

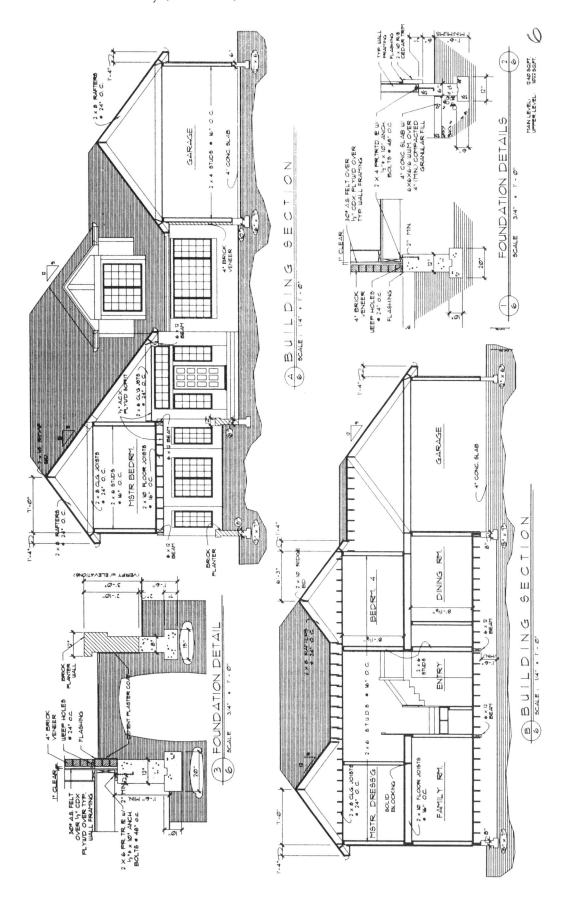

© 2011 Cengage Learning. All Rights Reserved. May not be scanned, copied or duplicated, or posted to a publicly accessible website, in whole or in part.

Problem 4   Two-story (Continued)

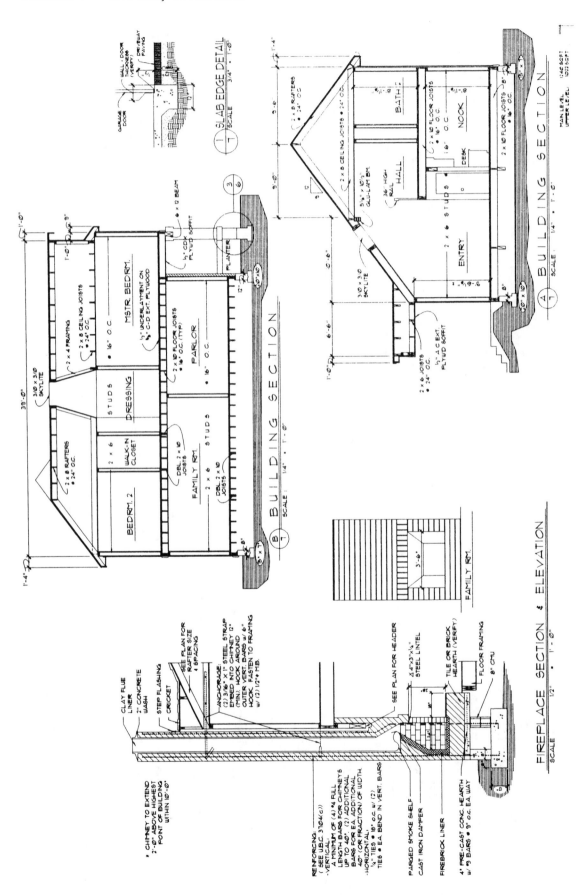

© 2011 Cengage Learning. All Rights Reserved. May not be scanned, copied or duplicated, or posted to a publicly accessible website, in whole or in part.

Problem 5   One-story with Full Basement

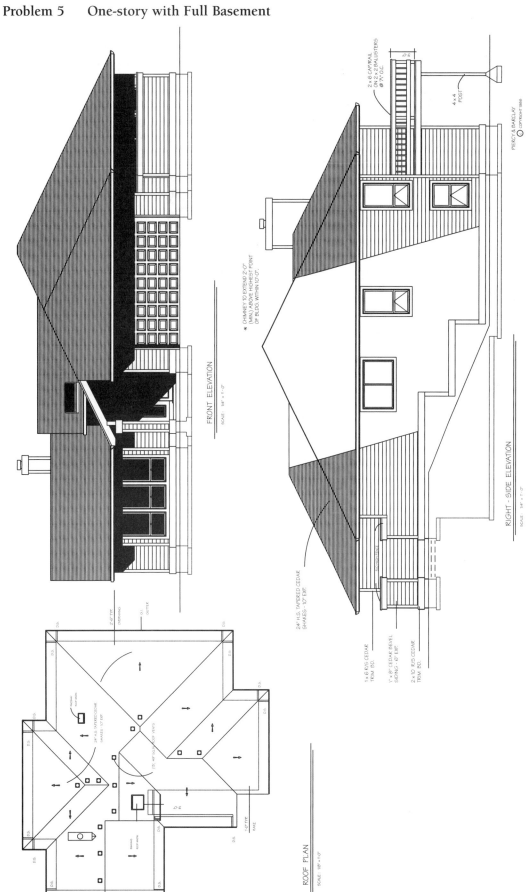

© 2011 Cengage Learning. All Rights Reserved. May not be scanned, copied or duplicated, or posted to a publicly accessible website, in whole or in part.

Problem 5   One-story with Full Basement (Continued)

REAR ELEVATION
SCALE: 1/4" = 1'-0"

* CHIMNEY TO EXTEND 2'-0" (MIN.) ABOVE HIGHEST POINT OF BLDG. WITHIN 10'-0".

24" H.S. TAPERED CEDAR SHAKES - 10" EXPOSED.

1 x 6 R/S CEDAR TRIM BOARD.

1" x 8" CEDAR BEVEL SIDING - 6" EXPOSED.

2 x 10 R/S CEDAR TRIM BOARD

RIGHT - SIDE ELEVATION
SCALE: 1/8" = 1'-0"

1" x 8" CEDAR BEVEL SIDING - 6" EXP.

24" H.S. TAPERED CEDAR SHAKES - 10" EXP.

1 x 6 R/S CEDAR TRIM BD.

2 x 6 CAP RAIL ON 2 x 2 BALUSTERS @ 7" O.C.

4 x 4 POST

2 x 10 R/S CEDAR TRIM BD.

ROOF FRAMING PLAN
SCALE: 1/8" = 1'-0"

NOTES:

1.   ALL RAFTERS TO BE 2 x 12 #2 & BTR. DF/L @ 24" O.C. (UNLESS OTHERWISE NOTED).

2.   ALL HIP & RIDGE BOARDS TO BE 2 x 14 #2 DF/L (UNLESS OTHERWISE NOTED).

3.   DOUBLE FRAMING AT ALL ROOF PENETRATIONS.

© 2011 Cengage Learning. All Rights Reserved. May not be scanned, copied or duplicated, or posted to a publicly accessible website, in whole or in part.

Problem 5   One-story with Full Basement (Continued)

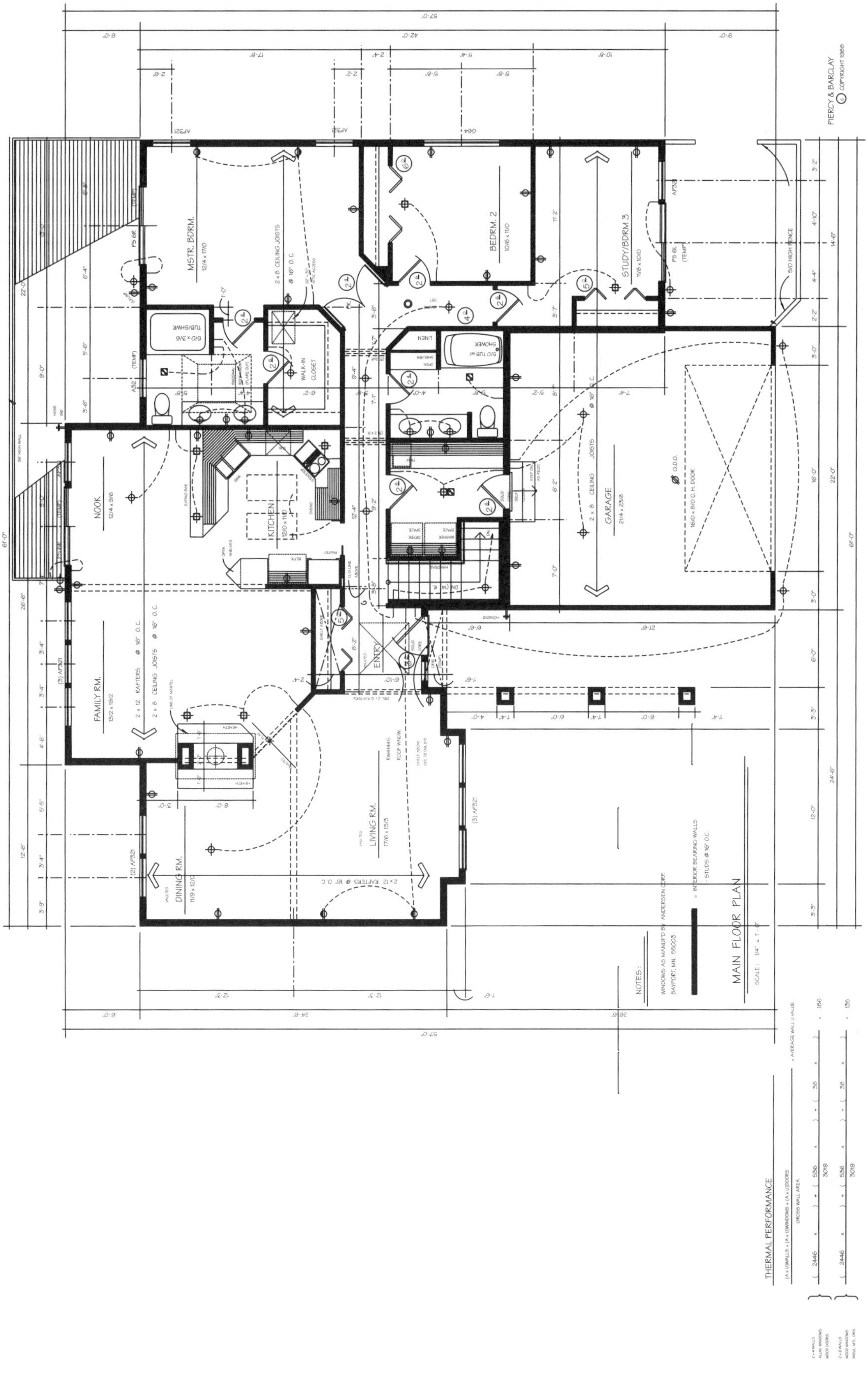

MAIN FLOOR PLAN

SCALE: 1/4" = 1'-0"

© 2011 Cengage Learning. All Rights Reserved. May not be scanned, copied or duplicated, or posted to a publicly accessible website, in whole or in part.

Problem 5   One-story with Full Basement (Continued)

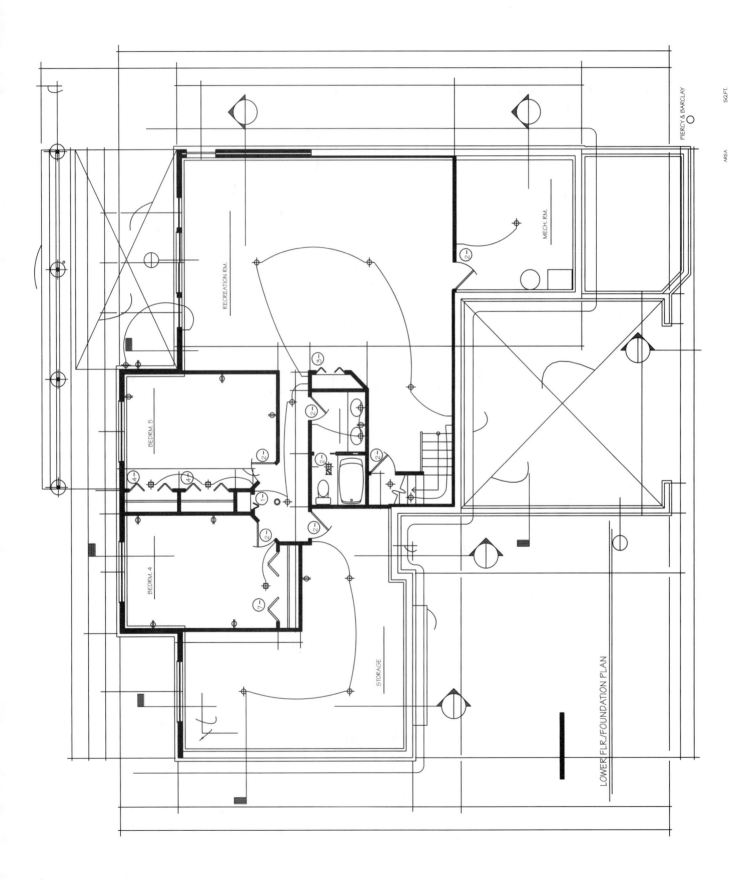

© 2011 Cengage Learning. All Rights Reserved. May not be scanned, copied or duplicated, or posted to a publicly accessible website, in whole or in part.

Problem 5   One-story with Full Basement (Continued)

© 2011 Cengage Learning. All Rights Reserved. May not be scanned, copied or duplicated, or posted to a publicly accessible website, in whole or in part.

Problem 5   One-story with Full Basement (Continued)

2 x 12 RAFTERS @ 16" O.C.

2 x 6 CEIL'G JOISTS @ 16" O.C.

2 x 6 STUDS @ 16" O.C.

8'-1"

MSTR. BEDRM.

RW2944V ROOF WINDOW

M. BATH

RECREATION RM.

2 x 12 FLOOR JOISTS @ 16" O.C.

2 x 14 RIDGE BD.

NOOK

BEDROOM 3

2 x 12 RAFTERS @ 16" O.C.

2 x 8 CEILING JOISTS @ 16" O.C.

SIMPSON U26

FAMILY RM.

BEDROOM 4

SUPERIOR BT-3840 FIREPLACE (SEE FLOOR PLAN)

4" CONC. SLAB

DINING RM.

2 x 6 STUDS @ 16" O.C.

UNFINISHED STORAGE

15" x 7"

15" x 7"

BUILDING SECTION

SCALE : 1/4" = 1'-0"

C
5

© 2011 Cengage Learning. All Rights Reserved. May not be scanned, copied or duplicated, or posted to a publicly accessible website, in whole or in part.

Problem 6   One-story with Optional Dual Master Bedroom

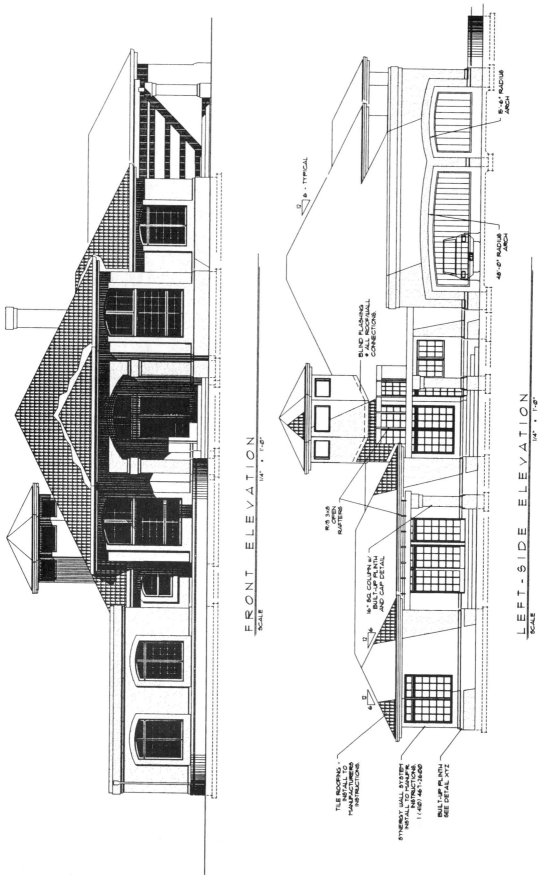

© 2011 Cengage Learning. All Rights Reserved. May not be scanned, copied or duplicated, or posted to a publicly accessible website, in whole or in part.

Problem 6   One-story with Optional Dual Master Bedroom (Continued)

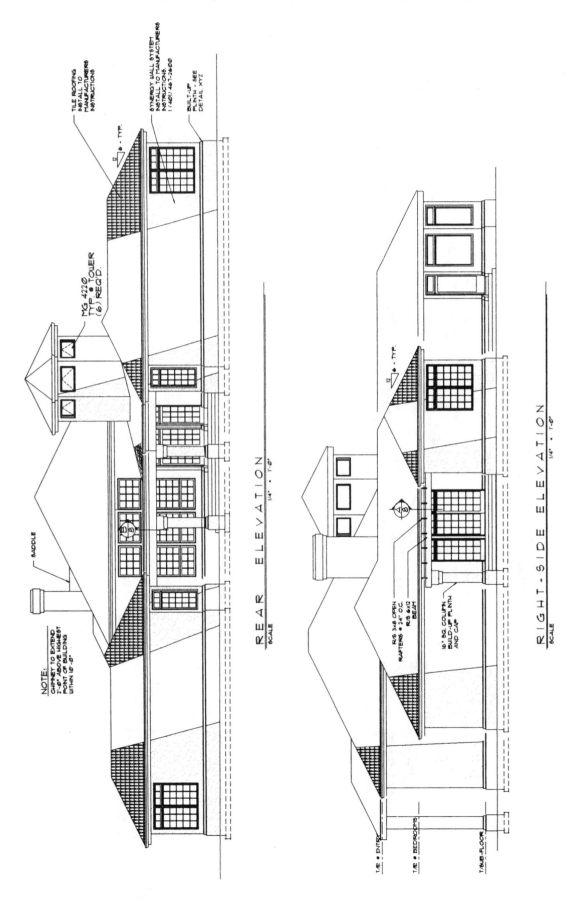

© 2011 Cengage Learning. All Rights Reserved. May not be scanned, copied or duplicated, or posted to a publicly accessible website, in whole or in part.

Problem 6   One-story with Optional Dual Master Bedroom (Continued)

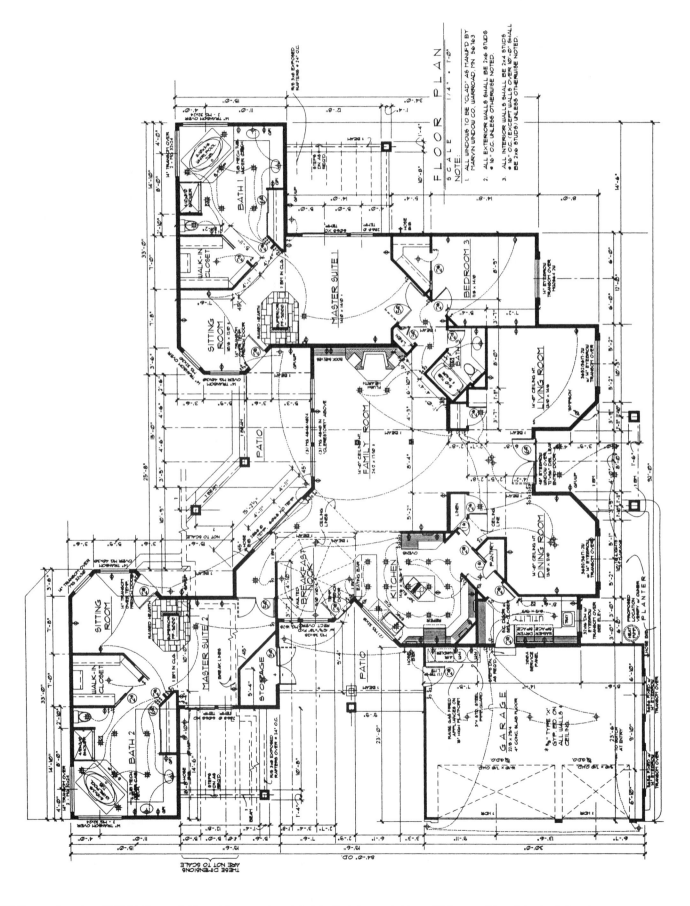

© 2011 Cengage Learning. All Rights Reserved. May not be scanned, copied or duplicated, or posted to a publicly accessible website, in whole or in part.

Problem 6 One-story with Optional Dual Master Bedroom (Continued)

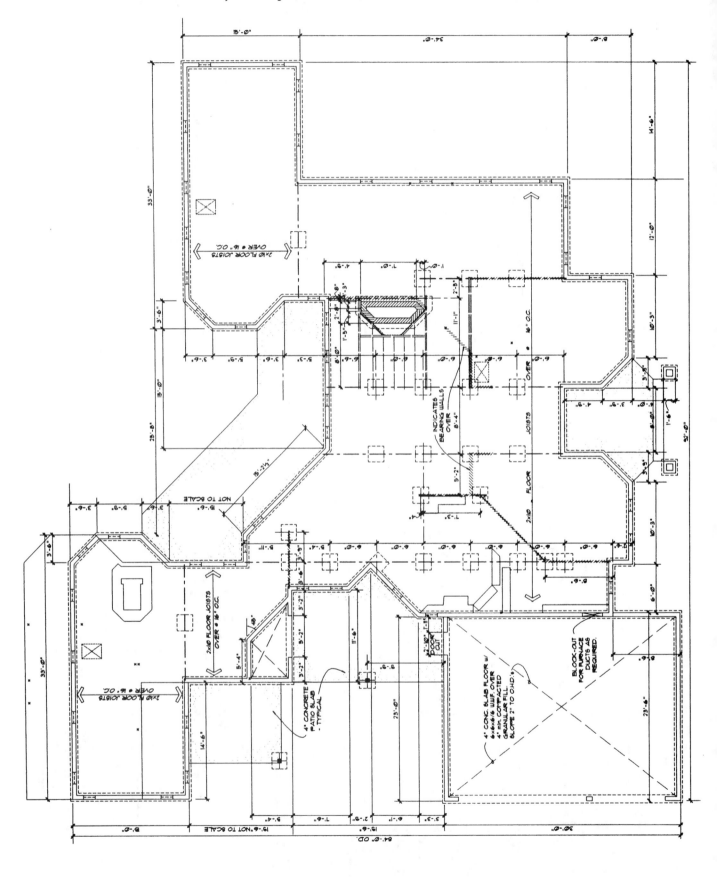

© 2011 Cengage Learning. All Rights Reserved. May not be scanned, copied or duplicated, or posted to a publicly accessible website, in whole or in part.

Problem 6   One-story with Optional Dual Master Bedroom (Continued)

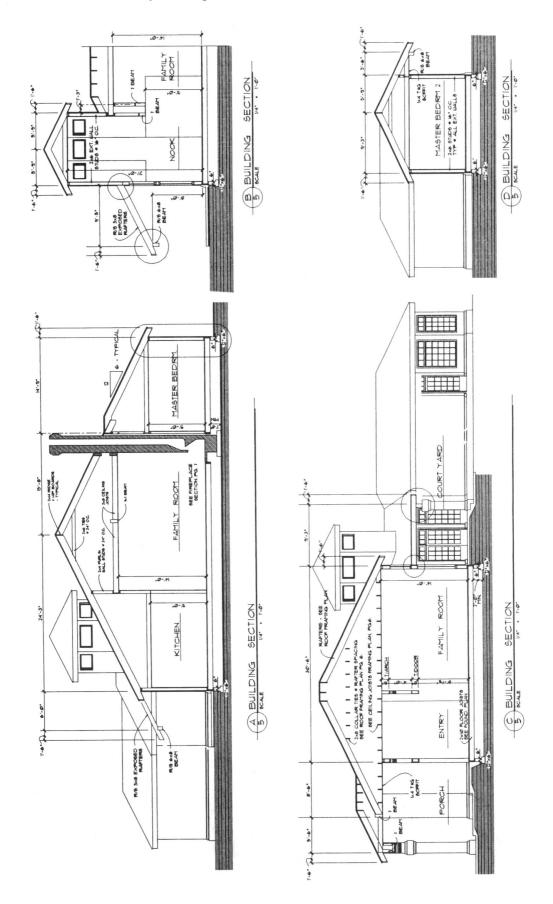

© 2011 Cengage Learning. All Rights Reserved. May not be scanned, copied or duplicated, or posted to a publicly accessible website, in whole or in part.

Problem 6   One-story with Optional Dual Master Bedroom (Continued)

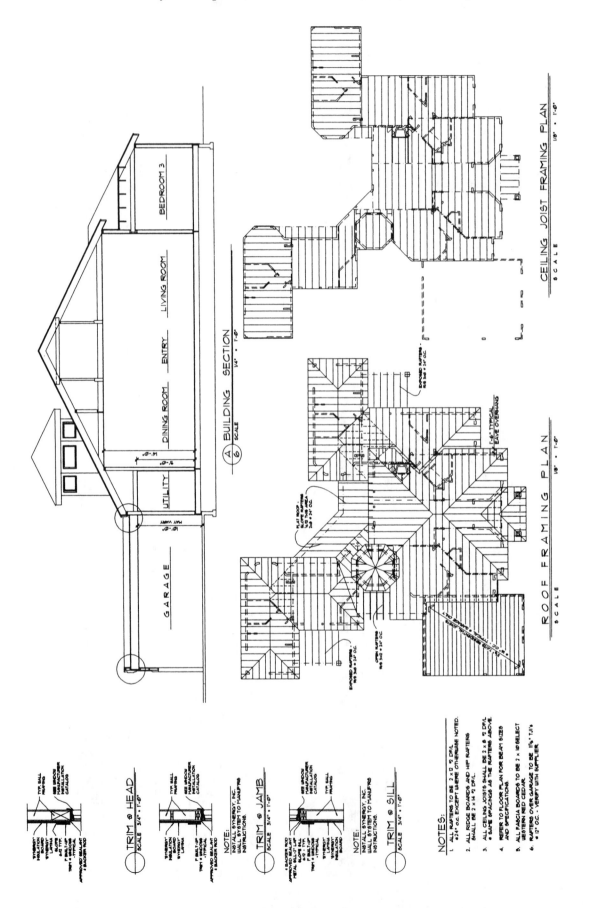

© 2011 Cengage Learning. All Rights Reserved. May not be scanned, copied or duplicated, or posted to a publicly accessible website, in whole or in part.

Problem 6   One-story with Optional Dual Master Bedroom (Continued)

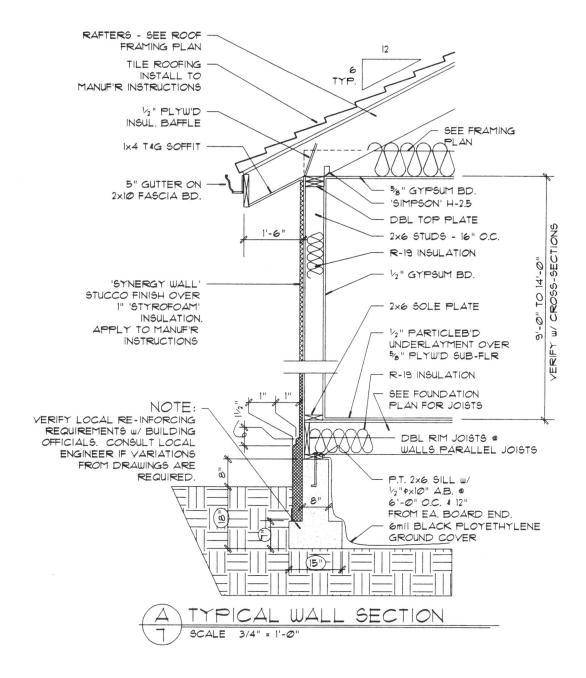

RAFTERS - SEE ROOF
FRAMING PLAN

TILE ROOFING
INSTALL TO
MANUF'R INSTRUCTIONS

½" PLYW'D
INSUL. BAFFLE

1x4 T&G SOFFIT

5" GUTTER ON
2x10 FASCIA BD.

'SYNERGY WALL'
STUCCO FINISH OVER
1" 'STYROFOAM'
INSULATION.
APPLY TO MANUF'R
INSTRUCTIONS

NOTE:
VERIFY LOCAL RE-INFORCING
REQUIREMENTS w/ BUILDING
OFFICIALS. CONSULT LOCAL
ENGINEER IF VARIATIONS
FROM DRAWINGS ARE
REQUIRED.

12
6
TYP.

SEE FRAMING
PLAN

⅝" GYPSUM BD.
'SIMPSON' H-2.5
DBL TOP PLATE
2x6 STUDS - 16" O.C.
R-19 INSULATION
½" GYPSUM BD.

2x6 SOLE PLATE

½" PARTICLEB'D
UNDERLAYMENT OVER
⅝" PLYW'D SUB-FLR

R-19 INSULATION

SEE FOUNDATION
PLAN FOR JOISTS

DBL RIM JOISTS @
WALLS PARALLEL JOISTS

P.T. 2x6 SILL w/
½"Φx10" A.B. @
6'-0" O.C. & 12"
FROM EA. BOARD END.

6mil BLACK POLYETHYLENE
GROUND COVER

1'-6"

1"   1"

1½"

8"

8"

18"

7"

15"

9'-0" TO 14'-0"
VERIFY w/ CROSS-SECTIONS

(A/7) TYPICAL WALL SECTION
SCALE 3/4" = 1'-0"

© 2011 Cengage Learning. All Rights Reserved. May not be scanned, copied or duplicated, or posted to a publicly accessible website, in whole or in part.

Problem 6   One-story with Optional Dual Master Bedroom (Continued)

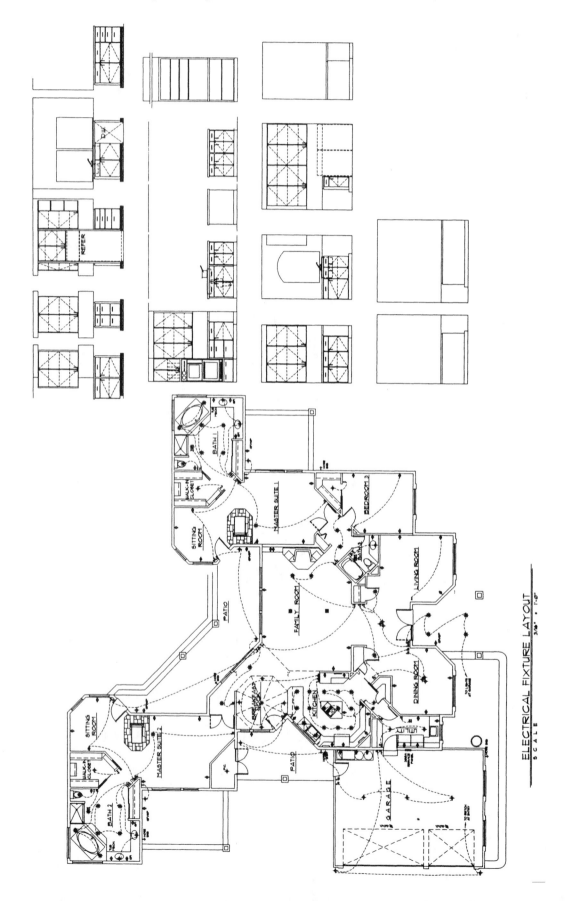

ELECTRICAL FIXTURE LAYOUT

© 2011 Cengage Learning. All Rights Reserved. May not be scanned, copied or duplicated, or posted to a publicly accessible website, in whole or in part.

Problem 7   Two-story

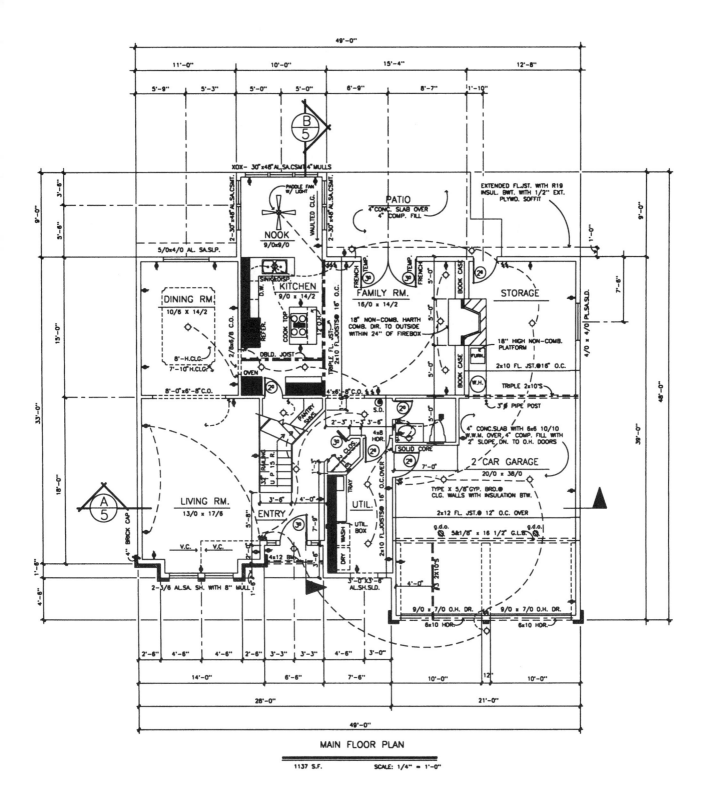

MAIN FLOOR PLAN

1137 S.F.   SCALE: 1/4" = 1'-0"

© 2011 Cengage Learning. All Rights Reserved. May not be scanned, copied or duplicated, or posted to a publicly accessible website, in whole or in part.

Problem 7   Two-story (Continued)

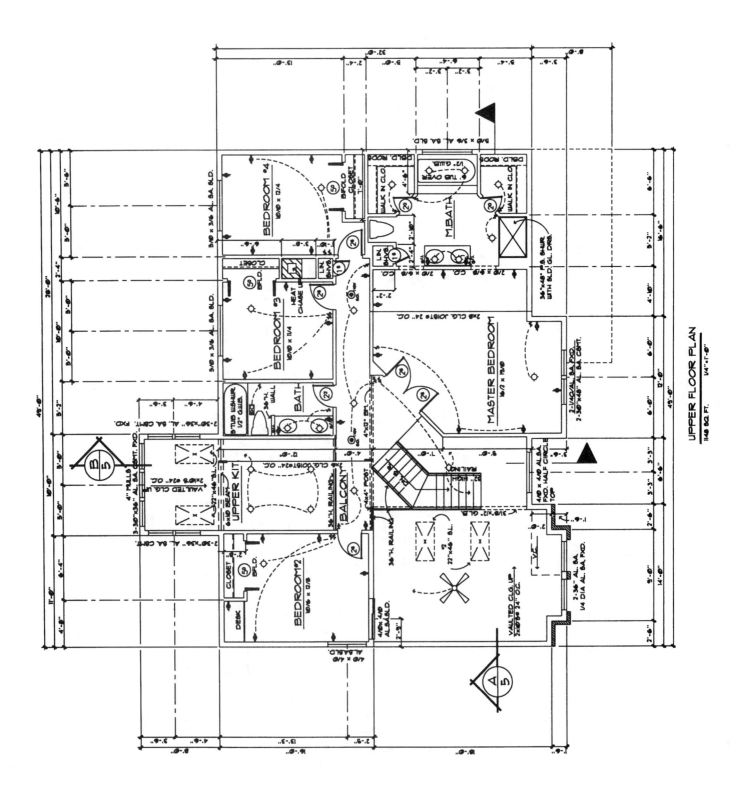

© 2011 Cengage Learning. All Rights Reserved. May not be scanned, copied or duplicated, or posted to a publicly accessible website, in whole or in part.

Problem 7   Two-story (Continued)

FRONT ELEVATION

1/4" = 1'-0"

© 2011 Cengage Learning. All Rights Reserved. May not be scanned, copied or duplicated, or posted to a publicly accessible website, in whole or in part.

Problem 7   Two-story (Continued)

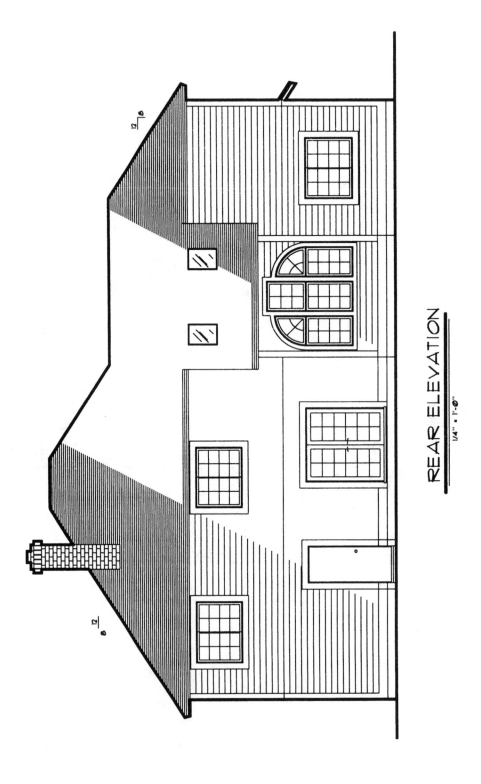

REAR ELEVATION
1/4" = 1'-0"

© 2011 Cengage Learning. All Rights Reserved. May not be scanned, copied or duplicated, or posted to a publicly accessible website, in whole or in part.

Problem 7   Two-story (Continued)

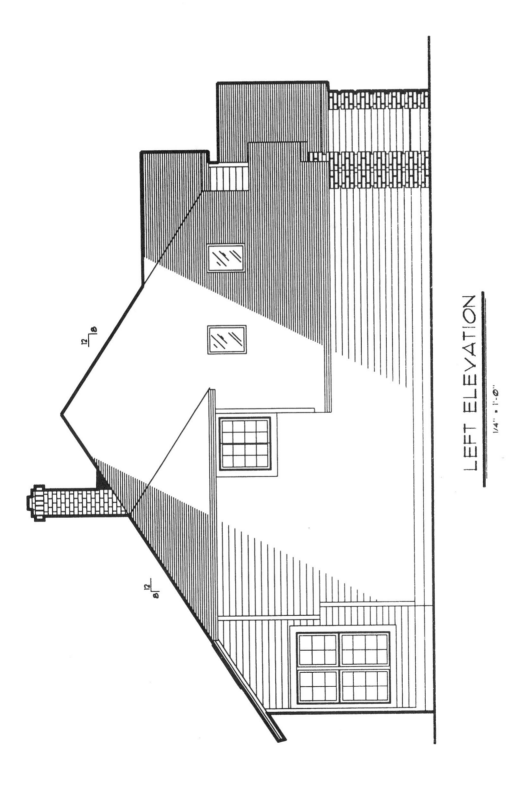

LEFT ELEVATION

1/4" = 1'-0"

© 2011 Cengage Learning. All Rights Reserved. May not be scanned, copied or duplicated, or posted to a publicly accessible website, in whole or in part.

Problem 7   Two-story (Continued)

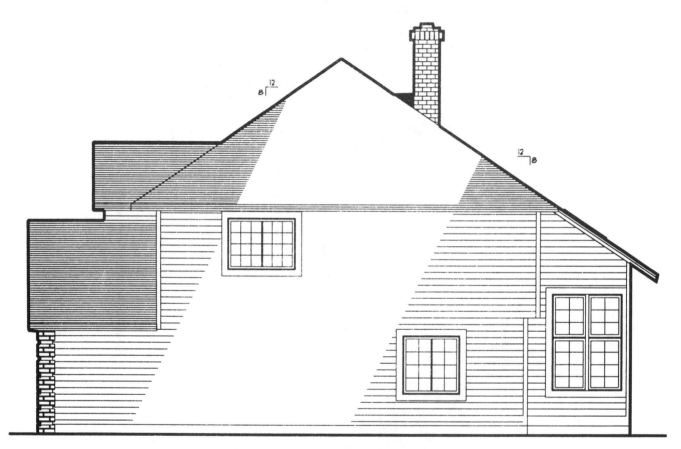

RIGHT ELEVATION

1/4" = 1'-0"

© 2011 Cengage Learning. All Rights Reserved. May not be scanned, copied or duplicated, or posted to a publicly accessible website, in whole or in part.

Problem 7   Two-story (Continued)

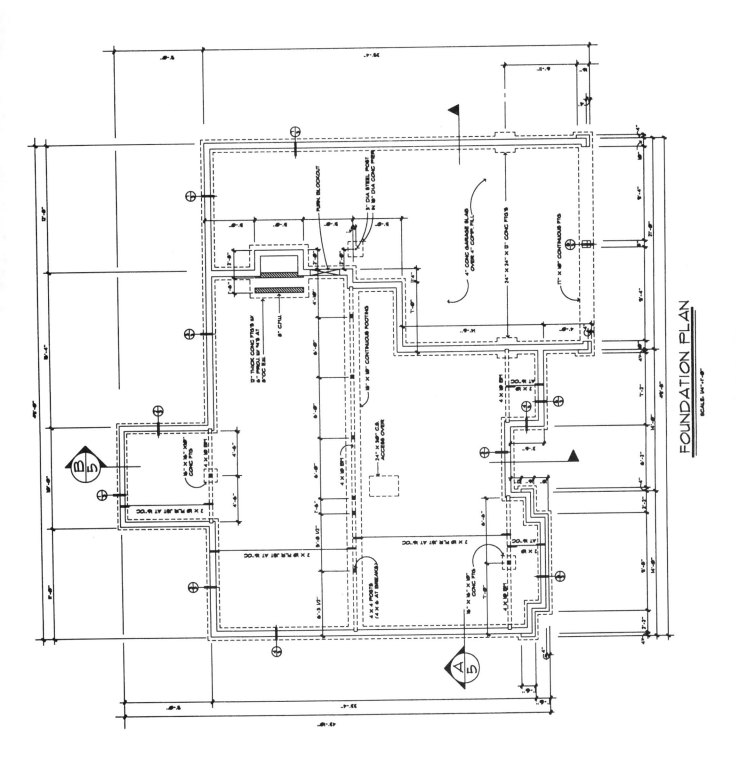

FOUNDATION PLAN
SCALE: 1/4" = 1'-0"

© 2011 Cengage Learning. All Rights Reserved. May not be scanned, copied or duplicated, or posted to a publicly accessible website, in whole or in part.

Problem 7   Two-story (Continued)

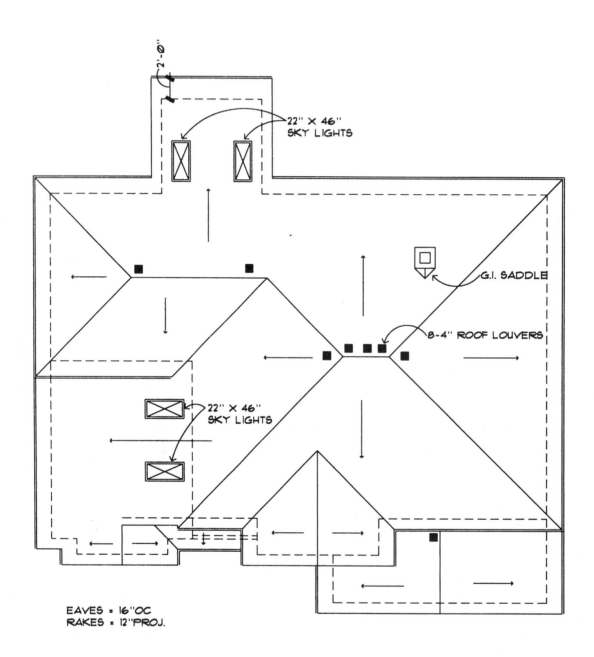

2'-0"

22" X 46"
SKY LIGHTS

G.I. SADDLE

8-4" ROOF LOUVERS

22" X 46"
SKY LIGHTS

EAVES = 16"OC
RAKES = 12"PROJ.

ROOF PLAN

SCALE: 1/8"=1'-0"

© 2011 Cengage Learning. All Rights Reserved. May not be scanned, copied or duplicated, or posted to a publicly accessible website, in whole or in part.

Problem 7   Two-story (Continued)

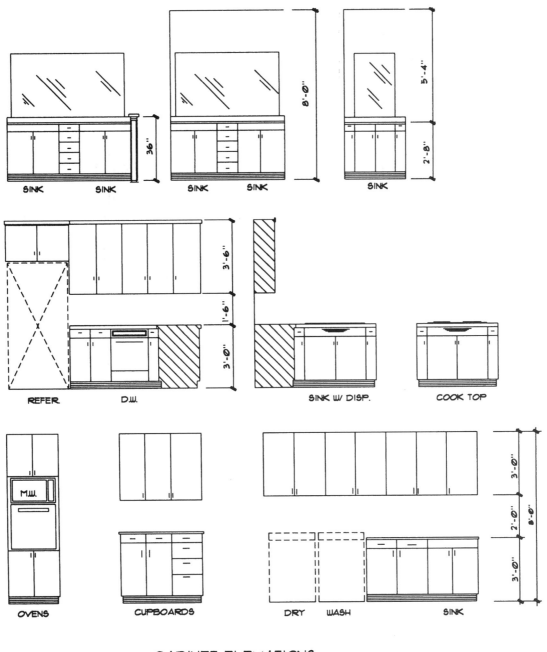

CABINET ELEVATIONS

SCALE: 3/8"=1'-0"

© 2011 Cengage Learning. All Rights Reserved. May not be scanned, copied or duplicated, or posted to a publicly accessible website, in whole or in part.

Problem 7   Two-story (Continued)

10" EXPOSED H.S. CEDAR SHAKES

12
8

R-38 INSULATION TYPICAL

MASTER BATH

8'-1"

DBLD. 6.B.

12"

GARAGE

2 X 6 CLG. JTS. AT 24" OC

2 X 12S AT 12" OC

5/8" TYPE 'X' GYP BOARD

2 X 4 STUDS AT 16" OC

4" CONC. SLAB WITH 6x6 10/10 WWM. OVER 4" COMP. FILL

MASTER BEDROOM

1/2" PARTICLE BOARD
5/8" C.D. PLYWOOD DECKING

1/2" G.W.B.

2 X 4 STUDS AT 16" OC

2 X 10S AT 16" OC

1/2" G.W.B. TYP.

UTILITY

R-19 INSULATION TYPICAL

3 1/2"X 12" G.L.B.

36" HT RAILING

5 15/16" MAX

LIVING ROOM

1/2" PARTICLE BOARD
2 X 6 T&G DECKING

2 X 10 FLR JST AT 16" OC

2 X 6 STUDS AT 16" OC

8'-1"

12
8

A
5

SECTION
SCALE: 1/4"=1'-0"

© 2011 Cengage Learning. All Rights Reserved. May not be scanned, copied or duplicated, or posted to a publicly accessible website, in whole or in part.

Problem 7   Two-story (Continued)

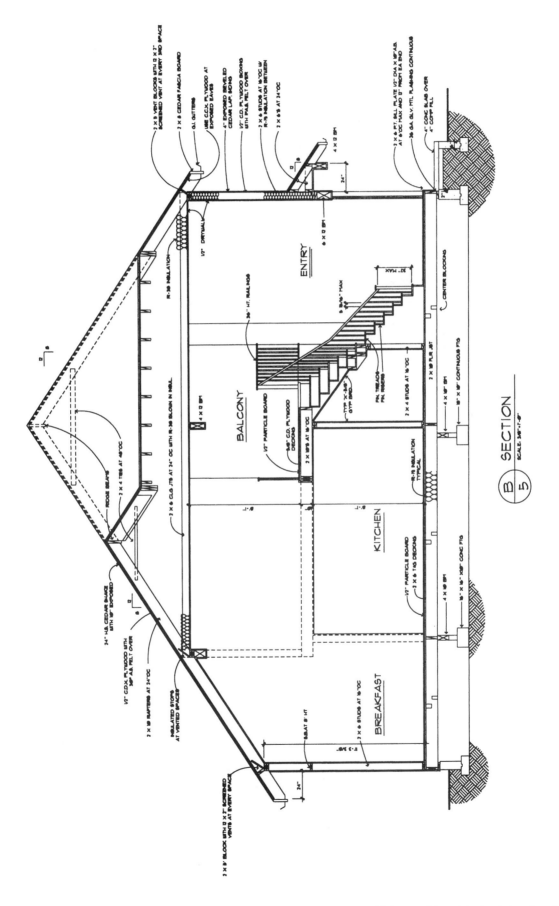

© 2011 Cengage Learning. All Rights Reserved. May not be scanned, copied or duplicated, or posted to a publicly accessible website, in whole or in part.

Problem 7   Two-story (Continued)

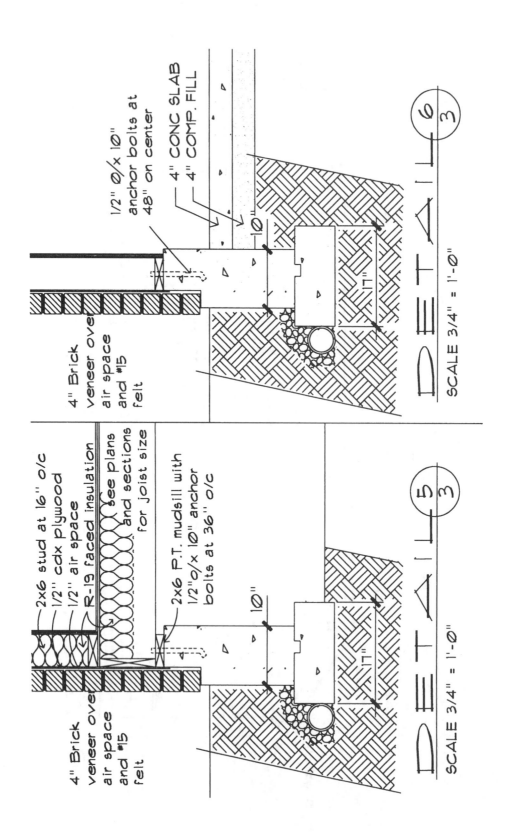

1/2" Ø/x 10" anchor bolts at 48" on center

4" CONC SLAB
4" COMP. FILL

DETAIL 6
3

SCALE 3/4" = 1'-0"

4" Brick veneer over air space and #15 felt

2x6 stud at 16" o/c
1/2" cdx plywood
1/2" air space
R-19 faced insulation
see plans and sections for joist size

2x6 P.T. mudsill with 1/2" o/x 10" anchor bolts at 36" o/c

10"

17"

4" Brick veneer over air space and #15 felt

DETAIL 5
3

SCALE 3/4" = 1'-0"

© 2011 Cengage Learning. All Rights Reserved. May not be scanned, copied or duplicated, or posted to a publicly accessible website, in whole or in part.

Problem 7   Two-story (Continued)

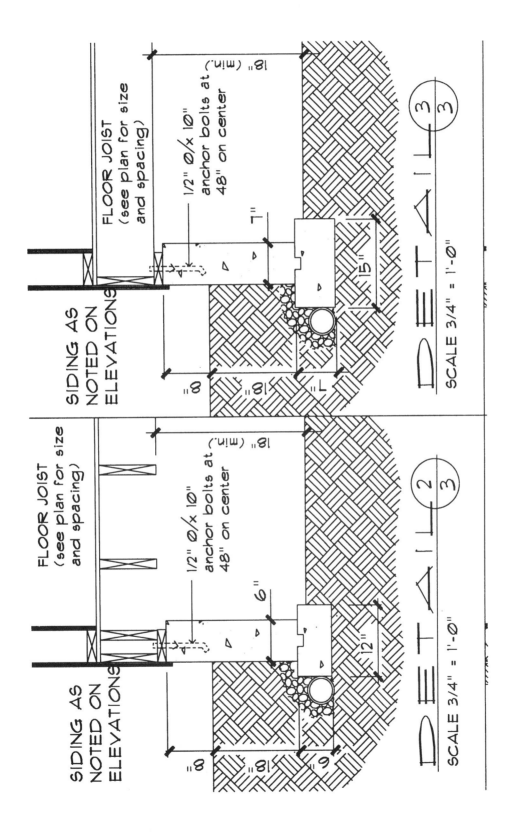

SIDING AS NOTED ON ELEVATIONS

FLOOR JOIST (see plan for size and spacing)

1/2" Ø/x 10" anchor bolts at 48" on center

18" (min.)

7"

15"

8"

18"

7"

DETAIL 3/3

SCALE 3/4" = 1'-0"

SIDING AS NOTED ON ELEVATIONS

FLOOR JOIST (see plan for size and spacing)

1/2" Ø/x 10" anchor bolts at 48" on center

18" (min.)

6"

12"

8"

18"

6"

DETAIL 2/3

SCALE 3/4" = 1'-0"

© 2011 Cengage Learning. All Rights Reserved. May not be scanned, copied or duplicated, or posted to a publicly accessible website, in whole or in part.

Problem 7   Two-story (Continued)

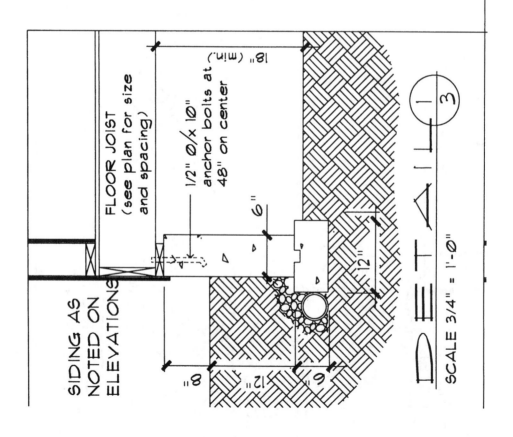

SIDING AS
NOTED ON
ELEVATIONS

FLOOR JOIST
(see plan for size
and spacing)

1/2" Ø/x 10"
anchor bolts at
48" on center

18" (min.)

6"

12"

8"

12"

6"

DETAIL 1/3

SCALE 3/4" = 1'-0"

© 2011 Cengage Learning. All Rights Reserved. May not be scanned, copied or duplicated, or posted to a publicly accessible website, in whole or in part.

Problem 7   Two-story (Continued)

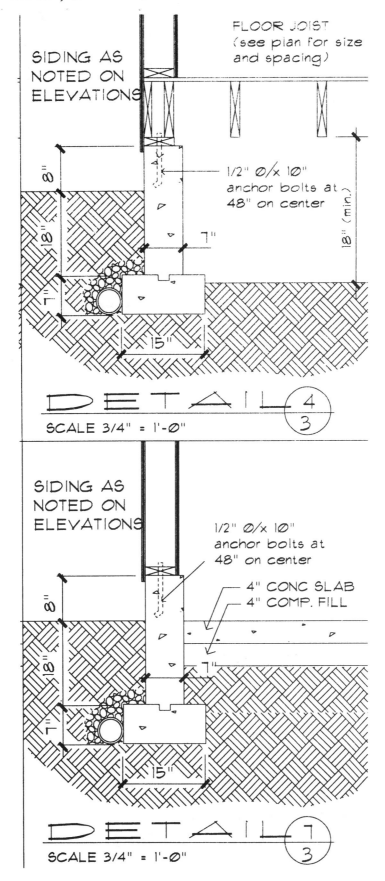

SIDING AS NOTED ON ELEVATIONS

FLOOR JOIST (see plan for size and spacing)

1/2" Ø/x 10" anchor bolts at 48" on center

8"

18"

7"

18" (min.)

7"

15"

D E T A I L ④/③

SCALE 3/4" = 1'-0"

SIDING AS NOTED ON ELEVATIONS

1/2" Ø/x 10" anchor bolts at 48" on center

4" CONC SLAB
4" COMP. FILL

8"

18"

7"

7"

15"

D E T A I L ⑦/③

SCALE 3/4" = 1'-0"

© 2011 Cengage Learning. All Rights Reserved. May not be Scanned, copied or duplicated, or posted to a publicly accessible website, in whole or in part.

Problem 7   Two-story (Continued)

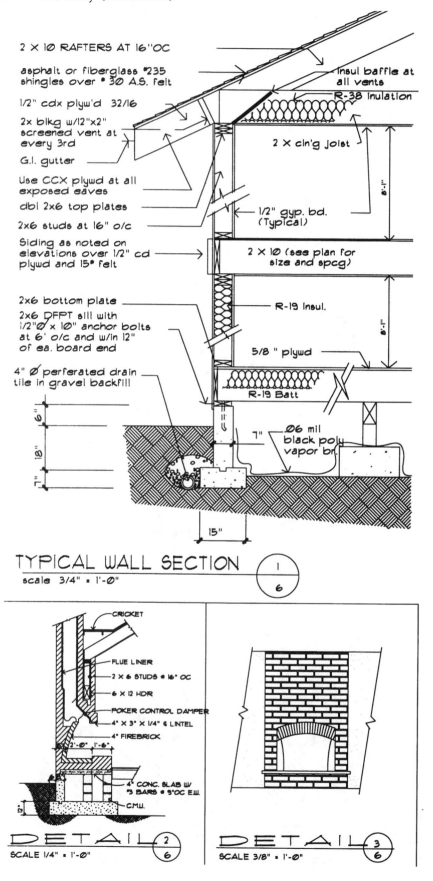

2 X 10 RAFTERS AT 16"OC

asphalt or fiberglass #235 shingles over # 30 A.S. felt

1/2" cdx plyw'd 32/16

2x blkg w/12"x2" screened vent at every 3rd

G.I. gutter

Use CCX plywd at all exposed eaves

dbl 2x6 top plates

2x6 studs at 16" o/c

Siding as noted on elevations over 1/2" cd plywd and 15# felt

2x6 bottom plate

2x6 DFPT sill with 1/2"Ø x 10" anchor bolts at 6' o/c and w/in 12" of ea. board end

4" Ø perferated drain tile in gravel backfill

Insul baffle at all vents

R-38 Inulation

2 X cln'g Joist

1/2" gyp. bd. (Typical)

2 X 10 (see plan for size and spcg)

R-19 Insul.

5/8 " plywd

R-19 Batt

8'-1"

8'-1"

6"

18"

7"

7"

.06 mil black poly vapor br.

15"

TYPICAL WALL SECTION   1/6
scale 3/4" = 1'-0"

CRICKET

FLUE LINER

2 X 6 STUDS @ 16" OC

6 X 12 HDR

POKER CONTROL DAMPER

4" X 3" X 1/4" 6 LINTEL

4" FIREBRICK

2'-0"   1'-6"

4" CONC. SLAB W/ #3 BARS @ 9"OC E.W.

12"

C.M.U.

DETAIL   2/6
SCALE 1/4" = 1'-0"

DETAIL   3/6
SCALE 3/8" = 1'-0"

© 2011 Cengage Learning. All Rights Reserved. May not be scanned, copied or duplicated, or posted to a publicly accessible website, in whole or in part.

Problem 8   Two-story

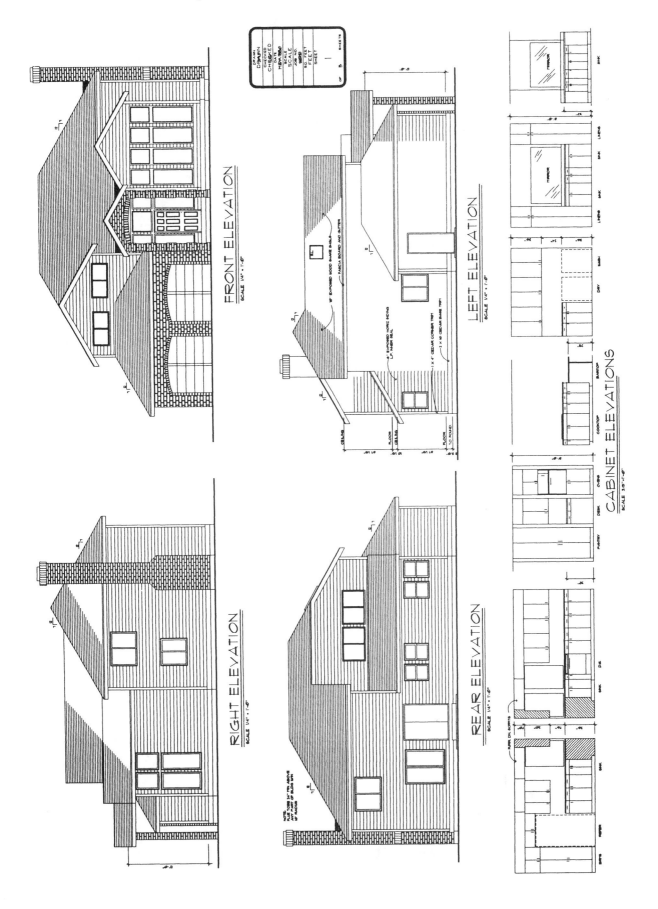

© 2011 Cengage Learning. All Rights Reserved. May not be scanned, copied or duplicated, or posted to a publicly accessible website, in whole or in part.

Problem 8   Two-story (Continued)

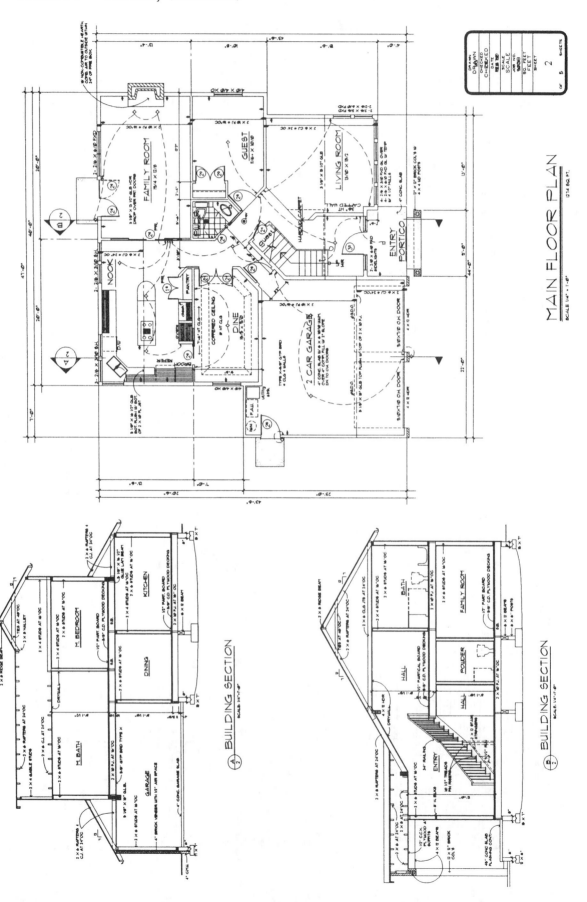

© 2011 Cengage Learning. All Rights Reserved. May not be scanned, copied or duplicated, or posted to a publicly accessible website, in whole or in part.

Problem 8   Two-story (Continued)

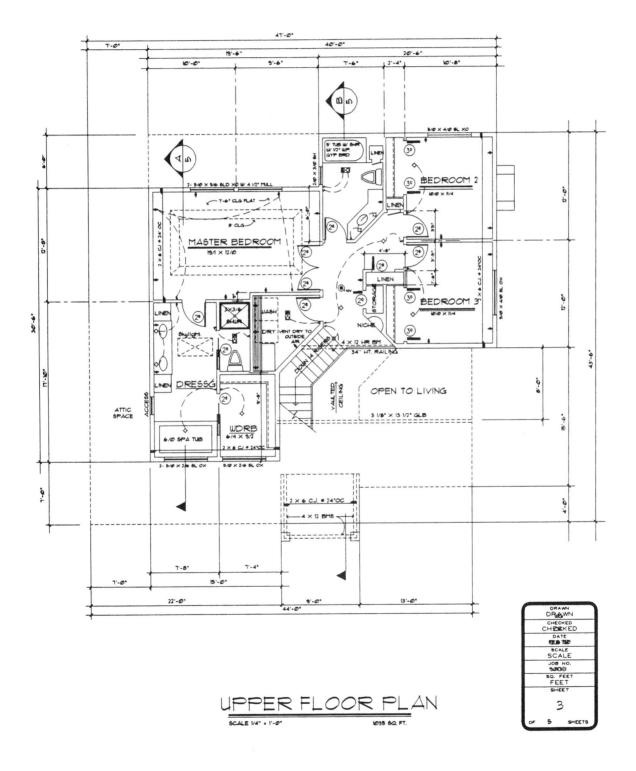

UPPER FLOOR PLAN

SCALE 1/4" = 1'-0"   1035 SQ. FT.

DRAWN
DRAWN
CHECKED
CHECKED
DATE
FEB TBD
SCALE
SCALE
JOB NO.
3008
SQ. FEET
FEET
SHEET
3
OF 5 SHEETS

© 2011 Cengage Learning. All Rights Reserved. May not be scanned, copied or duplicated, or posted to a publicly accessible website, in whole or in part.

Problem 8   Two-story (Continued)

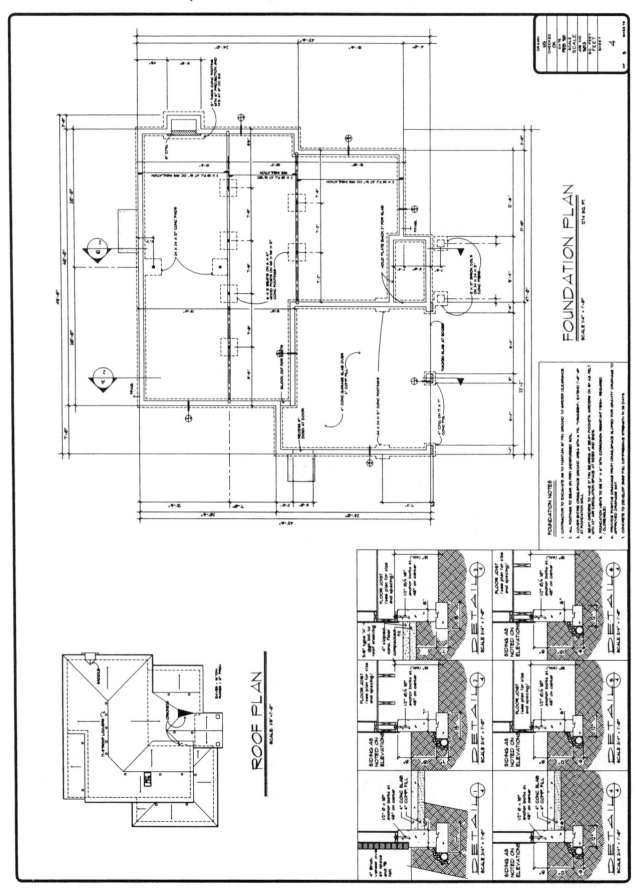

© 2011 Cengage Learning. All Rights Reserved. May not be scanned, copied or duplicated, or posted to a publicly accessible website, in whole or in part.

Problem 8   Two-story (Continued)

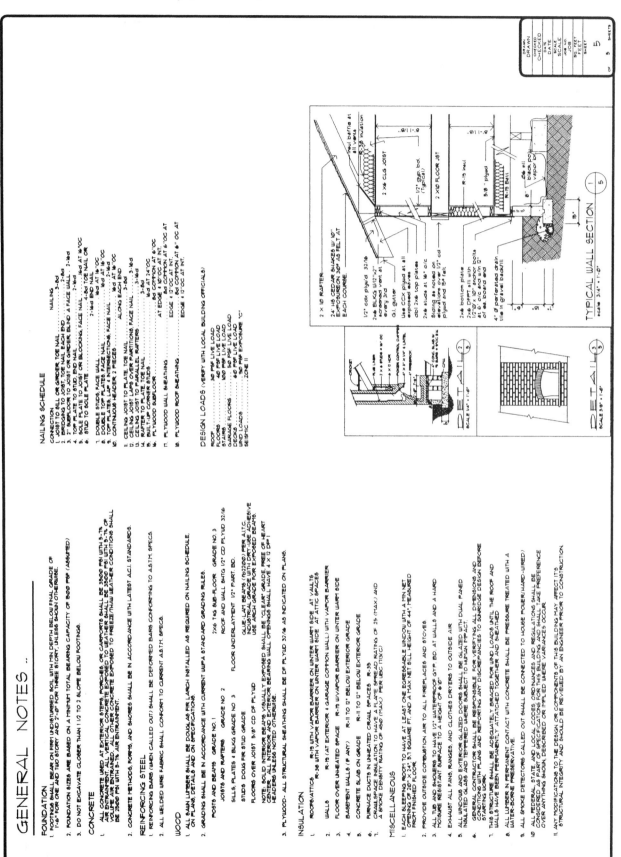

© 2011 Cengage Learning. All Rights Reserved. May not be scanned, copied or duplicated, or posted to a publicly accessible website, in whole or in part.

Problem 9 **One-story with Partial Basement**

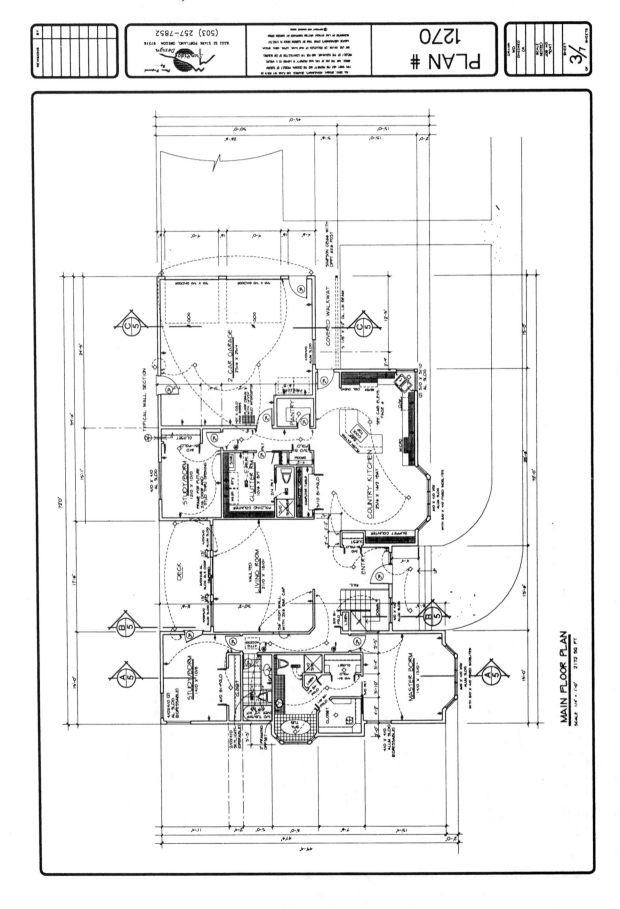

© 2011 Cengage Learning. All Rights Reserved. May not be scanned, copied or duplicated, or posted to a publicly accessible website, in whole or in part.

Problem 9   One-story with Partial Basement (Continued)

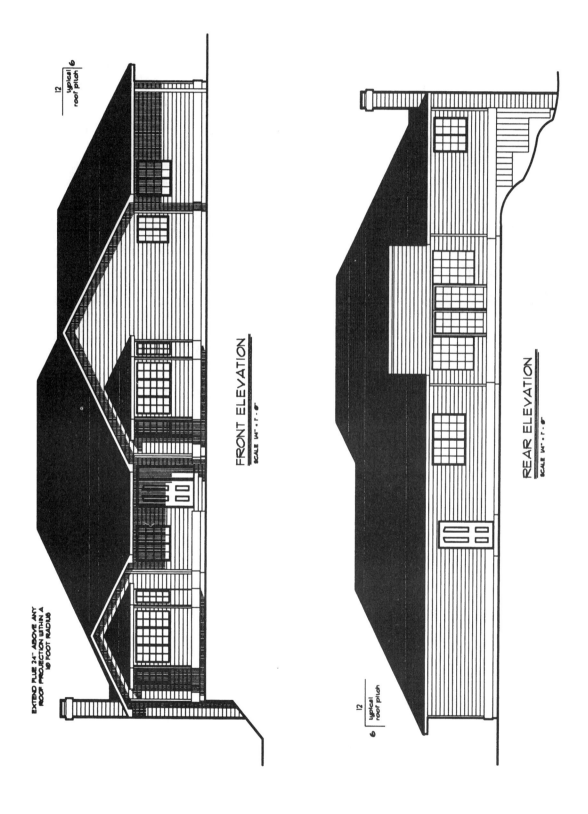

FRONT ELEVATION
SCALE 1/4" = 1'-0"

REAR ELEVATION
SCALE 1/4" = 1'-0"

EXTEND FLUE 24" ABOVE ANY
ROOF PROJECTION WITHIN A
10 FOOT RADIUS

typical
roof pitch

© 2011 Cengage Learning. All Rights Reserved. May not be scanned, copied or duplicated, or posted to a publicly accessible website, in whole or in part.

Problem 9   One-story with Partial Basement (Continued)

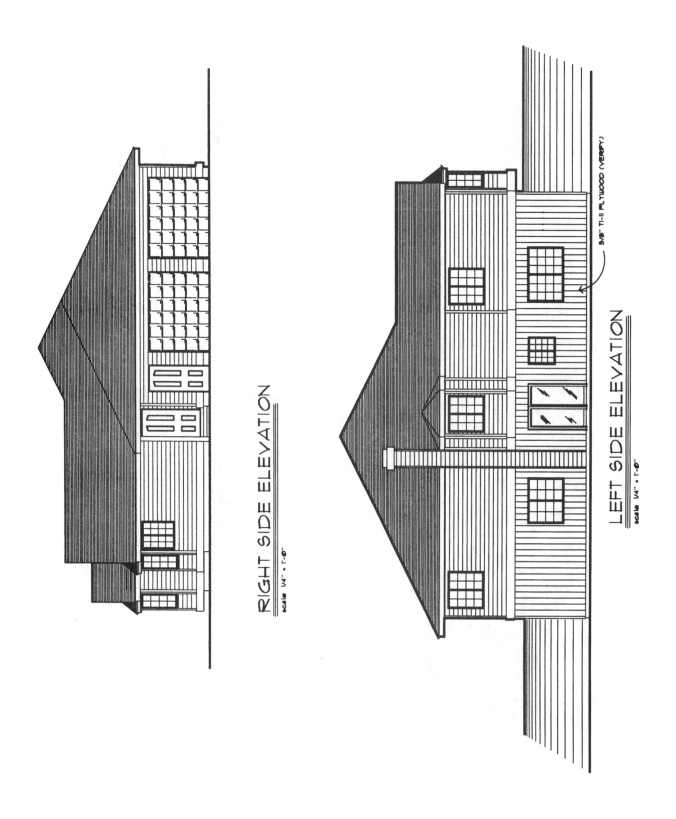

Problem 9 One-story with Partial Basement (Continued)

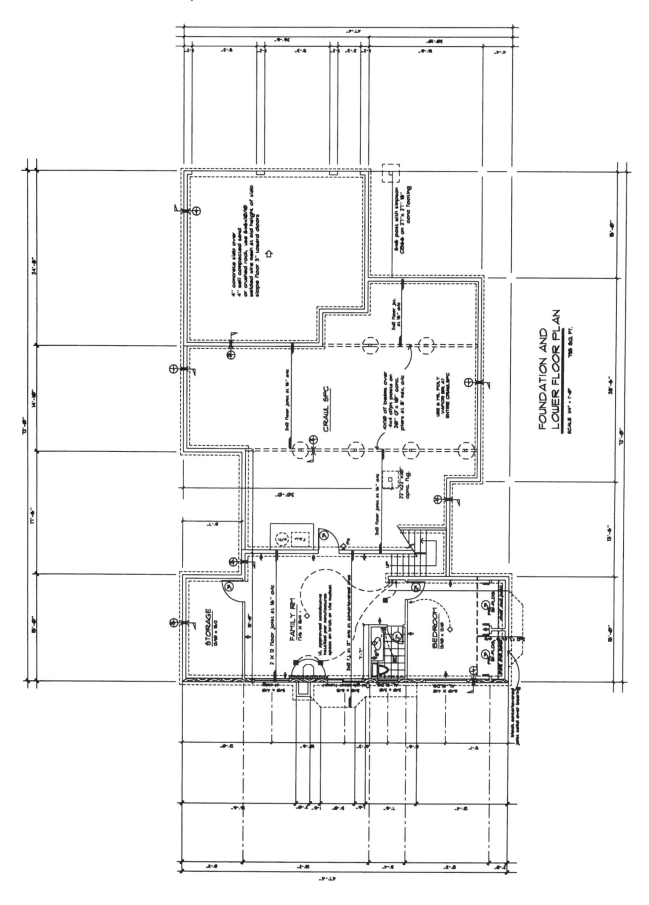

© 2011 Cengage Learning. All Rights Reserved. May not be scanned, copied or duplicated, or posted to a publicly accessible website, in whole or in part.

Problem 9   One-story with Partial Basement (Continued)

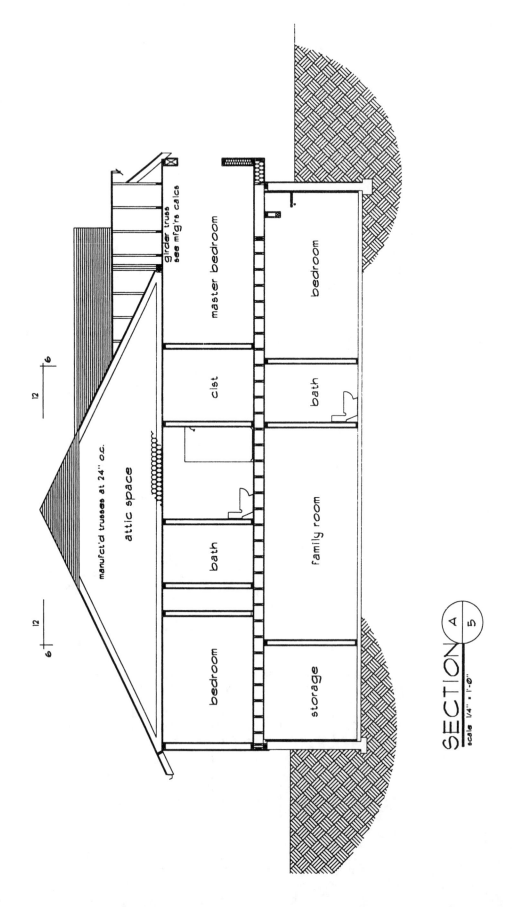

© 2011 Cengage Learning. All Rights Reserved. May not be scanned, copied or duplicated, or posted to a publicly accessible website, in whole or in part.

Problem 9   One-story with Partial Basement (Continued)

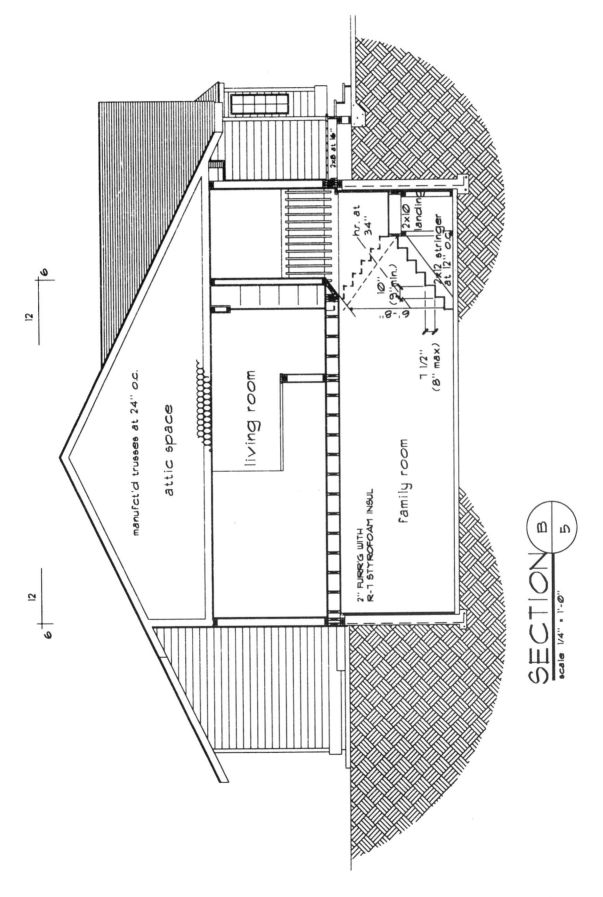

© 2011 Cengage Learning. All Rights Reserved. May not be scanned, copied or duplicated, or posted to a publicly accessible website, in whole or in part.

Problem 9   One-story with Partial Basement (Continued)

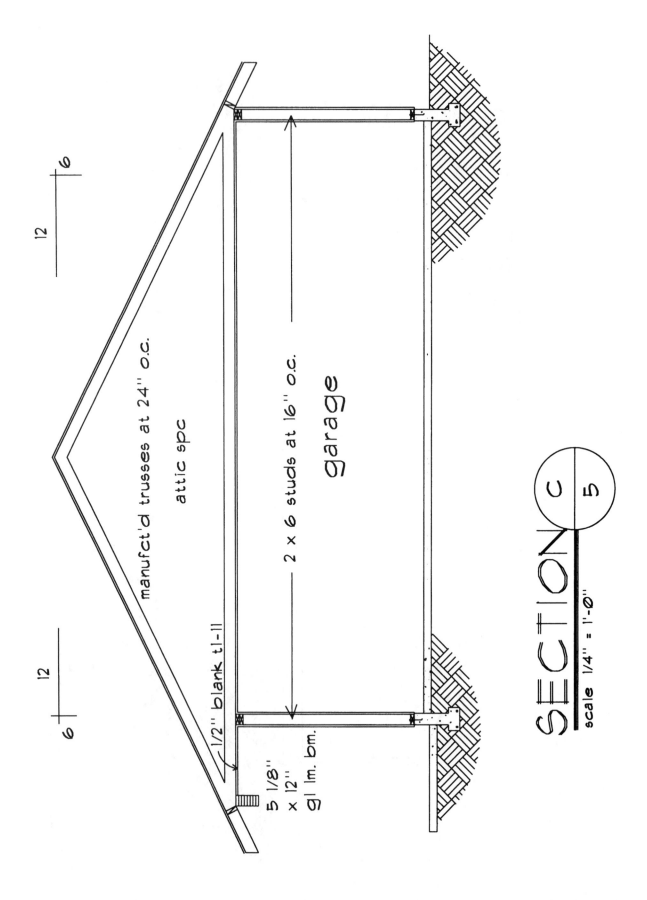

SECTION C 5

scale 1/4" = 1'-0"

manufct'd trusses at 24" o.c.

attic spc

1/2" blank t1-11

2 x 6 studs at 16" o.c.

garage

5 1/8" x 12" gl lm. bm.

12 6

12 6

© 2011 Cengage Learning. All Rights Reserved. May not be scanned, copied or duplicated, or posted to a publicly accessible website, in whole or in part.

Problem 9   One-story with Partial Basement (Continued)

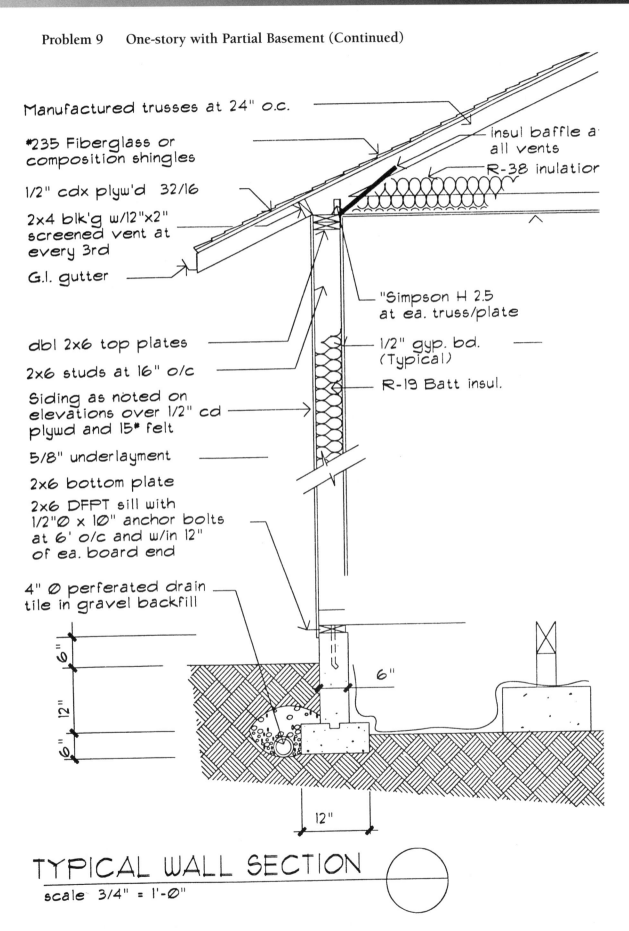

Manufactured trusses at 24" o.c.

#235 Fiberglass or composition shingles

1/2" cdx plyw'd 32/16

2x4 blk'g w/12"x2" screened vent at every 3rd

G.I. gutter

insul baffle a all vents

R-38 inulatior

"Simpson H 2.5 at ea. truss/plate

1/2" gyp. bd. (Typical)

R-19 Batt insul.

dbl 2x6 top plates

2x6 studs at 16" o/c

Siding as noted on elevations over 1/2" cd plywd and 15# felt

5/8" underlayment

2x6 bottom plate

2x6 DFPT sill with 1/2"∅ x 10" anchor bolts at 6' o/c and w/in 12" of ea. board end

4" ∅ perferated drain tile in gravel backfill

6"

12"

6"

6"

12"

TYPICAL WALL SECTION
scale 3/4" = 1'-0"

© 2011 Cengage Learning. All Rights Reserved. May not be scanned, copied or duplicated, or posted to a publicly accessible website, in whole or in part.

Problem 9   One-story with Partial Basement (Continued)

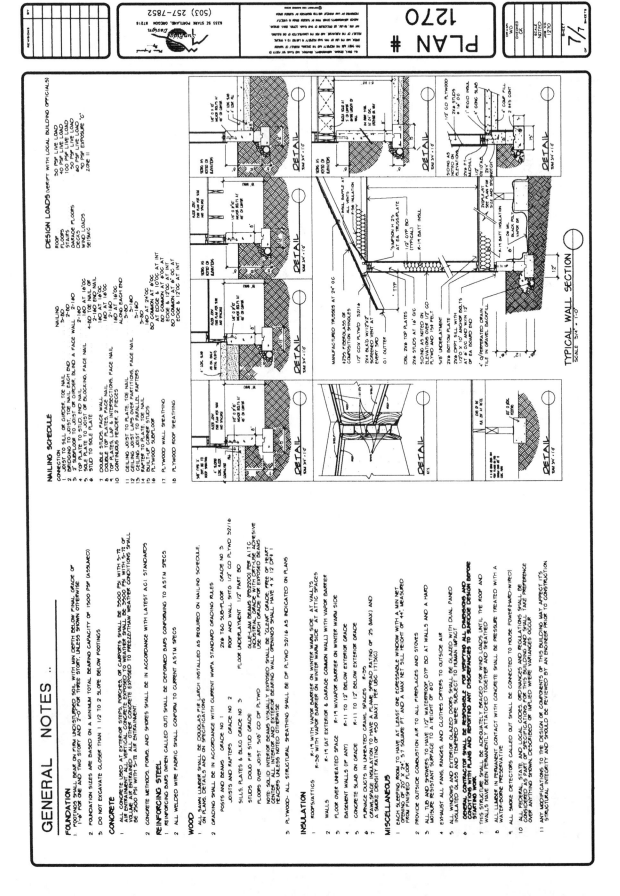

© 2011 Cengage Learning. All Rights Reserved. May not be scanned, copied or duplicated, or posted to a publicly accessible website, in whole or in part.

Problem 9   One-story with Partial Basement (Continued)

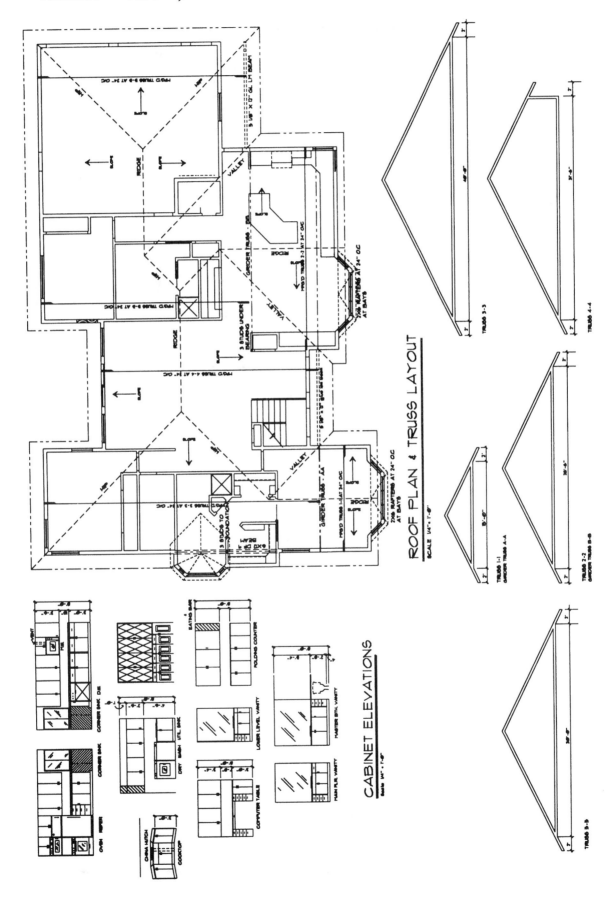

ROOF PLAN & TRUSS LAYOUT

SCALE 1/4" = 1'-0"

CABINET ELEVATIONS

© 2011 Cengage Learning. All Rights Reserved. May not be scanned, copied or duplicated, or posted to a publicly accessible website, in whole or in part.

Problem 10   Multi-level

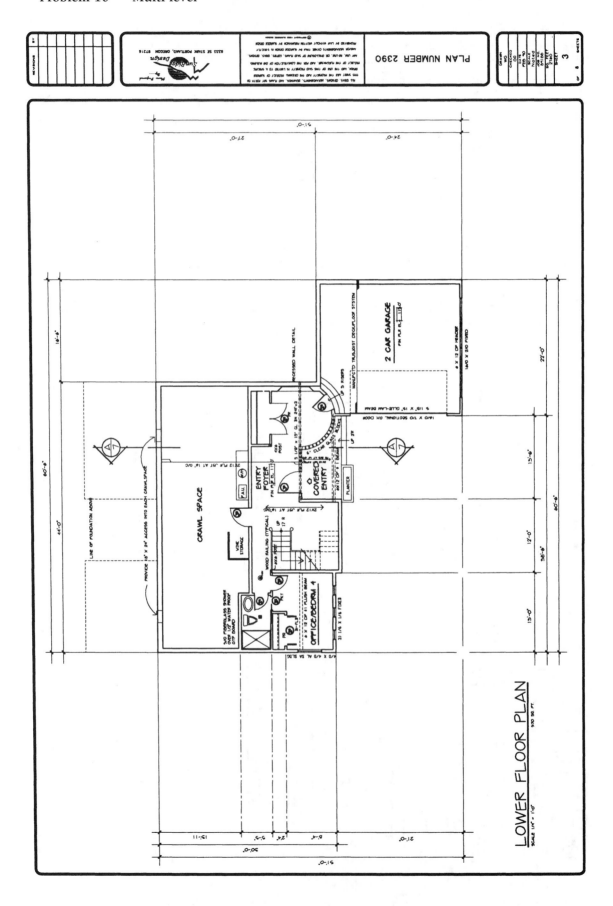

LOWER FLOOR PLAN
SCALE 1/4" = 1'-0"

© 2011 Cengage Learning. All Rights Reserved. May not be scanned, copied or duplicated, or posted to a publicly accessible website, in whole or in part.

Problem 10   Multi-level (Continued)

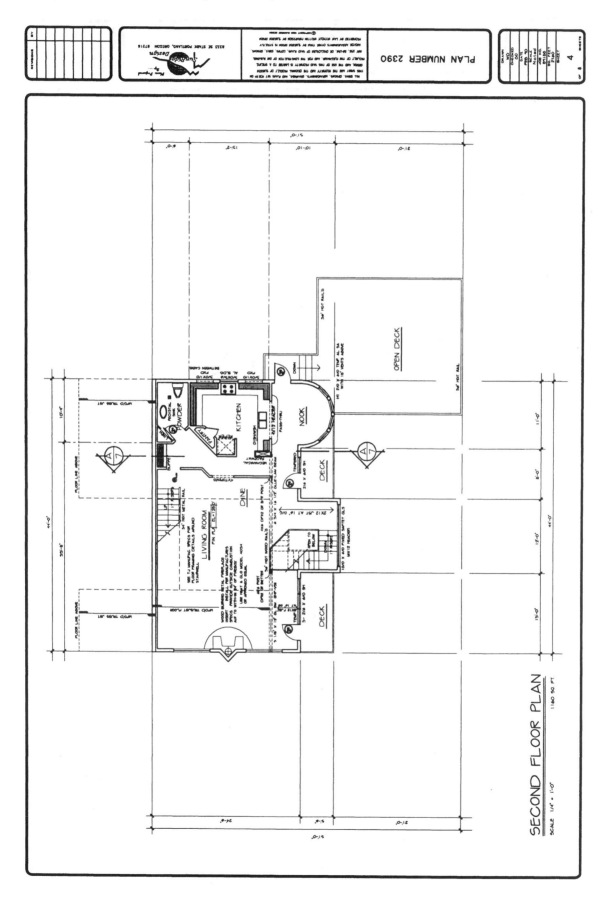

© 2011 Cengage Learning. All Rights Reserved. May not be scanned, copied or duplicated, or posted to a publicly accessible website, in whole or in part.

Problem 10   Multi-level (Continued)

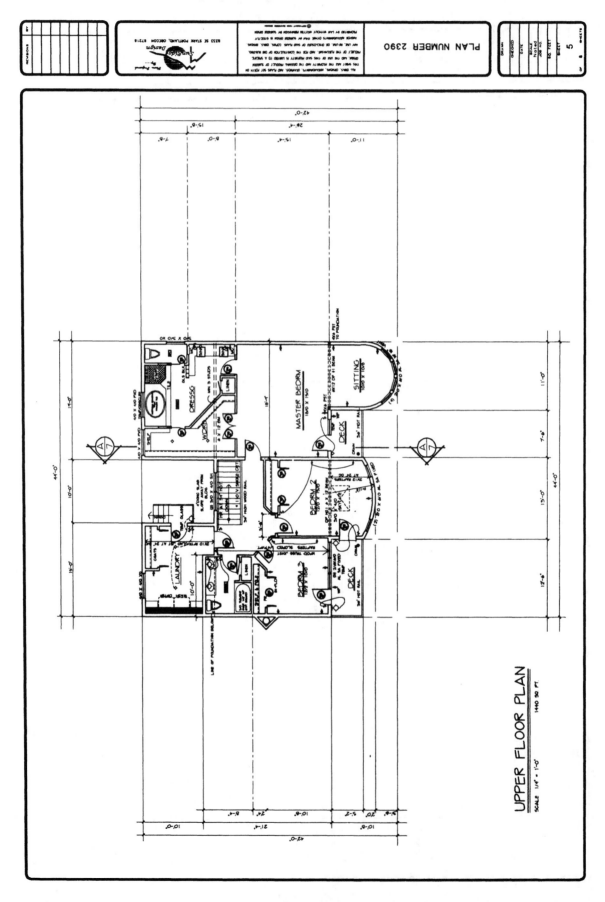

© 2011 Cengage Learning. All Rights Reserved. May not be scanned, copied or duplicated, or posted to a publicly accessible website, in whole or in part.

Problem 10   Multi-level (Continued)

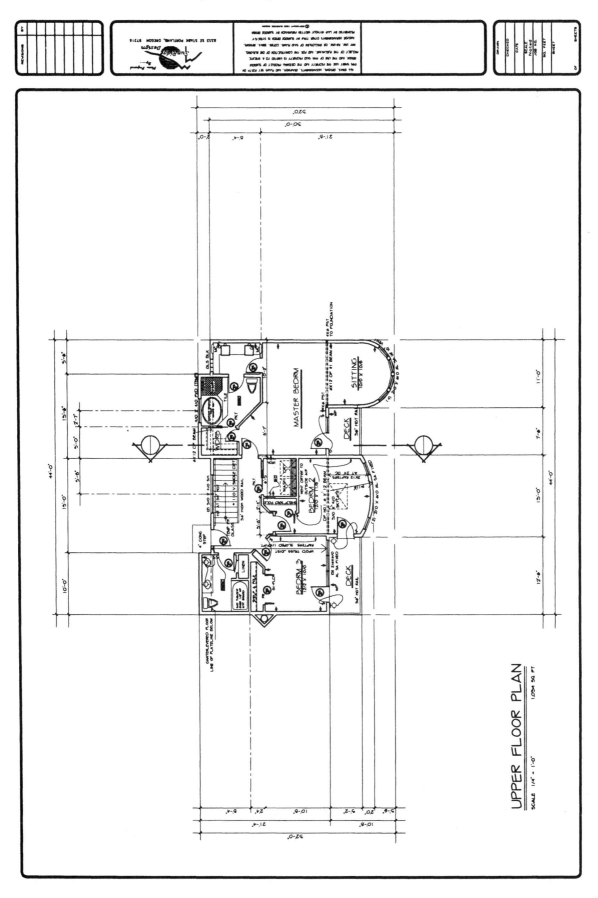

© 2011 Cengage Learning. All Rights Reserved. May not be scanned, copied or duplicated, or posted to a publicly accessible website, in whole or in part.

Problem 10   Multi-level (Continued)

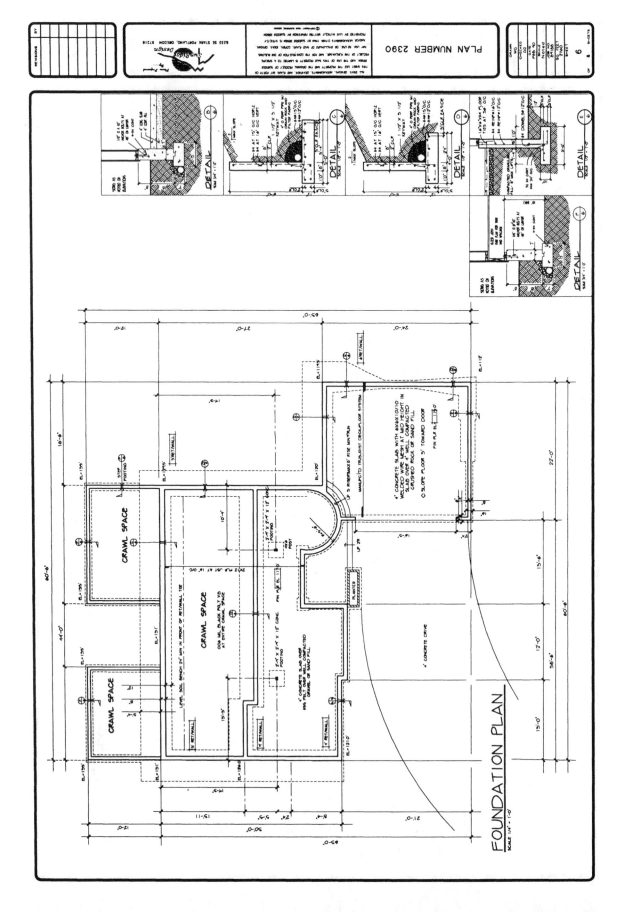

Problem 10   Multi-level (Continued)

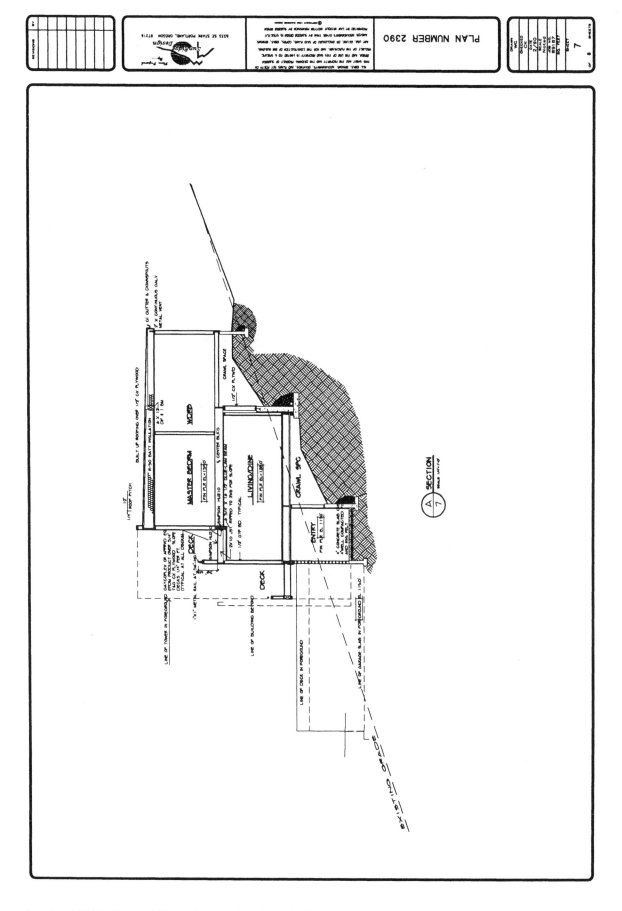

© 2011 Cengage Learning. All Rights Reserved. May not be scanned, copied or duplicated, or posted to a publicly accessible website, in whole or in part.

Problem 10   Multi-level (Continued)

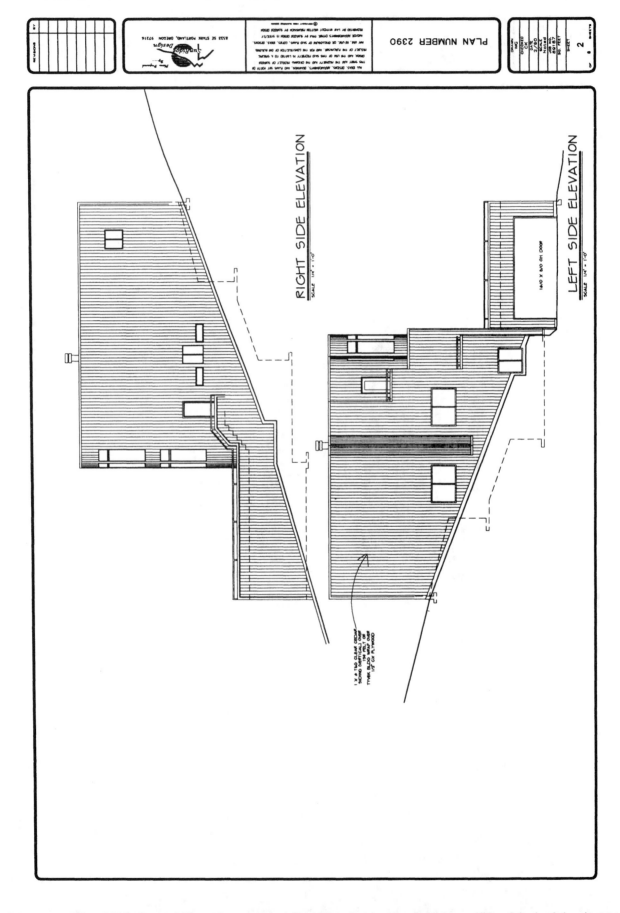

SECTION 3

Additional Advanced Residential Projects

Problem 3 Elevation

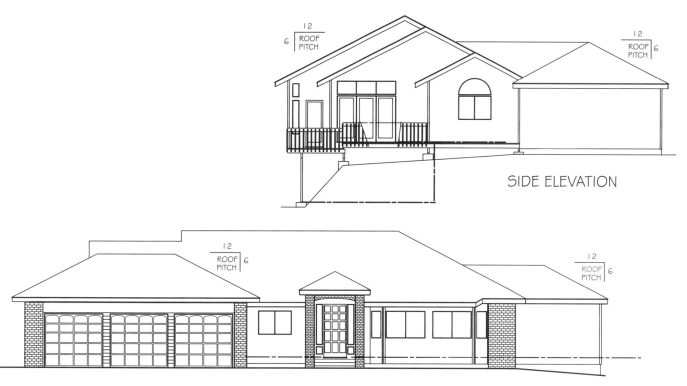

Problem 3—Lower Floor

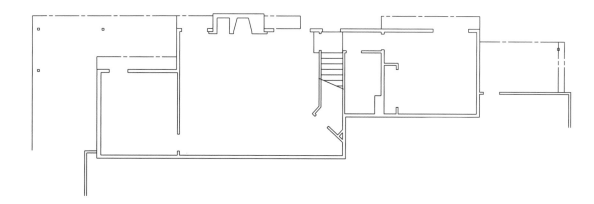

© 2011 Cengage Learning. All Rights Reserved. May not be scanned, copied or duplicated, or posted to a publicly accessible website, in whole or in part.

Problem 3   Main Floor

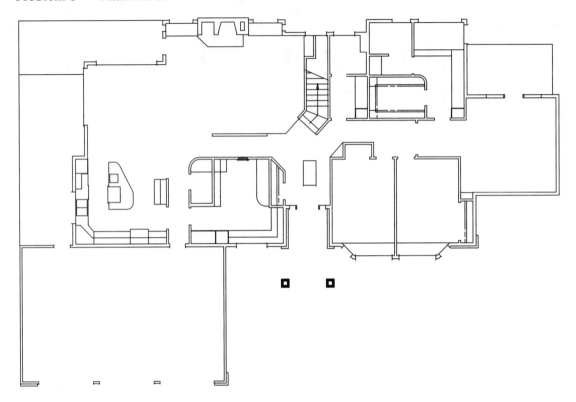

Problem 7   Elevations

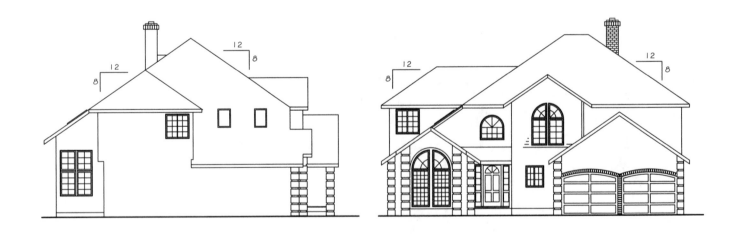

© 2011 Cengage Learning. All Rights Reserved. May not be scanned, copied or duplicated, or posted to a publicly accessible website, in whole or in part.

Problem 7   Main Floor

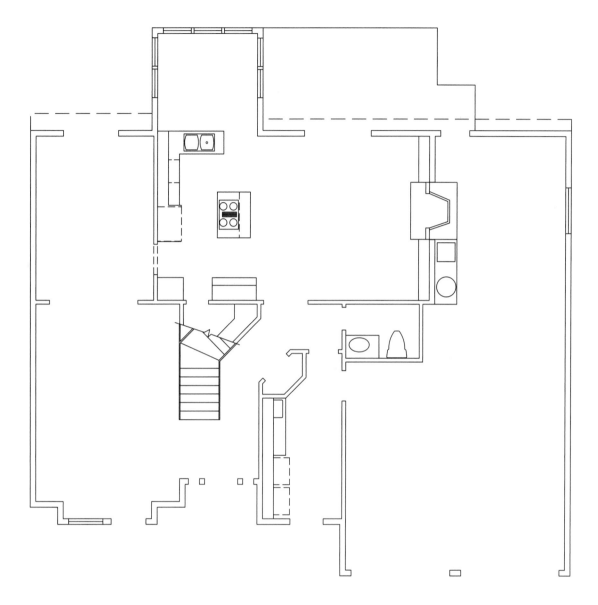

© 2011 Cengage Learning. All Rights Reserved. May not be scanned, copied or duplicated, or posted to a publicly accessible website, in whole or in part.

Problem 7   Upper Floor

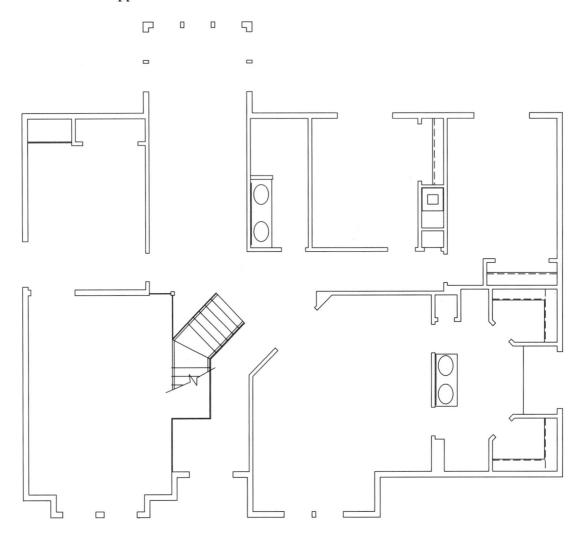

Problem 8   Elevations

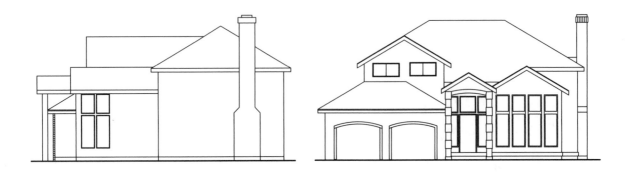

© 2011 Cengage Learning. All Rights Reserved. May not be scanned, copied or duplicated, or posted to a publicly accessible website, in whole or in part.

Problem 7   Main Floor

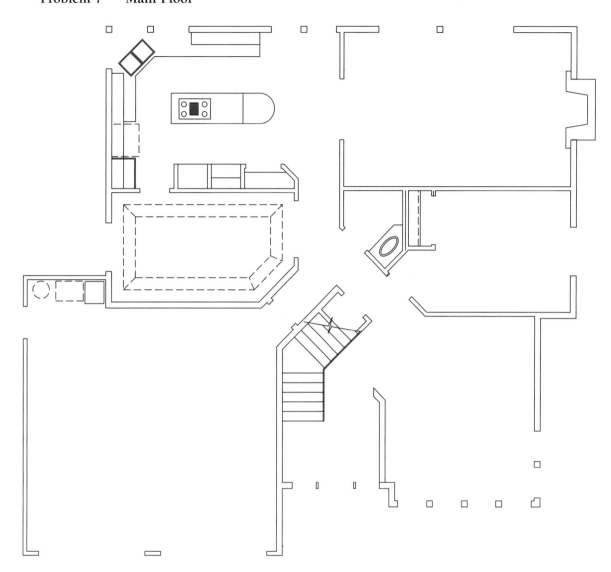

2011 Cengage Learning. All Rights Reserved. May not be scanned, copied or duplicated, or posted to a publicly accessible website, in whole or in part.

Problem 8   Upper Floor

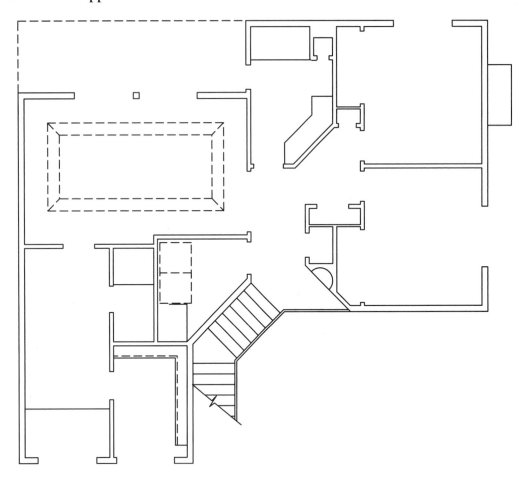

© 2011 Cengage Learning. All Rights Reserved. May not be scanned, copied or duplicated, or posted to a publicly accessible website, in whole or in part.

Problem 9   Elevations

Problem 9   LowerFloor/Foundation

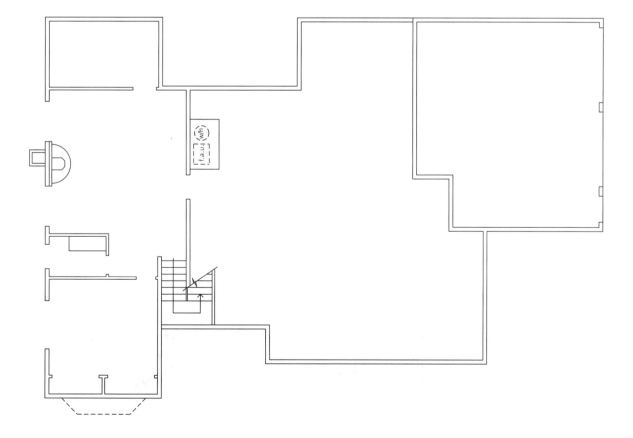

© 2011 Cengage Learning. All Rights Reserved. May not be scanned, copied or duplicated, or posted to a publicly accessible website, in whole or in part.

Problem 9   Main Floor

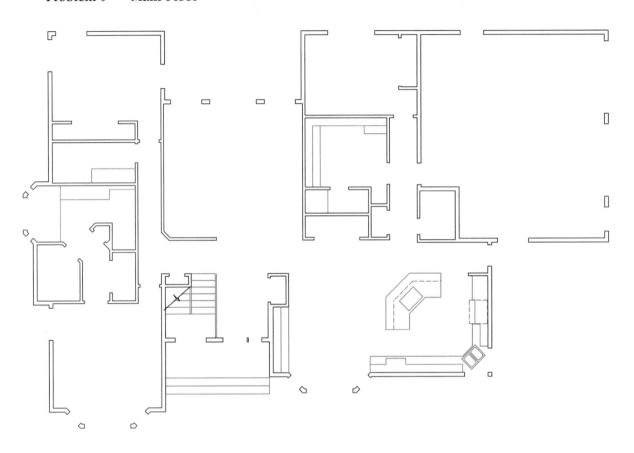

Problem 10   Elevations

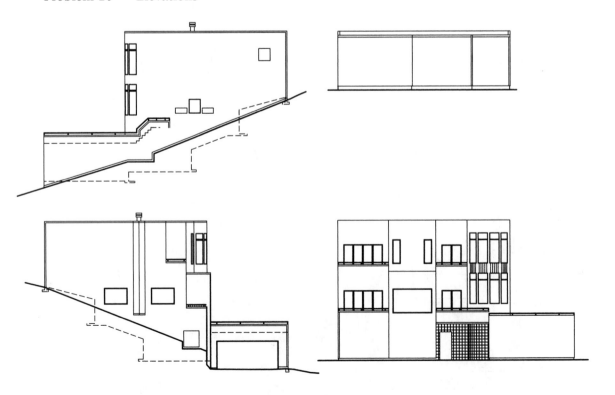

© 2011 Cengage Learning. All Rights Reserved. May not be scanned, copied or duplicated, or posted to a publicly accessible website, in whole or in part.

Problem 10   Lower Floor

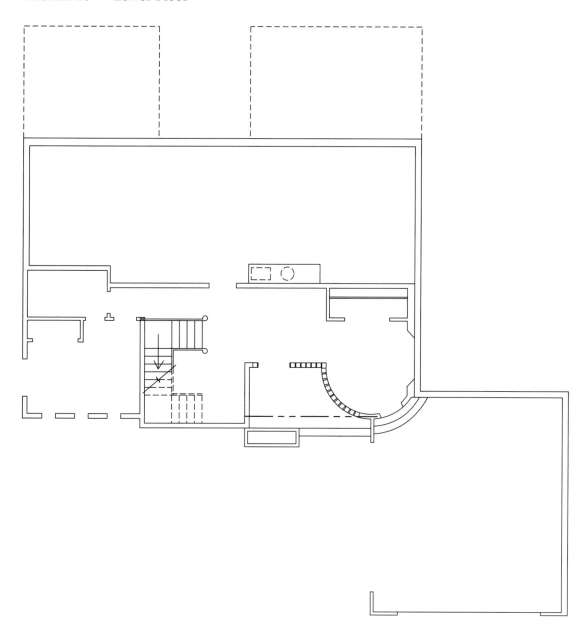

2011 Cengage Learning. All Rights Reserved. May not be scanned, copied or duplicated, or posted to a publicly accessible website, in whole or in part.

Problem 10   Second Floor

© 2011 Cengage Learning. All Rights Reserved. May not be scanned, copied or duplicated, or posted to a publicly accessible website, in whole or in part.

Problem 10   Upper Floor

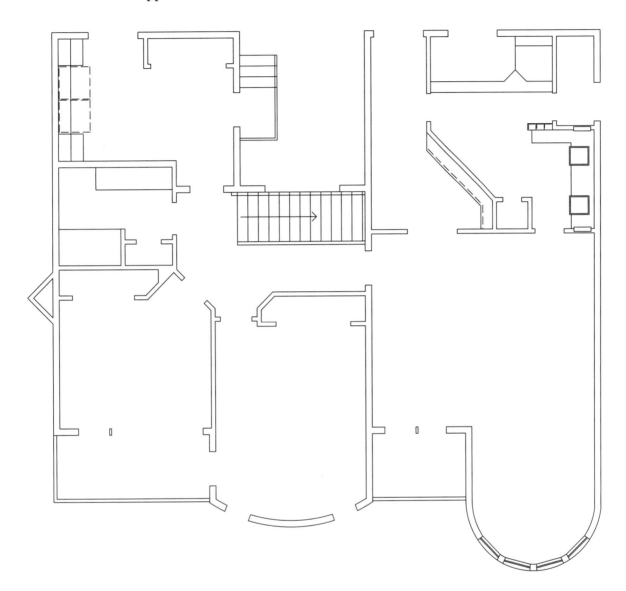

© 2011 Cengage Learning. All Rights Reserved. May not be scanned, copied or duplicated, or posted to a publicly accessible website, in whole or in part.

© 2011 Cengage Learning. All Rights Reserved. May not be scanned, copied or duplicated, or posted to a publicly accessible website, in whole or in part.

SECTION 4

Advanced Research Projects

Solutions vary based on a 500-page (or less) written report for each topic selected. Each report must be neatly typed using a word processing program, and each report must include at least two illustrations or drawings to support the content.

GOING GREEN RESEARCH PROJECTS

Problem 4–1   Automated green design software programs are available from CADD software companies. Identify one and write a complete report on the specific program, or select several and compare their applications.

Problem 4–2   Find a green design and construction project that uses a wide variety of green design features. Completely describe the project and provide illustrative examples of floor plans and elevations. Identify each green design and construction application used in the project.

Problem 4–3   Environmentally sound landscaping practices

Problem 4–4   Insulated windows

Problem 4–5   Small footprint home

Problem 4–6   Energy conservation electrical design and construction applications

Problem 4–7   Electricity generation from small-scale wind power

Problem 4–8   Electricity generation from small-scale geothermal power

Problem 4–9   Electricity generation from small-scale geothermal power

Problem 4–10   Electricity generation from small-scale hydroelectric power

Problem 4–11   Energy-conserving methods of construction that can be applied to the plumbing installation

Problem 4–12   Water conservation applications in residential design and construction

Problem 4–13   Water conservation applications in commercial design and construction

Problem 4–14   Factors that contribute to indoor air pollution and improving indoor air quality

© 2011 Cengage Learning. All Rights Reserved. May not be scanned, copied or duplicated, or posted to a publicly accessible website, in whole or in part.

© 2011 Cengage Learning. All Rights Reserved. May not be scanned, copied or duplicated, or posted to a publicly accessible website, in whole or in part.

Oracle Press™

Oracle
Data Guard 11*g*
Handbook

About the Authors

Larry Carpenter is a Distinguished Product Manager at Oracle USA and is a member of the Maximum Availability Architecture Product Management team in Server Technologies with a focus on Oracle's High Availability and Disaster Recovery technologies. Larry has 35 years of experience in the computer industry, with the last 20 years focused on the business continuity needs of critical databases and applications. He is recognized by the Oracle user community as a Data Guard expert, an HA Technical Evangelist, and a consultant to diverse Enterprise customers worldwide. Larry's expertise is ensuring the successful deployment of Oracle Disaster Recovery Solutions in diverse computing environments and bringing constantly evolving customer requirements to Oracle's development teams. Larry is conversant in English, Italian, French, and German.

Joe Meeks is a Director of Product Management with Oracle's Database High Availability Group in Server Technologies. Joe manages customer programs that focus on data protection and high availability solutions using Oracle Data Guard and the Oracle Maximum Availability Architecture. These programs ensure customer success through knowledge transfer of HA best practices while closely aligning future Oracle development priorities with customer requirements. Joe has 30 years of experience in the computer industry helping customers to address HA requirements of business critical applications in manufacturing, retail, finance, energy, telecommunications, healthcare, and public sectors. He has a BS in Environmental Science and an MBA.

Charles Kim is an Oracle ACE and an Oracle Certified DBA. Charles works predominately in the Maximum Availability Architecture (MAA) space (RAC, ASM, Data Guard, and other HA solutions). Charles released his first book, *Oracle Database 11g New Features for DBA and Developers,* in November 2007. Charles also co-authored *Linux Recipes for Oracle DBAs* with APress, published in November 2008. Charles is also the author of the MAA case study at Oracle's web site (www.oracle.com/technology/deploy/availability/htdocs/FNF_CaseStudy.html). He holds certifications in Oracle, Red Hat Linux, and Microsoft; has more than 18 years of IT experience; and has worked with Oracle since 1991. Charles blogs regularly at http://blog.dbaexpert.com and provides technical solutions to Oracle DBAs and developers.

Bill Burke is a Consulting Technical Director with Oracle's System Performance and Architecture consulting practice. More than half of his 25 years in the IT industry has been committed to volunteer leadership roles. He has served on the board of directors of the International Oracle Users Group, International Oracle Users Council, Oracle Development Tools User Group, has led the first and second IOUG/Oracle Database 10g beta test teams, and has been an active participant on the public boards, forums, and Oracle mailing lists where he was known as the "Kinder and Gentler DBA." Most of his work today in the SP&A Practice is in best practice audits and the implementation and performance tuning of Maximum Availability Architectures including Real Application Clusters (RAC), Data Guard, and their management with Enterprise Manager Grid Control. Bill has been an OCP-certified DBA since version 7 of Oracle.

Mr. Burke is a Certified Flight Instructor—Instrument and has logged hundreds of hours as a commercial pilot and flight instructor over the years. In his free time away from Oracle, he is an accomplished professional photographer who works with local youth sports organizations, non-profit organizations on a pro-bono basis, and specializes in scenic, wilderness, and travel photography with an emphasis on endangered species.

You can reach him at wburkejr@gmail.com.

Sonya Carothers is a Senior Oracle Database Administrator at PDX, Inc. She has more than 24 years of IT experience in database administration and software development. Sonya has worked as a senior database administrator, IT manager, and technical consultant. She has worked with several relational databases and has been working with Oracle since 1994. In addition, she has worked on a wide variety of projects in multi-platform environments. Her expertise includes high availability architecture, disaster recovery infrastructure, high performance database design, best practice database administration, and systems configuration.

Joydip Kundu is currently the Director of Development for Data Guard Logical Standby and LogMiner. He has been with Oracle since 1996 and is one of the original developers of Oracle LogMiner. Joydip is the architect of the log mining engine inside the Oracle RDBMS that underpins Data Guard Logical Standby, Streams Capture, and other redo-based features such as asynchronous Change Data Capture and Audit Vault. Joydip holds a Ph.D. in Computer Science from University of Massachusetts at Amherst.

Michael Smith is Principal Member of the technical staff in Oracle's Maximum Availability Architecture (MAA) team in Server Technologies. Mike has been with Oracle for 10 years, previously serving as the Data Guard Global Technical Lead within Oracle Global Support. Mike's current focus is developing, validating, and publishing HA best practices using Data Guard in an integrated fashion across all Oracle Database high availability features. His Data Guard technical specialties focus on network transport, recovery, role transitions, Active Data Guard, and client failover. He has published a dozen MAA Best Practice papers for Oracle 9*i*, 10*g*, and 11*g*. He has been a contributing author to other Oracle Press publications. Mike has also been speaker at the previous three Oracle Open World events held in San Francisco. His "What They Didn't Print in the DOC" best practice presentations covering Data Guard and MAA are a favorite among Oracle users, with attendance at the top of all Oracle Database technology presentations.

Nitin Vengurlekar, a consulting member of the technical staff at Oracle, is the author of *Oracle Automatic Storage Management* by Oracle Press. With more than 22 years of IT experience, including OS390 Systems Programming, UNIX Storage Administration, System and Database Administration, Nitin is a seasoned systems architect who has successfully assisted numerous customers to deploy highly available Oracle systems. He has worked for Oracle for more than 14 years, currently in the Real Application Clusters (RAC) engineering group, with specific emphasis on ASM and storage. He has written many papers on ASM usage and deployments on various storage array architectures and serves as a writer of and contributor to Oracle documentation as well as Oracle education material.

About the Technical Editors

Michael Powell is an OCP-certified DBA with more than 15 years of IT experience. He has more than 12 years of experience in implementing and administering Oracle for Fortune 500 companies. Michael has worked as lead DBA for RAC and Data Guard implementations. He is also a contributor to the "Maximum Availability Architecture Implementation Case Study for Fidelity National Financial (FNF)" and has been a participant in Oracle Database Beta programs. Michael specializes in database and Oracle Application implementations. Here's a link to a case study: www.oracle.com/technology/deploy/availability/htdocs/FNF_CaseStudy.html.

Sreekanth Chintala is an OCP-certified DBA, has been using Oracle technologies for more than a decade, and has more than 15 years of IT experience. Sreekanth specializes in Oracle high availability, disaster recovery, and grid computing. Sreekanth is an author of many technical white papers and a frequent speaker at Oracle OpenWorld, IOUG, and local user group meetings. Sreekanth is active in the Oracle community and is the current web seminar chair for the community-run Oracle Real Application Clusters Special Interest Group (www.ORACLERACSIG.org).